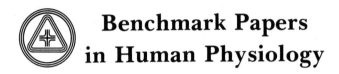

Benchmark Papers
in Human Physiology

Series Editor: L. L. Langley
National Library of Medicine

Published Volumes and Volumes in Preparation

Benchmark Papers
in Human Physiology

———— A *BENCHMARK* ₜₘ Books Series ————

CONTRACEPTION

Edited by
L. L. Langley
National Library of Medicine

Dowden, Hutchinson
& Ross, Inc.
Stroudsburg, Pennsylvania

Library of Congress Cataloging in Publication Data

Langley, Leroy Lester, comp.
    Contraception.

    (Benchmark papers in human physiology)
    1. Conception—Prevention.   2. Birth control.
I. Title.
RG136.L34   613.9'4   73–4256
ISBN 0–87933–025–2

Manufactured in the United States of America.

Exclusive distributor outside the United States and
Canada: John Wiley & Sons, Inc.

Acknowledgments
and Permissions

ACKNOWLEDGMENT
Indian Journal of Medical Research
  "Percutaneous Vasectomy: A Comparative Study Using a New Instrument and Technique"

PERMISSIONS
The following papers have been reprinted with the permission of the authors and copyright owners.

American College of Obstetrics and Gynecology—*Obstetrics and Gynecology*
  "Intrauterine Contraception: A New Approach"

American College of Physicians—*Annals of Internal Medicine*
  "Problems in Contraception"

American Medical Association—*Journal of the American Medical Association*
  "Tests of Spermicidal Activity"
  "The Postcoital Test as a Method of Evaluating a Contraceptive Jelly"

American Physiological Society—*American Journal of Physiology*
  "The Scrotum as a Temperature Regulator for the Testes"

Johann Ambrosius Barth—*Zentralblatt Gynaekologie*
  "Über den Konzeptionstermin des Weibes und seine Anwendung in der Praxis"

Cambridge University Press—*Journal of Hygiene*
  "The Spermicidal Powers of Chemical Contraceptives. I"
  "The Spermicidal Powers of Chemical Contraceptives. III"

J. B. Lippincott Company—*Endocrinology*
  "Studies of the Biological Activity of Certain 19-nor Steroids in Female Animals"

E & S Livingstone Ltd.—*British Journal of Urology*
  "A Simple Technique of Re-anastomosis After Vasectomy"

Excerpta Medica Foundation—*Proceedings of the Conference, Population Council: Intrauterine Contraceptive Devices*
  "A Study of Intra-Uterine Contraception: Development of a Plastic Loop"

Franklin H. Martin Memorial Foundation, London—*Surgery, Gynecology and Obstetrics*
  "Simple Sterilization of Women"

C. V. Mosby Company—*American Journal of Obstetrics and Gynecology*
  "Occlusion of the Fallopian Tubes with Tantalum Clips"
  "Prevention of Pregnancy by the Graefenberg Ring Method. A Re-evaluation After 28 Years' Experience"
  "Fertility Control with Oral Medication"
  "Psychology of the Misuse and Rejection of Contraception"

New York Academy of Science—*Annals of the New York Academy of Science*
  "Action of Prostaglandin in the Pregnant Woman"

Planned Parenthood Federation of America—*Family Planning Perspectives*
    "Contraceptive Research: A Male Chauvinist Plot?"
    "The Modernization of U.S. Contraceptive Practice"

Williams & Wilkins Company
    Journal of Urology
    "The Legal and Medical Aspects of Vasectomy"
    Manual of Contraceptive Practice
    "Coitus Interruptus"
    Obstetrical and Gynecological Survey
    "A Review of Tubal Sterilization Failures"
    Proceedings of the Seventh International Birth Control Conference: The Practice of Contraception
    "Intrauterine Methods. An Intrauterine Contraceptive Method"

Wistar Institute of Anatomy and Biology—*Journal of Experimental Zoology*
    "The Influence of High Temperature on the Guinea-Pig Testis"

Yokohama University School of Medicine—*Yokohama Medical Bulletin*
    "Clinical Studies of Intrauterine Rings, Especially the Present State of Contraception in Japan and the
    Experiences in the Use of Intrauterine Rings"

Preface

This is the second volume I have edited, put together, done . . . whatever is the appropriate word for these unique "Benchmark" books. The first was *Homeostasis: Origins of the Concept*. That was a labor of love since, as a physiologist, I have long appreciated the fact that homeostasis is the most fundamental, most important concept in physiology. To bring together, in one volume, the classic papers that were responsible for the development of the concept proved to be highly satisfying and rewarding.

My motivation for *Contraception* is quite different. Undeniably, anything that has to do with sex has fairly wide appeal, and certainly developments in this field have truly revolutionized attitudes toward sex. Beyond these considerations, though, the articles in this volume provide a fascinating overview of *homo sapiens* struggling for enlightenment as he takes his sometimes very halting steps toward independence, true independence that can only come through knowledge. And in this connotation, such knowledge has the very practical result that men and women can now, easily and successfully, separate sexual intercourse from reproduction; can, themselves, determine if they want children, when they want children, and how many children they want.

The "pill," the IUD, and sterilization have become so commonplace that one is apt to lose sight of the anguish that was an ever-continuing component of the lives of our predecessors. Many of the articles included in this volume poignantly recall that fact. "On Facultative Sterility" is particularly pertinent. This was written less than a century ago, yet the physician thought it prudent to use a pseudonym because his publication dealt with matters sexual. To my knowledge, this is the first time that the article has been translated into English, and it is here included in its entirety because it truly reveals the dire consequences of unwanted pregnancies. As pointed out later, the author gets a bit carried away with the subject but even that underscores the profound state of ignorance that persisted to that time, and unfortunately still does in certain quarters.

Along these same lines, the reader is directed to the paper by Donnelly and Ferber on "The Legal and Medical Aspects of Vasectomy." It was written in 1959 but incorporates views that carry forth the mythologies of prior centuries. The real problem, of course, is that we are not dealing simply with a medical situation but rather with a confluence of philosophy, theology, and sociology in addition to the underlying medical implications. This has greatly inhibited progress, has caused qualified investigators to shy away from the field, and has beclouded the undeniable advances that have come forth.

The final section in this volume is particularly revealing. It demonstrates, ever so vividly, that facts alone do not suffice. People are strange, ever-fascinating, complex beings, or, as someone stated: "You can lead a horse to water, but you can't always make him drink!"

I again had the full facilities of the incomparable National Library of Medicine at my disposal. I am particularly grateful to Mr. Berkowitz for his cooperation in this project and to Mr. Barnes, who has an eighth sense in locating books and journals that occasionally are misplaced on those endless stacks. Appreciation is also expressed to the great Countway Library at Harvard Medical School for making available a microfilm copy of the very rare Knowlton pamphlet. Unfortunately, a reader of that valuable document found it necessary to do a bit of underlining . . . herein all too faithfully reproduced!

L. L. Langley

Contents

I. COITUS INTERRUPTUS

II. ABORIGINES, MALTHUS, AND PLACE

III. THE CONDOM

VIII. FEMALE STERILIZATION

IX. MALE STERILIZATION

X. INTRAUTERINE DEVICES

Contents by Author

Introduction

There is the general belief that until relatively recently men desired children more than women. This is understandable on the basis that children, at least in primitive and agricultural societies, had value: thus the male desire. However, women in these societies found childbearing just one more onerous chore. There were three possibilities to limit the number of children—contraception, abortion, and infanticide. All three were practiced. The publications reproduced in this volume concern themselves primarily with contraception.

Knowledge of the physiology of reproduction is required for the rational prevention of conception. At the very least there must be awareness that conception and sexual intercourse have a relationship. Just when in the history of man this fact became known cannot be stated. The Bible, however, proves beyond question that this basic relationship was known in biblical times. Recall that the custom of levirate was practiced by the Jews, as well as by others. This custom required that a man must marry his brother's widow. The Bible informs us that when Onan's brother died, Onan married his brother's wife but rather than impregnate her he "spilled his seed upon the ground." He not only prevented conception but, in so doing, practiced a form of contraception that has been the most frequently utilized method throughout the world, a method referred to as "coitus interruptus." He also, unknowingly of course, gave his name to medical terminology in the form of "onanism," which properly means coitus interruptus but is frequently used as a synonym for masturbation.

If onanism is the most widely practiced method of contraception, the procedure utilized at one time by the Aborigines of Australia must be the least practiced. As detailed in a paper herein reproduced, an incision was made into the urethra immediately in front of the scrotum. During ejaculation, then, the semen would exit via this opening and therefore would not be introduced into the vagina.

Another very old method involved the introduction of various objects into the

1

vagina to serve as a barrier against the sperm. Sponges were most commonly, although by no means exclusively, used for this purpose. Cloth, animal skin, and various membranes were also employed. And speaking of animal membranes, the first condoms were made from them. Undoubtedly, such condoms were in use long before they were first mentioned in the 16th Century by the famous Italian anatomist, Fallopio.

Douching was also probably in general use before the earliest mention of it in the literature. Many fluids ranging from plain water to a variety of pleasantly scented chemical substances, and even to a popular soft drink, have been used. In the latter instance, just before the Second World War, the soft drink manufacturer was perplexed by the reported requests for but one or two bottles of their product, and always warm. After simple detective work disclosed the true purpose of these purchases the company had a study made of the spermicidal properties of their product and were surprised, no doubt, to learn that it did indeed possess such unsuspected abilities!

A volume could be filled with reports of strange or amusing contraceptive methods, some of which are still used by the uninformed. For example, a section of a 19th Century monograph on the physiology of sex is included in this collection. According to the "expert" who wrote the book, the woman only need sit bolt upright as soon as the man ejaculates and then cough violently. In this way the semen would be ejected from the vagina. Just how she was to remove the dead weight of the suddenly quiescent and rapturous male in order to carry out this rather disruptive procedure is not stated.

Real progress in contraception has been made in the past 100 years. First, reliable condoms have become more easily available at a very modest price. Next, the rubber diaphragm was introduced and developed great popularity in the more educated and affluent societies. Many chemicals were put on the market; some to be used as a douche, others to be introduced into the vagina just prior to intercourse. The biggest revolution, however, was brought about by "the pill." But because of undesirable side effects, the search goes on. The intrauterine device, of various shapes and materials, has proven remarkably effective and equally remarkably free of undesirable side effects. And most recently, prostaglandins have been used in an interesting way with excellent results. The paper describing its use is included in this collection even though one could argue that prostaglandins are abortifacients, not contraceptive agents.

Three articles are included more for physiologic interest than for their contribution to contraception. Man has long known that if the testes do not descend into the scrotum the individual is sexually potent but infertile. And man certainly has observed from the very beginning that the scrotal sac rises in cold weather and falls in hot weather. Yet it was not until 1923 that a Japanese investigator showed that sperm are heat sensitive. Subsequent studies confirmed and quantified this observation. Theoretically, then, the application of heat, or the prevention of cooling of the testes, could prevent conception.

The field of contraception is complicated by moral, social, psychological, and religious overtones. Several articles in this collection illuminate these factors. Also, at least one procedure, the so-called rhythm (safe period) method, owes whatever popularity it has to the Roman Catholic Church. The last word has not been written.

Simple procedures have been developed for sterilizing either the woman or the man. And the search for a male "pill" goes on. Because of an ever more enlightened society and of the potential profits a better idea promises, we can be certain of progress in this field. But technical progress, as the last paper in this collection amply demonstrates, is not self-sufficient. All too many fertile individuals simply reject contraceptives for many reasons. Progress on this front must be made too.

Looking back over the history of contraception and, at the same time studying the results in various countries, proves illuminating. The dominant fact is that, to date, contraception has not successfully controlled population. Consequently, there are those who are insisting, ever more vehemently, that since voluntary utilization of contraception has failed, coercion or, at the very least, adequate incentives must be used. Should there perhaps, instead of income tax deductions for children, be increasingly stiff penalties for each new birth?

Interestingly, widespread, unrestricted use of legal, safe abortion has proven to be the most effective way to control population. This has been particularly true in Japan. By way of contrast, in India which has had a very active birth control campaign for many years and where condoms, vasectomies, "the pill," and intrauterine devices have long been available, the population continues to explode.

The publications in this collection are arranged, for the most part, according to method rather than chronology, although the order of the methods themselves is in accord with the time in which they were developed. The original benchmark papers are easy to identify and select, but no field is ever established by a single publication. The problem in a book of this type is to select among great riches. That is risky. No doubt important articles have been omitted either because of limitations of space or ignorance of them. The purpose of this volume is illumination, not exhaustive treatment.

Coitus Interruptus

I

Editor's Comments on Papers 1 and 2

1 *The Bible: Genesis, Chapter 38, verses 8 and 9*

2 **Sjövall:** *Coitus Interruptus*

In view of the fact that coitus interruptus is said to be the oldest method of contraception and, in many parts of the world, is still the most frequently used, the section of the Bible bearing on this procedure is presented first. Interestingly, different bibles use different words to describe the act but there is general agreement in all of them that Onan, instead of ejaculating within the vagina of his brother's wife, withdrew and spilled his semen (seed in some versions) upon the ground. There is also no question but that he did this so as not to impregnate Tamar. Quite obviously, then, the relationship of sexual intercourse to pregnancy was well known, and coitus interruptus practiced.

That the method is widely used and is generally effective are facts without argument. Its use, however, has long been the subject of debate and much has been written concerning it. Rather than burden the reader with reams of mostly unsupportable prose, an excellent summary of the matter is presented here. In the *Manual of Contraceptive Practice,* edited by Mary Steichen Calderone, M.D., M.P.H., Medical Director of Planned Parenthood–World Population, there is included an article by Elisabet Sjövall of Sweden. In a few pages the pertinent physiology and psychology are discussed in a way that provides the intelligent reader with sufficient facts upon which to base his own conclusions.

The Babylonian Talmud was translated into English by Rabbi Dr. I. Epstein and published in London in 1936. In this work contraception is carefully considered. Coitus interruptus is recommended by Rabbi Eliezer (yev. 34b) as a contraceptive procedure to prevent dilution of the mother's milk during nursing, but is rejected by the other sages and is forbidden by all the law codes, beginning with that of Maimonides. Yet the factors of intent and constancy are considered, and the response would permit, for example, the continuance of marital relations where coitus interruptus is unintentional or irregular. On the other hand, the deviations of "unnatural" coitus are objected to on moral grounds.

According to the Talmud, three categories of women may use an "absorbent," that is a contraceptive such as a sponge, hackled wool, or flax, in marriage. These categories are: (1) a minor, because she might become pregnant and not survive; (2) a pregnant woman because she might "cause her foetus to degenerate into a sandal" (a sandal is translated to mean a "flat fish," i.e., "a flat, fish-shaped abortion due to superfetation"); and (3) a nursing woman because she might "have to wean her child prematurely and this would result in his death." A minor, in biblical days, was a girl "from the age of eleven years and one day until the age of twelve years and one day."

Outside of marriage, "a proselyte and an emancipated slave with whom harlotry is not unusual" may take contraceptive means. The "means" would be an absorbent, although there is the intriguing statement that "a woman playing the harlot turns over in order to prevent conception." Clearly, if a woman did not fall into one of the above categories she was "forbidden to use contraceptives and willfully destroy seed" because there is the obligation "to be fruitful and multiply."

Dr. M. Feldman, in *Birth Control in Jewish Law,* points out that sexual relations without procreative possibility is allowable, and contraception is preferable to abstinence. He also argues that an oral contraceptive, such as "the pill," is preferable to other methods. "The pill" will be considered later; here we are concerned with onanism.

1

THE

HOLY BIBLE

CONTAINING THE

OLD AND NEW TESTAMENTS

TRANSLATED OUT OF THE ORIGINAL TONGUES
AND WITH THE FORMER TRANSLATIONS
DILIGENTLY COMPARED AND REVISED BY
HIS MAJESTY'S SPECIAL COMMAND

Appointed to be read in churches

AUTHORIZED KING JAMES VERSION

CUM PRIVILEGIO

OXFORD
PRINTED AT THE UNIVERSITY PRESS
OXFORD UNIVERSITY PRESS
LONDON   NEW YORK   TORONTO

New Pica Royal Text
India Paper

8

8 And Judah said unto Onan, Go in unto thy brother's wife, and marry her, and raise up seed to thy brother.

9 And Onan knew that the seed should not be his; and it came to pass, when he went in unto his brother's wife, that he spilled *it* on the ground, lest that he should give seed to his brother.

Reprinted from *Manual of Contraceptive Practice*, 200–206 (1964)

Manual of
Contraceptive
2
Practice

Edited by

MARY STEICHEN CALDERONE, M.D., M.P.H.

Medical Director, Planned Parenthood-World Population (formerly
Planned Parenthood Federation of America, Inc.)

Introduction by

NICHOLSON J. EASTMAN, M.D.

Emeritus Obstetrician-in-Chief, The Johns Hopkins Hospital; Program Consultant, Physiology of Reproduction, The Ford Foundation

Editorial Consultation Committee

EDWARD C. MANN, M.D., Chairman
NATHANIEL H. COOPER, M.D., M.P.H.
JOHN M. COTTON, M.D.

THE WILLIAMS & WILKINS COMPANY
Baltimore · 1964

Editor's note on coitus interruptus

The following section on *coitus interruptus* by Elisabet Sjövall of Sweden is notable for its thoughtful approach to a subject that has until now received little study. Lief has pointed out the failure of medical schools to teach even the normal aspects of sexuality. The questions posed by Sjövall are among those that need answering before we can arrive at a clear concept of "normality" as regards the sexual process in the male.

Sjövall questions whether the woman can experience harmful effects if she does not reach orgasm. She does not, however, differentiate between the possible effects of such failure when a woman is not sexually aroused and when she is. In the former case it is doubtful that harm would result. Masters and Johnson in their pioneering studies of the human vagina in coitus and orgasm (see references p. 150), have clearly demonstrated the complex anatomical and physiological changes that occur with sexual excitation, not only in the vagina itself but in the entire genital and perigenital structures. These profound changes are shown to undergo an orderly re-solutional process after orgasm, a resolution that fails to occur in the same orderly and relatively rapid fashion if sexual excitation has *not* culminated in orgasm. It would be unrealistic to expect harm to result in the woman from occasional failure to reach climax after excitation, but it would be equally unrealistic to anticipate that repeated interruption of any normal physiological process, particularly one with so pressurized a buildup leading to such explosive release, would not result in some observable changes. The areas needing study here are obviously broad, particularly in a culture that, in contrast to others in which the woman is expected to be sexually passive, lays great stress on the privilege, in fact, the right and almost the obligation, of the woman to experience orgasm.

Harm to men from coitus interruptus has been widely assumed in this culture, particularly by urologists. The editor recently polled a small sampling of psychiatrists picked at random from the membership list of the American Association of Marriage Counselors, and of urologists from the membership list of the American Society for the Study of Sterility. The psychiatrists unanimously agreed that in their experience, coitus interruptus created no observable psychic difficulties in men, nor in women who regularly achieved orgasm before their partners' withdrawal.

The urologists, however, were just as unanimous in condemning the practice for men by attributing to it various prostatic difficulties. These opinions were based only upon their private practice observation of men who came to them with chronic prostatitis, some of whom admitted to habitual practice of coitus interruptus. Studies are obviously needed of an adequate group of men with various genitourinary complaints, and of a control group with none—as to which men have or have not practised coitus interruptus, and if they have, for what length of time. Such a study might easily and usefully include the practice of masturbation, and its findings might help to explain why France, a nation in which the birthrate since the Napoleonic era has been kept remarkably low mainly by the widespread use of coitus interruptus, has not reported a rate of prostatic disturbances significantly higher than that in countries where the practice is not widespread.

Coitus interruptus is a method that is always available and that costs nothing. It should be learned for those situations in which no other method is at hand.

Coitus Interruptus

ELISABET SJÖVALL

Translated by Christopher Tietze

Coitus interruptus, also known as *coitus incompletus* and, more popularly, as "withdrawal," is the oldest method of birth control known to be still in use, and even today it may well be the most widely used method.* Sometimes referred to as "being careful," this method requires the man to withdraw his penis when he feels ejaculation is imminent and to ejaculate outside the vagina.

General considerations. For about one-half of the men who practice it, coitus interruptus or withdrawal has proved an effective method of birth control. For the other half, it is unsatisfactory either because it is not practiced correctly or because it is unsuitable for a variety of reasons. Because scientists have made little or no effort to study the physiology of coitus, advice for a particular man must be based upon information obtainable in retrospect only. If a man practicing withdrawal has successfully avoided unwanted pregnancy over a period of 5 to 10 years, this method may be considered effective for him.

Effective coitus interruptus requires the man to be aware in advance just when ejaculation is about to occur. It is believed, however, that complete ejaculation in a single emission, usually in one powerful gush, occurs in less than 50 per cent of all men. Among other men, the semen is expelled intermittently or in a slow stream. Whether in these latter cases the man is aware of the exact moment when semen escape begins, or whether he feels only the last portion of ejaculation, is not known. Nor is it known whether a particular type of ejaculation is characteristic for a particular man. Illness, convalescence, fatigue, or the consumption of alcohol could presumably have at least a temporary effect on the type of ejaculation.

Spermatozoa may enter the urethra by escaping from the seminal vesicles either spontaneously or in response to erotic stimulation. They may also leak at the beginning of coitus and can be found in the drop of liquid produced by the mucous glands inside the urethral opening when erection occurs. Spermatozoa which have remained motile and viable for many

---

* In the United States, coitus interruptus has been less widely used than the condom, diaphragm, and rhythm methods. *Editor*.

hours have been found in these mucous drops as well as in ordinary urine specimens or in specimens taken from the anterior portion of the urethra. Because it is impossible for either man or woman to be aware that such a drop of moisture from the urethra was actually deposited in the vagina at the beginning of coitus, conception may possibly result although the coital episode is interrupted before ejaculation.

In view of the fact that even one drop of semen contains from 10,000 to 100,000 spermatozoa, the effectiveness of coitus interruptus as a contraceptive method among the men who use it requires some explanation. Robert L. Dickinson attempted to make such an explanation in terms of minor variations in nervous and muscular structures among men. A more likely explanation might be based upon the known facts derived from studies of infertile couples, in which low spermatozoa counts are related to the lack of success in achieving pregnancy. For the majority of successful users, however, the success probably stems from psychological factors: a conscientious man, with a thorough knowledge of the functioning of his own body, good self control, and a strong desire to protect his partner, is the best candidate for the successful practice of coitus interruptus.

Reasons for ineffectiveness. According to Alfred C. Kinsey, about one-half of all men either reach orgasm within 2 to 5 minutes or suffer from premature ejaculation. This group has much greater difficulty with coitus interruptus than men for whom coitus normally lasts 5 to 20 minutes or longer. However, men whose seminal emission is intermittent are found within both groups, although the condition is believed to be more common among older men.

Kinsey points out that, with the imminence of orgasm in both men and women, a condition is experienced that can vary from a mild to a considerable clouding of consciousness in which all coital movements lose their voluntary character and become involuntary. This condition may last for several seconds, and unless coitus is interrupted before the man reaches it, the opportunity to carry out such a conscious action as withdrawal is lost. The shorter the duration of coitus the more difficult it is for the man to recognize the boundary between the different phases of feeling and behavior. The failures reported for coitus interruptus may, thus, be partially explained on the basis of these factors, although there is no way in which their relative importance can be gauged.

That spermatozoa may enter the vagina although coitus is interrupted is a risk inherent in the withdrawal method. As pointed out, the entry of spermatozoa may occur through: (1) escape of a drop of semen containing a number of spermatozoa before ejaculation; (2) ejaculation in stages, or interruption of coitus after some portion of the semen has already been deposited in the vagina; (3) inability of some men to withdraw in time, for a variety of reasons; and (4) ejaculation at or close enough to, the external sexual organs of the woman so that spermatozoa can migrate into the vagina.

Ignorance of the fact that spermatozoa possess motility of their own is usual in cases of ejaculation close to the vulva. When semen is deposited between the labia, the moisture may be sufficient for the spermatozoa to retain and exercise their motility, whereas spermatozoa deposited on the skin quickly lose it. Both married couples and young unmarried people, in various forms of petting, often rely on intercourse between the labia or between the thighs in the mistaken belief that they do not run the risk of pregnancy. Cases are recorded of women, who, while participating in this type of sexual activity, became pregnant although the hymen remained intact.

It is often very difficult to convince a man that spermatozoa may escape before ejaculation, especially if on a particular occasion he is sure that he has withdrawn his penis in time. Some men present so aggressive a psychological resistance to this idea that one is forced to conclude that they believe themselves faced with impugnment of their willingness and ability to interrupt coitus. Thus, a problem that should be resolved simply on an anatomical and physiological basis becomes complicated with emotional and moral overtones.

Possible effects on the man. Many men and many women apparently overevaluate ejaculation as the sole measure of virility. Hence, denial of his right to ejaculate when and where he wishes seems to the man to be a deprivation of his most important and obvious male prerogative. A man who has this attitude, which may often be combined with an attitude that downgrades women, is not only resistant to the use of coitus interruptus but also difficult to instruct in the correct procedure.

If certain men refuse to accept coitus interruptus primarily because of an exaggerated self-indulgence, others do so because of a fairly obvious fear of impotence. Many cases of impotence which occur in connection with coitus interruptus can certainly be explained on a physiological basis, especially for those men who have a premature or early ejaculation. However, the major portion of the entire problem of impotence is probably far more closely linked to psychological factors. In the case of coitus interruptus, the man may be tense and anxious, afraid of not being able to control himself in time to withdraw, and at the same time afraid of a possible disturbance of potency. If he has even once been impotent while attempting coitus interruptus, he may soon find himself in the vicious circle so characteristic for the fixed impotent man in whom an "unsuccessful" coitus produces a strong fear that the next attempt will also be unsuccessful, thus, almost unavoidably, leading to exactly that which he fears. He soon believes himself "incapable" and overwhelmed at the thought that the woman will also believe it. This may form the core of an insoluble problem, especially at the beginning of a union before the partners know each other well.

Possible effects on the woman. The psychological stress in connection with coitus interruptus can also result in unresponsiveness in the woman. Frigidity in women certainly develops primarily on a psychological basis but may also result from physiological conditions just as impotence in men. It is certain that in most cases a combination of factors is present.

In the older literature, which continues to be cited in modern textbooks, it is stated that withdrawal of the man without orgasm for the woman can lead to a congestion of blood in her pelvic organs and eventually even to pelvic inflammation. That an interrupted coitus differs from a completed coitus only by seconds, or a fraction of a second, is overlooked. If the parners are in sexual harmony, the woman should be able to complete all or at least the greater part of the common experience, and the interruption can only mean that on some occasions her orgasm may be somewhat less strong than on others. Although this may become a psychological problem if the woman believes that she has missed something important, it cannot lead to physical damage. Considering the widespread use of coitus interruptus, it must be presumed that its dangers have been considerably exaggerated.

If one seeks a physiological explanation for the fact that a woman does not reach orgasm, the reason should be sought elsewhere than in the practice of coitus interruptus. Just as a man may need a shorter or a longer time to reach orgasm, women also differ in this respect. If a woman reacts very rapidly and the man slowly, she may reach her orgasm at the beginning of coitus, and further coital activity may become uncomfortable for her. If the man reaches his orgasm rapidly and the woman's reaction is slower, she may not achieve orgasm whether coitus is interrupted or not. In such cases, lack of harmony between the partners rather than the actual practice of withdrawal may be the cause of her failure to have orgasm.

Although coitus interruptus is the primary factor, it is certain that the woman's fear and lack of confidence are important contributing factors to her inability to respond. The woman may fear that she will be cheated of her orgasm or that the man may not withdraw in time, and thus, may be tense during the entire coitus. Thus, the same vicious circle—fear causing incapacity causing fear—is found in women as with men, but it should be remembered that in both sexes this vicious circle is not unique to coitus interruptus. It can and does operate with any form of conception control— or with none.

16

SUMMARY

Coitus interruptus may be recommended as an effective method of birth control if it has already been successfully used over a long period of time. It can also be recommended, even to young men, if they belong to that group who ejaculate in one portion and have learned how to achieve a protracted preejaculatory period. If the partners have experienced failures with coitus interruptus, attributable to a permanent condition which cannot be eliminated, they should be counseled against the use of withdrawal as a means of family limitation. The same is true for men with premature ejaculation or for those who reach orgasm within five minutes. The effectivenes of the method is very doubtful for those men who ejaculate in several stages. If these men nevertheless wish to practice coitus interruptus, they should be advised to interrupt coitus each time they feel that an ejaculation is imminent and to dry the glans and the opening of the urethra carefully with a towel or handkerchief before continuing.

The method is unsuitable in cases of impotence or frigidity that are diagnosed as primarily caused by the method itself. The same applies if the method produces substantial anxiety or fear in either partner although it is otherwise effective, unless the man and woman accept the possible loss of maximal orgasm with coitus interruptus as the price that must be paid for security.

17

Aborigines, Malthus, and Place

II

Editor's Comments on Papers 3, 4, and 5

The following three publications are grouped together, although the first may have little in common with the second and third. And this is true except for the fact that the first is obviously physically very primitive. The second, from an intellectual viewpoint would seem to be equally primitive. And the third, of course, is in reply to the second.

The first paper, on the deformation of the genital organs in certain Aborigines of Australia is included because, according to the author, J. G. Garson, M.D., the mutilation was performed not in accord with any religious rite but for the frank purpose of contraception. This procedure of placing an opening in the urethra close to the scrotum is, in all probability, very effective in preventing conception but one could have predicted that it would hardly become the method of choice throughout the world.

Turning to the Malthus and Place writings we have publications that have had widespread and lasting repercussions. Thomas Robert Malthus was an English economist and clergyman. He lived from 1766 to 1834. His most important and still quoted publication is *An Essay on the Principle of Population*. Rather than an essay in the sense that we use the word today, it is a two-volume monograph that went through several editions. The section that is relevant to this collection is taken from the sixth edition published in 1826 simply because only that edition was available to me. The first edition was published in 1798. The basic concept of the relationship of the availability of food to population permeates all editions, caused a sensation at the beginning of the 19th century, and is still relied upon by many who, for various reasons, argue for limitation of population.

The so-called Malthusian concept is that populations grow at a geometric rate whereas the food supply increases only on an arithmetic basis. Therefore, if human reproduction is not limited, the need of the populace for food will not be satisfied and famine will result, which in itself will limit the population. This is a compelling argument but one that is fraught with error, as numerous authorities have long since indicated. Here we are not concerned with the basic Malthusian concept but rather with the conclusions which Malthus derived from it. Because unrestrained reproduction must ultimately lead to famine, Malthus argues for "moral restraint." As will be seen in Chapter II of Volume I of his work, moral restraint means "restraint from marriage which is not followed by irregular gratifications." He goes on to state that "Promiscuous intercourse, unnatural passions, violations of the marriage bed, and improper arts to conceal the consequences of irregular connexions, are preventive checks that clearly come under the head of vice." And, he adds in a footnote, "the general consequence of vice is misery." In other words, if people restrain from marriage and do not indulge in intercourse outside of marriage, the growth of the population will be limited.

Actually this idea was not original with Malthus. As Bertrand Russell points out in his *History of Western Philosophy,* Jean-Antoine-Nicolas Caritat, the Marquis de Condorcet, invented it. His book, *Essai sur l'application de l'analyse aux probabilités,* was published in 1785. His solution, unlike that of Malthus, was to practice birth control.

Frances Place (1771–1854) is considered to be the founder of the birth-control movement in England. He was a self-taught workingman who eventually rose to prominence in English political life. Not only did he publish the work which is included here, but he also disseminated contraceptive handbills among the working classes. In the very early part of the 19th century that was a bold and dangerous activity.

In 1822, Place published his book entitled *Illustrations and Proofs of the Principle of Population: Including an Examination of the Proposed Remedies of Mr. Malthus, and a Reply to the Objections of Mr. Godwin and Others.* Chapter VI of that work is called "Means of Preventing the Numbers of Mankind from Increasing Faster than Food Is Provided." Section III of that chapter is reproduced in this collection. In it the author expounds upon his own ideas concerning this proposition. Place is clearly outraged by Malthus and others, such as the Mr. Godwin of the title, who advocate celibacy. He states that "if a hundredth, perhaps a thousandth part of the pains, were taken to teach these truths that are taken to teach dogmas, a great change for the better might, in no considerable space of time, be expected to take place in the appearance and habits of the people. If, above all, it were once clearly understood, that it was not disreputable for married persons to avail themselves of such precautionary means as would, without being injurious to health, or destructive of female delicacy, prevent conception, a sufficient check might at once be given to the increase of population beyond the means of subsistence, vice and misery, to a prodigious extent, might be removed from society, and the object of Mr. Malthus, Mr. Godwin, and of every philanthropic person, be promoted, by the increase of comfort, of intelligence, and of moral conduct, in the mass of the population." Later in the chapter he states: "If means were adopted to prevent the breeding of a larger number of children than a married couple might desire to have, and if the labouring part of the population could thus be kept below the demand for labour, wages would rise so as to afford the means of comfortable subsistence for all, and all might marry." Quite carried away with this theme, he concludes that "[m]arriage, under these circumstances would be, by far, the happiest of all conditions, as it would also be the most virtuous, and, consequently, the most beneficial to the whole community. . . ." Even, he insists, ". . . promiscuous intercourse carried on by means of open prostitution, now so excessively and extensively pernicious, would cease. . . ." Not even the most rabid of modern advocates of birth control are willing to go that far, but they would agree that the way to control population growth is via birth control as Place advocates, and not by the postponement of marriage coupled with celibacy as Malthus would have it.

Reprinted from *Med. Press Circular*, **108**, 189 (1894)

3

NOTES ON
DEFORMATIONS OF THE GENITAL ORGANS,
PRACTISED BY THE NATIVES OF AUSTRALIA. (a)

By. J. G. GARSON, M.D.

THE following notes on deformations of the male and female genital organs practised by the Aborigines of Australia may not be uninteresting to the Fellows of this Society. The information which I am about to communicate was collected and sent to the Anthropological Institute by Mr. B. H. Purcell, a gentleman who has, for the last 25 years, given great attention to the study of these natives amongst whom he resides.

Circumcision.—This operation is practised all over Australia, except in Victoria and New South Wales, on boys at the age of eight years. The operation is performed by one man seizing the prepuce between his forefingers and thumbs and stretching it to the fullest extent, while the head man of the tribe transfixes it with a flint knife of lancet shape, sharpened on both sides, and cuts it off with one circular sweep. After the bleeding has ceased the wound is dressed with the soft down of a duck or the eagle-hawk.

The Mylagoordi have a somewhat different method of performing the operation. They divide the prepuce by four longitudinal incisions and then dissect each segment backwards "to the butt of the penis," removing each separately.

In the Northern territory the prepuce is scored with a flint knife and is then dressed with irritating herbs so as to produce hypertrophy of the parts.

The operation is done for the purposes of cleanliness. The natives do not consider a person clean unless he has been circumcised, and a circumcising tribe will not eat food with one who is uncircumcised.

A *Mika* is a man upon whom an operation to produce artificial hypospadias has been practised for the purpose of preventing him from having any family. Three different operations are performed for this purpose.

1st.—On Corpus Christi Creek, Western Australia, the natives content themselves with making a small incision through the urethra immediately in front of the scrotum. Through this opening the semen is ejaculated during copulation, after the wound is healed.

2nd —On the Diamantina and Lower Georgiana the natives divide the urethra in front of the scrotum and again just below the glans penis, then cutting longitudinally along each side of the urethra dissect it out.

3rd.—The most general plan of mutilation is that of which I show you a photograph. It is performed by placing a narrow piece of wood along the dorsum of the penis and drawing the loose skin tightly backwards over the wood. A flint knife is then inserted into the orifice and the urethra is laid open to the scrotum. Before the operation is performed the penis is beaten till it is benumbed. After the operation the penis is bandaged against the abdomen ; should excessive inflammation of the wound occur during the healing process it is dressed with a kind of native clay or crushed eucalyptus leaves. The mortality after this operation is stated to be *nil*.

These operations are performed on youths at the age of 18 years, and only upon a certain number of them, namely, those who prove themselves indolent and the least useful members of their tribes.

A *Euriltha* is a woman upon whom the following operation has been performed for the purpose of rendering her barren :—

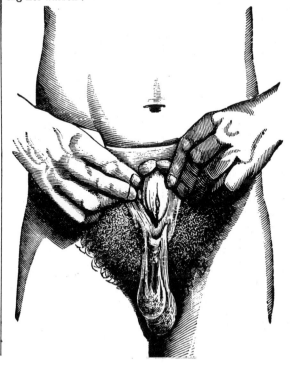

(a) Read before the Medical Society of London, Feb. 5th, 1894.

A roll of emu feathers is made, seven or eight inches long, thinner at one end than the other, it is lashed round with twine manufactured from opossum fur, and daubed with a mixture of fat and red ochre. To the smaller end a cord, made of human hair, is attached, looped over it, and brought down to the thicker end. The girl, who is between 10 and 12 years of age when the operation is performed, is placed upon her back, and the thin end of the roll with the loop is inserted into the vagina. With a flat piece of stick passed up the vagina along side of the roll the loop at its upper end is placed round the projecting end of the cervix uteri. The girl is watched for a while till the parts have become swollen, the free end of the cord is now twisted round the hand of the operator and the portion of the cervix included in the loop is forcibly severed and drawn out with the roll and loop. The girl is placed in camp for the next three weeks. At the end of that time a small flint knife, fixed to the end of a stick six inches long, is passed up the vagina and a vertical and transverse incision is made in the stump of the cervix. These incisions are then stuffed with down of the duck or eagle-hawk to keep them open, lumps of heated fat are now inserted to grease the parts and keep them clean. When the wounds have healed, the lower end of the posterior wall of the vagina is divided down to the anus, so as to make sexual intercourse with the Mikas more easy. The operators are the old men and women of the tribe.

This horrible operation is only practised by a few tribes in Central Australia. It has often been called spaying, but Mr. Purcell says "I have examined all the women of the tribes where these operations are done, but on none of them did I find a trace of the flint knife for spaying." Instead of performing the whole operation the natives content themselves with dividing the lower part of the posterior wall of the vagina. **Women on whom only this part of the operation has been done are called a Dindahs or Dindees.**

Reprinted from *An Essay on the Principle of Population; or, A View of Its Past and Present Effects on Human Happiness,* Vol. 1, 6th ed., 1–24 (1826)

4

AN ESSAY

ON THE

PRINCIPLE OF POPULATION;

OR,

A VIEW OF ITS PAST AND PRESENT EFFECTS

ON

HUMAN HAPPINESS;

WITH

AN INQUIRY INTO OUR PROSPECTS RESPECTING THE FUTURE REMOVAL OR MITIGATION OF THE EVILS WHICH IT OCCASIONS.

BY

THE REV. T. R. MALTHUS, A. M. F.R.S.

LATE FELLOW OF JESUS COLLEGE, CAMBRIDGE, AND PROFESSOR OF HISTORY AND POLITICAL ECONOMY IN THE EAST-INDIA COLLEGE, HERTFORDSHIRE

◆

SIXTH EDITION.

IN TWO VOLUMES.

VOL. I.

LONDON:

JOHN MURRAY, ALBEMARLE STREET.

MDCCCXXVI.

ESSAY,

&c. &c.

BOOK I.

OF THE CHECKS TO POPULATION IN THE LESS
CIVILIZED PARTS OF THE WORLD AND
IN PAST TIMES.

CHAP. I.

Statement of the Subject. Ratios of the Increase of Population and Food.

IN an inquiry concerning the improvement of society, the mode of conducting the subject which naturally presents itself, is,

1. To investigate the causes that have hitherto impeded the progress of mankind towards happiness; and,

2. To examine the probability of the total or partial removal of these causes in future.

To enter fully into this question, and to enumerate all the causes that have hitherto influenced human improvement, would be much beyond the power of an individual. The principal object of

VOL. I.   B

26

the present essay is to examine the effects of one great cause intimately united with the very nature of man; which, though it has been constantly and powerfully operating since the commencement of society, has been little noticed by the writers who have treated this subject. The facts which establish the existence of this cause have, indeed, been repeatedly stated and acknowledged; but its natural and necessary effects have been almost totally overlooked; though probably among these effects may be reckoned a very considerable portion of that vice and misery, and of that unequal distribution of the bounties of nature, which it has been the unceasing object of the enlightened philanthropist in all ages to correct.

The cause to which I allude, is the constant tendency in all animated life to increase beyond the nourishment prepared for it.

It is observed by Dr. Franklin, that there is no bound to the prolific nature of plants or animals, but what is made by their crowding and interfering with each other's means of subsistence. Were the face of the earth, he says, vacant of other plants, it might be gradually sowed and overspread with one kind only, as for instance with fennel: and were it empty of other inhabitants, it might in a few ages be replenished from one nation only, as for instance with Englishmen.*

This is incontrovertibly true. Through the animal and vegetable kingdoms Nature has scattered the seeds of life abroad with the most pro-

* Franklin's Miscell. p. 9.

27

fuse and liberal hand; but has been comparatively sparing in the room and the nourishment necessary to rear them. The germs of existence contained in this earth, if they could freely develope themselves, would fill millions of worlds in the course of a few thousand years. Necessity, that imperious, all-pervading law of nature, restrains them within the prescribed bounds. The race of plants and the race of animals shrink under this great restrictive law; and man cannot by any efforts of reason escape from it.

In plants and irrational animals, the view of the subject is simple. They are all impelled by a powerful instinct to the increase of their species; and this instinct is interrupted by no doubts about providing for their offspring. Wherever therefore there is liberty, the power of increase is exerted; and the superabundant effects are repressed afterwards by want of room and nourishment.

The effects of this check on man are more complicated. Impelled to the increase of his species by an equally powerful instinct, reason interrupts his career, and asks him whether he may not bring beings into the world, for whom he cannot provide the means of support. If he attend to this natural suggestion, the restriction too frequently produces vice. If he hear it not, the human race will be constantly endeavouring to increase beyond the means of subsistence. But as, by that law of our nature which makes food necessary to the life of man, population can never actually increase beyond the lowest nourishment capable of supporting

B 2

it, a strong check on population, from the difficulty of acquiring food, must be constantly in operation. This difficulty must fall somewhere, and must necessarily be severely felt in some or other of the various forms of misery, or the fear of misery, by a large portion of mankind.

That population has this constant tendency to increase beyond the means of subsistence, and that it is kept to its necessary level by these causes, will sufficiently appear from a review of the different states of society in which man has existed. But, before we proceed to this review, the subject will, perhaps, be seen in a clearer light, if we endeavour to ascertain what would be the natural increase of population, if left to exert itself with perfect freedom ; and what might be expected to be the rate of increase in the productions of the earth, under the most favourable circumstances of human industry.

It will be allowed that no country has hitherto been known, where the manners were so pure and simple, and the means of subsistence so abundant, that no check whatever has existed to early marriages from the difficulty of providing for a family. and that no waste of the human species has been occasioned by vicious customs, by towns, by unhealthy occupations, or too severe labour. Consequently in no state that we have yet known, has the power of population been left to exert itself with perfect freedom.

Whether the law of marriage be instituted, or not, the dictate of nature and virtue seems to be an early attachment to one woman; and where there were no impediments of any kind in the way of an union to which such an attachment would lead, and no causes of depopulation afterwards, the increase of the human species would be evidently much greater than any increase which has been hitherto known.

In the northern states of America, where the means of subsistence have been more ample, the manners of the people more pure, and the checks to early marriages fewer, than in any of the modern states of Europe, the population has been found to double itself, for above a century and a half successively, in less than twenty-five years.* Yet, even during these periods, in some of the towns, the deaths exceeded the births,† a circumstance which clearly proves that, in those parts of the country which supplied this deficiency, the increase must have been much more rapid than the general average.

In the back settlements, where the sole employment is agriculture, and vicious customs and unwholesome occupations are little known, the population has been found to double itself in fifteen years.‡ Even this extraordinary rate of increase is probably short of the utmost power of

* It appears, from some recent calculations and estimates, that from the first settlement of America, to the year 1800, the periods of doubling have been but very little above twenty years. See a note on the increase of American population in Book ii. chap. xi.

† Price's Observ. on Revers. Pay. vol. i. p. 274. 4th edit.

‡ Id. p. 282.

population. Very severe labour is requisite to clear a fresh country ; such situations are not in general considered as particularly healthy ; and the inhabitants, probably, are occasionally subject to the incursions of the Indians, which may destroy some lives, or at any rate diminish the fruits of industry.

According to a table of Euler, calculated on a mortality of 1 in 36, if the births be to the deaths in the proportion of 3 to 1, the period of doubling will be only 12 years and 4-5ths.*   And this proportion is not only a possible supposition, but has actually occurred for short periods in more countries than one.

Sir William Petty supposes a doubling possible in so short a time as ten years.†

But, to be perfectly sure that we are far within the truth, we will take the slowest of these rates of increase, a rate in which all concurring testimonies agree, and which has been repeatedly ascertained to be from procreation only.

It may safely be pronounced, therefore, that population, when unchecked, goes on doubling itself every twenty-five years, or increases in a geometrical ratio.

The rate according to which the productions of the earth may be supposed to increase, it will not be so easy to determine. Of this, however, we may be perfectly certain, that the ratio of their

* See this table at the end of chap. iv. book ii.
† Polit. Arith. p. 14.

increase in a limited territory must be of a totally different nature from the ratio of the increase of population. A thousand millions are just as easily doubled every twenty-five years by the power of population as a thousand. But the food to support the increase from the greater number will by no means be obtained with the same facility. Man is necessarily confined in room. When acre has been added to acre till all the fertile land is occupied, the yearly increase of food must depend upon the melioration of the land already in possession. This is a fund, which, from the nature of all soils, instead of increasing, must be gradually diminishing. But population, could it be supplied with food, would go on with unexhausted vigour; and the increase of one period would furnish the power of a greater increase the next, and this without any limit.

From the accounts we have of China and Japan, it may be fairly doubted, whether the best-directed efforts of human industry could double the produce of these countries even once in any number of years. There are many parts of the globe, indeed, hitherto uncultivated, and almost unoccupied; but the right of exterminating, or driving into a corner where they must starve, even the inhabitants of these thinly-peopled regions, will be questioned in a moral view. The process of improving their minds and directing their industry would necessarily be slow; and during this time, as population would regularly keep pace with the increasing produce, it would rarely happen that a great degree of knowledge and industry would have to operate at once upon rich unappropriated soil. Even where this might take place, as it does sometimes in new colonies, a geometrical ratio increases with such extraordinary rapidity, that the advantage could not last long. If the United States of America continue increasing, which they certainly will do, though not with the same rapidity as formerly, the Indians will be driven further and further back into the country, till the whole race is ultimately exterminated, and the territory is incapable of further extension.

These observations are, in a degree, applicable to all the parts of the earth, where the soil is imperfectly cultivated. To exterminate the inhabitants of the greatest part of Asia and Africa, is a thought that could not be admitted for a moment. To civilise and direct the industry of the various tribes of Tartars and Negroes, would certainly be a work of considerable time, and of variable and uncertain success.

Europe is by no means so fully peopled as it might be. In Europe there is the fairest chance that human industry may receive its best direction. The science of agriculture has been much studied in England and Scotland; and there is still a great portion of uncultivated land in these countries. Let us consider at what rate the produce of this island might be supposed to increase under circumstances the most favourable to improvement.

If it be allowed that by the best possible policy, and great encouragements to agriculture, the average produce of the island could be doubled in the first twenty-five years, it will be allowing, probably, a greater increase than could with reason be expected.

In the next twenty-five years, it is impossible to suppose that the produce could be quadrupled. It would be contrary to all our knowledge of the properties of land. The improvement of the barren parts would be a work of time and labour; and it must be evident to those who have the slightest acquaintance with agricultural subjects, that in proportion as cultivation extended, the additions that could yearly be made to the former average produce must be gradually and regularly diminishing. That we may be the better able to compare the increase of population and food, let us make a supposition, which, without pretending to accuracy, is clearly more favourable to the power of production in the earth, than any experience we have had of its qualities will warrant.

Let us suppose that the yearly additions which might be made to the former average produce, instead of decreasing, which they certainly would do, were to remain the same; and that the produce of this island might be increased every twenty-five years, by a quantity equal to what it at present produces. The most enthusiastic speculator cannot suppose a greater increase than this. In a few centuries it would make every acre of land in the island like a garden.

If this supposition be applied to the whole earth, and if it be allowed that the subsistence for man which the earth affords might be increased every twenty-five years by a quantity equal to what it at present produces, this will be supposing a rate of increase much greater than we can imagine that any possible exertions of mankind could make it.

It may be fairly pronounced, therefore, that, considering the present average state of the earth, the means of subsistence, under circumstances the most favourable to human industry, could not possibly be made to increase faster than in an arithmetical ratio.

The necessary effects of these two different rates of increase, when brought together, will be very striking. Let us call the population of this island eleven millions; and suppose the present produce equal to the easy support of such a number. In the first twenty-five years the population would be twenty-two millions, and the food being also doubled, the means of subsistence would be equal to this increase. In the next twenty-five years, the population would be forty-four millions, and the means of subsistence only equal to the support of thirty-three millions. In the next period the population would be eighty-eight millions, and the means of subsistence just equal to the support of half that number. And, at the conclusion of the first century, the population would be a hundred and seventy-six millions, and the means of subsistence only equal to the support of fifty-five millions, leaving a population of a hundred and twenty-one millions totally unprovided for.

Taking the whole earth, instead of this island, emigration would of course be excluded; and, supposing the present population equal to a thousand millions, the human species would increase as the numbers, 1, 2, 4, 8, 16, 32, 64, 128, 256, and subsistence as 1, 2, 3, 4, 5, 6, 7, 8, 9. In two centuries the population would be to the means of subsistence as 256 to 9; in three centuries as 4096 to 13, and in two thousand years the difference would be almost incalculable.

In this supposition no limits whatever are placed to the produce of the earth. It may increase for ever and be greater than any assignable quantity; yet still the power of population being in every period so much superior, the increase of the human species can only be kept down to the level of the means of subsistence by the constant operation of the strong law of necessity, acting as a check upon the greater power.

CHAP. II.

Of the general Checks to Population, and the Mode of their Operation.

T$_{HE}$ ultimate check to population appears then to be a want of food, arising necessarily from the different ratios according to which population and food increase. But this ultimate check is never the immediate check, except in cases of actual famine.

The immediate check may be stated to consist in all those customs, and all those diseases, which seem to be generated by a scarcity of the means of subsistence, and all those causes, independent of this scarcity, whether of a moral or physical nature, which tend prematurely to weaken and destroy the human frame.

These checks to population, which are constantly operating with more or less force in every society, and keep down the number to the level of the means of subsistence, may be classed under two general heads—the preventive, and the positive checks.

The preventive check, as far as it is voluntary, is peculiar to man, and arises from that distinctive superiority in his reasoning faculties, which enables him to calculate distant consequences. The checks to the indefinite increase of plants and irrational animals are all either positive, or, if preventive, involuntary.   But man cannot look around him, and see the distress which frequently presses upon those who have large families; he cannot contemplate his present possessions or earnings, which he now nearly consumes himself, and calculate the amount of each share, when with very little addition they must be divided, perhaps, among seven or eight, without feeling a doubt whether, if he follow the bent of his inclinations, he may be able to support the offspring which he will probably bring into the world.   In a state of equality, if such can exist, this would be the simple question.   In the present state of society other considerations occur.   Will he not lower his rank in life, and be obliged to give up in great measure his former habits?   Does any mode of employment present itself by which he may reasonably hope to maintain a family?   Will he not at any rate subject himself to greater difficulties, and more severe labour, than in his single state?   Will he not be unable to transmit to his children the same advantages of education and improvement that he had himself possessed?   Does he even feel secure that, should he have a large family, his utmost exertions can save them from rags and squalid poverty, and their consequent degradation in the community?   And may he not be reduced to the grating necessity of forfeiting his independence, and of being obliged to the sparing hand of Charity for support?

These considerations are calculated to prevent,

and certainly do prevent, a great number of persons in all civilized nations from pursuing the dictate of nature in an early attachment to one woman.

If this restraint do not produce vice, it is undoubtedly the least evil that can arise from the principle of population. Considered as a restraint on a strong natural inclination, it must be allowed to produce a certain degree of temporary unhappiness; but evidently slight, compared with the evils which result from any of the other checks to population; and merely of the same nature as many other sacrifices of temporary to permanent gratification, which it is the business of a moral agent continually to make.

When this restraint produces vice, the evils which follow are but too conspicuous. A promiscuous intercourse to such a degree as to prevent the birth of children, seems to lower, in the most marked manner, the dignity of human nature. It cannot be without its effect on men, and nothing can be more obvious than its tendency to degrade the female character, and to destroy all its most amiable and distinguishing characteristics. Add to which, that among those unfortunate females, with which all great towns abound, more real distress and aggravated misery are, perhaps, to be found, than in any other department of human life.

When a general corruption of morals, with regard to the sex, pervades all the classes of society, its effects must necessarily be, to poison the springs of domestic happiness, to weaken conjugal and parental affection, and to lessen the united exertions and ardour of parents in the care and education of their children;—effects which cannot take place without a decided diminution of the general happiness and virtue of the society; particularly as the necessity of art in the accomplishment and conduct of intrigues, and in the concealment of their consequences necessarily leads to many other vices.

The positive checks to population are extremely various, and include every cause, whether arising from vice or misery, which in any degree contributes to shorten the natural duration of human life.   Under this head, therefore, may be enumerated all unwholesome occupations, severe labour and exposure to the seasons, extreme poverty, bad nursing of children, great towns, excesses of all kinds, the whole train of common diseases and epidemics, wars, plague, and famine.

On examining these obstacles to the increase of population which I have classed under the heads of preventive and positive checks, it will appear that they are all resolvable into moral restraint, vice, and misery.

Of the preventive checks, the restraint from marriage which is not followed by irregular gratifications may properly be termed moral restraint.*

* It will be observed, that I here use the term *moral* in its most confined sense.   By moral restraint I would be understood to mean a restraint from marriage, from prudential motives, with a conduct strictly moral during the period of this restraint ; and I have never intentionally deviated from this sense.   When I have wished to

Promiscuous intercourse, unnatural passions, violations of the marriage bed, and improper arts to conceal the consequences of irregular connexions, are preventive checks that clearly come under the head of vice.

Of the positive checks, those which appear to arise unavoidably from the laws of nature, may be called exclusively misery; and those which we obviously bring upon ourselves, such as wars, excesses, and many others which it would be in our power to avoid, are of a mixed nature. They are brought upon us by vice, and their consequences are misery.*

consider the restraint from marriage unconnected with its consequences, I have either called it prudential restraint, or a part of the preventive check, of which indeed it forms the principal branch.

In my review of the different stages of society, I have been accused of not allowing sufficient weight in the prevention of population to moral restraint; but when the confined sense of the term, which I have here explained, is adverted to, I am fearful that I shall not be found to have erred much in this respect. I should be very glad to believe myself mistaken.

* As the general consequence of vice is misery, and as this consequence is the precise reason why an action is termed vicious, it may appear that the term misery alone would be here sufficient, and that it is superfluous to use both. But the rejection of the term vice would introduce a considerable confusion into our language and ideas. We want it particularly to distinguish those actions, the general tendency of which is to produce misery, and which are therefore prohibited by the commands of the Creator, and the precepts of the moralist, although, in their immediate or individual effects, they may produce perhaps exactly the contrary. The gratification of all our passions in its immediate effect is happiness, not misery, and, in individual instances, even the remote consequences (at least in this life) may possibly come under the

The sum of all these preventive and positive checks, taken together, forms the immediate check to population; and it is evident that, in every country where the whole of the procreative power cannot be called into action, the preventive and the positive checks must vary inversely as each other; that is, in countries either naturally unhealthy, or subject to a great mortality, from whatever cause it may arise, the preventive check will prevail very little. In those countries, on the contrary, which are naturally healthy, and where the preventive check is found to prevail with considerable force, the positive check will prevail very little, or the mortality be very small.

In every country some of these checks are, with more or less force, in constant operation; yet, notwithstanding their general prevalence, there are few states in which there is not a constant effort in the population to increase beyond the means of subsistence. This constant effort as constantly tends to subject the lower classes of society to distress, and to prevent any great permanent melioration of their condition.

same denomination. There may have been some irregular connexions with women, which have added to the happiness of both parties, and have injured no one. These individual actions, there-fore, cannot come under the head of misery. But they are still evidently vicious, because an action is so denominated, which violates an express precept, founded upon its general tendency to produce misery, whatever may be its individual effect; and no person can doubt the general tendency of an illicit intercuorse between the sexes, to injure the happiness of society.

VOL. I.　　　　　　C

These effects, in the present state of society, seem to be produced in the following manner. We will suppose the means of subsistence in any country just equal to the easy support of its inhabitants. The constant effort towards population, which is found to act even in the most vicious societies, increases the number of people before the means of subsistence are increased. The food, therefore, which before supported eleven millions, must now be divided among eleven millions and a half. The poor consequently must live much worse, and many of them be reduced to severe distress. The number of labourers also being above the proportion of work in the market, the price of labour must tend to fall, while the price of provisions would at the same time tend to rise. The labourer therefore must do more work, to earn the same as he did before. During this season of distress, the discouragements to marriage and the difficulty of rearing a family are so great, that the progress of population is retarded. In the mean time, the cheapness of labour, the plenty of labourers, and the necessity of an increased industry among them, encourage cultivators to employ more labour upon their land, to turn up fresh soil, and to manure and improve more completely what is already in tillage, till ultimately the means of subsistence may become in the same proportion to the population, as at the period from which we set out. The situation of the labourer being then again tolerably comfortable, the restraints to population are in some degree loosened; and, after a short period, the same retrograde and progressive movements, with respect to happiness, are repeated.

This sort of oscillation will not probably be obvious to common view; and it may be difficult even for the most attentive observer to calculate its periods.   Yet that, in the generality of old states, some alternation of this kind does exist though in a much less marked, and in a much more irregular manner, than I have described it, no reflecting man, who considers the subject deeply, can well doubt.

One principal reason why this oscillation has been less remarked, and less decidedly confirmed by experience than might naturally be expected, is, that the histories of mankind which we possess are, in general, histories only of the higher classes. We have not many accounts that can be depended upon, of the manners and customs of that part of mankind, where these retrograde and progressive movements chiefly take place.   A satisfactory history of this kind, of one people and of one period, would require the constant and minute attention of many observing minds in local and general remarks on the state of the lower classes of society, and the causes that influenced it; and, to draw accurate inferences upon this subject, a succession of such historians for some centuries would be necessary.   This branch of statistical knowledge has, of late years, been attended to in some countries,* and we may promise ourselves a

* The judicious questions which Sir John Sinclair circulated in Scotland, and the valuable accounts which he has collected in

c 2

clearer insight into the internal structure of human society from the progress of these inquiries.   But the science may be said yet to be in its infancy, and many of the objects, on which it would be desirable to have information, have been either omitted or not stated with sufficient accuracy. Among these, perhaps, may be reckoned the proportion of the number of adults to the number of marriages; the extent to which vicious customs have prevailed in consequence of the restraints upon matrimony; the comparative mortality among the children of the most distressed part of the community, and of those who live rather more at their ease; the variations in the real price of labour; the observable differences in the state of the lower classes of society, with respect to ease

that part of the island, do him the highest honour, and these accounts will ever remain an extraordinary monument of the learning, good sense, and general information of the clergy of Scotland.   It is to be regretted that the adjoining parishes are not put together in the work, which would have assisted the memory both in attaining and recollecting the state of particular districts.   The repetitions and contradictory opinions which occur are not in my opinion so objectionable; as, to the result of such testimony, more faith may be given than we could possibly give to the testimony of any individual.   Even were this result drawn for us by some master hand, though much valuable time would undoubtedly be saved, the information would not be so satisfactory.   If, with a few subordinate improvements, this work had contained accurate and complete registers for the last 150 years, it would have been inestimable, and would have exhibited a better picture of the internal state of a country than has yet been presented to the world. But this last most essential improvement no diligence could have effected.

and happiness, at different times during a certain period; and very accurate registers of births, deaths, and marriages, which are of the utmost importance in this subject.

A faithful history, including such particulars, would tend greatly to elucidate the manner in which the constant check upon population acts; and would probable prove the existence of the retrograde and progressive movements that have been mentioned; though the times of their vibration must necessarily be rendered irregular from the operation of many interrupting causes; such as, the introduction or failure of certain manufactures; a greater or less prevalent spirit of agricultural enterprise; years of plenty, or years of scarcity; wars, sickly seasons, poor-laws, emigrations and other causes of a similar nature.

A circumstance which has, perhaps, more than any other, contributed to conceal this oscillation from common view, is the difference between the nominal and real price of labour. It very rarely happens that the nominal price of labour universally falls; but we well know that it frequently remains the same, while the nominal price of provisions has been gradually rising. This, indeed, will generally be the case, if the increase of manufactures and commerce be sufficient to employ the new labourers that are thrown into the market, and to prevent the increased supply from lowering the money-price.*   But an increased

---

* If the new labourers thrown yearly into the market should

number of labourers receiving the same money-wages will necessarily, by their competition, increase the money-price of corn. This is, in fact, a real fall in the price of labour; and, during this period, the condition of the lower classes of the community must be gradually growing worse. But the farmers and capitalists are growing rich from the real cheapness of labour. Their increasing capitals enable them to employ a greater number of men; and, as the population had probably suffered some check from the greater difficulty of supporting a family, the demand for labour, after a certain period, would be great in proportion to the supply, and its price would of course rise, if left to find its natural level; and thus the wages of labour, and consequently the condition of the lower classes of society, might have progressive and retrograde movements, though the price of labour might never nominally fall.

In savage life, where there is no regular price of labour, it is little to be doubted that similar oscillations took place. When population has increased nearly to the utmost limits of the food, all the preventive and the positive checks will natu-

---

find no employment but in agriculture, their competition might so lower the money-price of labour, as to prevent the increase of population from occasioning an effective demand for more corn; or, in other words, if the landlords and farmers could get nothing but an additional quantity of agricultural labour in exchange for any additional produce which they could raise, they might not be tempted to raise it.

rally operate with increased force.   Vicious habits
with respect to the sex will be more general, the
exposing of children more frequent, and both the
probability and fatality of wars and epidemics will
be considerably greater;   and these causes will
probably continue their operation till the population is sunk below the level of the food; and then
the return to comparative plenty will again produce an increase, and, after a certain period, its
further progress will again be checked by the same
causes.*

But without attempting to establish these progressive and retrograde movements in different
countries, which would evidently require more
minute histories than we possess, and which the
progress of civilization naturally tends to counter-
act, the following propositions are intended to be
proved :—

1. Population is necessarily limited by the
means of subsistence.

2. Population invariably increases where the
means of subsistence increase, unless prevented
by some very powerful and obvious checks.†

---

* Sir James Stuart very justly compares the generative faculty
to a spring loaded with a variable weight, (Polit. Econ. vol. i.
b. i. c. 4. p. 20.) which would of course produce exactly that kind
of oscillation which has been mentioned.   In the first book of his
Political Economy, he has explained many parts of the subject of
population very ably.

† I have expressed myself in this cautious manner, because I
believe there are some instances, where population does not keep
up to the level of the means of subsistence.   But these are extreme
cases ; and, generally speaking, it might be said, that,

3. These checks, and the checks which repress the superior power of population, and keep its effects on a level with the means of subsistence, are all resolvable into moral restraint, vice and misery.

The first of these propositions scarcely needs illustration. The second and third will be sufficiently established by a review of the immediate checks to population in the past and present state of society.

This review will be the subject of the following chapters.

2. Population always increases where the means of subsistence increase.

3. The checks which repress the superior power of population, and keep its effects on a level with the means of subsistence, are all resolvable into moral restraint, vice and misery.

It should be observed, that, by an increase in the means of subsistence, is here meant such an increase as will enable the mass of the society to command more food. An increase might certainly take place, which in the actual state of a particular society would not be distributed to the lower classes, and consequently would give no stimulus to population.

––––––––

Reprinted from *Illustrations and Proofs of the Principle of Population: Including an Examination of the Proposed Remedies of Mr. Malthus, and a Reply to the Objections of Mr. Godwin and Others,* 157–179 (1822)

5

ILLUSTRATIONS AND PROOFS

OF THE

PRINCIPLE OF POPULATION:

INCLUDING

AN EXAMINATION OF THE

PROPOSED REMEDIES OF MR. MALTHUS,

AND A REPLY TO THE

OBJECTIONS OF MR. GODWIN

AND OTHERS.

By FRANCIS PLACE.

It to this day remains a problem, whether the number of our species
can be increased. GODWIN, p. 115.

LONDON:

PRINTED FOR

LONGMAN, HURST, REES, ORME, AND BROWN,
PATERNOSTER-ROW.

1822.

CHAPTER VI.

MEANS OF PREVENTING THE NUMBERS OF MAN-
KIND FROM INCREASING FASTER THAN FOOD
IS PROVIDED.

SECTION III.

IDEAS OF THE AUTHOR RELATIVE TO THE MEANS OF PREVENT-
ING THE PEOPLE FROM INCREASING FASTER THAN FOOD.

IN the preceding section we have seen one set of
propositions, and one mode of teaching the people
pointed out. Mr. Malthus, as has been shown,
insisted that, as previous steps, the poor should be
convinced they have no *right* to eat when out of
employment, and that we are bound in justice and
honour formally to disclaim their right to support,
and these proposals if adopted, he tells us, would
unite the rich and the poor more closely. The
futility of these modes of teaching and uniting have
been already shown. We will now proceed to
examine another set of propositions, which, if well
understood and steadily acted upon, would render
the former propositions altogether unnecessary.
They are, to be sure, somewhat at variance with
the former propositions, but this is by no means
an uncommon occurrence in the work of Mr.
Malthus.

Many of the facts and observations to be found in the work of Mr. Malthus, are of the greatest importance, but to make them useful to the high as well as to the low, they should be arranged so as to form a whole, and not be scattered through the work. They should be elucidated in the plainest manner, their practical consequences should be shown, as well as the way in which those consequences are to be brought about. The *higher* classes are quite as ignorant as the *lower* classes, and the middle classes are by no means too well-informed on the subject of population. Mr. Malthus himself has produced evidence of this. " It is," he says, " of the utmost importance, that the gentlemen of the country, and particularly the clergy, should not from *ignorance* aggravate the evils of scarcity every time that it unfortunately occurs. During the dearths of 1800 and 1801, half the gentlemen and clergymen in the kingdom richly deserved to have been prosecuted for sedition. After inflaming the minds of the common people against the farmers and corn-dealers, by the manner in which they talked of them or preached about them, it was but a feeble antidote to the poison they had infused, coldly to observe, that, however the poor might be oppressed or cheated, it was their duty to keep the peace."* Mr. Malthus observes, that " it does not seem entirely visionary to suppose, that if the true and permanent causes of poverty were clearly explained, and forcibly brought home to each man's bosom, it would have some and perhaps a conside-

* Vol. iii. p. 202, Note.

rable influence on his conduct, at least *the experiment has never yet been fairly tried.*"* "We must explain to them the true nature of their situation, and show them that the withholding the supplies of labour, is the only possible way of really raising its price, and that they themselves being the possessors of the commodity, have alone the power to do this."†—"We cannot justly accuse them of improvidence, and want of industry, (although he has himself accused them,) till they act as they now do, after it has been brought home to their comprehensions, that they are themselves the cause of their own poverty, that the means of redress are in their own hands, and in the hands of no other persons whatever.‡" This is all excellent; and thus has Mr. Malthus replied to himself, and proved the absurdity and cruelty of the propositions before noticed. Were what he has here proposed but properly followed up, no doubt need be entertained of a remedy. He goes on—"The population once overtaken by an increased quantity of food, and by proportioning the population to the food, we are not to relax our efforts to increase the quantity of food, and thus unite the two grand desiderata, a great actual population, and a state of society in which abject poverty and dependence are comparatively but little known ; two objects which are far from being incompatible."§

---

* Vol. iii. p. 108.   † Vol. iii. p. 114.
‡ Vol. iii. p. 108.   § Vol. iii. p. 113.

" This once effected, it (population) might then start afresh, and continue increasing for ages with the increase of food, maintaining always the same relative proportion to it.   I can conceive that this country, with a proper direction of the national industry, might in the course of some centuries contain two or three times its present population, and yet every man be much better fed, clothed (and he might have added instructed), than he is at present." *

" The prudential restraint from marriage, if it were generally adopted, by narrowing the supply of labour in the market, would soon raise its price. The period of delayed gratification would be passed in saving the earnings which were above the wants of a single man, and in acquiring habits of sobriety, industry, and economy, which would enable him in a few years to enter into the matrimonial contract without fear of its consequences. The operation of the preventive check in this way, by constantly keeping the population within the limits of the food, though constantly following its increase, would give a real value to the rise of wages. As the wages of labour would thus be sufficient to maintain a large family, every married couple would set out with a sum for contingencies, all abject poverty would be removed from society, or would be confined to a very few who had fallen into misfortunes, against which no prudence or foresight could provide."†

* Vol. iii. p. 116.   † Vol. iii. p. 86.

Yet, notwithstanding these and similar passages, Mr. Godwin accuses Mr. Malthus of being the enemy of the working man, " and *always* an advocate for low wages." Mr. Godwin, in his former reply, dwelt much upon the same topics as those which have just been noticed, but he brought his subject more home to the immediate attention of his readers, and did not obscure his statement by extraneous or irrelevant matter.

" Let us suppose (he says) that population was at this moment in England, or elsewhere, so far advanced, that the *public welfare* demanded that it should not increase." * Mr. Godwin enters into some calculations, to show how many would probably marry, and how many children each marriage *might be permitted to produce;* he then observes, that " The prejudice which at present prevails against a single life, and the notion so generally received, that a man or woman without progeny has failed in discharging one of their unquestionable duties to society, frightens many men and women into an inclination towards the marriage state. This prejudice the doctrines of the Essay on Population, when they shall come to be generally diffused and admitted, will tend to remove. If this subject were further pursued, it would lead to many observations and details, curious and important in their nature, but which would prove repulsive to the general reader, and would more properly find a place in a treatise on medicine or animal economy. †

* First Reply, p. 68.   † Ib. p. 69.

" *Another check* upon increasing population, *which operates very powerfully and extensively* in the country we inhabit, is that sentiment, whether virtue, prudence, or pride, which continually restrains the universality and frequent repetition of the marriage contract. Early marriages in this country, between a grown-up boy and girl, are of uncommon occurrence. Every one, possessed in the most ordinary degree of the gift of foresight, deliberates long before he engages in so momentous a transaction. He asks himself, again and again, how he shall be able to subsist the offspring of his union. I am persuaded, it very rarely happens in England that a marriage takes place, without this question having first undergone a repeated examination. There is a very numerous class in every great town, clerks to merchants and lawyers, journeymen in shops, and others, who either never marry, or refrain from marriage, till they have risen through the different gradations of their station to that degree of comparative opulence, which, they think, authorises them to take upon themselves the burthen of a family. *It is needless to remark, that where marriage takes place at a later period of life, the progeny may be expected to be less numerous.* If the check from virtue, prudence, or pride, operates less in the lower classes of life than in the class last described, it is that the members of those classes are rendered desperate by the oppression under which they groan ; they have no character of prudence or reflection to support, and they have nothing of that pride, arising from what is called the decent and respectable appearance a man makes among his neighbours, which should enable them to suppress the first sallies of passion, and the effervescence of a warm constitution."* Mr. Godwin anticipates the operation of the preventive check in an improved state of society, in which " The doctrines of the Essay on Population, if they be true, as J have no doubt that they are, will be fully understood, and in which no man would be able to live without character and the respect of his neighbours."† In such a state of society, the checks alluded to by Mr. Godwin would, no doubt, be sufficient, without resorting to infanticide. Mr. Malthus has also drawn a picture of an improved state of society, which, he thinks, may be realized, " in which there would be no improvident marriages, which would remove one of the principal causes of offensive war, and eradicate these two fatal disorders, internal tyranny and interal tumult, which mutually produce each other. Indisposed to a war of offence, in a war of defence, such a society would be strong as a rock of adamant. Where every family possessed the necessaries of life in plenty, and a decent portion of its comforts and conveniencies, there could not exist that desire for change, or, at best, that melancholy and disheartening indifference to it, which sometimes prompts the lower classes of the people to say, " Come what will, we can't be worse off."‡

* First Reply, p. 72.   † Ib. p. 74.
‡ Essay, vol. iii. p. 99.

"The master-spring of public prosperity," as Mr. Malthus has properly enough called the love of distinction; the hope of rising, and the fear of falling in the world, and in the moral estimation of his neighbours; "the decent pride," and the effect it produces, which has been so well spoken of by Mr. Godwin, and to which my intercourse with the world enables me to bear witness, and which would, no doubt, be equally efficacious among the commonest mechanics and labourers; if without any thing which should have the appearance of immediate self-interest in the teacher, at the expence of the scholar; if without what to the people may appear like canting; if without airs of superiority and dictation; if without figure and metaphor, means were adopted to show them how the market came to be overstocked with labour; that this was the cause of the low rate of wages — that it was impossible for real wages to rise, so as to enable them to live in comfort while they continued to keep the supply above the demand; — if it were clearly shown to them, that inevitable poverty and misery would result from marrying and having a family while this state of things continued; if familiar instances were collected of the poverty and misery, the crime and disgrace, to which indiscreet marriages too frequently led; if it were shown, that overstocking the market, even in a small degree, with labour, inevitably deteriorated the condition of every working man; — if all this were clearly and familiarly shown, on the one side, and if, on the other, it was as clearly shown, that by abstaining from marriage for even a few years, the supply of labour might be brought rather under the demand ; that, when so, its price, like that of bread, or meat, or potatoes, when scarce, would rise, and might, by their abstinence from marriage, be raised so high as to enable them to maintain themselves respectably, and give many of them a fair chance of rising in the world ; — if a hundredth, perhaps a thousandth part of the pains, were taken to teach these truths that are taken to teach dogmas, a great change for the better might, in no considerable space of time, be expected to take place in the appearance and the habits of the people. If, above all, it were once clearly understood, that it was not disreputable for married persons to avail themselves of such precautionary means as would, without being injurious to health, or destructive of female delicacy, prevent conception, a sufficient check might at once be given to the increase of population beyond the means of subsistence ; vice and misery, to a prodigious extent, might be removed from society, and the object of Mr. Malthus, Mr. Godwin, and of every philanthropic person, be promoted, by the increase of comfort, of intelligence, and of moral conduct, in the mass of the population.

The course recommended will, I am fully persuaded, at some period be pursued by the people, even if left to themselves. The intellectual progress they have for several years past been making, the desire for information of all kinds, which is

abroad in the world, and particularly in this country, cannot fail to lead them to the discovery of
the true causes of their poverty and degradation,
not the least of which they will find to be in
overstocking the market with labour, by too rapidly
producing children, and for which they will not
fail to find and to apply remedies.

" One objection to decreasing the supply of
labour (says Mr. Malthus) which perhaps will be
made, is, that *from which alone it derives its value
—a market rather understocked with labour.* This
must undoubtedly take place to a certain degree,
but by no means in such a degree as to affect the
wealth and prosperity of the country. But putting this subject of a market understocked in the
most unfavourable point of view, if the rich will
not submit to a slight inconvenience, necessarily
attendant on what they profess to desire, they cannot really be in earnest in their professions. Their
benevolence to the poor must be either childish
play or hypocrisy; it must be either to amuse
themselves, or to pacify the minds of the common
people with a mere show of attention to their
wants. To wish to better the condition of the
poor, by enabling them to command a greater
quantity of the necessaries and comforts of life,
and then to complain of high wages, is the act of
a silly boy, who gives his cake and then cries for
it. *A market overstocked with labour, and an
ample remuneration to each labourer, are objects
perfectly incompatible with each other.* In the
annals of the world they never existed together;

and to couple them even in imagination, betrays a gross ignorance of the simplest principles of political economy." *

This is all very true ; but hitherto the conduct of the rich has not only been quite as absurd as has been described, but it has also been directly in opposition to their professions. The very men who pretended to be most desirous to better the condition of the poor man, even while they were making professions to serve him, took the advantage the laws gave them to prevent even the remote possibility of a labouring man becoming chargeable to a parish, to which he did not at the moment belong by acquiring a legal settlement ; and when a man was found likely to obtain a new settlement, he was either expelled the parish, or transported back to his own ; no matter what were his prospects, or how well soever he was doing ; it was quite enough that in the opinion of the magistrates he might some day become chargeable to the parish in which he resided, if allowed to make a settlement. Thus he was imprisoned in his own parish. Having got him into this state, the next thing was to reduce him as low as possible, and to keep him so. For this purpose, the land-owners, magistrates, and principal farmers openly combined, and formed what the law in the case of the labourer treats as a conspiracy ; and having, in their capacity of conspirators, ascertained the smallest quantity of food necessary to keep the male human animal in barely working condition, this they said,

* Essay, vol. iii. p. 115.

or its equivalent in money, should be the wages paid to him ; * if he chose to marry and have children, then he was to receive from the parish " *a gallon loaf for feed, and 3d. in money for clothes, for his wife, and for each of his children once a week.*" But as this would not afford assistance to any of his family in sickness, he was to look for aid to private benevolence. But if at any time he dared to complain, he was to be punished; if he congregated, or made an attempt to congregate, for the purpose of preventing his own degradation, he was prosecuted as a felon, and told from the seat of justice, by the mouth of an English judge, that " *his crime was worse than felony, and as bad as murder,*" and sentenced to two years solitary confinement, separated from his family, and in some cases almost entirely debarred from even a knowledge of the deplorable distress and misery to which his unjust and cruel sentence had been the means of reducing them.

This has been the justice meted out by the rich to the poor ; this the intelligible proof of their desire, when associated together, to improve the condition of the working man. This is the practical lesson many are at the present moment learning in different gaols ; this is the recompence they have received at the hands of the rich, for attempting to perform their moral duties ; and this is the way, or,

* About twenty years ago a meeting so composed was held in Berkshire, and a table of wages, calculated by the price of bread, in order to ascertain the money-wages to be paid, was published, with a recommendation to those whom it might concern, not to pay more than was allowed by the table.

rather, one of the ways, the rich have taken to
" draw the bonds of society closer." Such were
the laws the British legislature thought it wise to
enact, and such the proceedings under them which
they sanctioned. Have not the poor, then, a right
to complain? Can it be of any use to preach to people thus treated, of the *law of nature excluding them
from all claim to support* under any circumstances?
Will they believe, merely because they are told so,
that these barbarous laws, savage denunciations,
cruel sentences, and conspiracies to degrade and
pauperize them, are any thing but wanton outrages
of power ; and ought any man to expect they will
be operated upon by those whom they have but too
much reason to believe are their decided enemies,
whenever their pride, their ignorance, and love of
power, induce them to suppose they have an interest in doing them mischief? Do they not know,
that the whole practice of the government, in respect to them, has been, and still is, an attempt to
keep down the wages of labour? Do they not
know that this has all along been recommended to
the government, by the gentry, the magistrates, and
the great manufacturers? Do they not know that
it has been the intention of all above them to
reduce them to the most abject state of dependence? Do they not know that, while they are
preached to, as it were, with one hand, they are
scourged with the other? Do they not know that
no attempt has been made to lead them, but that
on all occasions they have been driven? That the
laws and the magistrates have always treated them

as a seditious, dishonest, covetous, dissolute set of brutes, and that they have never been recognized in any other capacity ? *   Yes, all this they know,

---

* Among a thousand instances which might be given, the act of the 1st and 2d of the King, called the New Vagrant Act, may be cited as the most recent instance of unwise legislation. Under this act, if a man cannot find employment in his own parish, and either does not choose to become a pauper, or to remain one, but laudably endeavours to remove himself to some other place, in the hope of being able to maintain himself by the labour of his hands; if a man so circumstanced should fail to obtain employment, until his poverty had compelled him to commit an act, which any Justice of the Peace should deem to be an act of vagrancy, he may commit him to prison for any time not less than one month, nor more than three months, and there keep him to hard labour on the gaol allowance. A little time ago two men were brought before one of the Aldermen of the City of London; they had been found sleeping in the sheep pens in Smithfield Market. One of them stated that he was a farrier, and had travelled all the way from Alnwick in Northumberland, seeking employment in his business; he had endeavoured to obtain work all along the road, but without success, and had never been in London before. The other said that he had been shopman to a grocer in Shropshire, but having been long out of employment, had come to London in the hope of obtaining it. Both begged to be discharged, and promised to make their way home again in the best way they could; but to this request the magistrate would not accede. The act allows two magistrates to pass vagrants to their respective parishes at once, if they think the case requires it. The Alderman therefore, as this was the first case which had occurred under the act, carried it before the Lord Mayor. The Alderman observed that he did not like to form a precedent for his brother magistrates, yet he felt it was necessary that a rule should be laid down which might be uniformly adhered to in all future cases of this nature. In the present case he was of opinion the *prisoners* were *not justified* in coming to town without any pros-

and much more, and nothing can be so absurd as to expect their confidence can be obtained by those who treat them thus, whose pretensions to do them service are " *either childish play or hypocrisy.* "

Three things must be done, if there be where there ought to be a real desire to better the condition of the working people.

1. A repeal of all the laws relating to the combinations of workmen to increase their wages. No good reason has been or can be given for restrain-

---

pect before them, for they *must* have known that, in the present state of trade, no one would take them in, nor indeed would any one be justified in taking in a perfect stranger; and, therefore, they *must have been aware that they would ultimately become burthensome to the district where they fell. But whether their conduct arose solely from ignorance or not, he considered was immaterial ;* the magistrates could not know their minds, and could make no distinction.

The Lord Mayor agreed with the Alderman. The City Magistrates wished it to be known in the country at large, that in future they should feel themselves *bound to send all to hard labour for the term enacted, whether they were actuated by a vicious spirit of vagabondage, or with whatever professed object or speculation they came to town.* In short, *they would put the law in full force against all who could not prove reasonable assurance, or certainty of obtaining employment, as their motive for coming to London.* The men were passed home to their respective parishes. No comment is necessary, on a law which authorizes a magistrate to tell a labourer, or a journeyman mechanic, that if unable to live by the labour of his hands in his own parish, he seek it in another, and failing to obtain it, commits an act of vagrancy, he shall be punished as severely as he would be, after he had been convicted of one among many serious crimes. But it may be asked, if this be not one of those laws which induce men to commit crimes?

ing the workmen and their employers from making their bargains in their own way, as other bargains are made.

2. A repeal of the laws restraining emigration. These laws might all be repealed at once.

3. To repeal, as rapidly as possible, all restrictive laws on trade, commerce, and manufactures,* and particularly the corn laws.

Before, however, the latter sentence could be well pronounced, the rich, it might be expected, would rise in arms against both the proposition and the proposer. This would, however, only prove how very far we are from the desirable state contemplated, inasmuch as it depends upon the rich. If, however, the rich are not disposed to take this course, they, of all men, ought to cease complaining of the conduct of the poor, and the pressure of the poor's rate.

Were those in whose hands the power is held, to show a sincere desire to do but bare justice to the working people, they would find them not the last to acknowledge the intended benefit. They would be the first, not only to acknowledge the benefit intended them, but eagerly desirous to become acquainted with the truths on which their welfare so materially depends.

* There would be less difficulty and less inconvenience in carrying this recommendation into effect than is generally supposed. The committee of the House of Commons on "the depressed state of agriculture," says, " It may well be doubted whether, with the exception of silk, any of our considerable manufactures derive benefit from the *assumed protection* in the markets of this country." Report, folio 23.

Mr. Malthus seems to shrink from discussing the propriety of preventing conception, not so much it may be supposed from the abhorrence which he or any reasonable man can have to the practice, as from the possible fear of encountering the prejudices of others, has, towards the close of his work, resolved all his remedies into one, the efficacy of which he has all along doubted, and on which he seems afraid to rely. " He candidly confesses that if the people cannot be persuaded to defer marriage till they have a fair prospect of being able to maintain a family, *all our* former *efforts will be thrown away. It is not in the nature of things, that any permanent general improvement in the condition of the poor can be effected without an increase in the preventive check.* Nothing can be more true than the concluding clause of the sentence quoted, and we need give ourselves no further trouble to discuss the propriety or cruelty either of infanticide, or excluding children from parish aid. Neither would be adequate to the end proposed, and neither are likely to be adopted. Mr. Malthus confesses that his proposal to exclude them would not remove the evil, and both he and Mr. Godwin have declared that the true remedy can alone be found in preventives. It is nothing to the purpose that Mr. Godwin has, at length, persuaded himself that " we have more reason to fear a decrease than to expect an increase of people." It is time, however, that those who really understand the cause of

* Essay, vol. iii. p. 299.

a redundant, unhappy, miserable, and considerably vicious population, and the means of preventing the redundancy, should clearly, freely, openly, and fearlessly point out the means.   It is "childish" to shrink from proposing or developing any means, however repugnant they may at first appear to be; our only care should be, that we do not in removing one evil introduce another of greater magnitude.   He is a visionary who expects to remove vice altogether, and he is a driveller who, because he cannot accomplish what is impossible to be accomplished, sets himself down and refrains from doing the good which is in his power.

One circumstance deserves notice, as an objection which will probably be made—would not incontinence be increased, if the means recommended were adopted?   I am of opinion it would not; so much depends on manners, that it seems to be by no means an unreasonable expectation that if these were so improved, as greatly to increase the prudential habits, and to encourage the love of distinction, "the master spring of public prosperity," and if, in consequence of the course recommended, all could marry early, there would be less debauchery of any kind.   An improvement in manners would be an improvement in morals; and it seems absurd to suppose an increase of vice with improved morals.   Mr. Malthus has, however, set the question of continence in a very clear point of view; he says, "it may be objected, that, by endeavouring to urge the duty of moral restraint" " we may increase the quantity of vice relating to the sex.

I should be extremely sorry to say any thing which could either directly or remotely be construed unfavourably to the cause of virtue ; but *I certainly cannot think that the vices which relate to the sex are the only vices which are to be considered in a moral question, or that they are even the greatest and most degrading to the human character.* They can rarely or never be committed without producing unhappiness somewhere or other, and, therefore, ought always to be strongly reprobrated. But there are other vices, the effects of which are still more pernicious ; and there are other situations which lead more certainly to moral offences than refraining from marriage. *Powerful as may be the temptations to a breach of chastity, I am inclined to think that they are impotent in comparison with the temptations arising from continued distress. A large class of women and many men, I have no doubt, pass a considerable part of their lives consistently with the laws of chastity ; but I believe there will be found very few who pass through the ordeal of squalid and* HOPELESS *poverty, or even of long-continued embarrassed circumstances, without a great moral degradation of character.*"*

The most effectual mode of diminishing promiscuous intercourse is marriage, if all could be married while young, with reasonable hopes that propriety of conduct and a fair share of industry would save them from degradation, and the multiplied evils of the wretched poverty which exist in a poor

* Essay, vol. iii. p. 117.

man's family, and which, although much talked about, cannot be fully appretiated, even by the imagination of those whose situation precludes them from witnessing those evils for any long-continued period, as well as from feeling them. * If means were adopted to prevent the breeding of a larger number of children than a married couple might desire to have, and if the labouring part of the population could thus be kept below the demand for labour, wages would rise so as to afford the means of comfortable subsistence for all, and all might marry.   Marriage,

* Abject poverty sometimes paralizes all exertion, destroys all hope.   The extent to which it produces hard-heartedness, and extinguishes even the love of parents for their offspring, would scarcely be believed, without actual knowledge of the facts.   I have known but too many instances.   A few years ago, upon an investigation made from house to house, and from room to room, in the upper part of Drury Lane, and the courts and alleys adjoining, for the purpose of ascertaining the real state of the people, Mr. Edward Wakefield, one of the investigators, after reporting many instances, sums up his report by observing, that he "witnessed great wretchedness and misery, which appeared to be permanent.   The unhealthy appearance of the majority of the children was too apparent ; it would seem as if they came into the world to exist for a few years in a state of torture, since by no other name can I call the dirt, ignorance, want of food, and sickness, which I found to prevail."

Mr. Wakefield met with several parents evidently not bad people, yet so reckless, that all regard for themselves or their children was nearly or entirely extinguished. In a family where one child was dying and another sick, the father, who had not been always in extreme poverty, confessed that he had no hope of being able to bring up his family, and had made no application for medical aid, since death, he said, would be a relief both to the children and himself.

under these circumstances, would be, by far, the happiest of all conditions, as it would also be the most virtuous, and, consequently, the most beneficial to the whole community ; the benefits which might reasonably be calculated upon are very extensive and very numerous ; the poors rate would soon be reduced to a minimum, and the poor laws might, with the greatest ease, be remodeled and confined to the aged and helpless, or might, if it should appear advisable, be wholly abolished.   Much even of that sort of promiscuous intercourse carried on by means of open prostitution, now so excessively and extensively pernicious, would cease, and means might be found which, without greatly infringing on personal freedom, might render so much of this sort of promiscuous intercourse, as could not be prevented, less pernicious, even to those females, the most degraded and most unfortunate of all human beings ; a vast many of whom, in large towns, are doomed to continual prostitution, and of whom a very competent judge says, " With respect to the prostitutes, there are such innumerable instances of extreme misery, that I could almost cut my hand off, before I could commit so poor a wretch to additional misery ; they are miserable in the extreme. — Within our present district of Westminster, or half way down the Strand, towards Temple Bar, there may every night be found above 500 to 1000 of that description of wretches. How they can gain any profit by their prostitution, one can hardly conceive ; but they are the most hardened and despicable of the whole, notwithstanding the misery which makes them objects of compassion."*

I cannot for a moment admit the observation, however general, of well meaning people to have any weight, namely, that we are not to mitigate, by means of regulations, such a horrid mass of misery, or remove, as much as is possible, the temptation to promiscuous intercourse, as it is now indulged in, an indulgence excessively pernicious to young men, and to which a prodigious number of young women are sacrificed, lest we should seem to countenance the course of life followed by common prostitutes. A large portion of the mischief done to society by these women, and the exceedingly gross and vicious conduct they adopt, might, to a considerable extent, be prevented, were we not restrained from making the attempt, by our mistaken apprehensions, that, by interfering, our virtuous notions might be deteriorated, and our detestation of vice be diminished. But as this, as well as many other vices, owes its extent, both as to enormity and number, to the too great proportional increase of population, its great corrective must be looked for in proportioning the labourers to the demand for labour, and to the increase of the means of subsistence.

There appears, upon a view of the whole case, no just cause for despair, but much for hope, that

* The late William Fielding, Esq., chief magistrate at the Police Office, Queen Square, Westminster, in his evidence before the Police Committee of the House of Commons, in 1817, fol. 405.

moral restraint will increase, and that such physical means of prevention will be adopted, as prudence may point out and reason may sanction, and the supply of labour be thus constantly kept below the demand for labour, and the amount of the population be always such as the means of comfortable subsistence can be provided for. The improvement which, under very adverse circumstances, the mass of the people have acquired the general desire for information which exists, and the means of instruction which have been of late adopted, would be increased, and would produce a high state of knowledge, of case, and comfort, among all classes, and this country would attain an eminence in wealth, in strength, and in wisdom, far beyond any which has hitherto been known.

The Condom

III

Editor's Comments on Papers 6 Through 9

Until "the pill," the intrauterine device, and sterilization became the methods of choice, the condom was used almost everywhere and in incredible numbers. Because it is inexpensive and available, can be easily and secretly carried, and provides not only contraceptive protection but also protection against venereal disease, the condom is still widely used.

Undoubtedly, before recorded history, various animal membranes were used as condoms. The first record is generally attributed to the famous Italian anatomist, Fallopius. In 1564 he published *De Morbo Gallico, Liber Absolutissimus.* The title page and the pertinent section are reproduced along with a translation of the key paragraph. The "condom" of Fallopius was a linen cloth designed to fit only the glans of the penis. One can only surmise that he limited the sheath to the glans so that after it was put on the prepuce could be drawn "forward over the glans." This would hold it in place and, most importantly, would obviate the bother of putting it on just prior to intercourse. At any rate, as Fallopius makes clear, the purpose of the sheath was not contraception, but prevention of syphilis.

This is also true in the recommendation made by Dr. Daniel Turner in his dissertation on venereal disease, published in 1717. In the section reproduced the reader will be amused by Turner's observation that many men decline to use a condom, preferring to risk "a Clap" rather than to engage "with spears thus sheathed."

Just where the word "condom" comes from has never been resolved and is not likely to be. An interesting article, entitled "Who Was Condom?", is reproduced here. The author, E. Lennard Bernstein, M.D., goes over the well-trodden ground and concludes that there was indeed someone by the name of Cundum, an Englishman, most likely an army officer, who lived around 1700. On the other hand, the noted historian and authority on the history of contraception, Norman E. Himes, Ph.D., does not think the evidence justifies that conclusion.

Whatever the origin of the term, the development of vulcanization of rubber in 1843 revolutionized the condom. The development of this contraceptive device since that date is succinctly discussed by Dr. Himes in a section of his book, *Medical History of Contraception,* and is reproduced here.

Reprinted from *De Morbo Gallico, Liber Absolutissimus*, 52, (1564)

6

GABRIELIS

FALLOPPII MVTINENSIS

PHYSICI, ET CHIRVRGICI NO-

, STRORVM TEMPORVM EXIMII

DE MORBO GALLLICO

LIBER ABSOLVTISSIMVS

A` Petro Argelo Agatho Materate, (eo legente)
ſcriptus , iàm in gratiam hominum editus ,
& ſcholiis marginalibus illuſtratus .

*A quo etiam additæ ſunt exercitationes quædam
nobiles paſſim inſertæ , paſſim hac nota [ ]
à reliquo orationis contextu ſecretæ .*

Additus etiam 'eſt in calce de Morbo Gallico traɗatus ,
Antonii Fracanciani Bononiæ in loco eminentis
ſcientiæ Fæliciter legentis .

EDITIO PRIMA.

Non ſine Priuilegijs.

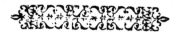

PATAVII, *Apud Lucam Bertellum* , & ſocios ,
M D L X I I I I.

78

Quoties ergo quis coiuerit abluat (fi potest) pudendum, uel panno de-
tergat: postea habeat linteolum ad menfuram glandis praeparatum; demum
cum coiuerit ponat fupra glandem, & recurrat praeputium: fi potest ma-
dere fputo, uel lotio bonum est, tamen non refert: fi timetis, ne caries oria-
tur in medio canali, habeatis huius lintei inuolucrum, & in canali ponatis,
ego feci experimentum in centum, & mille hominibus, & Deum testor im-
mortalem nullum eorum injectum.

As often as a man has intercourse, he should (if possible) wash the genitals, or wipe them with a cloth; afterward he should use a small linen cloth made to fit the glans, and draw forward the prepuce over the glans; if he can do so it is well to moisten it with saliva or with a lotion; however, it does not matter: If you fear lest caries be produced in the canal, take the sheath of this linen cloth and place it in the canal; I tried the experiment on eleven hundred men, and I call immortal God to witness that not one of them was infected.

7

SYPHILIS.

A

PRACTICAL DISSERTATION

ON THE

Venereal Difeafe.

In which, after a fhort Account of its *Nature* and *Original*; the *Diagnoftick* and *Prognoftick* SIGNS, with the beft WAYS of Curing the feveral Degrees of that Diftemper, together with fome *Hyftorial Obfervations* relating to the fame, are Candidly and without Referve communicated

In TWO PARTS

By *DANIEL TURNER*, of the College of Phyficians, *London*.

Tour Doom is paft, black Styx has heard him Swear,
This Plague fhould never be extinguifh'd here :
Since then your Soil muft ne'er be wholly free ;
Beg Heav'n at leaft to yield fome Remedy. Tate's Poem.

The Remedy is found, yet fuch thy Fate,
Poor Sinner ! That it often comes too late :
For what, alas ! avails the Art, if ftill [*fhall kill.*
Thofe whom the Pox would fpare, the wretched Quack

LONDON:

Printed for *R. Bonwicke,* Tim. *Goodwin,* J. *Walthoe,* M. *Wotton,* Manfhip, *Richard Wilkin,* Benj. *Tooke,* R. *Smith* and Tho. *Ward,* 1717.

As to the Preservative in general, I have *The Pre-* this only to add farther, that whether any *servative* such Thing be possible or not, I shall not take *from this* upon me absolutely to determine. But when *first In-* a certain Gentleman tells us, *That it will be-* *fection.* *come every Man to be modest, when at any time a* *Method of preventing may be recommended upon* *due Experience :* I can't forbear Enquiring, whe- ther we may expect the Discovery from a Mo- dest Man, or what Reward even a common moral Man will deem him worthy, (without consulting Casuists) that shall first, publish it to the World ? and indeed when it is revealed, I leave every honest Man to judge of the Con- sequence ; tho' I think there is no great Danger of such an Invention. The *Condum* being the best, if not the only Preservative our Liber- tines have found out at present ; and yet, by reason of its blunting the Sensation, I have heard some of them acknowledge, that they had often chose to risque a *Clap*, rather than engage *cum Hastis sic clypeatis.*

Reprinted from *Human Fertility*, **5**, 172–175, 186 (1940)

WHO WAS CONDOM?

By E. LENNARD BERNSTEIN, M.D.

Westport, Conn.

I

THE condom was popularized about 1840, in the time of Goodyear and Hancock, when mass production of rubber goods became possible. Similar devices, used as contraceptives, prophylactics, or talismans, were known for centuries before that time, being made of whatever material was most available, in accordance with the industrial culture of the time and place (1). The Chinese used oiled silk paper; linen was popular in Renaissance Italy; while the natives of Dutch Guiana sometimes used vegetable pods.

Here we are concerned with the origin of the name "condom," generally agreed to be derived from the name of a person never clearly identified, though certainly he is a historical figure of the first importance. In attempting to establish his identity, we must first consider the question asked by Cabanes (2). "Did Condom ever exist?" There are some who would deny him altogether. Bloch (3), for instance, suggests that the name of the instrument comes from the name of the French town of Condom, in Gascony, made famous by Bossuet; Hans Ferdy derives it from "condus," "that which preserves" (4); while Paul Richter thinks it may have come, by way of a mediaeval pun, from the Persian "kendu," or "kondu," animal guts used for storing seeds and grain (5). These impersonal derivations, however, are undocumented and find no support from other authors, who nearly all agree that Condom was a man.

In an appendix to an article on Parisian vendors of quack remedies for venereal diseases, Cabanes, in answering his own question, states:

> To the 18th century, the most gallant century of all, we owe the hatching of an invention which some consider a benefit, while others feel that it encourages prostitution; we speak of that protective covering which still carries the name of the man to whom the invention is attributed: the condom. The question has been under discussion for some time in the scientific journals as to whether Condom ever existed. Dr. Brémond, who claims to have made a minute enquiry on this subject, says that he has searched vainly for the name of this unappreciated philanthropist in the most accredited biographical dictionaries of France as well as England.

He then goes on to quote Méras on this subject:

> "*Redingotes Anglaises:* In Paris, they give this name to little bags prepared from the caecum of several quadrupeds, and which serve to protect the genital organs from absorbing the venereal virus. . . . It is about 65 years ago that this invention was originated in London by a man named Condom, and it has kept his name attached to it in this country. M. Swediaur remarks that this discoverer, whose invention made him worthy of the gratitude of his compatriots, was only dishonored in public opinion, and even had to change his name, even though he published his discovery without any mercenary motives and never made it an object of mercantile speculation."

And Cabanes concludes that:

> This article being written towards 1812, Condom, therefore, must have been born in the early years of the 18th century, since the invention dates from the middle of the same century (2).

This conclusion, however, is erroneous. The use of the condom, under that name, was well established before the middle of the eighteenth century. The first mention of the condom by name appears to occur in an English treatise on syphilis, by Dan Turner (quoted by Norman Himes) (5). This book was published in 1717. Condom, therefore, whoever he was, must have been developing his invention in the early 1700's, at the latest; possibly 30 or 40 years earlier, as we shall see. But before we return to this main question, let us read a few items which are interesting because they indicate what might be called the "social position" of the condom in the 18th century, and how well known it was at that time.

Bachaumont (6), the French Pepys, though of a later date, quotes from a letter written by a celebrated advocate of the period (1773), Linguet, who apparently became infected with a venereal disease at the famous establishment of Mme. Gourdan. Linguet puts into Mme. Gourdan's mouth a reproach to one of her ladies for not using the condom, as she had been taught, ending with the injunction: "Le Condon, c'est la loi, ma fille, et les prophètes!" (The condom is the law, young lady, and the prophets!") By this time, therefore, the condom, under that name, was part of the recognized apparatus of professional venery.

Matron Phillips had an establishment at the Green Canister in Halfmoon Street in the Strand, where she prepared condoms from dried sheep-gut. She made a fortune and retired, like other wealthy manufacturers. Then she heard that her successors were selling a product of inferior quality, whereupon, in 1776, she issued handbills deploring this deterioration, and expressing her intention of resuming business; not, however, from selfish motives, but only "out of a patriotic zeal for the public welfare." (7)

Opinion as to the desirability of the condom was, as it is today, divided. Some were enthusiastically in its favor; Linguet, Mrs. Phillips, naturally, and

the unknown author of the "Panegyrick upon Cundums," which we shall discuss later, belonged to this camp. Many, however, were not enthusiastic about the device, among them Casanova, who referred to it "as a piece of dead skin," and Dr. Turner, who mentioned that some of his friends often chose to risk infection rather than "to fight in armor," an expression current at the time which illustrates this hostile attitude (8). Condoms were, also perhaps somewhat contemptuously, called "machines." (8) Cabanes reflects this hostile outlook when he points out that as in the case of syphilis, each nation does its best to shift the responsibility for it on to its dearest enemy (2). The French called them "redingotes anglaises"; the English called them "French cloaks," "French letters," "French preservatives." As usual, Albion muddled through to victory; in France, they are now called "preservatives," nationality generally unstated, and "*English* riding-coat" is all but dead, though far more picturesque; while the dull and prosaic "*French* letter" persists in the English language, very much alive to this day.

II

Who was Condom? M. Swediaur's circumstantial account, as quoted by Méras, is undocumented, and since it is not mentioned, except in passing, by any of the modern historians of the subject, apparently it has not been taken very seriously. Méras appears to be simply following Swediaur, and has no sources of his own. Cabanes himself, placing the invention in the 18th century, invokes no authorities to his support other than Méras. Dr. Brémond, we are told, made a minute biographical inquiry in both France and England, without result.

Himes, a leading authority on the

history of contraception, says: "In the literature of venereology it is most commonly stated that the condom was invented by and named after, one Dr. Condom or Conton, a physician at the court of Charles II (1660–1685) . . . Charles II was beginning to be annoyed at the number of his illegitimate children . . . Dr. C. invented the instrument for Charles in return for which Charles with great gratitude, knighted him." (5)

Havelock Ellis states that the name "condom" dates from the 18th century and first appeared in France, and is generally considered to be that of an English physician or surgeon who invented or rather improved the appliance. He does not, however, mention his French authority. "It appears," he says at another point, "that a considerable improvement in the manufacture took place in the seventeenth or eighteenth century, and this improvement was generally associated with England." (4)

Foster (9), quoting Littré and Robin, says that Conton was the name of the inventor, and gives no further details. Bloch (3) dismisses the question by saying that "Conton" did not invent it, since it was known to Fallopius in the 16th century.

Barrere and Leland (10) state that "Condum" lived in the time of Queen Anne, and that he was simply a person noted for selling an already developed product. Several authorities, including Havelock Ellis, are said to have searched the records of the Royal Colleges of Physicians and Surgeons in vain for a Condom or Condon. Hyrtl (4) says that the name was "Gondom," a cavalier of the Restoration, who first prepared one from the amnion of a sheep. But Gondom does not appear in the records either.

The best guess, since it is at least partially documented, is given by Farmer (11):

Cundum: An obsolete appliance worn in the act of coitus to prevent infection; so called from the name of its inventor, a colonel in the Guards, *temp.*, Charles II: the modern equivalent is known as a *French Letter*.

As the source of his information, Farmer gives the following reference: "1767. Rochester, Roscommon, and Dorset, "A Panegyric Upon Cundum," p. 208."

The book referred to by Farmer is extremely rare, and does not exist, for example, in the Widener Library at Harvard. In the Sterling Library at Yale, however, we find an edition of 1777; but even more interesting, an edition of 1739, with the following title: "Poems by the Earls of Roscommon and Dorset; the Dukes of Devonshire, Buckinghamshire, &c., Vol. II. London: Printed in the year MDCC.-XXXIX."

Since the Panegyric is so difficult to find, and since it has apparently been overlooked by all the historians of the subject hitherto, some of it is quoted here. The whole poem is several hundred lines in length.

A PANEGYRICK UPON CUNDUMS

Hear, and Attend: In Cundum's might praise
I sing, for sure, 'tis worthy of a Song . . .

Hail, happy Albion, in whose fruitful Land
The wondrous (Procurer) arose, from whose
    strange Skill
In inmost Nature thou hast reap'd more Fame,
More Solid Glory, than from *Newton's* Toil,
Newton who next is England's Noblest Boast:
    (Just as Smyrna, Chios, Colophon, Rhodes,
      Argos, Salamis, and Athens, fought for
      the honor of being Homer's birthplace)
In after Times, so shall with warm Dispute,
Europa's rival Cities proudly strive,
Ambitious each of being deemed the Seat
Where *Cundums* first drew vital Air.

Curse of Disease! how many gallant Youths
Have fallen by the Iron Hand of Death,
Untimely, immature; As if, to Love,
Your everlasting Purpose, were a Crime.
But O, ye Youths born under happier Stars . . .
Be cautious, stay awhile till fitly arm'd
With *Cundum* shield, at Rummer best supply'd,
Or never-failing Rose;
By me forewarn'd, thus may you ever tread
Love's pleasing Paths in blest Security.

When was this poem written? Partridge (12) says: "In 1667 those aristocratic courtiers, wits, and poets, Rochester, Roscommon, and Dorset, issued 'A Panegyric Upon Cundum'." This is wrong. Partridge seems to have copied Farmer, and inaccurately. In the first place, the mention of Newton as "England's Noblest Boast" rules it out, since the "Principia" did not appear until 1687, and England did not boast of him enough to make him President of the Royal Society until 1703. In the second place, a footnote explains that certain lines in the poem which begin with the words "Happy the Man," are an allusion to "The Splendid Shilling," a poem beginning with the same words, and much imitated in the early years of the eighteenth century. Since Philips first published "The Splendid Shilling" in 1705, we can definitely place the Panegyric between 1705 and 1739. Its author we do not know. In the book it appears anonymously. A search of the collected works of the various Earls and Dukes included in the volume gives us no clue.

A second footnote, to the line about "the wondrous Procurer", says: "Colonel Cundum who invented them; call'd so, from his Name." Apparently this footnote was the source of Farmer's information, but why Farmer places the Colonel in the Restoration period he does not say, although the poem does tell us that in 1739 the Colonel was "Long since deceas'd."

Thompson (7), Cary (13), Partridge (12), and others, who state that the Colonel lived during the Restoration, are apparently simply following Farmer, since none of them mentions any other source. But a search of the poems of the Restoration Rakes, especially Rochester, both published and in manuscript, fails to reveal any mention of condoms or similar devices, though otherwise the whole gamut of Restoration debauchery is described in intimate detail, with several references to coitus interruptus and ejaculatio praecox, both occurring in the absence of condoms. Those who know Rochester would agree that he would undoubtedly have mentioned them somewhere if he had known about them; especially if they had been invented by a contemporary, and above all, if they had been invented at the special request of King Charles. He would not have let such a perfect occasion pass unsung, and the fact that there is no song is almost proof that there was no such occasion. Condoms are not mentioned by Pepys, Evelyn, or Wycherley, either. It is therefore very doubtful if they were sold in England during the Restoration.

Trusting the Panegyric, then, and taking it in conjunction with our other sources, we can surmise the following:

1. Cundum did exist. He was an Englishman, most likely an army officer.[1] He was probably not a physician, since his name is not recorded as such. He may have been a "procurer," unless this is only a figure of speech in the Panegyric.

[1] An English correspondent writes me: "I spent one rather fruitless morning in the Public Records Office chasing the elusive Colonel through the Domestic Papers and Army Lists of Charles II. Condon seems to have been a fairly common name then, as I came across three or four, but all of them in much inferior ranks than Colonel. I did not see any Condoms or Cundums."

(Continued on page 186)

inued from page 175)

2. He popularized or improved the "machine" some time between Rochester's death in 1680, and Dan Turner's book in 1717; so he must have been born before 1700. In 1739, he was "Long since deceas'd."

BIBLIOGRAPHY

(1) Himes, Norman E.: "Forerunners of the Modern Condom." *Janus, 42:* 1938.
(2) Cabanes, A.: "Indiscrétions de l'histoire." Paris, 1903. Vol. 1.
(3) Bloch, Iwan: "Sexual Life of Our Time." William Heinemann, Ltd., London, 1908.
(4) Ellis, Havelock: "Studies in the Psychology of Sex." Vol. VI. F. A. Davis & Co., Philadelphia, 1927.
(5) Himes, Norman E.: "Medical History of Contraception." Williams & Wilkins, Baltimore, 1936.
(6) Bachaumont, L.: "Anecdotes Piquantes." Bruxelles, 1881.
(7) Thompson, C. J. S.: "The Quacks of Old London." Brentano's, London, 1928.
(8) Grose, Francis: "Lexicon Balatronicum." London, 1811.
(9) Foster, F. P.: "Encyclopaedic Medical Dictionary." New York, 1892.
(10) Barrere, A., and Leland, C. G.: "Dictionary of Slang, Jargon, and Cant." London, 1889.
(11) Farmer, J. S.: "Slang and Its Analogues." Privately Printed, 1891.
(12) Partridge, E.: "Dictionary of Slang, etc.," New York, 1937.
(13) Cary, H. N.: "Slang of Venery and Its Analogues." Chicago, 1916.

Reprinted from *Medical History of Contraception*, 201–206 (1963)

9

MEDICAL
HISTORY OF
CONTRACEPTION

by

Norman E. Himes, Ph.D.

Foreword by
Robert Latou Dickinson, M.D., F.A.C.S.

Preface by
Alan F. Guttmacher, M.D.

GAMUT PRESS, INC.

New York

1963

§5 THE CONDOM SINCE THE VULCANIZATION OF RUBBER

Widespread, common use of the condom, however, had to await the vulcanization of rubber, first successfully carried out by Goodyear and Hancock in 1843–44.[56] This lowered costs so materially that the condom immediately won a place for itself.[57] Thereafter virtually every late nineteenth century treatise, and certainly every twentieth century treatise, dealing with technique gave it a prominent place. There are at least a hundred such pamphlets and volumes; and no useful purpose would be served by citing the literature, for many of them are mentioned in Part Five, which discusses briefly the developments since 1800.

The use of liquid latex and the introduction of automatic machinery has cheapened the condom still further in the last decade. Sales are enormous. There are no statistics available of the number manufactured in England and Germany, but in the United States sales approach 317 million annually. In fact it has recently come to light in an American Circuit Court of Appeals that one American manufacturer sold 20,000,000 in *one year* to druggists and doctors.[58] J. Schmid of New York says that the fifteen chief manufacturers in the United States produce a million and a half a day. Harmsen reports[59] that one German firm put twenty-four million rubber condoms on the market every year. He declares that since the war there has been an extraordinary increase in their use in Germany. Though the birth-control clinics seldom recommend the condom,[60] it is increasingly used by the general populace, doubtless because

[56] As early as 1872, Proksch (*op. cit.*, pp. 50–51) proposed the feasibility of rubber condoms. It is difficult to credit the statement of Streich [*Sudhoff's Archiv. f. Gesch. d. Med.*, xxii (1929), 210] that the rubber glans condom was first introduced into Europe from America through the World Exposition held in Philadelphia in 1876. Must Yankee inventive genius be credited with this also? I doubt it; yet the fact that rubber was first vulcanized here may lend credence to the view. The English claim Hancock invented the process, but the honor is generally (and I believe correctly) attached to Goodyear's name.

[57] Though those made in our time of animal membranes are undoubtedly superior in strength, they have never, for economic and sanitary reasons, proved as popular. Butherand and Duchesne give a description of the manufacture of condoms in *Lyon Médicale*, Oct. 21 and 28; Nov. 4, 1877.

[58] The official citation is Youngs Rubber Corporation, Inc., v. C. I. Lee & Co., et al, 45 Federal Reporter, 2nd Series, 103. *Cf.*, Morris L. Ernst, "How We Nullify." [New York] *Nation*, cxxxiv, 113–114 (January 27, 1932). See p. 114.

[59] In Sanger and Stone [Eds.], *Practice of Contraception*, p. 153.

[60] The Cambridge, England, clinic and the Russian clinics are exceptions. Since this was written the English clinics are using sheaths increasingly. A recent statistical study by Enid Charles supports well, though I do not think it conclusively proves, the thesis that the condom is the most reliable contraceptive we have. Havelock Ellis took this view many years ago.

it is cheap, easily available, generally known, and also the best protection against infection. The height of mechanized diffusion of contraceptives seems to have been reached in one respect in Germany and Holland, where for many years condoms have been sold by coin slot-machines! In the United States vending machines have likewise been introduced; and more are sold in gasoline stations and tobacco shops than in drug stores. Thus enters a new problem in social control.

§6   MODERN ECONOMIC ASPECTS OF THE INDUSTRY[61]

We have spoken of the revolution following the vulcanization of rubber, which caused, in turn, all but the disappearance of the skin condom. Sales and use expanded enormously, facilitated by substantially lowered costs. In the last half decade (1930–1935) the industry has experienced another technological revolution: the manufacture of condoms from liquid latex instead of from crepe rubber. We have noted the sales results. It remains now to sketch certain other aspects of this change: the processes involved, the problems of distribution, cost, competition, price and quality; the methods of testing.

The processes of modern manufacture are of interest. The substitution of liquid latex for crepe rubber is one of the most important recent technical changes, the introduction of automatic machinery being another. The latex is the whole sap of the rubber tree, suspended in water, concentrated by evaporation, stabilized by ammonia. Until recently rubber condoms were made of crepe rubber masticated and dissolved. There were difficulties incident to mastication, solution and fire hazard. Now all American manufacturers save one has ceased to make the "cement" rubber condom of crepe rubber. The latex product resists aging from three to five years, is odorless and often thinner. The new process requires constant attention of highly skilled chemists and technicians since the use of colloidal suspensions in this industry is new. Even the old processes have been so modified through changes in compounding, and in the use of the "hot" cure instead of the "cold" cure utilizing sulphur chloride gas, that the newer product does not deteriorate so rapidly. Accompanying these changes has been the introduction of continuous, automatic machinery which has also contributed to lower costs and hence to a doubled market. (See below for an estimate of prices and the total value of the output of the industry.)

In the Killian process, glass tubes (also called "forms" and "bottles") about 14 inches long and $1\frac{1}{4}$ inches in diameter dip into tanks filled with

---

[61] Parts of this section are extracted from a report of Mr. Randolph Cautley to the National Committee on Maternal Health, and almost the entire section is based on his report.

ivory-colored latex at the rate of 1 per second on each side of a dual machine which operates 24 hours per day. Rotating smoothly through the compound, they gather a dripping film of latex and rise out of the tank elevating their angle with the continuous chain to which they are attached, distributing the running liquid evenly about the blunt end of the form and preventing the formation of a drop at the tip. They are dried by hot air, dipped a second time, and dried again. The protective bead or ring at the open end is then rolled by rotating cylindrical brushes, after which vulcanization takes place in a long overhead hot air duct followed by a hot water bath. The films of latex are partially dried and dusted with talc, and are then stripped from the forms by brushes quite like the bead-rollers but so placed as to roll the condoms completely off the forms whence they fall to continuous belt-conveyors. The belts take them into an adjacent room and deposit them on a table where women unroll and snap them to remove the wrinkles (induced by the rolling) before they have time to result in permanent sticking. Meanwhile the glass forms have been cleaned by having passed through brushes and hot water, and are beginning to dip again. The entire conveyor, about 500 feet long, and containing about 4,000 glass forms in two series, one on either side of the machine, is driven at a constant rate of speed by two large cogs set about 250 feet apart in a completely air-conditioned room.

The Shunk process differs principally in the method of dipping and in the method of cure. Where the Killian machine rotates the forms through the compound at an angle of 45° with the level of the fluid, the Shunk unit dips the forms vertically into the compound through the elevation and lowering of the compound tanks, and the forms remain perfectly stationary except for rotation. The compound runs down the form and forms a hard, thick tip at the very end of the condom. The process is not completely automatic, in that labor is required to transfer the forms back and forth between the dipping machine and the conveyor, which unifies the whole process. The forms, instead of being fastened to one conveyor, are divided into units of 24, each unit being a separate board or rack. Four of these racks are placed on the dipping arm and taken off after the dipping. Finally, after vulcanization in hot water, the forms and condoms are cooled by a spray of cold water before dipping. The Killian machine is the larger of the two, being adapted to produce 1200 gross per day, while the Shunk unit will produce in the neighborhood of 700 gross per day.

Each step in the compounding, dipping and curing presents opportunities for wide variations in the properties of the resulting condoms. The pH, viscosity and ingredients of the compound are especially important in their influence upon the final product. Continuous agitation of the compound is sometimes necessary to prevent "creaming," a condition in which the rubber particles rise to the top as do the fat particles in milk. Humidity and temperature must be controlled in the dipping, and the temperature of the cure or vulcanization is also quite important. Particles of dust, oil or other foreign matter in the compound at the time of dipping conduce to defective condoms. The cure affects the aging characteristics and other physical properties. With a viscosity too high, the compound is likely to permit the formation of fine bubbles, which in the finished condom are seen as holes, thin spots and blisters. Weight, size, thickness, elasticity, tensile strength, aging quality, resistance to abrasion, reaction with physiological fluids, reaction with lubricants, porosity, presence of foreign matter, etc., are all determined by the technological processing, equipment and supervision.

American condoms are generally much thinner than the European product, for the latter are predominantly of the "cement" type. Those produced in air-conditioned rooms are remarkably free from dirt and foreign matter.

The patents of the industry are chiefly in the hands of three competing producers; and while there has been talk of a patent pool this has not materialized.

Production costs and prices are of importance. Figures on manufacturing costs are extremely difficult to obtain, and they vary, of course, not only with efficiency in production, with control of patents, but with size of overhead (generally speaking, the smaller the output the larger the overhead), with care taken in testing, means of marketing, etc. It is a common economic phenomenon that marketing costs are high in relation to manufacturing costs. This is illustrated very well in the industry under consideration. In a preliminary cost estimate[62] of $2.17 per gross, distribution is roughly as follows: $1.30 is for salesmen, a conservative estimate; 41¢ for overhead (perhaps higher than average); and 20¢ for raw materials. The small balance is for stamping, rolling, packaging, etc. Testing costs vary between nothing and 23¢–25¢, with an average probably around 5¢.

Distributors all over the country can now buy bulk condoms from the leading manufacturers for less than 50¢ a gross, and most of them are sold in bulk by manufacturers to distributors who then resell them, using their own brands and packages. There are countless numbers of brands on the market varying greatly in quality and selling to the retailer mainly from 50¢ to $1.50 a gross, though some run as high as $5.50 or $10.80 a gross.

Retail prices vary greatly in this anarchical industry. One brand sells at retail 3 for 75¢. The retail price of a gross is $36. These can be pur-

[62] Of tentative value only. It is very difficult to get at cost figures in the industry.

chased from the manufacturer for $6. Is it any wonder that the druggists are being undersold, and that today retail druggists sell only about one-third of the condoms annually produced in the United States? In the face of these economic facts it hardly seems possible that the trade can be restricted to regular retail drug outlets.

It is estimated that the druggists sell in the vicinity of 700,000 gross annually at an average price of around $16 per gross, or approximately $11,000,000. Other retail outlets and peddlers sell about 1,400,000 gross annually at an average price of about $10 per gross, or about $14,000,000 per year. Thus we have an annual retail value of $25,000,000. At the price of 3 for 50¢, or $24 a gross retail, the annual sales to consumers would be valued at roughly $50,000,000. But since the present average price, under the conditions of cut-throat competition prevailing in the industry, is probably nearer $12 a gross or $1 per dozen, the annual value of sales to consumers is probably nearer $25,000,000 annually. An annual export quota of about 200,000 gross must be allowed for in estimating domestic consumption.

As is often the case in a modern industry a few producers have cornered the major portion of the market. The three leading manufacturers are responsible for 70 per cent of the daily production; the leading four for 80 per cent; the leading six for 88 per cent of the output; and all others for 12 per cent.

In this anarchically competitive industry emphasis is upon production at a low price rather than upon quality of output. Price factors have likewise led to a more than proportional increase in sales through non-drug-store channels (pool rooms, food stores, gasoline stations, etc.). Drug stores are being undersold. They have considered condoms "whisper items," and have consequently insisted on margins of profit approaching those on drugs. It is a common saying in the drug trade that the sale of condoms pays the store rent.

There are four chief methods of testing; a fifth is used in England. (1) During the "Flip Test" an operator sits at a table with bulk condoms at her left elbow using her right hand to pick up individual condoms. As they fill with air this is imprisoned in the tip end by a scissor-like action of two fingers of the left hand. The entire condom is thus elongated and the tip distended. This is supposed to show up holes and facilitate rejection of those containing wrinkles or creases. Sometimes the condom is turned over. However, holes, weak spots and dirt specks are not well perceived by this method of testing, which is the least satisfactory of the methods now in use. None the less, this is all the testing most "tested" condoms ever get. (2) An operator fills a dozen condoms with air from a compressed air jet, squeezing them against the body, bursting some and leaving others intact.   Visual examination may or may not follow.   (3) An operator blows down a condom held vertically with open end up, imprisons some air, and turns the inflated tip to the cheek to detect air streams.   (4) A cheek test follows full inflation.   At the same time there is a visual examination for dirt, wrinkles, creases, etc.   There is a careful, deliberate visual examination of the condom inflated and uninflated, about 15 seconds being spent upon each one.   This is the best test in general commercial use in the U. S. A. today.   (5) The following test is used by an English manufacturer. Condoms are inflated to about 6 x 8 inches and placed on moving belts about 5 or 6 inches apart.   As they are carried slowly across the room—transit occupies 20 to 30 minutes—those which become deflated because of holes or defects drop to the floor between the belts.   Several distributors in this country employ visual examination before a frosted glass pane.   The laboratory of a certain manufacturer occasionally tests for tensile strength by stretching a portion of his product on a vertical rod; another claims to inflate every third condom with smoke, the outpourings of which are more readily visible.

Testing by the consumer is usually difficult because of his inexperience. Inflation with water and breath are commonly used.   The disadvantage of the latter is that exhalation into the condom sometimes causes the powder thereon to form a sticky paste and thus to cover up defects.   The percentage of condoms which meet high standards of manufacture vary greatly with different brands.   And even some of the good ones are not uniformly good. The habits of consumers militate against effective purchasing of quality products only.   These devices are usually purchased rolled, and never examined until the crucial moment.   Until the habits of consumers change, it is probably not likely that manufacturers and distributors will consider it commercially advisable to maintain more rigid testing standards.

It seems clear from the data presented above that the economic, social and medical problems of the production, sale and distribution of condoms are considerable.   Certainly we have in the greatly increased use of this instrument nothing short of a revolution in the sexual relations of mankind. How astounded Fallopius would be, could he return to earth and observe what a change has taken place since he invented his linen glans covering! Little did he realize how social forces would catch up his invention and improve and diffuse it until its use became common knowledge.   This process of democratization is the subject of the next Part.

Rhythm and Safety

IV

Editor's Comments on Papers 10, 11, and 12

Any consideration of the so-called rhythm, or safe period, method of contraception must pay homage to Saint Thomas Aquinas (1225–1274). His philosophy is said, by the Roman Catholic Church, to be the only right one, so that his writings are still of great interest today. Saint Thomas' most important publication is *Summa contra Gentiles*, which he began in 1259 and finished in 1264. Therein is to be found the prohibition of birth control. And the reason given is that it is "against nature." Bertrand Russell wonders, rather slyly, why Saint Thomas does not prohibit life-long celibacy as being against nature!

The scope of this book does not permit a discussion of how the Catholic Church concluded that the rhythm method is not really birth control in the usual sense and thus is not proscribed. Suffice it to say that because this method does have the blessing of the Church, it has enjoyed widespread popularity if not universal success.

Until Ogino, a Japanese investigator, straightened things out with his publication in 1932, little luck was had with the method because the prevailing concept of the involved physiology was wrong. The work of Annie Besant (1847–1933), an English theosophist who spent much of her life attempting to convey birth control information to the masses, provides an example. She carefully quotes a statement by a Dr. Tyler Smith: "In the middle of the interval between the (menstrual) periods, there is little chance of impregnation taking place." In this section, two more key papers are presented to show just how wrong that physiology was.

F. A. Pouchet, M.D., was a French zoologist of considerable distinction and international reputation. In 1842, he published his classic paper on the "Positive Theory of Fertilization among Animals." There are no data, so that what we see is more philosophical than physiological, yet Pouchet came close to the truth. Early in his paper he points out that the menstrual flow results from ovarian activity. As proof he cites the fact that following removal of the ovaries, menstruation stops as well as the sexual appetite. But after making this correct start he falls into the old trap of assuming that sexual excitement in the woman reaches its peak during menstruation and therefore "the menstrual period of the woman also has very close and incontestable ties with conception. . . ." He concludes that the ova are released "somewhat after the menstrual period . . ." which is, of course, correct but he sides with his predecessors in believing that this release occurs very close to the menstrual period as shown by his statement ". . . the union which occurs at the end of the menstrual period often determines conception. . . ." However, astute observer that he obviously was, he cautioned that conception may take place several days later. In short, he came close. At the very least, his paper is important because it establishes that conception occurs only at a certain time during the cycle, not throughout it.

Next we turn to a popular textbook by R. T. Trall, M.D., an American physician. Chapter XII of his *Sexual Physiology* is reproduced here. He begins that chapter by continuing the Malthus-Place battle, in which he argues that women have a right to enjoy sexual intercourse while regulating the number of children they bear. Then he discusses methods of contraception and begins with the rhythm method. But first he laments the lack of knowledge and the fact that the subject is not taught in the medical schools. Warming up to his subject he states that ". . . if sexual intercourse is limited to about one-half of each month, pregnancy will seldom occur." More specifically he advises that one abstain for about 12 days following the cessation of the menstrual flow. In view of the fact that ovulation occurs about nine days following the cessation of the flow in a woman with a regular 28-day cycle, this is sound advice, although it calls for abstinence during the immediate post-menstrual period which is generally a very safe time. Trall insists that the majority of women can tell when the ovum passes the *os uteri* and therefore can calculate their own period of fertility. This is to be questioned for many reasons, including the data he reports which show that the ovum passes into the vagina on about the sixth day after cessation of the menstrual flow. Leaving the safe-period method, the author addresses himself to other possibilities, and here we see that ". . . coughing, sneezing, jumping, lifting, injections, etc., prevent pregnancy . . . because they occasion the uterus to contract, and if its contractions are sufficiently vigorous and prolonged the egg surely expelled." Were it only that simple!

As already stated, basic knowledge was lacking until Ogino in Japan and Knaus in America published their papers in 1932 and 1933, respectively. The article by Ogino is reproduced here without translation simply because no translation is required to decipher his graphs, which clearly show the period of ovulation in his subjects. He recommends a period of abstinence of seven days, while Knaus trims it down to three days. Also, as Ogino emphasizes, if there is irregularity in the cycle, abstinence would have to be for a longer period. There is still another factor. Sexual stimulation can bring about ovulation earlier than would have occurred in the absence of such stimulation. This too will throw the calculation off.

In summary, although the Catholic Church only sanctions the rhythm method, it has not gained great and lasting popularity because of the requirement of a period of abstinence and because of the margin for error.

Reprinted from *Librairie encyclopédique de Roret*, 99–107 (1842)

10

THÉORIE POSITIVE

DE LA

FÉCONDATION

DES

MAMMIFÈRES,

Basée sur l'observation de toute la série animale;

PAR

F.-A. POUCHET,

DOCTEUR MÉDECIN,

PROFESSEUR DE ZOOLOGIE AU MUSÉUM D'HISTOIRE NATURELLE DE ROUEN,
MEMBRE DE L'ACADÉMIE DES SCIENCES, LETTRES ET ARTS DE CETTE VILLE,
ET DE PLUSIEURS ACADÉMIES FRANÇAISES ET ÉTRANGÈRES, ETC.

La nature obéit à des lois et à des règles
dans l'immense variété de ses productions
(TIEDEMANN. *Physiolog.* Tome I, p. 44.)

PARIS.

LIBRAIRIE ENCYCLOPÉDIQUE DE RORET,

RUE HAUTEFEUILLE, N° 10 BIS.

1842.

Positive Theory of Fertilization Among Mammals

Ninth Fundamental Law

Fertilization shows an unvarying relation to the emission of menstrual fluid; such is manifest in the human species where it is easy to indicate precisely the definite intermenstrual period when conception is physically impossible and the period when conception has a greater probability of occurrence.

If, as has become evident due to the authoritative studies of Buffon, F. Cuvier, Geoffroy St.-Hilaire, Burdach, Garnot, Lesson and our own observations, it has been shown that there exists a relation between the menstrual period of the woman and the love-making period of mammals and if, as we now believe, it has also been indubitably established that this period makes its presence known among members of the highest ranks by a true menstruation, it becomes incontestable that, since these phenomena are the outward expression of generative power and since they are the unique indicators of the organic procésses involved here, the appearance of menstrual flow in the woman also bears an extremely close and indisputable relation to the ability to conceive children. It seems to us that one cannot push aside these rational propositions without ignoring all the laws of logic.

M. Magendie [1] and all physiologists have noted the connection here.

Burdach [2] has analyzed the problem with extreme preciseness in this way: "Given that mestruation entails a heightened activity of the genital organs, it appears furthermore," he says, "as a sign and condition of the generative ability in the woman and it is always an exception to the rule that a woman who has no menstrual flow whatsoever is fertile. Menstruation is without a doubt rather the effect than the cause of the generative ability because it is none other than the manifestation of a vital activity in the organs whose only function is to reproduce, but in life any effect stems from its cause and each force establishes its presence only by its outward

manifestations. Therefore, the generative ability of the woman is kept up by menstruation, seeing that it periodically excites the vitality of the genital organs and since the tubes of the ovaries further show turgescence during this activity, it can be considered, in accord with Schweighaeuser [3], as a periodic maturation of the very substance that produces the fruit."

The entire rational theory of fertilization is contained in these few words.

Menstruation happens only during the time when the woman is able to conceive. We should naturally conclude that this function has an obvious close relation to the activities taking place in the ovaries and the emission of eggs which is the product of it. This, then, is a quite natural physiological result. With the support of this assertion one can add that we know women who never become regulated and generally have no children: the absence of menstruation indicating without doubt a weakness in the organic forces of the genital apparatus and the impotence in which this occurs either in failure to secrete or in failure to nourish its products or the ova.

Physiologists and doctors delivering babies, following Levret [4], Delamotte [5] and Baudelocque [6], are unanimous on this point and further state that the deprivation of these conditions is an almost certain cause of sterility.

Parent-Duchatelet [7] and the statisticians who have studied prostitutes have shown that they ordinarily have no children during the time they are so engaged, regardless of whether it should at first seem to be entirely otherwise. But the sterility of "public women" can be explained several ways; it is due either to the fact that they keep the genital organs in a state of continual orgasm which prevents the ova from attaching or to the fact that among these women, exceedingly early in life, the emission of ova ceases to occur, which is evidenced by the absence of menstrual flow that is often observed among them. Parent-Duchatelet makes this assertion: "And what is for sure," he says, "is that all those who are led to repent in renouncing prostitution enter the Bon-Pasteur convent without being regular, and what is even more extraordinary is that menstruation does not reestablish itself during their stay in this place despite the rest which they enjoy and the good food they are given." Finally, this sterility, as Morgagni [8] has seen, can be tied to the fact that the fallopian tubes are found to be thickened or obstructed by the continued excitation that the courtesans maintain in their genital organs.

In the works of Rondelet and Joubert are listed cases, it is true, of women who conceive without ever being regular; D. Wiel [9], de la Motte [10], M. Maygrier [11], M. Mondat [12] and M. Velpeau [13] report similar examples. But, in those cases, if the constitution of these women did not permit the monthly period to show itself by an apparent flow of blood, certainly the internal sex organs did not experience excitation any less periodically during the time the ovaries emitted their products. However, everything happened in the natural way, following processes analogous to those that are observed normally among a great number of mammals, of which the procreative ability does not reveal itself except in the turgescence of the internal organs and the intense activity which accompanies it, but which never discloses itself with the aid of any apparent exterior indication and very often is not known except for the simple expulsion of an abundance of mucus.

The emission of blood constitutes such a tiny part of the phenomenon that often, after it has stopped, one discovers that the menstrual process nonetheless does not yet occur for a certain length of time, but that the changes which it inaugurates in the organization are confined to the internal apparatus without giving any outer clues in a trace of blood. Cabanis [14], who has clearly understood this periodic internal plethora, even says he has sometimes seen it continue in certain women for several years after the cessation of flow.

According to what we observe in the majority of mammals and following the various exceptions that have been pointed out with regard to the human species, among which certain groups manage to perpetuate themselves even though the women extrude only an insignificant quantity of blood during the menstruation period, and further considering the point that some non-regular women have at times conceived, it becomes manifest that the emission of blood does not constitute the major part of the phenomenon, and that it is only a secondary feature.

Nevertheless, if the emission of blood is not in any way one of the essential activities of the menstrual period, this emission, among the species that experience it, serves to act as a revealing witness of the organic movement which is happening in the ovaries. But this fluid is not a regulator of uterine activity nor a pool of blood put on reserve for nutrition of the fetus, because many animals that never experience this periodic evacuation yet nevertheless produce a great number of off-spring. What offers a powerful argument in favor of this opinion is that following the extirpation of ovaries, menstruation stops as well as the sexual appetite [15].

Yet, as we have previously proved, if the rutting time is not marked for the majority of mammals by an emission of blood, this happens at least with many animals of this category; the analogy is everywhere obvious because among those where no blood flows from the vulva, as states Cuvier [16], the swelling which is observed in the genital parts clearly announces the presence of this fluid, and this proves that the period of conception is tied to rutting and the emission of blood.

In following the laws of analogy and without separating our reason from the authority of facts and observation, if we admit, as unimpeachable proof, that periodic sexual excitation in mammals and the menstrual period are identical, since from another angle it is well known that the excitable period of mammals is the only time when conception is possible, we find ourselves obliged to conclude, as I previously stated, that the menstrual period of the woman also has very close and incontestable ties with conception; it remains only to determine them in a positive manner, and to establish precisely the intermenstrual period during which the ova are emitted by the ovaries, and during which conception is consequently possible. This is where we have arrived after detailed consideration in studying the internal and external phenomena which accompany this important activity.

The law which we are the first to announce is so absolutely true, so obvious, that the scholars of every century have conceded its existence with respect to animals; and with women themselves where so many sources of error could have led observers astray, all the physiologists seem to have detected it beforehand, from the time when the men of antiquity established the bases of science up to our own epoch where men have illustrated this point so brilliantly. In fact, when we read the works of Aristotle [17], Richerand [18], Adelon [19], Brachet [20], Burdach [21], Pell-etier [22], Dugès [23], we realize that all are unanimous in considering conception as occurring usually most readily around the time which follows the menstrual period. The authors who have written on childbirth state the exact same opinion when they deal with this matter, as we note particularly in the writings of M. Maygrier [24].

As we see it, the scholars who preceded us have left us nothing less than the glory of illustrating in a definitive way a fact which, in their minds, existed only as a vague presentiment, engendered by the influence of observations, but stated with no precision whatsoever, and which they in no way attempted to associate with a general and fundamental law.

However, while granting that the scholars we have just cited presented a fact almost exactly, in declaring that a union which occurs at the end of the menstrual period often determines conception, it is necessary to add further that it is nevertheless not always immediately following this period that the process occurs, and that very often the actual fertilization itself, or impregnation of the ova by seminal fluid, happens quite a long time afterward. Indeed, it is necessary essentially to recognize the fact that impregnation does not always take place, as is popularly believed, at the moment of union of the sexes but frequently a fairly good while later and only when the product of the ovary, detached from its secreting source, traverses the organs filled with fertilizing fluid. But even though the exact time of fertilization may vary, one can still confirm the fact that there are definite signs which indicate clearly and positively the moment when this act is physically impossible, for there are precise indices announcing the moment of the original release of the ova, which occurs somewhat after the menstrual period, and others that attest to the fact that the uterus is no longer capable of accepting the product of the ovary and that the latter has gone by without being fertilized.

In summary, we see therefore that all authors (we can say this because there are few exceptions) have conceded a positive fact in admitting that conception occurs at one certain period in particular, and that on the sole authority of observation; but they have not defined this point in detail because, being dominated by an erroneous idea, they found themselves obliged to respect it; namely, that fertilization takes place in the ovary and that it is the ovary which controls the maturation of the ova and their eventual release. To generalize the fundamental laws of this function, therefore, it took courage to rise up against the theories which flourished not long ago in the schools and whose foundations we are gradually undermining. Perhaps our efforts may appear premature, but soon the truth will make itself known, and our work, so courageous today, at times so hopeless, and for which we fight against the authority of so many previous centuries and against the power of so many scholars, our work will receive justice. Then, all our work, at first bitterly censured, will attract attention and will be hallowed as a new truth acquired for science.

References

1. Précis élémentaire de physiologie [Basic summary of physiology], Paris, 1817, Vol. 2, p. 416.
2. Traité de physiologie considérée comme science d'observation [Treatise on physiology considered as a science of observation], Paris, 1837, Vol. 1, p. 294.
3. Sur quelques points de physiologie relatifs au foetus [On several points of physiology relative to the fetus], p. 2.
4. L'art des accouchements démontré par des principes physiques et mécaniques [The art of childbirth illustrated by principles of physics and mechanics], Paris, 1766, p. 41.

5. Traité complet des accouchements [Complete treatise on childbirth], Paris, 1765, Vol. 1, p. 35.
6. L'art des accouchements [The art of childbirth], Paris, 1815, Vol. 1, p. 181.
7. De la prostitution dans la ville de Paris, considérée sous le rapport de l'hygiène publique, de la morale et de l'administration [On prostitution in the city of Paris, considered in relation to public hygiene, morality and administration], Paris.
8. De sedibus et causis morborum, etc., etc. Naples, 1762.
9. Observ. rar., Vol. 2, p. 323.
10. Traité complet des accouchements [Complete treatise on childbirth] p. 53.
11. Dictionnaire des sciences médicales [Dictionary of medical sciences], Vol. 32, p. 377.
12. De la stérilité [On sterility], 1833, p. 144.
13. Traité complet des accouchements [Complete treatise on childbirth], Vol. 2, p. 117.
14. Rapport du physique et du moral de l'homme [Relation of the physical and the mental in man], Paris, 1824, Vol. 1, p. 328.
15. Burdach, Physiologie considéreé comme science d'observation [Physiology considered as a science of observation], Vol. 1, p. 35.
16. Leçons d'anatomie comparée [Lessons on comparative anatomy], Paris, 1805, Vol. 5, p. 125.
17. Histoire des animaux [History of the animals], Book 8, p. 423.
18. Nouveaux éléments de physiologie [New elements of physiology], Paris, 1833, Vol. 3, p. 293.
19. Physiologie de l'homme [Physiology of man], Vol. 3, p. 126.
20. Physiologie [Physiology], p. 350.
21. Traité de physiologie considérée comme science d'observation [Treatise on physiology considered as a science of observation], Vol. 1, p. 295; Vol. 2, p. 118.
22. Physologie médicale et philosophique [Medical and philosophical physiology], Vol. 4, p. 322.
23. Physiologie comparée de l'homme et des animaux [Comparative physiology of man and the animals], Paris, Vol. 3, p. 258.
24. Dictionnaire des sciences médicales [Dictionary of medical sciences], Vol. 32, p. 371.

Reprinted from *Sexual Physiology: A Scientific and Popular Exposition of the Fundamental Problems in Sociology*, 5th ed., 201–214 (1867)

11

SEXUAL PHYSIOLOGY:

A Scientific and Popular Exposition

OF THE

FUNDAMENTAL PROBLEMS IN SOCIOLOGY

By R. T. TRALL, M. D.,

AUTHOR OF THE "HYDROPATHIC ENCYCLOPEDIA;" "HAND-BOOK OF HYGIENIC MEDI-
CATION;" "UTERINE DISEASES AND DISPLACEMENTS;" "PATHOLOGY OF THE REPRO-
DUCTIVE ORGANS," AND OTHER WORKS; PRINCIPAL AND FOUNDER OF THE NEW
YORK AND MINNESOTA HYGEIO-THERAPEUTIC COLLEGES; MEMBER OF THE
NEW YORK ASSOCIATION FOR ADVANCEMENT OF SCIENCE AND ART, ETC.

FIFTH EDITION.

NEW YORK:
MILLER, WOOD & CO., PUBLISHERS,
No. 15 LAIGHT STREET.
LONDON: J. BURNS, 1 WELLINGTON ROAD, CAMBERWELL.

1867.

CHAPTER XII.

REGULATION OF THE NUMBER OF OFFSPRING.

"WOMAN'S RIGHTS."—No truth is to my mind more self-evident, no rule of right more plain, no law of Nature more demonstrable, than the right of a woman to her own person. Nor can this right be alienated by marriage. "Life, liberty, and the pursuit of happiness," and also health—without which life and liberty are of little account, and the pursuit of happiness impossible—are God-given prerogatives, and inhere in the person, male or female; and all statutes, ceremonies, creeds, institutions or usages, which in any respect contravene the fundamental law of absolute personal freedom, in all the relations of life, are in derogation of the laws of Nature, and in opposition to the best good of the human family. The great want of the age, of humanity—the great need of man as well as of woman—is, the recognition of woman's equality. Would it not excite the just indignation of a *man* to be told by any person, even though that person were his "lawful-wedded" wife, that he must beget children when he did not desire them? or that he must perform the act of sexual intercourse when he did not feel inclined to? Certainly, he would never submit to such dictation, such tyranny, nor should he. And why should woman? It ought to be understood by all men and women that the sexual embrace, when either party is averse to it—when both parties are not inclined to it—is an outrage. It is a lustful not a love indulgence. And whether the consequences are sexual diseases of one or both parties, or personal alienation, or depraved offspring, or all, there is no possible escape from the penalties.

9*   (201)

A more pernicious doctrine was never taught than that of absolution from the penalties of our misdeeds. Causes and consequences are as unalterably related in the organic as in the inorganic world. Nature punishes always, and pardons never, when her laws are violated, or rather disregarded. In the vital domain, as in the moral, "no good deed is ever lost;" nor can any wrong act be performed without an evil result. When this great primary truth is recognized practically; when it is taught in our schools and exemplified in our lives, we shall have the true basis on which to prosecute our physiological redemption. "Cease to do evil," is the first and greatest lesson to be learned. This is emphatically true as applied to the sexual relations, for the reason that the organic laws are more disregarded in these relations than in any other, perhaps than in all other respects. And this disobedience, with its train of untold miseries and its wide-spread sensuality and degradation, is, like most other evils of an earthly existence, attributable mainly to ignorance; and people are ignorant on this subject simply because they have not studied it at all, or have studied it from the wrong stand-points. Woman's equality in all the relations of life implies her absolute supremacy in the sexual relation. It is for her to nourish and sustain the new being; it is her health and life that are directly imperiled by being compelled to bear children when she is unfitted and unwilling for the sacred office; it is her happiness that is more especially destroyed when forced to bring into the world sickly and deformed children, who can be nothing but a torment to themselves, of no use to the world, and nothing but a grief and a shame to their parents. For these reasons it is her absolute and indefeasible right to determine when she will, and when she will not, be exposed to pregnancy.

In the sensuous world around us, habit and fashion rule in the matter of sexual intercourse as much as they do in the matter of eating, or drinking, or dressing. The fashionable world recognizes no rule or principle of dress except "the latest fashion." The why or wherefore is never thought of, and in dietetic habits the masses of people follow no law except that of perverted appetency. They eat and drink to gratify alimentiveness, regardless of all physiological considerations and without knowing or thinking whether their appetites are normal or morbid, or whether the viands are wholesome or otherwise.

And as no propensity is more abused and abnormal, as the world is now constituted, than that of amativeness, and as sexual intercourse has become in married life, to a very great extent, a mere habit, to be indulged whenever the *man* feels the inclination, it follows that woman must be degraded to a mere machine in all that pertains to her highest interest and holiest aspirations.

In the animal kingdom the female does exercise her supremacy in this respect. No male animal offers violence to the female. But when she is in proper condition for his embrace, and desires it, she solicits it, and he invariably responds. So it should be, so it is in the order of Nature with man and woman. And when her supremacy is fully recognized, there will soon be an end of stillbirths, and of frail and malformed offspring who can seldom be reared to adult age, or, if they can. are only curses to themselves and to the world.

It may be objected, that to leave this great and important question of having children entirely with woman would endanger the extinction of the race. But such an objection implies little knowledge of woman and less of Nature. The desire for offspring, with all women who are in normal conditions, is the strongest of her nature. It is all-absorbing, all-controlling. It is only in diseased conditions that the pains and perils of childbirth and the cares of maternity are dreaded. It is well understood by physicians that the health of a majority of women in civilized society is seriously impaired and their lives greatly abbreviated by too frequent pregnancies. Thousands are brought to their graves in five, ten or fifteen years after marriage, and rendered miserable while they do live, for this reason.   And so general has this conviction become, that women all over the civilized world, and in all classes of society, are more and more resorting to numerous expedients, more or less injurious, to prevent pregnancy or produce abortion.   Nor does it avail for the moralist to declaim against the practice as wicked.   All laws are equally sacred in the sight of the Lawgiver, and woman's instincts can recognize no higher law (whatever she may assent to intellectually) than that of self-preservation, and no duty greater than that of bringing into the world children of sound and vigorous constitutions, or none at all.

Restore woman to health, and give her what God has ordained as her birthright—the control of her own person—and the trade of the abortionist will soon cease; but until then not only will the abortionist flourish, but the larger race of empirics in every city, who sell useless or injurious specifics for the prevention of pregnancy, will drive a profitable trade.

THE SCIENCE OF PROPAGATION.—Certain modern writers have suggested the idea that, as the propagation of human beings, like that of animals, is governed by laws which can be understood and influenced by conditions within human control, the subject ought to be studied as an " exact science" and its principles applied as a " true art."   Why not ?   This subject has been studied as a science and practised as an art for centuries—in fact, more or less in all ages—as applied to domestic animals and plants ; indeed, as applied to all living things with which man has to deal with the single exception of his own offspring.

What intelligent farmer would be willing to have his cattle begotten, born and bred under circumstances as unphysiological as are his children ?   The art of raising domestic animals—horses, cattle, sheep and even swine—has attained a great degree of perfection.   And the success which has attended this art is due to the recognition of certain principles in physiology which constitute the theory of the science.

The laws of life, the conditions of health, and the rules for normal development are precisely the same in all living organisms. And certainly it is of as much more importance that they should be recognized and applied, in relation to the propagation of human beings, as human beings are more important than animals.

But it happens, unfortunately, that while the whole subject is most assiduously investigated in relation to the animal kingdom, and to a great extent the vegetable kingdom also, it is almost entirely ignored in its application to human beings. The subject is not even alluded to in our text-books on Physiology; it is not taught in medical schools; it has no place in the current medical literature of the world; it is scarcely ever mentioned in the family circle; the good minister never hints at it, and, with the exception of a few of the more progressive of the Health Reformers, nobody tries to disturb the unthinking tranquillity of the public mind. Yet it lies at the foundation of all human improvement and all enduring progress, and is intrinsically the most important problem that can occupy the human mind.

PREVENTION OF PREGNANCY.—Assuming that woman is not morally nor physiologically bound to bear children unless she is fitted for that office, both by normal bodily condition and mental inclination, the question how she can help herself becomes important. Many women will not, and some can not, have the control of themselves in this matter. And the number of married women is by no means inconsiderable, who, because of malformation, constitutional frailty, or local disease, can not become pregnant without endangering their lives; while some are so contaminated with scrofula, so disorganized by the effects of drug medicines, or so devitalized by tight lacing, sedentary habits and constipating food, that they ought not to become mothers. Abstinence is, indeed, infallible; but this is not always possible, nor is it always proper. If sexual intercourse is intended as a love act, independent of reproduction, instead of a mere generative act, as is the case with animals (a subject I shall consider hereafter), then it becomes expedient and proper, in all cases where married women do not desire children, and in all cases where they are not fitted bodily and mentally to nourish and train them properly, as well as in all cases where extreme poverty deprives them of the means of either mental or physical culture, to prevent pregnancy without interdicting sexual intercourse.

It is true that if sexual intercourse is limited to about one-half of each month, pregnancy will seldom occur. But this rule is not infallible, for the reason that sexual diseases and weaknesses are so prevalent. The rule which I published in the Hydropathic Encyclopædia, fifteen years ago, has been relied on by thousands of married persons, with very few failures. The theory there advanced is, that the ovum usually passes off in a few days after the cessation of the menstrual flow, and that if intercourse is abstained from until ten or twelve days after the cessation of the menstrual flow, pregnancy will not occur. This is doubtless true in the great majority of cases; and I am inclined to think that it is true in all cases where the sexual organism is in a healthy condition. All of the failures which I have known (and on this subject my correspondence has been very extensive) occurred in those who had suffered of leucorrhœa, displacement, constitutional plethora, or torpor of the uterine system. In those cases the process of ovulation would be slower, and the female liable to impregnation for a longer period after the catamenial discharge had subsided. In one case wherein I had an opportunity to investigate the patient's condition and history, pregnancy occurred sixteen days after the cessation of the monthly discharge. She had long been the subject of uterine disease, the uterine system was exceedingly weak and torpid, and so feeble was the muscular tissue that it required nearly the whole month for the egg to be transported from the ovary to the external world.

How the Woman can Ascertain her Liability to Pregnancy.—A majority of women (and all who are not and have not been the subjects of uterine disease) can easily ascertain by a little attention, which will occasion them no trouble whatever, when their liability to pregnancy terminates, during each monthly ovulation.

When the egg passes the os uteri there is, in most cases, a sense of weight, stricture or bearing down, followed by instant relief. The egg is propelled from its ovarian bed through the Fallopian tube and uterus by a regular peristaltic contraction, of which the woman is wholly unconscious. But, as it passes the sphincter muscles at the mouth of the womb the resistance is greater, and the sensibility of the outlet is greater, than that of any part of the utero-Fallopian channel. It is true that women who have had leucorrhœa, or who have suffered much of any form of mismenstruation, have less sensibility of the part and exert a less vigorous contractile effort, while the egg meets less obstruction at the os uteri, so that in such cases the bearing-down effort might not be noticed. Nor would it always be noticed by women in perfect health, unless their attention were called to it. But many women, probably a great majority, by watching themselves for a few days after the cessation of the menstrual flow, can determine the exact moment when the egg passes off, and from that time until the commencement of the next menstrual period they will not be liable to impregnation.

But suppose she can not in this manner ascertain the important fact. She can in almost all cases—possibly in all cases, except when the egg is so disorganized that impregnation would be impossible—by watching the cloth (which should be continued for this purpose) for a few days, discover a clot, something like partially concreted mucus tinged with a drop of blood, which is the egg in a more or less advanced stage of decay. By noticing the time for two or three successive periods at which the egg or clot passes off, she will ascertain her menstrual habit; and as this rarely varies more than a day or two (except from protracted disease, in which case she should repeat her observations), she will have an infallible guide.

From the statistics of several hundreds of cases which I have gathered and tabulated, the results are as follows: In nearly one-fourth of all the cases, the egg passed into the vagina on the fifth, sixth and seventh days after the cessation of the flux, the greatest number passing on the sixth day. The days next in the order of frequency were the eighth, fourth, ninth, third and tenth. None passed before the third day, and less than half a dozen after the twelfth. Not one passed after the fourteenth.

These observations are quite irreconcilable with many of the doctrines taught by our standard physiologists. A majority of physiologists seem still inclined to the opinion that conception may occur at any time, although they acknowledge that, during the menstrual excitement, and for a few days preceding and succeeding the menstrual flow, it is more liable to occur. But this subject involves a further consideration of the problem briefly treated in a preceding chapter, viz., Where does conception occur normally?

UTERINE IMPREGNATION.—Notwithstanding the formidable array of objections and experiments collated in the chapter just referred to, I am of the opinion that, normally, conception, and even impregnation, takes place in the uterus. The prevalent doctrine is, as we have seen, that the semen traverses the uterine canal, passes along the Fallopian tube to the ovary, and there impregnates the ripened ovum, which, because of impregnation, is arrested in the uterine cavity and there developed. But there are many facts utterly irreconcilable with this theory, and among them are the various methods successfully resorted to for the prevention of pregnancy.

It is well known that, very soon after impregnation, or even conception, any sudden and violent motions which agitate the pelvic viscera and cause the uterus to contract vigorously, will prevent pregnancy. Drastic purgatives will have the same effect, and are occasionally employed to produce abortion; sometimes violent coughing or sneezing will have the same effect. Running, jumping, lifting and dancing are often resorted to successfully, immediately after connection. Vaginal injections of cold water, or quite warm water, employed within a minute or two after coition, prevent pregnancy in a majority of cases. Many tons of drugs—bicarbonate of soda, and other alkaline preparations—are annually sold at exorbitant prices for the prevention of pregnancy. They are injected into the vagina on the supposition that they destroy the vitality of the semen, or the life of the spermatozoids or animalcules.

But what is the rationale? How do these various processes and agents prevent conception? Though none of them can be relied on as infallible, no one will dispute that they sometimes occasion the effect pretended.

If impregnation occurred in the ovary, I can not see how it is possible for these things to have any appreciable effect. And as it requires several days for the ovum to pass from the ovary to the uterus (two weeks or more, according to the authorities), the preventive measures, to be most effectual, should not be employed until the ovum arrives in the cavity of the uterus, for until then it is impossible for the uterus to expel it. But all observation, experience and authority, concur in the conclusion that all preventive measures, whether motions, shocks, drugs or injections, are most efficacious when employed immediately after sexual intercourse. "The sooner the surer," is a maxim very generally understood.

Now, on the theory that impregnation occurs in the uterus, all of these facts are easily explained. And here let me repeat the distinction between impregnation and conception. Impregnation is the meeting and commingling of the sperm-cell and the germ-cell—the male semen and the female ovum. Conception is the attachment of the impregnated ovum to the

place wherein it is to be developed until the period of birth.
All agree that the uterus is the proper place for such development. And as an egg passes into the uterus every month,
whether sexual commerce is had or not, why should it not
there meet and mingle with the spermatozoa? This would
seem to be a very simple, I had almost said *natural* arrangement. Why should the sperm-cell, so long as its *mate* is sure
to be in the uterine cavity in a short space of time, be sent on
a dubious and difficult voyage to the ovary? All that is
necessary for impregnation, as we have seen, is the contact
of the sperm and germ. And as the ovum will be several
days in the uterine cavity, in normal menstruation, it seems
the most convenient and *natural* thing in the world for impregnation to occur there.

On the theory that the egg is in the uterine cavity at the
moment of impregnation, it is easy to understand the effects
of preventives. Whatever excites *motion* in the uterus causes
it to expel its contents. If an egg is present, and is impregnated, it must adhere or become fixed to the uterine wall or it
can not develop—there is no conception. But if from any
cause the uterus, immediately after impregnation, is so disturbed as to cause it to contract vigorously, it will expel the
egg notwithstanding the impregnation. This is why coughing, sneezing, jumping, lifting, injections, etc., prevent pregnancy; not because they expel the semen, as some have supposed; nor because they destroy its life, as others have
imagined; but because they occasion the uterus to contract,
and if its contractions are sufficiently vigorous and prolonged
the egg is surely expelled. Of course the more powerful the
exertions, or the larger the doses, or the colder or hotter the
injections, the more certain the effect.

It is probable that adhesion or fixation occurs very soon—
in a few minutes after impregnation. No sooner are the
sperm and germ elements blended by commixture than the
process of adhesion commences; and unless uterine contractions be excited immediately, the attachment may become so

firm as to resist all ordinary measures for detaching it. The introduction then of the uterine probe, giving it two or three turns so as to break up whatever adhesions have occurred, will insure its expulsion within a few days.

Some women have that flexibility and vigor of the whole muscular system that they can, by an effort of will, prevent conception! They can, by a voluntary bearing-down effort, so compress the abdominal muscles upon the pelvic viscera as to cause the uterus to contract with a degree of force that expels the impregnated egg, or at least causes it to be moved from the point where impregnation occurred, and where adhesion would soon have occurred.

This is, in effect, precisely the same as are the abdominal manipulations which have been successfully practised both to prevent conception and to cause abortion. And precisely the same effect results from the administration of many acrid and narcotic drugs—cayenne pepper, savin, ergot, cotton seed, quinine, etc.

Women in various parts of the world, and without the benefit of physicians or the aid of physiologists, have discovered methods of causing the uterus to expel its contents at any period of gestation, by compressing and squeezing the uterus by hand manipulations applied to the abdomen. The operation is usually quite painful, but the result is certain. And the same process immediately after impregnation would tend to prevent conception by moving the egg along so that it could not adhere.

I have read a statement in some medical journal to the effect that the women of Iceland seldom had more than two or three children, and the reason assigned was the fact that, after having children enough, and finding themselves pregnant, they would subject themselves to such an abdominal kneading and squeezing as would result in abortion. And a few years ago the Boston *Medical and Surgical Journal* published a statement, apparently well authenticated, that the women of the Friendly Islands, in the Pacific, were very expert in this method of relieving themselves or their neighbors from the prospective burden of unwelcome children. Some practitioners among them had acquired great skill in this method of "movement cure," and could "carry their patients through" with invariable punctuality in about three days.

The fact that the Jewish women are required by their religious creed to abstain from sexual intercourse for eight days after menstruation, is sometimes brought forward as an overwhelming objection to the doctrine that impregnation takes place normally in the uterus, as well as to the theory that women are most liable to conception soon after the menstrual flow has ceased. But in reply to this it may be remarked that good Jews, like good Christians, are not always scrupulously exact, in the literal sense, in conforming to religious ordinances, when these ordinances apply to "the lusts of the flesh." The law, as given by MOSES, was predicated on the idea that menstruation is a purifying process, and that for a certain number of days thereafter the woman was unclean. Although as a practical physiologist MOSES was far in advance of the physicians of the present day, yet modern science has abundantly demonstrated that menstruation is in no sense a depurating process. The restraint, however, that MOSES imposed on the Jews in this respect was no doubt eminently salutary, considering their depraved and sensuous habits and inclinations, as were all of his regulations and ordinances concerning their personal habits. If we had one MOSES in New York, he would do more to rid the city of contagion and pestilence than all the doctors are doing !

EXCEPTIONAL CASES.—The information given in this chapter will enable nine-tenths of all the women to whom the subject is important to know their own condition, whether liable to pregnancy or not, and to employ such means as may be most convenient under the circumstances when compelled to expose herself. There will be some exceptional cases, dependent on constitutional peculiarities or local derangement, to whom no general rules will apply. And I can only advise such by professional correspondence on learning their condition and peculiarities. But as this volume may fall into the hands of those who have no means or no time for such correspondence, and whose lives are hazarded continually, it may be proper to suggest that any mechanical obstruction placed against the os uteri which will prevent the seminal fluid from coming in contact with the ovum, will be an infallible preventive. A medical friend of mine labored for a year or two on an invention for plugging the os uteri, and although it answered admirably in some cases, it was not adapted to all without a degree of trouble and inconvenience fatal to its general introduction. A piece of soft sponge introduced as high up the vaginal canal as possible may prove efficacious. The empirics of most of our large cities sell extensively articles made of caoutchouc or other soft and elastic material. They are introduced against the os uteri and worn during sexual intercourse, and when they keep their position so as completely to cover the os uteri they are a sure preventive. But they are liable to become so far displaced as to expose the os uteri, thereby rendering contact possible between the semen and ovum. These suggestions, however, may enable the ingenious woman to adopt some device on emergencies that will accomplish the object.

Let it be distinctly understood that I do not approve any method for preventing pregnancy except that of abstinence, nor any means for producing abortion, on the ground that it is or can be in any sense physiological. It is only the least of two evils. When people will live physiologically, as will be seen in the succeeding chapter, there will be no need of preventive measures, nor will there then be any need for works of this kind.

Several thousands of women in the United States have written me the sad—sometimes terrible—story of their sufferings and blasted hopes, some of which have caused the tears to flow, when some of my confidential friends and co-laborers have read them, because they were compelled to bear children which could not possibly be reared, and which were a constant drain upon their life-forces. They have implored me for a remedy, and so long as the present ignorance prevails, or the present false habits of society exist, so long will there be a demand for relief in this direction. And if these sufferers can not find the desired remedy in the knowledge imparted by this work, they will seek it in more desperate and more dangerous measures. Who can blame them?

Reprinted from *Zentr. Gynaekol.*, **56**, 721–732 (1932)

12

ZENTRALBLATT

FÜR

GYNÄKOLOGIE

GEGRÜNDET VON HEINRICH FRITSCH

HERAUSGEGEBEN VON

WALTER STOECKEL

BERLIN

56. JAHRGANG / NR. 1-18 / 1932 / JANUAR-APRIL

MIT 260 ABBILDUNGEN UND 1 TITELBILD

1 9 3 2

LEIPZIG / JOHANN AMBROSIUS BARTH

Über den Konzeptionstermin des Weibes und seine Anwendung in der Praxis

Von Dr. med. **K. Ogino,** Chefarzt der Gynäkologischen Abteilung des Takeyama-Krankenhauses zu Niigata (Japan)

Nachdem die von Capellmann aufgestellte Behauptung von der fakultativen Sterilität der Frau nicht anerkannt worden ist, und auch die von Siegel vertretene Ansicht über das Bestehen einer prämenstruellen Sterilität durch Statistiken anderer Autoren und später von Siegel selbst widerlegt worden ist, ist man jetzt in Europa allgemein der Ansicht, daß die Frau zu jeder Zeit zwischen zwei Perioden befruchtet werden kann, und daß das Konzeptionsoptimum in das postmenstruelle Stadium fällt.

So wird ein Fall, wo z. B. am 25. Tage nach Beginn der letzten Menses eine Konzeption stattfindet, als Beweis dafür angesehen, daß die Frau sogar noch 4 Tage vor den nächsten Menses konzipieren kann, ohne daß man sich über den Menstruationszyklus der Frau genauer unterrichtet hätte. Nach meinen Beobachtungen handelt es sich bei solchen Fällen von verspäteter Ovulation oder auch von sogenannter prämenstrueller Konzeption stets um einen besonders langen Menstruationszyklus.

Wenn es richtig ist, daß eine Frau 4 Tage vor den nächsten Menses befruchtet werden kann, so stößt man auf die Schwierigkeit, wie man das Ausbleiben der am 5. Tage nach der Konzeption erwarteten Menses erklären soll. Dafür zog man früher die Theorie vom Primat der Eizelle heran; dieses scheint aber jetzt durch die Untersuchungen von Zondek, Knaus u. a. widerlegt zu sein.

Auch die Konzeptionskurven von Pryll, Siegel u. a. werden zum Beweis dafür herangezogen, daß die Frau zu jeder Zeit zwischen zwei Perioden befruchtet werden kann. Es sind aber in ihren Tabellen die Menstruationszyklen verschiedener Zeitdauer nicht voneinander getrennt. Die nächsten Menses fallen also nicht bei

12³ 721

allen Frauen auf den 29. Tag nach Beginn der letzten Menses, so daß die wenigen Fälle von Konzeption nach dem 20. Tag nach Beginn der letzten Menses nicht als Beweis der prämenstruellen Konzeption gewertet werden können.

Im vorigen Jahrhundert herrschte die Ansicht, daß die Ovulation mit den Menses zusammenfalle. Man nahm daher immer die den Menses naheliegende Kohabitation als die befruchtende an. Das Material aus dieser Zeit, das Pryll in seiner Statistik verwendet, ist also für die Deutung eines Konzeptionsoptimum im Postmenstruum nicht beweiskräftig.

Auch bei Statistiken, in denen Schwangerschaften verwertet worden sind, die bei 9tägigem Urlaub des Befruchtenden eintraten, kann insofern eine Ungenauigkeit resultieren, als die Konzeptionskurve im Postmenstruum scheinbar eine bedeutende Höhe erreichen mag, während in Wirklichkeit die Befruchtung in dieser Zeit gar nicht stattgefunden hat.

Die Konzeptionskurve von Siegel, die schon am 6. Tage nach Beginn der Menses den Gipfel zeigt, ist aus demselben Grunde nicht beweisend.

Bei Annahme eines postmenstruellen Konzeptionsoptimum besteht zwischen diesem und dem Ovulationstermin eine schwer zu deutende Dissonanz. Um diese Kluft überbrücken zu können, überträgt man die durch den Koitus provozierte Ovulation, die bei Kaninchen und Katzen physiologisch ist, auf den Menschen, während man es sonst im allgemeinen vermeidet, aus dem Tierversuch ohne weiteres auf den Menschen zu schließen. Beim Menschen ist jedenfalls eine provozierte Ovulation bisher nicht sicher nachgewiesen.

Bei Anlegung einer wissenschaftlichen Kritik machen sich jedenfalls gegen die bisherigen Behauptungen über den Konzeptionstermin berechtigte Zweifel bemerkbar.

Die Lösung der Frage vom Konzeptionstermin hängt ab von der Feststellung des Ovulationstermines, der Zeitdauer der Befruchtungsfähigkeit der Eizelle und der Spermatozoen. Im Zbl. Gynäk. 1930, Nr 8 habe ich hinsichtlich des Ovulationstermins festgestellt, daß er unter physiologischen Verhältnissen bei allen mensuellen Zyklen derjenige 5tägige Zeitabschnitt ist, der zwischen dem 12.—16. Tag vor den nächsten Menses liegt; mit anderen Worten treten die nächsten Menses bei Ausbleiben der Konzeption am 13.—17. Tag nach der Ovulation auf. Durch diese Definition können die bisher veröffentlichten, sehr widerspruchsvollen Angaben vieler Autoren glatt in Übereinstimmung gebracht werden. Ohne meine früher gemachten Darlegungen zu wiederholen, will ich als Beweis für die Richtigkeit meiner Behauptungen nur einen Fall von Mittelschmerz anführen, der von Ando als Bestätigung meiner Theorie in der Japanischen Zeitschrift angeführt worden ist. (Tabelle I.)

Über die Dauer der Befruchtungsfähigkeit der menschlichen Eizelle nach der Ovulation wußten wir bisher so gut wie gar nichts. Bei Säugetieren war zwar durch die Studien verschiedener Forscher bekannt geworden, daß die Befruchtungsfähigkeit der Eizelle nach der Ovulation nur wenige Stunden dauere; doch scheute man sich, diesen Befund beim Tier auf den Menschen zu übertragen. Nachdem jetzt aber die Frage des Ovulationstermins durch meine Untersuchungen geklärt ist, und hier kaum Widersprüche zu dem Material anderer Autoren bestehen, kann man nunmehr die Frage der Dauer der Befruchtungsfähigkeit der Eizelle am Menschen selbst studieren, indem man den Geschlechtsverkehr, der nach dem Ovulationstermin stattfindet, systematisch auf seine Befruchtungsfähigkeit prüft.

722

121

Tabelle I
Fall von Mittelschmerz, nach Ando

Tag des Mittelschmerzes	Datum der Menses	Tag des Mittelschmerzes vor den nächsten Menses	Tag des Mittelschmerzes nach Beginn der letzten Menses	Menstrualzyklus
11. IX.	26. IX.	15	—	—
12. X.	27. X.	15	17	31
14. XI.	30. XI.	15	19	34
15. XII.	30. XII.	15	16	30
13. I.	28. I.	15	15	29
13. II.	1. III.	16	17	32
13. III.	29. III.	16	13	28
14. IV.	28. IV.	14	17	30

Über die Dauer der Befruchtungsfähigkeit der menschlichen Spermatozoen bestanden ebenfalls wenig sichere Angaben. Zwar haben die Untersuchungen von Hoehne, Behne, Schwarski, Hausmann, Zweifel, Percy. Charpentier, Schultze, Ahlfeld, Sims, Birch-Hirschfeld, Nürnberger, Dührssen und Fraenkel ergeben, daß die Lebensdauer der Spermatozoen in den weiblichen Genitalien gewöhnlich nur 3 Tage, selten 4—8 Tage und ganz ausnahmsweise 2 Wochen und darüber dauere, wobei man sich darüber klar sein muß, daß die Lebensdauer der Spermatozoen keinesfalls mit der Imprägnationsfähigkeit gleichzusetzen ist, und daß man auch hier die Verhältnisse vom Tier nicht auf den Menschen übertragen darf. Doch können wir jetzt diese Frage auch direkt am Menschen studieren, indem wir auch hier den vor dem Ovulationstermin ausgeführten Koitus auf seine Befruchtungsfähigkeit prüfen.

In der obengenannten Arbeit habe ich diesbezügliche Beobachtungen veröffentlicht und bin zu dem Schluß gekommen, daß der Konzeptionstermin des Weibes derjenige 8tägige Zeitabschnitt ist, welcher zwischen dem 12. und 19. Tag vor den nächsten Menses liegt, daß die Konzeption in dem 5tägigen Zeitabschnitt vor diesem genannten Konzeptionstermin nur selten möglich ist, und daß in der sonstigen Zeitspanne die Frau steril bleibt. Diese meine Ansicht habe ich schon 1924 in der Japanischen Zeitschrift mitgeteilt und viele Anhänger gefunden. In Europa hat Schroeder (1930 brieflich) sich inhaltlich durchaus mit meiner Ansicht einverstanden erklärt, bis auf die Fälle von verfrühter Regel; auch Smulders hat meine Theorie mit Ausnahme der Fälle des seltenen Konzeptionstermins bestätigt; er hat sogar durch eine Monographie auf meine Arbeit aufmerksam gemacht. Bekanntlich wich die Ansicht von Knaus anfänglich etwas von meiner Theorie ab, doch befinden sich seit 1931 seine Behauptungen, abgesehen von den Fällen des seltenen Konzeptionstermins, mit meiner Theorie durchaus in Übereinstimmung.

Meine Beobachtungen haben sich seitdem noch vermehrt, so daß ich mich veranlaßt fühle, sie hier mitzuteilen und gleichzeitig die praktische Anwendung meiner Regeln zu empfehlen mit der Bitte, sie einer Nachprüfung zu unterziehen.

Eigene Beobachtungen

Gruppe 1. Beobachtungen bei bekanntem Konzeptionstermin

Im Zbl. Gynäk. **1930**, Nr 8 habe ich 9 derartige Fälle mitgeteilt. Hier folgen 5 weitere Beobachtungen.

723

Fall 10. K. T., 25 Jahre, Primipara, bisherige Menstruationszyklen 26 bis 36 Tage. Letzte Menses am 20. VIII. 1930, 4 Tage dauernd. Geschlechtsverkehr am 12. VI., 7. IX. und 5. X. Am 27. I. 1931 Schwangerschaft im 6. Monat. Der Ovulationstermin liegt in diesem Fall zwischen 30. VIII. und 13. IX., der Konzeptionstag (7. IX.) liegt innerhalb des Ovulationstermins.

Fall 11. T. S., 21 Jahre, bisherige Menstruationszyklen 29—33 Tage dauernd. Vorletzte Menses am 27. XII. 1925, letzte Menses am 29. I. 1926, 4 Tage dauernd. Einzige Kohabitation am 16. II. 1926, seitdem Amenorrhöe. Am 7. VIII. Schwangerschaft im 7. Monat. Der errechnete Ovulationstermin reicht vom 11.—19. II., der Konzeptionstag (16. II.) liegt innerhalb dieses Zeitraums.

Fall 12. K. T., 37 Jahre, IVpara, Phthisikerin. Bisherige Menstruationszyklen 25—33 Tage dauernd (32, 29, 33, 25, 32, 32, 25). Letzte Menses am 21. VI., danach ein einziger Koitus am 9. VII. Seit 28. VII. Übelkeit und Erbrechen. Am 31. VII. wurde ein junges Ei durch Abrasio entfernt. Der Ovulationstermin liegt in diesem Fall zwischen dem 30. VI. und dem 12. VII., der Konzeptionstag (9. VII.) liegt auch hier innerhalb des Ovulationstermins.

Fall 13. Y. H., 32 Jahre, VIpara, 4 normale Geburten, 2 künstliche Aborte wegen Lungentuberkulose. Letzter Abort am 21. III. 1929. Seit April 1929 hat diese Frau ihren Geschlechtsverkehr mit ungenügendem Verständnis meiner Theorie vom Konzeptionstermin geregelt und wurde durch Kohabitationen innerhalb des Konzeptionstermins geschwängert. Die zeitlichen Verhältnisse zwischen Ovulationstermin und Kohabitationen werden auf Tabelle II gezeigt.

Tabelle II

Gruppe I. Fall 13. Y. H.

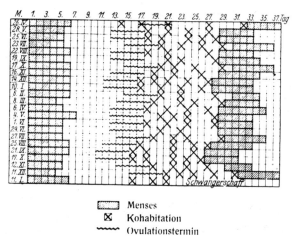

▨ Menses
☒ Kohabitation
〜 Ovulationstermin

Wie die Tabelle zeigt, hatte diese Pat. Menstruationszyklen von 26—32 Tagen Dauer, und folglich lag der Konzeptionstermin zwischen dem 8.—21. Tag nach Beginn der letzten Menses. Wenn sie die Schwangerschaft verhüten wollte, so durfte sie während dieses Termins (8.—21. Tag) keinen Verkehr haben. Trotzdem hatten die Kohabitationen innerhalb dieses Zeitraumes stattgefunden; doch fielen die Kohabitationstage, wenn man sie auf das Auftreten der nächsten Menses bezieht, glücklicherweise auf die Tage nach dem Ovulationstermin; es dauerte aber

724

dieses Glück nicht lange; sie wurde schließlich durch Kohabitation entweder am 26. oder am 29. I. geschwängert.

Fall 14. I. K., 43 Jahre, VIIIpara. Bisherige Menstrualzyklen 30—31 Tage dauernd. Vorletzte Menses am 10. VI., letzte Menses am 10. VII. 1931, 3 Tage dauernd. Der Ehemann war seit Mitte Juni auf Reisen und kehrte am 26. VII. heim, um vom nächsten Tag ab wieder auf 2 Monate von seiner Frau getrennt zu sein. Schwangerschaft durch die Kohabitation am 26. VII. Der errechnete Ovulations- termin reicht vom 23.—28. VII., den Konzeptionstag (26. VII.) umfassend.

Tabelle III

Gruppe II. Fall I. A. P.

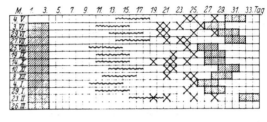

Zusammenfassung der beobachteten 14 Fälle: Bei 13 von 14 Fällen liegt der Tag der Konzeption inner- halb des Ovulationstermins

	Menses
	Kohabitation
	Ovulationstermin

und der vorangehenden 3 Tage, d. h. innerhalb des nach meiner Theorie be- stimmten Konzeptionstermins. Nur bei einem einzigen Fall fällt der Tag der Konzeption auf den 4. Tag vor dem Ovulationstermin.

Gruppe 2. Beobach- tungen an zeitlich ge- regelten Kohabitatio- nen beim Menschen

Fall 1. A. P., 25 Jahre. Das prämenstruelle Sterili- tätsstadium wurde von die- sen Eheleuten mit Erfolg zur Konzeptionsverhütung angewandt. Das Protokoll ist in Tabelle III ersichtlich.

Fall 2. T. M., 40 Jahre, Vpara. Bei dieser Frau wurde nicht nur das prä- menstruelle, sondern auch

Tabelle IV

Gruppe II. Fall II. T. M.

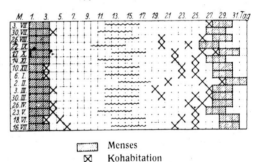

	Menses
	Kohabitation
	Ovulationstermin

das postmenstruelle Sterilitätsstadium für die Kohabitation freigegeben; der Zweck der Konzeptionsverhütung wurde damit erfüllt. Tabelle IV zeigt die genauen Verhältnisse.

Außer diesen beiden Fällen können noch der Fall 13 in der Gruppe 1 und 2 Fälle in meiner früheren Mitteilung im Zbl. Gynäk. 1930 (Tabelle VI und VII) als Ko- habitationsversuche im sterilen Stadium verwertet werden. Zusammenfassend werden diese 5 Fälle in Tabelle V übersichtlich dargestellt.

Diese Tabelle zeigt die Ergebnisse von insgesamt 274 Kohabitationen, die in 5 fruchtbaren Ehen innerhalb von 115 Monaten stattfanden. Von den prämen- struellen Kohabitationen fanden 29 am 1., 26 am 2., 24 am 3., 23 am 4., 29

725

Tabelle

Übersichtstabelle der Konzeptionsversuche beim Menschen. Die

	12	11	10	9	8	7	6	5	4	3	2	1
Fall VIII. O. T. (54 Monate)				1	3	8	5	3				
Fall IX. E. N. (12 Monate)							1				1	
Gruppe I. Fall XIII. Y. H. (22 Monate)												
Gruppe II. Fall I. A. P. (12 Monate)												
Gruppe II. Fall II. T. M. (15 Monate)				1	2	3	3					
Summe (115 Monate)				2	5	11	9	3			1	
						30						

am 5., 23 am 6., 20 am 7., 25 am 8., 17 am 9., 3 am 10. und 23 Kohabitationen am 11. Tag vor den nächsten Menses statt. Kein einziger Beischlaf, der in diesen 11 prämenstruellen Tagen ausgeführt wurde, führte zur Befruchtung. Von den postmenstruellen Kohabitationen verliefen 30, die in der Zeit zwischen 6.—10. Tag vor dem nach meiner Theorie errechneten Ovulationstermin stattfanden, sämtlich steril, während bei 3 unter diesen 5 Ehen Schwangerschaften durch Kohabitationen innerhalb des von mir errechneten Konzeptionstermins auftraten.

Gruppe 3. Beobachtungen von Schwangerschaften, entstanden aus Konzeptionen nach der Verheiratung, ohne daß nach der Verheiratung noch einmal die Menses auftraten.

11 derartige Fälle habe ich früher mitgeteilt, hier folgen 6 weitere Fälle:

Fall 12. T. N., 21 Jahre. Bisherige Menstruationszyklen 37—38 Tage dauernd, letzte Menstruation am 20. VII. Verheiratung am 27. VII., seitdem Amenorrhöe. Am 25. XII. 1930 Schwangerschaft im 6. Monat. Der Ovulationstermin liegt in diesem Fall zwischen 10. und 15. VIII., der Tag der Verheiratung liegt vor dem Ovulationstermin.

Fall 13. N. M., 24 Jahre. Bisherige Zyklen 33—35 Tage dauernd. Letzte Menses am 20. VI., 4 Tage dauernd. Verheiratung am 1. VII., seitdem Amenorrhöe und Schwangerschaft. Der Ovulationstermin reicht vom 7.—13. VII., der Tag der Heirat (1. VII.) liegt vor dem Ovulationstermin.

Fall 14. Y. M., 25 Jahre. Bisherige Zyklen 28—30 Tage dauernd, letzte Menses am 5. XI. 1930. Heirat am 17. XI., seitdem Amenorrhöe und Schwangerschaft. Der Tag der Heirat (17. XI.) liegt innerhalb des Ovulationstermins (17.—23. XI.).

Fall 15. U. A., 26 Jahre. Menstruationszyklen 29—31 Tage dauernd. Letzte Regel am 30. IX. 1930. Heirat am 17. X., seitdem Amenorrhöe und Schwangerschaft. Der Tag der Heirat (17. X.) liegt innerhalb des Ovulationstermins (13.—19. X.)

Fall 16. S. T., 22 Jahre. Menstruationszyklen ca. 42 Tage dauernd. Vorletzte Menses am 23. I., letzte Menses am 6. III., 6 Tage dauernd. Heirat am 11. III. 1931, seitdem Amenorrhöe und Schwangerschaft. Der Tag der Heirat liegt vor dem Ovulationstermin.

Fall 17. I. H., 23 Jahre, Menstruationszyklen 31—37 Tage dauernd. Letzte Menses am 12. I., Verheiratung am 24. I. 1931, seitdem Amenorrhöe und Schwangerschaft. Der Tag der Heirat (24. I.) liegt vor dem Ovulationstermin (27. I.—6. II.).

Zusammenfassung von Gruppe 3: 1) Innerhalb von 6 Jahren konnte ich 17 Fälle von Schwangerschaften beobachten, die aus einer Befruchtung entstanden waren,

726

V

mit Zahlen bezeichneten Kohabitationen erwiesen sich als steril

Ovulationstermin	11	10	9	8	7	6	5	4	3	2	1	Menses
	2	1	2	4	2	6	5	8	7	7	8	
	3	1	3	6	6	5	7	5	4	4	2	
	17	1	8	9	5	7	9	2	6	7	11	
	1	0	2	3	5	4	3	4	3	3	3	
	0	0	2	2	2	1	4	4	4	5	5	
	23	3	17	24	20	23	28	23	24	26	29	

240

ohne daß nach der Heirat die Menses wieder auftraten. Bei allen 17 Fällen lag der Tag der Konzeption innerhalb oder vor dem Ovulationstermin. Kein Fall von Schwangerschaft wurde beobachtet, wenn die Heirat nach dem Ovulationstermin stattfand. Es trat dann stets zur erwarteten Zeit die Regel wieder ein.

2) Während 4 Jahren konnte ich 88 Fälle von Schwangerschaft zusammenstellen, bei denen die Konzeption innerhalb der ersten 2—3 Monate der Ehe stattfand und bei denen der Tag der Heirat, der Tag der ersten Menses — falls nach der Verheiratung wieder aufgetreten —, und die Dauer der bisherigen Menstruationszyklen einwandfrei feststanden. Bei 49 von diesen 88 Fällen wurden die Eheschließungen vor oder innerhalb des Ovulationstermins vorgenommen, davon wurden 11 Frauen geschwängert, ohne daß die Menses nach der Verheiratung noch einmal auftraten. Die anderen 39 Frauen traten erst nach dem Ovulationstermin in die Ehe; in keinem einzigen Fall trat Konzeption ein, ohne daß die Menses nach der Verheiratung wiederkehrten.

Gruppe 4. Statistische Beobachtungen über die Menstruationszyklen

a. Statistik der Menstruationszyklen genitalgesunder Frauen, die mehr als einmal geboren haben.

Die allgemein herrschende Ansicht, daß der 28tägige Zyklus der häufigste sei, wird neuerdings in Japan von Obata, Nakagawa und mir angezweifelt. Ich habe eine Zusammenstellung von Menstrualzyklen genitalgesunder, pluriparer Frauen vorgenommen, bei denen die Menstruationsdaten 2—3mal hintereinander zu Protokoll genommen wurden. Die Ergebnisse folgen in Tabelle VI.

Tabelle VI

Statistik der Menstrualzyklen
(883 Zyklen bei 694 Frauen)

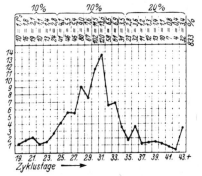

Es ist beachtenswert, daß die Menses von 28tägiger Dauer nur bei 9% der Fälle vorkommen, und daß die Zyklen von mehr als 34 Tagen ca. 20% und die von weniger als 25 Tagen ca. 10% der Fälle ausmachen. Obata und Nakagawa kamen zu den gleichen Ergebnissen.

b. Beobachtungen der Zyklusserien bei ein und derselben Frau.

727

126

Fall 1. N. M., genitalgesunde, fruchtbare Frau, 8jährige Beobachtung. Ihre Zyklusserien sind aus Tabelle VII, Fall 1, zu ersehen. Daraus geht hervor, daß die nächsten Menses häufig nicht im Rahmen der Schwankungsbreite der vorangegangenen 3—4 Zyklen auftreten, daß aber die nächsten Menses sich mit großer Sicherheit innerhalb der Schwankungsbreite der letzten 12 Zyklusserien erwarten lassen.

Fall 2. B. N., genitalgesunde, fruchtbare Frau. 5jährige Beobachtungsdauer. Zyklusserie ist aus Tabelle VII, Fall 2, zu ersehen. Diese Frau zeigt in der Laktationsperiode 2mal hintereinander normale, 28tägige Zyklen, dann aber unerwartet lange Zyklen von 42 und 45 Tagen, ein Beweis dafür, daß man den Eintritt der nächsten Menses nicht immer mit Sicherheit bestimmen kann, besonders während der Laktationsperiode und auch, wenn man die letzten Menstruationszyklen nur grob berücksichtigt.

Tabelle VII

Zyklusserien bei 2 Frauen

Fall I.							Fall II.		
	30	27	26	27	28	26		26	26
	28	Geburt	27	28	27	27		26	32
26	40	28	28	26	25			27	30
	26	41	26	26	25	28	23	27	28
31	27	30	27	25	26	26	25	26	26
29	26	33	29	28	25	27	21	Geburt	28
28	27	27	27	28	26	27	29	28	30
29	27	25	27	27	26	29	55	28	27
26	30	26	28	27	32	27	Heirat	42	25
26	27	27	28	27	27	27	20	45	
27	27	25	26	27	27	27	25	27	
24	28	27	25	27	29	26	29	31	
28	25	25	29	27	27	28	26	Geburt	
28	27	27	28	25	28	28	28	29	
27	27	27	25	28	27		25	40	
29	27	26	32	31	27		26	29	

Zusammenfassung aus Gruppe 4

1) Es gibt verhältnismäßig wenige Frauen, deren Menstrualzyklus stets die gleiche Dauer hat.

2) Will man den Menstrualzyklus einer Frau genau kennzeichnen, so muß man ihre maximale und minimale Zyklusdauer angeben, wodurch man ein Bild über die Schwankungsbreite ihrer Menstrualzyklen bekommt. Dabei muß man die maximale und minimale Zyklusdauer aus mindestens 12 vorangegangenen Zyklusserien kennen; 3—4 Zyklusserien sind für diesen Zweck ungenügend.

3) Bei Beurteilung der statistisch gewonnenen Konzeptionskurven muß man unbedingt darauf Rücksicht nehmen, daß das zugrunde liegende Material nur aus Fällen mit 28tägigem Zyklus besteht. Bei Zusammenstellung von Fällen mit allen möglichen Zyklusformen, wie dies bei den Konzeptionskurven von Pryll und Siegel der Fall ist, bedeutet z. B. der 21. Tag nach Beginn der letzten Menses nicht immer den 8. Tag vor der nächsten Regel, ebensowenig sind natürlich auch die Konzeptionsfälle an diesen oder noch späteren Tagen als beweiskräftig für die Möglichkeit einer prämenstruellen Konzeption anzusehen.

728

Zusammenfassung meiner Beobachtungen

Als Ausgangspunkt meiner Studien über den Konzeptionstermin wähle ich den von mir bestimmten Ovulationstermin.

Wie ich eingangs erörtert habe, können wir nunmehr die Dauer der Imprägnationsfähigkeit der menschlichen Eizelle am Menschen direkt studieren. Das Resultat meiner diesbezüglichen, systematischen Beobachtungen ist folgendes:

1) Unter 14 Schwangerschaften mit bekanntem Konzeptionstag fiel der Tag der befruchtenden Kohabitation niemals auf die Zeit nach dem Ovulationstermin. (Beobachtungsgruppe 1.)

2) Es wurden bei 5 fruchtbaren Ehen während einer Beobachtungsdauer von 115 Monaten gewissermaßen experimentelle Studien über die Konzeption ausgeführt mit dem Resultat, daß sich 242 Kohabitationen nach dem Ovulationstermin, d. h. während der 11 Tage vor den erwarteten, nächsten Menses, immer als steril erwiesen. (Beobachtungsgruppe 2.)

3) Von 88 innerhalb von 3 Monaten nach der Verheiratung geschwängerten Frauen traten 39 Frauen nach dem Ovulationstermin in die Ehe ein; diese blieben zunächst unbefruchtet, bis sie dann nach Eintritt der nächsten Menses geschwängert wurden. (Beobachtungsgruppe 3:)

4) 17 Frauen, bei denen die Befruchtung eintrat, ohne daß nach der Verheiratung die Menses noch einmal auftraten, hatten alle während oder vor dem Ovulationstermin, aber niemals nach dem Ovulationstermin geheiratet. (Beobachtungsgruppe 3.)

Dieses Resultat meiner Beobachtungen berechtigt mich zu der Behauptung, daß die Dauer der Imprägnationsfähigkeit der menschlichen Eizelle ebenso kurzfristig ist wie die des Säugetieres. Die klinischen Beobachtungen von Knaus und Smulders führten zu den gleichen Ergebnissen. Siegel hat 1917 berichtet, daß bei 65 Fällen, bei denen die Hochzeit innerhalb der letzten 8 Tage vor der Menstruation stattfand, nach der Hochzeit die Menstruation wiederkehrte und erst danach die Empfängnis eintrat. Meines Erachtens kann man diesen Befund als Beweis einer prämenstruellen Sterilität bewerten; Siegel aber hat seinen Befund dahin gedeutet, daß er darin nur eine prämenstruelle Fertilitätsverminderung erblickte.

Bezüglich der Dauer der Befruchtungsfähigkeit der menschlichen Spermatozoen sind folgende Beobachtungen zu verwerten:

1) Bei 13 von 14 Schwangerschaftsfällen mit bekanntem Konzeptionstag fielen die Tage der befruchtenden Kohabitationen auf die Zeitspanne des Ovulationstermins oder innerhalb der 3 ihm vorangehenden Tage; nur in einem Fall wurde die Frau am 4. Tage vor dem Ovulationstermin befruchtet.

2) Bei den Konzeptionsstudien an zwei fruchtbaren Ehen verliefen 30 Kohabitationen, die in der Zeit zwischen 6. und 10. Tag vor dem Ovulationstermin stattfanden, steril. Die Beobachtungsdauer betrug ca. 30 Monate.

Auf Grund dieser Beobachtungen und unter Berücksichtigung der eingangs gemachten Ausführungen über die Lebensdauer der menschlichen Spermatozoen komme ich zu der Ansicht, daß die Befruchtungsfähigkeit der menschlichen Spermatozoen im allgemeinen 3 Tage andauert. Die Ergebnisse der Beobachtungen von Knaus und Smulders stimmen damit überein. Doch steht die Entscheidung der Frage, ob die Spermatozoen ausnahmsweise 4—8 Tage befruchtungsfähig bleiben können oder nicht, noch aus, sofern man die Resultate des Tierversuches nicht direkt auf den Menschen übertragen will.

Damit komme ich bezüglich des Konzeptionstermins zu folgendem Schluß:

1) Der Konzeptionstermin des Weibes ist in der Regel derjenige 8tägige Zeitabschnitt, welcher zwischen 12. und 19. Tag vor den nächsten Menses liegt (5tägiger Ovulationstermin plus 3 Tage davor).

2) Innerhalb des Zeitabschnittes, welcher zwischen 20. und 24. Tag vor den nächsten Menses liegt, ist eine Konzeption selten möglich (4.—8. Tag vor der Ovulation). Es fehlen noch genügende Beobachtungen beim Menschen, um diese Möglichkeit vollkommen ausschließen zu können. Wegen der Seltenheit einer Befruchtung in diesem Zeitraum möchte ich ihn jedoch praktisch als steril bezeichnen.

3) Während des 11tägigen Zeitabschnittes vor den nächsten Menses ist die Konzeption unmöglich.

Praktische Anwendung

Ich bin der Überzeugung, daß wir mit Hilfe meiner Feststellungen befähigt sind, diejenigen Frauen, die zur sexuellen Abstinenz, zum Gebrauch antikonzeptioneller Apparate und Medikamente gezwungen sind, wenigstens zeitweise davon zu befreien, um sie somit vor etwaigen psychischen und somatischen Gesundheitsschädigungen zu bewahren.

Für die Praxis bewährt es sich, den Konzeptionstermin vom Beginn der letzten Menses ab zu errechnen. Bei 28tägigem Zyklus ist dann der Konzeptionstermin die Zeit vom 10.—17. Tag nach Beginn der letzten Menses. Wenn der Zyklus länger oder kürzer als 28 Tage dauert, so verschiebt sich der Konzeptionstermin um so viele Tage nach hinten oder nach vorn. Da die Menstruationszyklen einer Frau im allgemeinen ungleichmäßig sind, so muß man die Formel für den Konzeptionstermin folgendermaßen ausdrücken:

Beginn des Konzeptionstermins = 10 + (Minimalzyklus — 28 Tage).

Ende des Konzeptionstermins = 17 + (Maximalzyklus — 28 Tage).

Das Resultat gibt den betreffenden Tag nach Beginn der letzten Menses an; die maximale und minimale Zyklusdauer sind aus den vorausgegangenen 12 Zyklusserien zu errechnen; die Berücksichtigung von nur 3—4 Zyklen ist, wie oben angeführt, ungenügend. Die seltenen Konzeptionstermine habe ich hierbei außer Acht gelassen, da sie für die Praxis keine große Rolle spielen.

Da aber die meisten Frauen keine genauen Aufzeichnungen ihrer menstruellen Zyklen besitzen, so kann man auch so vorgehen, daß man sie nach ihrem Gedächtnis die maximale und minimale Zyklusdauer angeben läßt, um daraus provisorisch ihren Konzeptionstermin bestimmen zu können. Danach muß natürlich jeder mensuelle Zyklus aufgeschrieben und berücksichtigt werden. Man muß sich bei diesem Vorgehen darüber klar sein, daß etwaige Fehlschläge von Gedächtnistäuschungen herrühren können.

Die oben angeführte Formel für den Konzeptionstermin ist theoretisch für alle Frauen gültig; in Wahrheit aber ist sie nur auf Frauen mit Zyklusschwankungen von maximal 10 Tagen anwendbar; je größer die Zyklusschwankungen werden, um so geringer ist der praktische Wert. So fällt z. B. bei Frauen mit einem Menstrualzyklus von 26—36 Tagen der Beginn des Konzeptionstermins auf den 10. + (26—28) = 8. Tag; das Ende auf den 17. + (36—28) = 25. Tag nach Beginn der letzten Menses. Nun können die nächsten Menses, wenn jetzt der Zyklus von minimaler Dauer ist, schon am 27. Tag wiederkehren; daraus folgt, daß von den prämenstruellen Sterilitätstagen nur 1 Tag als solcher brauchbar ist. Kehren die nächsten Menses dagegen erst nach maximal langer Zyklusdauer wieder, so können

730

11 volle Tage des Prämenstruum ausgenutzt werden. Außerdem steht in diesem Falle auch noch die postmenstruelle, sterile Periode zum Gebrauch. Ich möchte jedenfalls einen solchen Fall als Grenze für den praktischen Wert meiner Theorie betrachten. Wieviel Frauen weisen nun Zyklusschwankungen von maximal 10 Tagen auf? Unter Zyklusschwankungen verstehe ich dabei die Differenz in der Zahl der Tage bei maximal und minimal langer Zyklusdauer ein und derselben Frau. Nach Obata (Japan) weisen die Zyklusschwankungen bei 960 Schülerinnen, bei denen 3—10 genau aufgeschriebene Zyklusserien berücksichtigt wurden, und die schon länger als 2 Jahre menstruiert waren, folgende Zahlen auf:

Zyklusschwankungen	0 Tag	0,7 %
»	bis 3 Tage	10,0 %
»	» 7 »	30 %
»	» 10 »	44 %
»	über 11 »	56 %

Diese Statistik umfaßt natürlich auch Fälle von Hypoplasia uteri und Hypofunktion des Ovarium, während bei solchen Frauen aus leicht verständlichen Gründen eine Konzeptionsverhütung nicht in Frage kommt. Es würde sich infolgedessen bei fruchtbaren Frauen der Prozentsatz noch etwas steigern. Bei Berücksichtigung dieser Umstände geht man nicht fehl, wenn man die in Frage kommenden Fälle vorläufig als auf die Hälfte der Frauen schätzt.

Können diese Frauen den Konzeptionstermin praktisch mit Sicherheit bestimmen? Die praktische Anwendungsmethode beruht auf der Voraussetzung, daß man die nächsten Menses bzw. die nächste Ovulation unter Berücksichtigung der vorangegangenen Menstrualzyklen bestimmen kann. Nun hat, wie wir wissen, die Ovulation nur mit den nächsten Menses einen zeitlichen Zusammenhang, aber nicht mit den vorangegangenen Menses. Daraus muß man logisch folgern, daß man eine absolute Sicherheit für die praktische Anwendung nicht gewähren kann. Aber ich fühle mich berechtigt zu behaupten, daß bei Frauen, deren nächste Menses sich in einer bestimmten Zyklusschwankung mit Sicherheit erwarten lassen, auch mit gleicher Sicherheit dieser Konzeptionstermin in praxi bestimmt werden kann. Wer in der Konzeptionsverhütung eine absolute Sicherheit verlangt, der darf ebensowenig die Schlußfolgerungen meiner Theorie, wie auch sonst die jetzt gebräuchlichen Medikamente, Pessare, Kondome und Tubensterilisationsoperationen in Anwendung bringen. Verständlich ist es auch, daß man während der Laktationsperiode, nach schweren Krankheiten und bei durchgreifender Veränderung der Lebensweise bei Bestimmung des Konzeptionstermins in praxi die stärkste Vorsicht walten lassen muß.

Smulders hat in seiner Monographie »Periodieke Onthouding in hat Huwelijk« (1930) eine Methode angegeben, nach der der von mir bestimmte Konzeptionstermin nach Kalendertagen bezeichnet werden kann. Für manche Frauen scheint dies bequem zu sein. Bekanntlich hat Knaus unabhängig von mir eine ähnliche Ansicht über den Zeitpunkt der Konzeptionsfähigkeit des Weibes veröffentlicht, dahingehend, daß eine regelmäßig, 4wöchentlich menstruierende Frau nur in der Zeit vom 11.—17. Tage des mensuellen Zyklus empfangen könne. Über die Verhältnisse bei anderer Zyklusdauer machte er keine bestimmten Angaben. 1931 äußerte er sich dahin, daß bei Frauen mit 26—30tägigen Zyklen das Konzeptionsoptimum auf den 9.—17. Tag nach Beginn der letzten Menses falle. Damit ist es zwischen Knaus und mir, abgesehen von den seltenen Konzeptionsterminen, zur Übereinstimmung gekommen.

Ich hoffe, daß meine Angaben, nachdem sie von vielen Seiten kritisiert und nachgeprüft worden sind, allgemeine Anwendung bei geeigneten Frauen finden können, und daß dadurch diese Frauen, wenn auch nur periodisch und in beschränktem Zeitumfang, von dem widernatürlichen Gebrauch antikonzeptioneller Mittel befreit und vor Gesundheitsschädigungen bewahrt werden können.

Literatur

1) Ando, Chiryo oyobi shoho 4, H. 5. — 2) Bauer, Med. Klin. 1930, Nr 1. — 3) Capellmann, Die fakultative Sterilität. 1883. — 4) Dickinson, Amer. J. obstetr. 1, Nr 6. — 5) Fels, Zbl. Gynäk. 1931, Nr 9. — 6) Fraenkel, Arch. Gynäk. 144, H. 1. — 7) Greenhill, Amer. J. obstetr. 22, Nr 1. — 8) Grosser, Halban-Seitz, Handbuch der Biologie und Pathologie des Weibes 6. — 9) Haire, Zbl. Gynäk. 1930, Nr 37. — 10) Hermstein, Zbl. Gynäk. 1931, Nr 39. — 11) Hartmann u. Störring, Arch. Gynäk. 145, H. 3. — 12) Jaeger, Zbl. Gynäk. 1917. — 13) Kräuter, Z. ärztl. Fortbildg 28 (1931). — 14) Keller, Halban-Seitz, Handbuch der Biologie und Pathologie des Weibes 1. — 15) Kehrer, Halban-Seitz, Handbuch der Biologie und Pathologie des Weibes 2. — 16) Knaus, Zbl. Gynäk. 1929, Nr 35. — 17) Knaus, Med. Welt 1930, Nr 10. — 18) Knaus, Münch. med. Wschr. 1929, Nr 28. — 19) Knaus, Münch. med. Wschr. 1931, Nr 9. — 20) Knaus, Arch. Gynäk. 146, H. 2. — 21) Knaus, Zbl. Gynäk. 1931, Nr 39. — 22) Knaus, Mitt. Volksgesdh.amt 1931, H. 10. — 23) Meixner, Zbl. Gynäk. 1930, Nr 50. — 24) Max Hirsch, Zbl. Gynäk. 1931, Nr 41. — 25) Nürnberger, Münch. med. Wschr. 1918, 252. — 26) Nürnberger, Halban-Seitz, Handbuch der Biologie und Pathologie des Weibes 3. — 27) Nürnberger, Mschr. Geburtsh. 53 (1920). — 28) Nakagawa, Jap. J. of Obstetr. 14, Nr 3. — 29) Obata, Nihon fujinkagakukai zassi 24, Nr 8. — 30) Ogino, Hokuetsu igakukaizassi 1923, Nr 1. — 31) Ogino, Nipon fujinkagakukai zassi 1924, Nr 6. — 32) Ogino, Zbl. Gynäk. 1930, Nr 8. — 33) Ogino, Rinsho Sanfujinka 1931, Nr 6. — 34) Pryll, Z. Geburtsh. 79. — 35) Pryll, Münch. med. Wschr. 1916. — 36) Siegel, Dtsch. med. Wschr. 1915, Nr 42. — 37) Siegel, Münch. med. Wschr. 1916, Nr 21. — 38) Siegel, Gewollte und ungewollte Schwankungen der weiblichen Fruchtbarkeit. Julius Springer, 1917. — 39) Smulders, Perodieke Onthouding in het Huwelijk, 1930. — 40) Smulders, Tijdschr. Geneesk. (holl.) 1931, August. — 41) Smulders, Vox medicorum Nr 16/17. — 42) Schröder, Handbuch der mikroskopischen Anatomie des Menschen 7I. — 43) Treutler, Anat. Anz. 71. — 44) Van de Velde, Die Fruchtbarkeit in der Ehe und ihre wunschgemäße Beeinflussung. 1929. — 45) Wittenbeck, Arch. Gynäk. 142, H. 2. — 46) Schultze, Zbl. Gynäk. 1931, Nr 42. — 47) Zondek, Die Hormone des Ovariums und des Hypophysenvorderlappens. Julius Springer, 1931.

Douches and Spermicides

V

Editor's Comments on Papers 13 Through 18

Charles Knowlton, M.D., was a 19th Century American physician who stepped forth to take up the cudgel in the controversy set off by the Malthus publication. The popular word for the practice of contraception in those days, as may be seen in the writings of Malthus and Place, was "check." Any method that prevented pregnancy was called a check. This is seen again in the classic Knowlton pamphlet, which first appeared in 1833, was revised and republished several times, and, as late as 1880, was to appear again in a thin monograph by Charles Bradlaugh and the tireless Annie Besant. The original pamphlet had a stormy course. It was first published in England, at first without challenge, but ultimately it ran afoul of the law. Bradlaugh and Besant republished it to test the right of publication and because ". . . honestly believing that on all questions affecting the happiness of the people, whether they be theological, political, or social, fullest right of free discussion ought to be maintained at all hazards." The Bradlaugh and Besant preface is reproduced here after the Knowlton article. Unfortunately, these copies are rare and the available one is in poor shape, but still legible.

Knowlton begins his document with a comment on population. He notes that the world population was then (1833) about one billion. If growth were unrestrained he said that it would be eight billion at the end of 100 years and 64 billion in 200 years. Now, some 140 years later world population is only about four billion; thus, if his figures have validity various "checks" must be working. Be that as it may, Knowlton recites for us the usual objections to Malthus' suggestion of celibacy, points out the joys of sex and of early marriage, and concludes, as did Place, that if one could indulge in sexual intercourse without the consequence of pregnancy, population growth would be controlled, joy would reign, masturbation and prostitution would vanish. He then provides a detailed lesson on the anatomy and physiology of reproduction. His knowledge of anatomy is impeccable, but in physiology he simply reflects the ignorance of the times. He states that the semen excites the female genital organs in a peculiar manner, and that "public women" (prostitutes) rarely conceive, owing probably to a weakened state of the genital system induced by too frequent and promiscuous intercourse. There is no supporting evidence for these statements. But then he really goes overboard when he sets out in great detail the reasons why he believes that semen does not enter the uterus and does not traverse the fallopian tubes, but rather is absorbed by special vessels in the inner surface of the labia externa to be carried directly to the ovaries. He may be technically correct in stating that "semen" does not travel through the fallopian tubes but he apparently did not differentiate semen and sperm. He also clings to the concept that the most fertile period is immediately following the end of the menstrual flow. However, he says there are exceptions.

Finally, Knowlton addresses himself to checking conception. But first he has a few words about how conception can be promoted. He suggests several procedures—exercise in the open air, purging the bowels, nourishing food, temperance and, best of all, an ample dose of Spanish Flies "to arouse the genital organs." As for "checks," he dismisses coitus interruptus, the condom, and the sponge. Best he says is "syringing the vagina immediately after connection with a solution of sulphate of zinc, of alum, pearl-ash, or any salt that acts chemically on the semen. . . ." He realizes that this requires the woman ". . . to leave her bed for a few moments, but this is its only objection; and it would be unreasonable to suppose that any check can ever be devised entirely free of objections."

Also fascinating in this publication is the concluding section in which the good doctor discusses the reproductive instinct. He states that it should be gratified only after the age of about 18 and then in moderation, otherwise the whole system will be debilitated, mental energies impaired, with consumption and other diseases to follow. Warming up to this subject he insists that one may ". . . enjoy (sex) with impunity, were he a laboring man, or a man whose business requires but little mental exercise. . . ." Further, "[e]very young married woman ought to know that the male system is exhausted in a far greater degree than the female by gratification." Then he quotes the old canard that "one ounce of semen is equal in its effects upon the system of 40 ounces of blood." In short, here we see all the misconceptions that have persisted till today—that sex is debilitating and can lead to decreased mental powers, that masturbation results in insanity, and that oysters and other foods recharge the man. In the 1972 Olympics at least one athlete was castigated by his coach for getting married just before the games!

Knowlton suggested substances that would act chemically on the semen. But since he did not have a clear concept of sperm he could not carry the suggestion forward. Not until 1841 was this clarified by the Swiss zoologist, Kölliker. After that the search was on for substances that would inactivate sperm. Leaders in the field were Gustav Günther (1905) in Vienna, E. Gellhorn (1931) in the United States, and John Baker in England, who carried out an extensive investigation that culminated in a series of articles and a monograph. Two of Baker's articles are reproduced here.

Baker tried to establish laboratory conditions that would closely approximate the vaginal environment. To do so he made several assumptions concerning the volume of vaginal fluid and its acidity. He mixed in the chemical agent, then added a volume of semen, kept the mixture at body temperature, and then counted dead and surviving sperm at various time intervals. Not surprisingly he found some products totally useless, others highly effective and the remainder somewhere in between. Another authority in this field, Clarence J. Gamble, M.D., carried out similar tests using more sophisticated methodology. His results do not agree with those of Baker, which indicates that the methodology itself is the key factor. Accordingly, the whole question of effectiveness remained unanswered, leaving physicians and users little alternative but to depend upon the claims of the manufacturers.

The next paper, by Drs. Melvin Cohen and Bernard Kaye, is unique because in vivo rather than in vitro conditions were used. Their results, therefore, are more meaningful, but the time lag between coitus and examination leaves much to be desired.

Johnson and Masters entered this controversy using a direct test. In their article, published in 1963, a variety of commercially available products were evaluated. Female subjects in this investigation followed the manufacturers' instructions. After the product was introduced into the vagina the subjects engaged in artificial coital activity through a complete cycle of sexual response. At orgasm a previously examined seminal specimen was injected into the vaginal barrel simulating the male act of ejaculation. Vaginal specimens were collected at various time intervals and checked for sperm motility. The whole sequence was repeated an hour later and a third time five to eight hours after the initial sequence. Only two of the seven products tested provided adequate protection. In addition, this investigation showed that most products must be used before each sexual contact even if only separated by a few hours. Finally, esthetically there are objections. In short, chemical contraception presents many shortcomings.

Publisher's Note: We have tried repeatedly to obtain an unmarked copy of this paper, but without success. We ask your indulgence when reading it and hope that your attention is not distracted by an earlier reader's fast-moving pencil.

Reprinted from *Fruits of Philosophy. A Treatise on the Population Question*, 2–23 (1833)

13

FRUITS

OF

PHILOSOPHY:

OR,

THE PRIVATE COMPANION

OF

YOUNG MARRIED PEOPLE

BY CHARLES KNOWLTON, M.D.

Author of " Modern Materialism."

" Knowledge is Wealth." OLD SAYING.

REPRINTED FROM THE AMERICAN EDITION.

SECOND EDITION.

London :

J. WATSON, 18, COMMERCIAL PLACE,

CITY ROAD, FINSBURY.

Adjoining the Mechanics' Hall of Science.

137

PREFACE,

BY THE PUBLISHER.

———

IT is a notorious fact that the families of the married often increase beyond what a regard for the young beings coming into existence, or the happiness of those who gave them birth, would dictate; and philanthropists, of first rate moral character, in different parts of the world, have for years been endeavouring to obtain and disseminate a knowledge of means whereby men and women may refrain at will from becoming parents, without even a partial sacrifice of the pleasure which attends the gratification of their productive instinct. But no satisfactory means of fulfilling this object were discovered until the subject received the attention of a physician, who had devoted years to the investigation of the most recondite phenomena of the human system, as well as to chemistry. The idea occurred to him of destroying the fecundating property of the sperm by chemical agents; and upon this principle he devised " checks," which reason alone would convince us must be effectual, and which have been proved to be so by actual experience.

This work, besides conveying a knowledge of these and other checks, treats of Generation, Sterility, Impotency, &c. &c. It is written in a plain, yet chaste style. The great utility of such a work as this, especially to the poor, is ample apology, if apology be needed, for its publication.

E 2

138

CHAPTER 1.

Showing how desirable it is, both in a political and a social point of view, for mankind to be able to limit, at will, the number of their offspring, without sacrificing the pleasure that attends the gratification of the reproductive instinct.

FIRST.—*In a political point of view.*—If population be not restrained by some great physical calamity, such as we have reason to hope will not hereafter be visited upon the children of men, or by some *moral restraint*, the time will come, when the earth cannot support its inhabitants. Population, unrestrained, will double three times in a century. Hence, computing the present population of the earth at 1000 millions, there would be at the end of 100 years from the present time, 8000 millions.

At the end of 200 ,, 64,000 ,,
,, 300 ,, 512,000 ,,

And so on, multiplying by eight for every additional hundred years. So that in 500 years from the present time, there would be thirty-two thousand seven hundred and sixty-eight times as many inhabitants as at present. If the natural increase should go on without check for 1500 years, one single pair would increase to more than *thirty-five thousand one hundred and eighty-four* times as many as the present population of the whole earth !

Some check, then, there must be, or the time will come when millions will be born but to suffer and to perish for the necessaries of life. To what an inconceivable amount of human misery would such a state of things give rise ! And must we say that vice, war, pestilence, and famine, are desirable to prevent it ? Must the friends of temperance and domestic happiness stay their efforts ? Must peace societies excite to war and bloodshed ? Must the physician cease to investigate the nature of contagion, and to search for the means of destroying its baneful influence ? Must he that becomes diseased, be marked as a victim to die for the public good, without the privilege of making an effort to restore him to health ? And in case of a failure of crops in one part of the world, must the other parts withhold the means of supporting life, that the far greater evil of excessive population throughout the globe may be prevented ? Can there be no effectual moral restraint, attended with far less human misery than such physical calamities as these ? Most surely there can. But what is it ? Malthus, an English writer on the subject of population, gives us none but celibacy to a late age. But how foolish it is to suppose that men and women will become as monks and nuns during the very holiday of their

139

existence, and abjure during the fairest years of life, the nearest
and dearest of social relations, to avert a catastrophe, which they,
and perhaps their children, will not live to witness. But, besides
being ineffectual, or if effectual, requiring a great sacrifice of enjoyment, this restraint is highly objectionable on the score of its
demoralizing tendency. It would give rise to a frightful increase
of prostitution, of intemperance and onanism, and prove destructive to health and moral feelings. In spite of preaching, human
nature will ever remain the same; and that restraint which forbids
the gratification of the reproductive instinct, will avail but little
with the mass of mankind. The checks to be hereafter mentioned,
are the only moral restraints to population known to the writer,
that are unattended with serious objections.

Besides starvation with all its accompanying evils, over-population
is attended with other public evils, of which may be mentioned,
ignorance and slavery. Where the mass of the people must toil
incessantly to obtain support, they must remain ignorant: and
where ignorance prevails, tyranny reigns.

Second.—*In a social point of view.*—" Is it not notorious that
the families of the married often increase beyond what a regard for
the young beings coming into the world, or the happiness of those
who give them birth, would dictate? In how many instances does
the hard-working father, and more especially the mother, of a poor
family, remain slaves throughout their lives, tugging at the oar of
incessant labour, toiling to live, and living but to toil; when if
their offspring had been limited to two or three only, they might
have enjoyed comfort and comparative affluence? How often is
the health of the mother, giving birth every year to an infant—
happy if it be not twins—and compelled to toil on, even at those
times, when nature imperiously calls for some relief from daily
drudgery. How often is the mother's comfort, health, nay, even
her life thus sacrificed! Or if care and toil have weighed down
the spirit, and at last broken the health of the father, how often is
the widow left, unable, with the most virtuous intentions, to save
her fatherless offspring from becoming degraded objects of charity,
or profligate votaries of vice!

" Nor is this all. Many women are so constituted that they
cannot give birth to healthy—sometimes not to living children. Is
it desirable—is it *moral*, that such women should become pregnant?
Yet this is continually the case. Others there are, who ought
never to become parents; because, if they do, it is only to
transmit to their offspring grievous hereditary diseases, which
render such offspring mere subjects of misery throughout their
sickly existence. Yet such women will not lead a life of celibacy.
They marry. They become parents, and the sum of human misery
is increased by their doing so. But it is folly to expect we can
induce such persons to live the lives of Shakers. Nor is it necessary;—all that duty requires of them is to refrain from becoming

parents. Who can estimate the beneficial effect which a rational moral restraint may thus have on the health, and beauty, and physical improvement of our race throughout future generations."

Let us now turn our attention to the case of unmarried youth.

"Almost all young persons, on reaching the age of maturity, desire to marry. That heart must be very cold, or very isolated, that does not find some object on which to bestow its affections. Thus, early marriages would be almost universal, did not prudential considerations interfere. The young man thinks, 'I cannot marry yet; I cannot support a family. I must make money first, and think of a matrimonial settlement afterwards.'

"And so he goes to making money, fully and sincerely resolved, in a few years, to share it with her whom he now loves. But passions are strong and temptations great. Curiosity, perhaps, introduces him into the company of those poor creatures whom society first reduces to a dependence on the most miserable of mercenary trades, and then curses for being what she has made them. There his health and moral feelings alike make shipwreck. The affections he had thought to treasure up for their first object are chilled by dissipation and blunted by excess. He scarcely retains a passion but avarice. Years pass on—years of profligacy and speculation—and his first wish is accomplished ; his fortune is made. Where now are the feelings and resolves of his youth ?

—"Like the dew on the mountain,
Like the foam on the river,
Like the bubble on the fountain,
They are gone—and for ever !"

"He is a man of pleasure—a man of the world. He laughs at the romance of his youth, and marries a fortune. If gaudy equipage and gay parties confer happiness, he is happy. But if they be only the sunshine on the stormy sea below, he is a victim to that system of morality which forbids a reputable connexion until the period when provision has been made for a large expected family. Had he married the first object of his choice, and simply delayed becoming a father until his prospects seemed to warrant it, how different might have been his lot! Until men and women are absolved from the fear of becoming parents, except when they themselves desire it, they ever will form mercenary and demoralizing connexions, and seek in dissipation the happiness they might have found in domestic life.

"I know that this, however common, is not a universal case. Sometimes the heavy responsibilities of a family are incurred at all risks ; and who shall say how often a life of unremitting toil and poverty is the consequence? Sometimes if even rarely the young mind *does* hold to its first resolves. The youth plods through years of cold celibacy and solitary anxiety ; happy, if before the best hours of his life are gone, and its warmest feelings withered, he may return to claim the reward of his forbearance and his industry. But even in this comparatively happy case, shall we count for nothing the years of ascetic sacrifice at which after happiness is purchased ? The days of youth are not too many, nor its affections too lasting. We may, indeed, if a great object require it, sacrifice the one and mortify the other. But is this, in itself, desirable ? Does not wisdom tell us that such a sacrifice is a dead loss—to the warm-hearted, often a grievous one ? Does not wisdom bid us temperately enjoy the spring-time of life, ' while the evil days come not, nor the years draw nigh, when we shall say, we have no pleasure in them ?'

" Let us say, then, if we will, that the youth who thus sacrifices the present for the future, chooses wisely between the two evils, profligacy and asceticism. This is true. But let us not imagine the lesser evil to be a good. It is *not* good for man to be alone. It is for no man's or woman's happiness or benefit, that they should be condemned to Shakerism. It is a violence done to the feelings, and an injury to the character. A life of rigid celibacy, though infinitely preferable to a life of dissipation, is yet fraught with many evils. Peevishness, restlessness, vague longings, and instability of character, are amongst the least of these. The mind is unsettled, and the judgment warped. Even the very instinct which is thus mortified, assumes an undue importance, and occupies a portion of the thoughts which does not of right or nature belong to it; and which, during a life of satisfied affection, it would not obtain."

In many instances the genital organs are rendered so irritable by the repletion to which unnatural continency gives rise, and by the *much thinking*, caused by such repletion, as to induce a disease known to medical men by the name of *Gonorrhœa Dormientium*. It consists in an emission or discharge of the semen during sleep. This discharge is immediately excited in most instances by a lascivious dream; but such dream is caused by the repletion and irratibility of the genital organs. It is truly astonishing to what a degree of mental anguish this disease gives rise in young men. They do not understand the nature, or rather, the cause of it. They think it depends on a weakness—indeed, the disease is often called "a seminal weakness"—and that the least gratification in a natural way would but serve to increase it. Their anxiety about it weakens the whole system. This weakness they erroneously attribute to the discharges : they think themselves totally disqualified for entering into or enjoying the married state. Finally, the genital and mental organs act and react upon each other so perniciously, as to cause a degree of nervousness, debility, emaciation, and melancholy—in a word, a *wretchedness* that sets description at defiance. Nothing is so effectual in curing this diseased state of body and mind, in *young* men, as marriage. All restraint, fear, and solicitude should be removed.

" Inasmuch, then, as the scruples of incurring heavy responsibilities deter from forming moral connections, and encourages intemperance and prostitution, the knowledge which enables man to limit the number of his offspring, would in the present state of things save much unhappiness, and prevent many crimes. Young persons sincerely attached to each other, and who might wish to marry, would marry early ; merely resolving not to become parents until prudence permitted it. The young man, instead of solitary toil and vulgar dissipation, would enjoy the society and the assistance of her he had chosen as his companion ; and the best years of life, whose pleasures never return, would not be squandered in riot, nor lost through mortification."

CHAPTER II.

On Generation.

I HOLD the following to be important and undeniable truths :—That every man has a natural right both to receive and to convey a knowledge of all the facts and discoveries of every art and science, excepting such only as may be secured to some particular person or persons by copyright or patent. That a *physical truth* in its general effect cannot be a *moral evil.* " That *no* fact in physics or in morals ought to be concealed from the inquiring mind."

Some may make a misuse of knowledge, but that is *their* fault ; and it is *not right* that one person should be deprived of knowledge ; of spirits, of razors, or of any thing else which is harmless in itself and may be useful to him, because another may misuse it.

The subject of generation is not only interesting as a branch of science, but it is so connected with the happiness of mankind that it is highly important in a practical point of view. Such, to be sure, is the custom of the age that it is not considered a proper subject to investigate before a popular assembly, nor is it proper to attend the calls of nature in a like place ; yet they must and ought to be attended to, for the good—the happiness of mankind requires it ; so, too, for like reason, the subject of generation ought to be investigated until it be rightly understood by all people, but at such opportunities as the good sense of every individual will easily decide to be proper. This I presume to say, not simply upon the abstract principle that all knowledge of nature's workings is useful, and the want of it disadvantageous ; but from the known moral fact, that ignorance of this process has in many instances proved the cause of lamentable " mishap ;" and more especially as it is essential to the attainment of the great advantages which it is the chief object of this work to bestow upon mankind.

People generally, as was the case with physicians until of late years, entertain a very erroneous idea of what takes place in the process of conception. Agreeable to this idea, the " check" which I consider far preferable to any other, would not be effectual, as would be obvious to all. Consequently, entertaining this idea, people would not have due confidence in it. Hence it is necessary to correct a long held and widely extended error. But this I cannot expect to do by simply saying it is an error. Deep rooted and heretofore undisputed opinions are not so easily eradicated. If I would convince any one that the steps in one of the most recondite processes of nature e not such as he has always believed, it will greatly serve my purpose to show what these steps *are*. I must first prepare him to be reasoned with, and then reason the matter all over with him—I must point out the facts which disprove his opinion, and show that my own is unattended with difficulties.

But what can be more obvious than that it is absolutely impossible to explain any process or function of the animal economy so as to be understood, before the names of the organs which perform this function has been defined, that is, before the organs themselves have been described? Now it is well known to every anatomist, and indeed it must be obvious to all, that in describing any organ or system of organs we must always begin with some external and known part, and proceed regularly, step by step to the internal and unknown. As in arithmetic, " every thing must be understood as you go along."

Fully to effect the objects of this work, it is, therefore, a matter of necessity that I give an anatomical description of certain parts— even external parts—which some, but for what I have just said, might think it useless to mention. It is not to gratify the idle curiosity of the light minded that this book is written: it is for *utility* in the broad and truly philosophical sense of the term ; nay, farther, it shall, with the exception of here and there a little spicing, be confined to *practical utility*. I shall therefore endeavour to treat of the subject in this chapter so as to be understood, without giving any description of the male organs of generation : though I hold it an accomplishment for one to be able to speak of those organs, as diseases often put them under the necessity of doing, without being compelled to use low and vulgar language. But I must briefly describe the female organs; in doing which, I must, of course, speak as do other anatomists and physiologists ; and whoever to this objects, will discover more affectation and prudery than good sense and good will to mankind.

The adipose or fatty matter immediately over the share bone, forms a considerable prominence in females, which, at the age of puberty, is covered with hair, as in males. This prominence is called *Mons Veneris*.

The exterior orifice commences immediately below this. On each side of this orifice is a prominence continued from the mons veneris, which is largest above and gradually diminishes as it descends. These two prominences are called the Labia Externa, or external lips. Near the latter end of pregnancy they become somewhat enlarged and relaxed, so that they sustain little or no injury during parturition. Just within the upper or anterior commissure formed by the junction of these lips, a little round oblong body is situated. This body is called the Clitoris. Most of its length is bound down, as it were, pretty closely to the bone; and it is of very variable size in different females. Instances have occurred where it was so enlarged as to enable the female to have venereal commerce with others; and in Paris this fact was once made a public exhibition of to the medical faculty. Women thus formed appear to partake in their general form of the male character, and are termed hermaphrodites. The idea of human beings, called hermaphrodites, which could be either father, or mother, is, doubtless, erroneous. The clitoris is analogous in its structure to the penis, and like it, is exquisitely sensible, being, as it is supposed, the principal seat of pleasure. It is subject to erection or distension, like the penis, and from like causes.

The skin which lines the internal surface of the external lips is folded in such a manner as to form two flat bodies, the exterior edges of which are convex. They are called the Nymphæ. They extend downward, one on each side, from the clitoris to near the middle of the external orifice, somewhat diverging from each other. Their use is not very evident. The orifice of the urethra (the canal, short in females, which leads to the bladder) is situated an inch or more farther inward than the clitoris, and is a little protuberant.

Passing by the external lips, the clitoris, the nymphæ, and the orifice of the urethra, we come to the membrane called the Hymen. It is situated just at or a trifle behind the orifice of the urethra. It is stretched across the passage, and were it a complete septum, it would close up the anterior extremity of that portion of the passage which is called the Vagina. But the instances in which this septum or partition is complete, are very rare; there being, in almost all cases, an aperture either in its centre, or, more frequently in its anterior edge, giving the membrane the form of a crescent. Through this aperture passes the menstrual fluid. Sometimes, however, this septum is complete, and the menstrual fluid is retained month after month, until appearances and symptoms much like those of pregnancy are produced, giving rise perhaps to unjust suspicions. Such cases require the simple operation of dividing the hymen. In many instances the hymen is very imperfect. insomuch that some have doubted whether it is to be found in the generality of virgins. Where it exists, it is generally ruptured in the first intercourse of the sexes and the female is said to lose her virginity. In some rare instances it is so very strong as not to be ruptured by such intercourse: and the nature of the difficulty not being understood, the husband has sued for a divorce. But every thing may be put to rights by a slight surgical operation. The parts here described are among those called the *external* parts of generation.

The *Internal* organs of generation, consist, in the female, of the Vagina, the Uterus, the Ovaries and their appendages.

The *Vagina* is a membranous canal commencing at the hymen, and extending to the uterus. It is a little curved, and extends backwards and upwards between the bladder, which lies before and above it, and that extreme portion of the bowels, called the *rectum*, which lies behind it. The coat or membrane which lines the internal surface of the vagina, forms a number of transverse ridges. These ridges are to be found only in the lower or anterior half of the vagina, and they do not extend all round the vagina, but are situated on its anterior and posterior sides, while their lateral sides are smooth. I mention these ridges, because a knowledge of them may lead to a more effectual use of one of the checks to be made known hereafter.

The *Uterus*, or womb, is also situated between the bladder and the rectum, but above the vagina. Such is its shape that it has been compared to a pear with a long neck. There is, of course, considerable difference between the body and the neck, the first being twice as broad as the last. Each of these parts is somewhat flattened. In subjects of mature age, who have never been pregnant, the whole of the uterus is about two inches and a half in length, and more than an inch and a half in breadth at the broadest part of the body. It is near an inch in thickness. The neck of the uterus is situated downwards, and may be said to be inserted into the upper extremity of the vagina. It extends down into the vagina the better part of an inch. In the uterus is a cavity, which approaches the triangular form, and from which a canal passes down through the neck of the uterus into the vagina. This cavity is so small that its sides are almost in contact. So that the uterus is a thick firm organ for so small a one. Comparing the cavity of the uterus to a triangle, we say the upper side or line of this triangle, is transverse with respect to the body, and the other two lines pass downwards and inwards, so that they would form an angle below, did they not, before they meet, take a turn more directly downwards to form the canal just mentioned. In each of the upper angles there is an orifice of such size as to admit of a hog's bristle. These little orifices are the mouths of two tubes, called the *Fallopian* tubes, of which more will be said presently. The canal which passes through the neck of the uterus, connecting the cavity of this organ with that of the vagina, is about a quarter of an inch in diameter. It is different from other ducts, for it seems to be a part of the cavity from which it extends, inasmuch as when the cavity or the uterus is enlarged in the progress of pregnancy, this canal is gradually converted into a part of that cavity.

The lower extremity of the neck of the uterus is irregularly convex and tumid. The orifice of the canal in it, is oval, and so situated that it divides the convex surface of the lower extremity of the neck in two portions, which are called the *lips* of the uterus. The anterior is thicker than the posterior. The orifice itself is called *os tincæ*, or *os uteri*, or in English, *the mouth of the womb*. When the parts are in a weak relaxed state the mouth or neck of the uterus is quite low, and, in almost all cases, it may be reached by a finger introduced into the vagina, especially by a second person who carries his hand behind.

The *Ovaries* are two bodies of a flattened or oval form, one of which is situated on each side of the uterus, at a little distance from it, and about as high up as where the uterus becomes narrow, to form its neck. The longest diameter of the ovarium is about an inch. Each ovarium has a firm coat of membrane. In those who have not been pregnant, it contains from ten to twenty *vesicles*, which are little round bodies, formed of a delicate membrane, and filled with a transparent fluid. Some of these vesicles are situated so near the surface of the ovarium as to be prominent on its surface. They are of different sizes, the largest nearly a quarter of an inch in diameter.

In those in whom conception has ever taken place, some of these vesicles are removed, and in their place a cicatrix or scar is formed which continues through life. However, the number of cicatrices does not always correspond with the number of conceptions. They often exceed it, and are sometimes found where conception has not been known to have taken place.

The *Fallopian Tubes* are two canals four or five inches in length, proceeding from the upper angles of the cavity of the uterus, in a transverse direction, in respect to the body. Having so proceeded for some distance, they turn downwards towards the ovaries. At their commencement in the uterus they are very small; but they enlarge as much as they progress. The large ends which hang loose, terminate in open mouths, the margins of which consist of fimbriated processes, and nearly to the ovaria.

We are now prepared to treat of conception. Yet as menstruation is closely connected with it, and as a knowledge of many things concerning menstruation may contribute much to the well being of females, for whom this work is at least as much designed as for males, I shall first briefly treat of this subject.

Menstruation. When females arrive at the age of puberty, they begin to have a discharge once every month, by way of the vagina, of the colour of blood. This discharge is termed the *menses*. To have it, is to *menstruate*. The age at which menstruatiom commenses varies with different individuals, and also in different climates. The warmer the climate the earlier it commences and ceases. In temperate climates it generally commences at the age of fourteen or fifteen, and ceases at forty-four, or a little later. Whenever it commences, the girl acquires a more womanly appearance. It is a secretion of the uterus, or, in other words, the minute vessels distributed to the inner coat of the uterus, select, as it were, from the blood, and pour out in a gradual manner, the materials of this fluid. It has one of the properties, colour, of blood, but it does not coagulate, nor separate into different parts like blood, and cannot properly be called blood. When this discharge is in all respects regular, it amounts in most females to six or eight ounces, and is from two to four days continuance. During its continuance the woman is said to be *unwell*, or *out of order*. Various unpleasant feelings are liable to attend it; but when it is attended with severe pain, as it not unfrequently is, it becomes a disease, and the woman is not likely to conceive until it be cured. During the existence of the "turns," or the "monthlys," as they are often called, indigestible food, dancing in warm rooms. sudden exposure to cold or wet, and mental agitations should be avoided as much as possible. The "turns" do not continue during pregnancy, nor nursing, unless nursing be continued too long. The milk becomes bad if nursing be continued after the turns recommence. Some women, it is true, are subject to a slight hermorrhage that sometimes occurs with considerable regularity during pregnancy, and has led them to suppose they have their turns at such times; but it is not so; the discharge at such times is real blood.

The use of the menstrual discharge seems to be, to prepare the uterine system for conception. For females do not become pregnant before they commence, nor after they cease having their turns; nor while they are suppressed by some disease, by cold or by nursing. Some credible women, however, have said that they become pregnant while nursing, without having had any turn since their last lying-in. It is believed that in these cases, they had *some* discharge, colourless perhaps, which they did not notice, but which answered the purposes of the common one. Women are not near so likely to conceive during the week before a monthly, as during the week immediately after. But although the use of this secretion seems to be to prepare for conception, it is not to be inferred that the reproductive instinct ceases at the " turn of life," or when the woman ceases to menstruate. On the contrary, it is said that this passion often increases at this period, and continues in a greater or less degree to an extreme age.

Conception. The part performed by the male in the reproduction of the species consists in exciting the orgasm of the female, and depositing the semen in the vagina. Before I inquire what takes place in the females, I propose to speak of the semen.

This fluid, which is secreted by the testicles, may be said to possess three kinds of properties, physical, chemical, physiological. Its physical properties are known to every one—it is a thickish, nearly opake fluid, of a peculiar odour, saltish taste, &c. As to its chemical properties, it is found by analysis to consist of 900 parts of water, 60 of animal mucillage, 10 of soda, 30 of phosphate of lime. Its physiological property is that of exciting the female genital organs in a peculiar manner. *See note at back of Title Page*

When the semen is examined by a microscope, there can be distinguished a multitude of small animalculæ, which appear to have a rounded head and a long tail. These animalculæ move with a certain degree of rapidity. They appear to avoid the light and to delight in the shade. Leeuwenhoek, if not the discoverer of the seminal animalculæ, was the first who brought the fact of their existence fully before the public. With respect to their size, he remarked that ten thousand of them might exist in a space not larger than a grain of sand. They have a definite figure, and are obviously different from the animalcules found in any other fluid. Leeuwenhoek believed them to be the beginnings of future animals —that they are of different sexes, and even thought he could discover a difference of sex, upon which depends the future sex of the fœtus. Be this as it may, it appears to be admitted on all hands, that the animalcules are present in the semen of the various species of male animals, and that they cannot be detected when either from age or disease the animals are rendered sterile. " Hence," says Bostock, " we can scarcely refuse our assent to the position, that these animalcules are in some way or other instrumental to the production of the fœtus." The secretion of the semen commences at the age of puberty. Before this period the testicles secrete a viscid, transparent fluid, which has never been analysed, but which is doubtless essentially different from semen. The revolution which the whole economy undergoes at this period, such as the tone of the voice, the development of hairs, the beard, the increase of the muscles and bones, &c., is intimately connected with the existence of the testicles and the secretion of this fluid. " Eunuchs preserve the same form as in childhood ; their voice is effeminate, they have no beard, their disposition is generally timid ; and finally their physical and moral character very nearly resembles that of females. Nevertheless, many of them take delight in venereal intercourse, and give themselves up with ardour to a connexion which must always be unfruitful."*

The part performed by the female in the reproduction of the species is far more complicated than that performed by the male. It consists, in the first instance, in providing a substance, which in connexion with the male secretion, is to constitute the fœtus; in furnishing a suitable situation in which the fœtus may be

* Magendie's Physiology

developed; in affording due nourishment for its growth; in bringing it forth; and afterwards furnishing it with food especially adapted to the digestive organs of the young animal. Some parts of this process are not well understood, and such a variety of hypotheses have been proposed to explain them that Drelincourt, who lived in the latter part of the 17th century, is said to have collected 260 hypotheses of generation.

It ought to be known that women have conceived when the semen was merely applied to the parts anterior to the hymen, as the internal surface of the external lips, the nymphæ, &c. This is proved by the fact that several cases of pregnancy have occurred when the hymen was entire. This fact need not surprise us; for, agreeable to the theory of absorption, we have, to account for it, only to suppose that some of the absorbent vessels are situated anterior to the hymen—a supposition by no means unreasonable.

There are two peculiarities of the human species respecting conception, which I will notice. First, unlike other animals, they are liable—and for what has yet been proved to the contrary, *equally* liable to conceive at all seasons of the year. Second, a woman rarely, if ever, conceives until after having had several sexual connections; nor does one connexion in fifty cause conception in the matrimonial state, where the husband and wife live together uninterruptedly. Public women rarely conceive, owing probably to a weakened state of the genital system, induced by too frequent and promiscuous intercourse.

A woman is most likely to conceive, first, when she is in health; second, between the ages of twenty-six and thirty; third, after she has for a season been deprived of those intercourses she had previously enjoyed; fourth, soon after a monthly turn.

It is universally agreed, that sometime after a fruitful connexion, a vesicle (two in case of twins) of one or the other ovary becomes so enlarged, that it bursts forth from the ovary, and takes the name of *ovum*; which is taken up, or rather received as it bursts forth, by the fimbriated extremity of the fallopian tube, and is then slowly conducted along the tube into the uterus, to the inner surface of which it attaches itself. Here it becomes developed into a full grown fœtus, and is brought forth about forty-two weeks from the time of conception, by a process termed parturition. But one grand question is how the semen operates in causing the vesicle to enlarge, &c.; whether the semen itself or any part thereof reaches the ovary, and if so, in what way it is conveyed to them. It was long the opinion, that the semen was ejected into the uterus in the act of coition; and that it afterwards by some unknown means finds its way into and along the fallopian tubes to the ovary. But there are several facts which weigh heavily against this opinion, and some that entirely forbid it. In the first place, there are several well attested instances in which impregnation took place while the hymen remained entire; where the vagina terminated in the rectum; and where it was so contracted by a cicatrix as not to admit the penis. In all these cases the semen could not have been lodged any where near the mouth of the uterus, much less ejected into it. Secondly, it has followed a connexion where, from some defect in the male organs, as the urethra terminating some inches behind the end of the penis, it is clear that the semen could not have been injected into the uterus, nor even near its mouth. Third, the neck of the unimpregnated uterus is so narrow as merely to admit a probe, and is filled with a thick tenacious fluid, which seemingly could not be forced away by any force which the male organ possesses of ejecting the semen, even if the mouth of the male urethra were in apposition with that of the uterus. But, fourth, the mouth of the uterus is by no means fixed. By various causes it is made to assume various situations, and probably the mouth of the urethra rarely comes in contact with it.

Fifth. "The tenacity of the male semen is such as renders its passage through the small aperture in the neck of the uterus impossible, even by a power or force much superior to that which we may rationally suppose to reside in the male organs of generation."

Sixth. "Harvey and De Graaf dissected animals at almost every period after coition, for the express purpose of discovering the semen, but were never able to detect the smallest vestige of it in the uterus in any one instance."*

Aware of the insurmountable objections to this view of the manner in which the semen reaches the ovary, it has been supposed by some physiologists that the semen is absorbed from the vagina into the great circulating system, where it is mixed, of course, with the blood, and goes the whole round of the circulation, subject to the influence of those causes which produce great changes in the latter fluid.

To this hypothesis it may be objected, that while there is no direct evidence in support of it, it is exceedingly unreasonable, inasmuch as we can scarcely believe that the semen can go the whole round of the circulation, and then find its way to the ovary in such a pure unaltered state as the experiments of Spallanzani prove it must be in, that it may impregnate.

A third set of theorists have maintained that an imperceptible something, which they called *aura seminalis*, passes from the semen lodged in the vagina to the ovary, and excites those actions which are essential to the development of an ovum. Others, again, have told us, that it is all done by sympathy. That neither the semen nor any volatile part of it finds its way to the ovary; but that the semen excites the parts with which it is in contact

* Dewees' "Essay on Superfoetation."

c 2

in a peculiar manner, and by a law of the animal economy, termed sympathy or consent of parts, a peculiar action commences in the ovary, by which an ovum is developed, &c.

To both these conjectures it may be objected, that they have no other foundation but the supposed necessity of adopting them, to account for the effect of impregnation ; and further, they '' make no provision for the formation of mules ; for the peculiarities of, and likeness to parents, and for the propagation of predisposition to disease, from parent to child ; for the production of mulattoes, &c.''

A fifth, and to me far more satisfactory view of the subject than any other, is that advanced by our distinguished countryman, Dr. Dewees, of Philadelphia. It appears to harmonise with all known facts relating to the subject of conception ; and something from analogy may also be drawn in its favour. It is this: that there is a set of absorbent vessels leading directly from the inner surface of the labia externa and the vagina to the ovaries, the whole office of which vessels is, to absorb the semen and convey it to the ovaries. I do not know that these vessels have yet been fully discovered ; but in a note on the sixteenth page of his '' Essays on Various Subjects,'' the doctor says :—'' The existence of these vessels is now rendered almost certain, as Dr. Gartner, of Copenhagen, has discovered a duct leading from the ovary to the vagina.''

Another question of considerable moment relating to generation is, from which parent are the first rudiments of the fœtus derived.

The earliest hypothesis with which we are acquainted, and which has received the support of some of the most eminent of the moderns, ascribes the original formation of the fœtus to the combination of particles of matter derived from each of the parents. This hypothesis naturally presents itself to the mind as the obvious method of explaining the necessity for the co-operation of the two sexes, and the resemblance in external form, and even in mind and character, which the offspring frequently bears to the male parent. ''The principal objections,'' says Bostock, '' to this hypothesis, independent of the want of any direct proof of a female seminal fluid, are of two descriptions, those which depend upon the supposed impossibility of unorganized matter forming an organized being ; and those which are derived from observations and experiments of Haller and Spallanzani, which they brought forward in support of their theory of pre-existent germs.

In relation to these objections I remark, first, that those whose experience has been with hale females, I suspect can have no doubt but that the female orgasm increases like that of the male, until an emission of fluid of some kind or other takes place. But whether this secretion may properly be called semen, whether any part of it unites with the male semen in forming the rudiments of the fœtus, is another question. For my own part I am inclined to the opinion that it does not. I rather regard it as the result of exalted excitation, analogous to the increased secretion of other organs from increased stimulation ; and if it be for any object or use, as it probably is, it is that of affording nature a means of relieving herself ; or, in other words, of quieting the venereal passion. If this passion, being once roused, could not by some means or other be calmed, it would command by far too great a proportion of our thoughts, and with many constitutions, the individuals, whether male or female, could not conduct themselves with due decorum. One fact which leads me to think that the female secretion in the act of coition is not essential to impregnation, is, that many females have conceived, (if their unbiassed testimony may be relied on,) when they experienced no pleasure. In these cases it is more than probable that there was no orgasm, nor any secretion or emission of fluid on the part of the female.

As to the objection of " the *supposed* impossibility of unorganized matter forming an organized being." I do not conceive that it weighs at all against the hypothesis before us ; for I do not believe such a thing takes place, even if we admit that " the original formation of the fœtus is a combination of particles of matter derived from each of the parents." What do, or rather, what ought we to mean by organized matter ? Not, surely, that it exhibits some obvious physical structure, unlike what is to be found in inorganic matter, but that it exhibits phenomena, and of course may be said to possess properties unlike any kind of inorganic matter. Matter unites with matter in three ways, mechanically, chemically, and organically ; and each mode of union gives rise to properties peculiar to itself. When matter unites organically, the substance or being so formed exhibits some phenomena essentially different from what inorganic bodies exhibit. It is on this account that we ascribe to organic bodies certain properties, which we call physiological properties, such as contractility, sensibility, life, &c. When from any cause these bodies have undergone such a change that they no longer exhibit the phenomena peculiar to them, they are said to have lost these properties, and to be dead. A substance need not possess *all* the physiological properties of an animal of the higher orders, to entitle it to the name of an organized or living substance, nor need it possess the physical property of solidity. The blood, as well as many of the secretions, does several things, exhibits several phenomena, which no mechanical or mere chemical combinations of matter do exhibit. We must therefore ascribe to it certain physiological properties, and regard it as an organised, a· *living* fluid, as was contended by the celebrated John Hunter. So with respect to the semen, it certainly possesses physiological properties, one in particular, peculiar to itself, namely, the property of impetrnating the female ; and upon no sound principle can it be regarded in any other light than as an organized, and of course a living fluid. And if the female secretion or any part of it unite with the male secretion in the formation of the rudiments of the fœtus, in a different manner than any other substance would, then it certainly has the property of doing so, whether we give this property a name or not; and a regard to the soundest principles of physiology compels us to class this property with the physiological or vital, and of course to regard this secretion as an organized and living fluid. So, then, unorganized matter does not form an organized being, admitting the hypothesis before us as correct.

That organized beings should give rise to other organized beings under favourable circumstances as to nourishment, warmth, &c. is no more wonderful than that fire should give rise to fire when air and fuel are present. To be sure, there are some minute steps in the process which are not fully known to us; still, if they ever should be known, we should unquestionably see that there is a natural cause for every one of them; and that they are all consonant with certain laws of the animal economy. We should see no necessity of attempting to explain the process of generation by bringing to our aid (or rather to the darkening of the subject, any imaginary principle, as the *nisus formativus* of Blumenbach.

As to the " observations and experiments of Haller and Spallanzani," I think with Dr. Bostock that they weigh but little, if any, against the theory before us. I shall not be to the labour of bringing them forward, and shewing their futility as objections to this theory, for I am far from insisting on the correctness of it; that is, I do not insist that any part of the female secretion, during coition, unites with the male semen in the formation of the rudiments of the fœtus.

The second hypothesis or theory I shall notice, as to the rudiments of the fœtus, is that of Leeuwenhoek, who regarded the seminal animalcules of the male semen : the proper rudiments of the fœtus ; and that the office of the female is to afford them a suitable receptacle, where they may be supported and nourished until they are able to exist by the exercise of their own functions. This is essentially the view of the subject which I adopt, and which I intend to give more particularly presently.

I know of no serious objection to this hypothesis, nothing but the " extreme improbability." as its opponents say, " that these animalcules should be the rudiments of beings so totally dissimilar to them." But I wish to know if there is more difference between a fœtus and a seminal animalcule, than there is between a fœtus and a few material particles in some other form than that of such animalcule ?

The third hypothesis, or that of pre-existing germs, proceeds upon a precisely opposite view of the subject to that of Leeuwenhoek, namely, that the fœtus is properly the production of the female; that it exists previous to sexual congress, with all its organs, in some part of the uterine system ; and that it receives no proper addition from the male, but that the seminal fluid acts merely by exciting the powers of the fœtus, or endowing it with vitality.

It is not known who first proposed this hypothesis; but, strange as it may appear, it has had the support of such names as Bonnet, Haller, and Spallanzani, and met with a favourable reception in the middle of the last century. Agreeable to this hypothesis, our common mother, Eve, contained a number of homuncules [little men] one within another, like a nest of boxes, and all within her ovaries, equal to the number of all the births that ever have been, or ever will be, not to reckon abortions! Were I to bring forward all the facts and arguments that have been advanced in support of this idea, it seems to me I should fail to convince sound minds of its correctness, and as to arguments against it, they surely seem uncalled for.

Having now presented several hypotheses of generation, some as to the manner in which the semen reaches or influences the ovary, and others as to the rudiments of the foetus, I shall now bring together those views which upon the whole appear to me the most satisfactory.

I believe with Dr. Dewees that a set of absorbent vessels extend from the innermost surface of the labia externa, and from the vagina to the ovary, the whole office of which is to take up the semen or some part thereof, and convey it to the ovary. I believe with Leenwenhoek, that the seminal animalcules are the proper rudiments of the foetus, and are perhaps of different sexes, that in case of impregnation one of them is carried not only to, but *into* a vesicle of an ovary, which is in a condition to receive, and be duly affected by it. It is here surrounded by the albuminous fluid which the vesicle contains. This fluid being somewhat changed in its qualities by its new comer, stimulates the minute vessels of the parts which surround it, and thus causes more of this fluid to be formed, and while it affords the animalcule materials for its development, it puts the delicate membrane of the ovary which retains it in its place, upon the stretch, and finally bursts forth surrounded, probably by an exceedingly delicate membrane of its own. This membrane with the albuminous fluid it contains, and the animalcule in the centre of it, constitutes the ovum or egg. It is received by the fimbriated extremity of the fallopian tube, which by this time has grasped the ovary, and is by this tube, slowly conveyed into the uterus, to the inner surface of which it attaches itself, through the medium of a membrane, which is formed by the uterus itself in the interim, between impregnation and the arriving of the ovum in the way I have just mentioned.

The idea that a seminal animalcule enters an ovum while it remains in the ovary, was never before advanced to my knowledge; hence I consider it incumbent upon me to advance some reasons for this opinion. First, it is admitted on all hands, that the seminal animalcule are essential to impregnation, since "they cannot be detected when either from age or disease the animal is rendered sterile." Second, the ovum is impregnated while it remains in the ovary. True, those who have never met with Dr. Dewees' theory, and who, consequently, have adopted the idea that the semen is ejected into the uterus, as the least improbable of any with which they were acquainted, have found it very difficult to dispose of the fact that the ovum is impregnated in the ovary; and have consequently presumed this is not *generally* the case. They admit it is certainly so sometimes, and that it is difficult to reject the conclusion that it is always so. Dr. Bostock, who doubtless had not met with Dewees' theory at the time he wrote, and who admits it impossible to conceive how the semen can find its way along the fallopian tubes—how it can find its way towards the ovary farther, at most, than into the uterus, and consequently cannot see how the ovum can be impregnated in the ovary, says, " Perhaps the most rational supposition may be, that the ovum is transmitted to the uterus in the unimpregnated state; but there are certain facts which seem almost incompatible with this idea, especially the cases which not unfrequently occur of perfect fœtuses having been found in the tubes, or where they escaped them into the cavity of the abdomen. Hence it is demonstrated that the ovum is occasionally impregnated in the *tubes* [why did he not say ovaria?], and we can scarcely resist the conclusion that it must always be the case." * * * " Haller discusses this hypothesis, [Bostock's " most natural supposition, perhaps,"] and decides against it." * * * " The experiments of Cruikshank which were very numerous, and appear to have been made with the requisite degree of skill and correctness, lead to the conclusion that the rudiment of the young animal is perfected in the ovarium." * * * " A case is detailed by Dr. Granville of a fœtus, which appears to have been lodged in the body of the ovarium itself; and it is considered by its author as a proof that conception always takes place in this organ." The above quotations are from the third volume of Bostock's Physiology.

Now as the seminal animalcules are essential to impregnation, and as the ovum is impregnated in the ovarium, what more probable conjecture can we form that an animalcule, as the real proper rudiment of the fœtus, enters the ovum, where, being surrounded with albuminous fluid with which it is nourished, it gradually becomes developed? It may be noticed that Leeuwenhoek estimates that ten thousand animalcules of the human semen may exist in a space not larger than a grain of sand. There can, therefore, be no difficulty in admitting that they may find their way along exceedingly minute vessels from the vagina, not only to, but into the ovum, while situated in the ovarium.

I think no one can be disposed to maintain that the animalcule merely reaches the surface of the ovum,* and thus impregnates it.

* I say *surface* of the ovum, for it is probably not a mere drop of fluid, but fluid surrounded with an exceedingly delicate membrane.

But possibly some may contend that its sole office is to *stimulate* the ovum, and in this way set a going that train of actions which are essential to impregnation. But there is no evidence in favour of this last idea, and certainly it does not so well harmonize with the fact that the offspring generally partakes more or less of the character of its male parent. As Dr. Dewees says of the doctrine of sympathy, "It makes no provision for the formation of mules; for the peculiarities of, and likeness to, parents; and for the propagation of predisposition to disease from parent to child; for the production of mulattoes, &c.

Considering it important to do away the popular and mischievous error, that the semen must enter the uterus to effect impregnation, I shall, in addition to what has been already advanced, here notice the experiments of Dr. Haighton. He divided the fallopian tubes in numerous instances, and found that after this operation a foetus is never produced, but that corpora lutea were formed. The obvious conclusions from these facts are, that the semen does not traverse the fallopian tubes to reach the ovaria; yet that the ovum becomes impregnated while in the ovarium, and consequently that the semen reaches the ovarium in some way, except by the uterus and fallopian tubes. I may remark, however, that a corpus luteum is not positive proof that impregnation, at some time or other, has taken place; yet they are so rarely found in virgins that they were regarded as such proof until the time of Blumenbach, a writer of the present century.

"Harvey and De Graaf dissected animals at almost every period after coition, for the express purpose of discovering the semen, but were never able to detect the smallest vestige of it in the uterus in any one instance."—*Dewees' Essay on Superfoetation.*

The fact of superfoetation furnishes a very strong argument against the idea that the semen enters the uterus in impregnation.

A woman being impregnated while she is already impregnated, constitutes superfoetation. It is established beyond a doubt that such instances have occurred, yet those who have supposed that it is necessary for the semen to pass through the mouth of the uterus to produce conception, have urged that superfoetation could not take place, because, say they, and they say correctly, "so soon as impregnation shall have taken place, the os uteri closes, and becomes impervious to the semen, ejected in subsequent acts of coition."

Dr. Dewees relates two cases, evidently cases of superfoetation, that occurred to his own personal knowledge. The first shews, that agreeable to the old theory, the semen must have met with other difficulties than a closed mouth of the uterus—it must have passed through several membranes, as well as the waters surrounding the foetus, to have reached even the uterine extremity of a fallopian tube. The second case I will give in his own words.

"A white woman, servant to Mr. H. of Abington township,

Montgomery county, was delivered about five and twenty years since of twins ; one of which was perfectly white, the other perfectly black.　When I resided in that neighbourhood I was in the habit of seeing them almost daily, and also had frequent conversations with Mrs. H. respecting them.　She was present at their birth, so that no possible deception could have been practised respecting them.　The white girl is delicate, fair skinned, light hair, and blue eyed, and it is said very much to resemble the mother.　The other has all the characteristic marks of the African ; short of stature, flat, broad nosed, thick lipped, woolly headed, flat footed, and projecting heels ; she is said to resemble a negro they had on the farm, but with whom the woman never would acknowledge an intimacy : but of this there was no doubt, as both he and the white man with whom her connexion was detected, ran from the neighbourhood so soon as it was known the girl was with child."

I am aware that some have thought they had actually discovered semen in the uterus, while Ruysch, an anatomist of considerable eminence, who flourished at the close of the 17th century, asserted in the most unequivocal manner, that he found the semen in its gross white state in one of the fallopian tubes of a woman, who died very soon after, or during the act of coition ; but, says Dewees, " the semen, after it has escaped from the penis, very quickly loses its albuminous appearance, and becomes as thin and transparent as water.　And we are certain that Ruysch was mistaken.　Some alteration in the natural secretion of the parts was mistaken for semen ; this was nowise difficult for him to do, as he had a particular theory to support—and more especially as this supposed discovery made so much for it.　It is not merely speculative, when we say that some change in the natural secretion of the parts may be mistaken for semen ; for we have the testimony of Morgagni on our side.　He tells us he has seen similar appearances in several instances in virgins and others, who had been subject during their lives to leucorrhœa, and that it has been mistaken by some for male semen."

On the whole I would say, that in some instances, where the mouth of the uterus is uncommonly relaxed, the semen may as it were accidentally have found its way into it : but that is not generally the case, nor is it essential to impregnation ; and further, that whatever of semen may at any time be lodged in the uterus, has nothing to do with conception.　It is not consistent with analogy to suppose that the uterus has vessels for absorbing the semen and conveying it to the ovaria, considering the other important functions which we know it performs.

The circumstances under which a female is most likely to conceive, are, first, when she is in health ; second, between the ages of twenty-six and thirty ; third, after she has for a season been deprived of those intercourses she had previously enjoyed ; fourth, soon after menstruating.　Respecting this latter circumstance, Dr.

Dewees remarks: " Perhaps it is not erring greatly to say, that the woman is .able to conceive at any part of the menstrual interval. It is generally supposed, however, that the most favourable instant is, immediately after the catamenia have ceased ; perhaps this is so as a general rule, but it is certainly liable to exceptions;" and he relates the following case which occured to his own notice. " The husband of a lady who was obliged to absent himself many months, in consequence of the embarrassment of his affairs, returned one night clandestinely ; his visit being only known to his wife, his mother, and myself. The consequence of this visit was the impregnation of his wife. The lady was at this time within a week of her menstrual period ; and as this did not fail to take place, she was led to hope she had not suffered by the visit of her husband. But her catamenia not appearing at the next period, gave rise to a fear she had not escaped ; and the birth of a child nine months and thirteen days from the night of this clandestine visit, proved her apprehensions too well grounded."

I think this case is an exception to a general rule ; and, furthermore, favours an idea which reason and a limited observation, rather than positive knowledge, has led me to advance above, namely, that a woman is more likely to conceive, other things being the same, after being deprived for a season of those intercourses she had previously enjoyed. Had this lady's husband remained constantly at home, she would probably either not have conceived at all, or have done so a fortnight sooner than she did.

This case is also remarkable for two other facts; one, " that a woman in perfect health, and pregnant with a healthy child, may exceed the period of nine months by several days; the other, that a check is not always immediately given to the catamenial flow, by an ovum being impregnated." Probably it is not so generally so as many suppose.

The *term* of *utero-gestation*, or the length of time from conception, to the commencement of labour, is not precisely determined by physiologists. " It seems, however, says Dr. Dewees, " from the best calculations that can be made, that nine calendar months, or forty weeks, approaches the truth so nearly, that we can scarcely need desire more accuracy, could it be obtained." Unquestionably, however, some cases exceed this period by many days or even weeks, and it has been a question much agitated, how far this period is ever exceeded. It is a question of some moment in a legal point of view. Cases are reported where the usual period was exceeded by five or six months; cases, too, where the circumstances attending them, and the respectability of their reporters are such as to command our belief. Dr. Dewees has paid much attention to this subject, and he declares himself entirely convinced, " that the commonly fixed period may be extended from thirteen days to six weeks, under the influence of certain causes or peculiarities of constitution.

These occasional departures from the general rule will, perhaps, be the more readily admitted when we consider that they are not confined to the human species. From the experiment of Tessier, it appears that the term of utero-gestation varies greatly with the cow, sheep, horse, swine, and other animals to which his attention was directed.

Properly connected with the subject of generation, are the *signs of pregnancy*. Dr. Dewees remarks, that "our experience furnishes no certain mark by which the moment conception takes place is to be distinguished. All appeals by the women to particular sensations experienced at the instant, should be very guardedly received, for we are certain they cannot be relied upon ; for enjoyment and indifference are alike fallacious. Nor are certain nervous tremblings, nausea, palpitation of the heart, the sensation of something flowing from them during coition, &c. more to be relied upon." Burns, however, says, "some women feel, immediately after conception, a peculiar sensation, which apprises them of their situation ; but such instances are not frequent, and generally the first circumstances which lead a woman to suppose herself pregnant, are the suppression of the menses ;" a fickle appetite, some sickness, perhaps vomiting, especially in the morning; returning qualms, or of languor in the afternoon ; she is liable to heartburn, and to disturbed sleep. The mind becomes sometimes irritable, sometimes melancholy. The breasts at first often become smaller, sometimes tender; but about the third month they enlarge, and occasionally become painful. The nipple is surrounded with an areola or circle of a brown colour, or at least of a colour sensibly deeper or darker than before. She loses her looks, becomes paler, and the under part of the lower eyelid is often somewhat of a leaden hue. The features become sharper, and sometimes the whole body begins to emaciate, while the pulse quickens. In many instances particular sympathies take place, causing salivation, toothache, jaundice, &c. In other cases very little disturbance is produced, and the woman is not certain of her condition until the time of quickening, which is generally about four months from conception. It is possible for women to mistake the effects of wind for the motion of a child, especially if they have never borne children, and be anxious for a family ; but the sensation produced by wind in the bowels is not confined to one spot, but is often felt at a part of the abdomen where the motion of a child could not possibly be felt. Quite as frequently, perhaps, do fleshy women think themselves dropsical, and mistake motions of the child for movements of water within the abdominal cavity. The motion of the child is not to be confounded with the sensation sometimes produced by the uterus rising out of the pelvis, which precedes the feeling of fluttering. At the end of the fourth month the uterus becomes so large that it is obliged to rise out of the pelvis, and if this elevation take place suddenly, the sensation accompanying it is pretty strong, and the woman at the time often feels sick or faint, and in irritable habits, even a hysterical fit may accompany it. After this, the morning sickness and other sympathetic effects of pregnancy generally abate, and the health improves.

Very soon after impregnation, if blood be drawn, and suffered to stand a short time undisturbed, it will become sizy, of a yellowish or blueish colour, and somewhat of an oily appearance. But we cannot from such appearances of the blood alone pronounce a woman pregnant; for a suppression of the menses, accompanied with a febrile state, may give the blood a like appearance as pregnancy, so also may some local disease. Of the above mentioned symptoms, perhaps there is no *one* on which we can place more reliance than the increased colour of the circle around the nipple.

Six or eight weeks after conception, the most sure way of ascertaining pregnancy is, to examine the mouth and neck of the uterus, by way of the vagina. The uterus will be found lower down than formerly; its mouth is not directed so much forward as before impregnation; it is more completely closed, and the neck is felt to be thicker, or increased in circumference. When raised on the finger, it is found to be heavier, or more resisting. Whoever makes this examination must have examined the same uterus in an unimpregnated state, and retained a tolerably correct idea of its feeling at that time, or he will be liable to uncertainty; because the uterus of one woman is naturally different in magnitude from that of another; and the uterus is frequently lower down than natural, from other cause than pregnancy.

It has not been fully ascertained how long it is after a fruitful connexion before any effect is produced upon the ovaria, that is, before any alteration could be discovered, were the female to be dissected. But Haighton's experiments have established the fact, that with rabbits, whose term of utero-gestation is but thirty days, no effect is propagated to the ovaria until nearly fifty hours after coition; we should judge, therefore, that with the human species it must be several days, and it is generally estimated by physiologists, that the ovum does not reach the uterus until the expiration of twenty days from the time of connexion.

It is probable that in all cases in which any matter is absorbed from any part of the animal system, some little time is required for such matter, after its application, to stimulate and arouse the absorbent vessels to action; hence it is probable, that after the semen is lodged in the vagina, it is many minutes, possibly some hours, before any part of it is absorbed.

CHAPTER III.

Of Promoting and Checking Conception.

STERILITY depends either on imperfect organization, or imperfect action of the organs of generation. In the former cases, which are rare, the menses do not generally appear; the breasts are not developed, and the sexual desire is inconsiderable. There is no remedy in these cases.

The *action* may be imperfect in several respects. The menses may be obstructed or sparing, or they may be too profuse or frequent. It is extremely rare for a woman to conceive who does not menstruate regularly. Hence where this is the case, the first step is to regulate this periodical discharge. For this purpose the advice of a physician will generally be required, for these irregularities depend upon such various causes, and require such variety of treatment, it would be inconsistent with the plan of this work to attempt to give instructions for remedying them. A state of exhaustion or weakness of the uterine system, occasioned by too frequent intercourse, is a frequent cause of sterility. The sterility of prostitutes is attributed to this cause, but I doubt it being the only one. With females who are apparently healthy, the most frequent cause is a *torpor*, rather than weakness of the genital organs. For the removal of sterility from this cause, I shall give some instructions, and this I do the more readily because the requisite means are such as will also regulate the menses, in many cases, where they do not appear so early in life, so freely, or so frequently, as they ought.

In the first place it will generally be necessary to do something towards invigorating the system by exercise in the open air; by nourishing food of easy digestion; by sufficient dress, particularly flannel; and especially by strict temperance in *all* things. With this view, also, some scales which fall from the blacksmith's anvil, or some steel filings, may be put into old cider or wine, (cider the best.) and after standing a week or so, as much may be taken two or three times a day as can be borne without disturbing the stomach. All the while the bowels are to be kept rather open, by taking from one to three of *Pill rufi* every night on going to bed. These pills consist of four parts of aloes, two parts of myrrh, and one of saffron, by weight. These measures having been regularly pursued until the system be brought into a vigorous state, medicines which are more particularly calculated to arouse the genital organs from a state of torpor may be commenced, and continued for months, if necessary. The cheapest, most simple, and I am not prepared to say it is not the most effectual in many cases, is cayenne. All the virtues of this article are not generally known, even to physicians. I *know* it does not have the effect upon the coats of the stomach that many have conjectured. It may be taken in the quantity of from one to two rising tea-spoonsful, or even ...ore, every day, upon food, or in any liquid vehicle. Another medicine of much efficacy, as I have reason to believe, is Dewees' Volatile Tincture of Guac. It is generally kept by apothecaries: and is prepared as follows:—

Take of Gum Guaicum, in powder, eight ounces; carbonate of Potash, or of Soda, or (what will answer) Salaeratus, three drachms; Allspice, in powder, two ounces; any common spirits of good strength, two pounds, or what is about the same, two pints and a gill. Put all into a bottle, which may be shaken now and then, and the use of it may be commenced in a few days. To every gill of this, at least a large tea-spoonful of *Spirits of Ammonia* is to be added. A tea-spoonful is to be taken for a dose, three times a day, in a glass of milk, cider, or wine. It is usually given before eating; but if it should chance to offend the stomach when taken before breakfast, it may in this case be taken an hour after.

Dr. Dewees found this tincture, taken perhaps for months, the most effectual remedy for painful menstruation, which is an obstinate complaint. If there be frequent strong pulse, heat, thirst, florid countenance, &c., it is not to be taken until these symptoms be removed by low diet, a few doses of salts, and bleeding, if required.

A third medicine for arousing the genital organs, is tincture of Spanish Flies. But I doubt its being equal, in sterility, to the above-mentioned medicines, (though it may exceed them in some cases, and may be tried if these fail,) a drachm of them may be put to two gills of spirits. Dose, 25 drops, in water, three times a day, increasing each one by two or three drops, until some degree of stranguary occurs, then omit until this pass off, as it will in a day or two. Should the stranguary be severe, drink freely of milk and water, slippery elm, or flax seed tea.

In many cases of sterility, where the general health is considerably in fault, and especially where the digestive organs are torpid, I should have much confidence in a Thomsonian Course. It is calculated to arouse the capillary vessels throughout the whole system, and thus to open the secretions, to remove obstructions, and free the blood of those effete and phlegmy materials which nature requires to be thrown off. The views of the Thomsonians as to heat and cold, appear to me, unphilosophical. But this has nothing to do with the efficiency of their measures.

In relation to sterility, I would here bring to mind, what has been before stated, that a woman is most likely to conceive immediately after a menstrual turn. And now, also, let me suggest the idea that nature's delicate beginnings *may be* frustrated by the same means that put her a-going. This idea is certainly important when the woman is *known* to have miscarried a number of times. Sterility is *sometimes* to be attributed to the male, though he apparently be in perfect health. It would be an interesting fact to ascertain if there be no seminal animalcules in these cases ; and whether medicines of any kind are available.

It has been ascertained that a male and female may be sterile in relation to each other, though neither of them be so with others.

The foregoing measures for sterility are also suitable in cases of *impotency*. This term, I believe, is generally confined to, and defined a want of desire or ability, or both, on the part of the *male ;* but I see no good reason why it should not comprehend the cases in which there is neither desire nor pleasure with the female. Such females, it is true, may be fruitful ; but so, on the other hand, the semen may not have lost its fecundating **pro**perty. Impotency, at a young or middle age, and in some situations in life especially, is certainly a serious misfortune, to say the least of it. The whole evil by no means consists, in every case, in the loss of a source of pleasure. All young people ought to be apprized of the causes of it—causes which in *many* instances greatly lessen one's ability of giving and receiving that pleasure which is the root of domestic happiness. I shall allude to one cause, that of premature, and especially solitary gratification, in another place. Intemperance in the use of spirits is another powerful cause. Even a moderate use of spirits, and also of *tobacco*, in any form, have some effect. It is a law of the animal economy, that no one part of the system can be stimulated or excited, without an expense of *vitality*, as it is termed. That part which is stimulated draws the *energy* from other parts. And hence it is, that close and deep study, as well as all the mental passions when excessive, impair the venereal appetite. All excesses, all diseases and modes of life, which impair the general health, impair this appetite, but some things more directly and powerfully than others.

As to the *remedies* for impotency, they are much the same as for sterility. It is of the first importance that the mind be relieved from all care and anxiety. The general health is to be improved by temperance, proper exercise in the open air, cheerful company, change of scenery, or some occupation to divert the mind without requiring much exercise of it : nourishing food of easy digestion : flannel worn next to the skin. The cold bath may be tried, and if it be followed by agreeable feelings, it will do good. The bowels may be gently stimulated by the pills before mentioned ; and the preparation of iron also, already mentioned, should be taken.

To stimulate the genital organs more directly, cayenne, Dewees' tincture of guac, or tincture of flies may be taken. I have given directions for making and taking the tincture of flies, chiefly because it is esteemed one of the best remedies for impotency caused by or connected with nocturnal emissions, to which I have before alluded.

It is in cases where little or no pleasure nor erection attend these emissions—cases brought on by debauchery, or in elderly persons, that I would recommend tincture of flies, and the other measures above mentioned. In some bad cases, enormous doses of this tincture are required, say two or three hundred drops. Yet the best rule for taking it is that already given, namely, begin with small doses, and gradually increase until some stranguary be felt, or some benefit be received. In this affection, as well as in all cases of impaired virility, the means I have mentioned are to be pursued for a long time, unless relief be obtained. These have cured after having been taken for a year or more without this result. In all cases of impotency, not evidently depending upon disease of some part besides the genital organs, I should have much confidence in blisters applied to the lower part of the spine.

Occasional nocturnal emissions, accompanied with erection and pleasure, are by no means to be considered a disease ; though they have given many a one much uneasiness. Even if they be frequent, and the system considerably debilitated, if not caused by debauch, and the person be young, marriage is the proper measure.

There have been several means proposed and practised for *checking* conception. I shall briefly notice them, though a knowledge of the *best* is what most concerns us. That of withdrawal immediately before emission is certainly effectual, if practised with sufficient care. But if, (as I believe), Dr. Dewees' theory of conception be correct ; and as Spallanzani's experiments show that only a trifle of semen even largely diluted with water, may impregnate by being injected into the vagina, it is clear that nothing short of entire withdrawal is to be depended on. But the old notion that the semen must enter the uterus to cause conception, has led many to believe that a partial withdrawal is sufficient, and it is on this account that this error has proved mischievous, as all important errors generally do. It is said by those who speak from experience, that the practice of withdrawal has an effect upon the health similar to temperance in eating. As the subsequent exhaustion is, probably, mainly owing to the shock the nervous system sustains in the act of coition, this opinion may be correct. It is further said this practice serves to keep alive those fine feelings with which married people first come together. Still I leave it for every one to decide for himself whether this check be so far satisfactory, as not to render some other very desirable.

As to the baudruche, which consists in a covering used by the male, made of very delicate skin, it is by no means calculated to come into general use. It has been used to secure from syphilitic affections.

Another check which the old idea of conception has led some to recommend with considerable confidence, consists in introducing into the vagina, previous to connexion, a very delicate piece of sponge, moistened with water, to be immediately afterwards withdrawn by means of a very narrow ribbon attached to it. But as our views would lead us to expect, this check has not proved a sure preventive. As there are many little ridges or folds in the vagina, we cannot suppose the withdrawal of the sponge would dislodge all the semen in every instance. If, however, it were well moistened with some liquid which acts chemically upon the semen, it would be pretty likely to destroy the fecundating property of what might remain. But if this check were ever so sure, it would, in my opinion, fall short of being equal, all things considered, to the one I am about to mention—one which not only dislodges the semen pretty effectually, but at the same time destroys the fecundating property of the whole of it.

It consists in syringing the vagina immediately after connexion, with a solution of sulphate of zinc, of alum, pearlash, or any salt that acts chemically on the semen, and at the same time produces no unfavourable effect on the female. In all probability, a vegetable astringent would answer—as an infusion of white oak bark of red rose leaves, of nutgalls, and the like. A lump of either of the above-mentioned salts, of the size of a chesnut, may be dissolved in a pint of water, making the solution weaker or stronger, as it may be borne without producing any irritation of the parts to which it is applied. These solutions will not lose their virtues by age. A *female syringe*, which will be required in the use of this check, may be had at the shop of an apothecary, for a shilling or less. If preferred, the semen may be dislodged, as far as it can be by syringing with simple water, after which some of the solution is to be injected, to destroy the fecundating property of what may remain lodged between the ridges of the vagina, &c.

I know the use of this check requires the woman to leave her bed for a few moments, but this is its only objection ; and it would be unreasonable to suppose that any check can ever be devised entirely free of objections. In its favour, it may be said, it costs nearly nothing ; it is sure ; it requires no sacrifice of pleasure ; it is in the hands of the female ; it is to be used *after*, instead of before connexion, a weighty consideration in its favour, as a moment's reflection will convince any one ; and last, but not least, it is conducive to cleanliness, and preserves the parts from relaxation and disease. The vagina may be very much contracted by a persevering use of astringent injections, and they are frequently used for this purpose, in cases of *procidentia uteri*, or a sinking down of the womb. Subject as women are to fluor albus and other diseases of the genital organs, it is rather a matter of wonder they are not more so, considering the prevailing practices. Those who have used this check, (and some have used it to my certain knowledge, with entire success, for nine or ten years, and under such circumstances as leave no room to doubt its efficacy), affirm they would be at the trouble of using injections merely for the purposes of health and cleanliness.

By actual experiment it has been rendered highly probable that pregnancy may, in many instances, be prevented by injections of simple water, applied with a tolerable degree of care. But simple water *has* failed, and its occasional failure is what we should expect, considering the anatomy of the parts, and the results of Spallanzani's experiments, heretofore alluded to.

Thus much did I say respecting this check in the first edition of this work. This is what I call the chemical check. The idea of destroying the fecundating property of the semen was *original*, if it did not *originate* with me. My attention was drawn to the subject by the perusal of " Moral Physiology." Such was my confidence in the chemical idea, that I sat down and wrote this work in July, 1831. But the reflection that I did not *know* that this check would never fail, and that if it should, I might do some one an injury in recommending it, caused the manuscript to lie on hand until the following December. Sometime in November I fell in with an old acquaintance, who agreeably surprised me by stating, that to his own personal knowledge, this last check had been used as above stated. I have since conversed with a gentleman, with whom I was unacquainted, who stated that, being in Baltimore some few years ago, he was there informed of this check by those who have no doubt of its efficacy. From what has as yet fell under my own observation, I am not warranted in drawing any conclusion. I can only say I have not known it to fail. Such are my views on the whole subject, that it would require many instances of its reputed failure to satisfy me that such failures were not owing to an insufficient use of it. I even believe that quite cold water alone, if thoroughly used, would be sufficient. In Spallanzani's experiments, warm water was unquestionably used. As the seminal animalcules are essential to impregnation, all we have to do is change the condition of, or, (if you will), to kill them; and as they are so exceedingly small and delicate, this is doubtless easily done, and hence *cold* water *may* be sufficient.

What has now been advanced in this work will enable the reader to judge for himself, or herself, of the efficacy of the chemical or syringe check, and time will probably determine whether I am correct in this matter; for I do know that those married females who have much desire to escape, will not stand for the little trouble of using this check, especially when they consider that on the score of cleanliness and health alone, it is worth all this trouble. A great part of the time no check is necessary, and women of experience and observation, with the information conveyed by this work, will be able to judge pretty correctly when it is and when it is not. They may rest assured that none of the salts mentioned will have any deleterious effect. The sulphate of zinc is commonly

D 2

known by the name of white vitriol. This, as well as alum, have been much used for leucorrhœa. Acetate of lead, would doubtless be effectual—indeed, it has proved to be so; but I do not recommend it, because I conceive it possible that a long continued use of it might impair the instinct.

I hope that no failures will be charged to inefficacy of this check which ought to be attributed to negligence, or insufficient use of it. I will therefore recommend at least two applications of the syringe, the sooner the surer; yet it is my opinion that five minutes delay would nc rove mischievous, perhaps not ten.

CHAPTER IV.

Remarks on the Reproductive Instinct.

I SCARCELY need observe that by this instinct is meant the desire for sexual intercourse. Blumenbach speaks of this instinct as "superior to all others in universality and violence." Perhaps hunger is an exception. But, surely, no instinct commands a greater proportion of our thoughts, or has a greater influence upon our happiness for better or for worse. "Controlled by reason and cha.cened by good feeling, it gives to social intercourse much of its charm and zest; but directed by selfishness or governed by force, it is prolific of misery and degradation. In itself, it appears to be the most social and least selfish of all our instincts. It fits us to give, even while receiving pleasure; and among cultivated beings, the former power is even more highly valued than the latter. Not one of our instincts, perhaps, affords larger scope for the exercise of disinterestedness, or fitter play for the best moral feelings of our race. Not one gives birth to relations more gentle, more humanizing and endearing: not one lies more immediately at the root of the kindliest charities and most generous impulses that honour and bless human nature. It is a much more noble, because less purely selfish, instinct, than hunger or thirst. It is an instinct that entwines itself around the warmest feelings and best affections of the heart."—*Moral Physiology.*

But too frequently its strength, together with a want of moral culture, is such that it is not "controlled by reason;" and consequently, from time immemorial, it has been gratified, either in such a mischievous manner, or to such an intemperate degree, or under such improper circumstances, as to give rise to an incalculable amount of human misery. For this reason it has, by some, been regarded as a low, degrading, and "carnal" passion, with which a holy life must ever be at war. But, in the instinct itself, the philosopher sees nothing deserving of degrading epithets. He sees not that nature should war against herself. He believes that in savage life it *is*, and in wisely organized societies of duly enlightened and civilized beings it *would be*, a source of tenfold more happiness than misery.

A part of the evil consequences to which this instinct is daily giving rise under the present state of things, it belongs more particularly to the moralist to point out; whilst, of others, it falls within the province of the physician to treat. But let me first remark, that physicians have heretofore fell far short of giving those instructions concerning this instinct which its importance demands. In books, pamphlets, journals, &c. they have laid much before the public respecting eating, drinking, bathing, lacing, air, exercise, &c.; but have passed by the still more important subject now before us, giving only here and there some faint allusion to it. This, it is true, the customs, not to say pruderies, of the age, have compelled them to do, in publications designed for the public eye, yet, in some small work, indicated by its title to be for private perusal, they might, with the utmost propriety, have embodied much highly useful instruction in relation to this instinct.

This instinct is liable to be gratified at improper times, to an intemperate degree, and in a mischievous manner.

True philosophy dictates that this and all other appetites be so gratified as will most conduce to human happiness—not merely the happiness attending the gratification of one of the senses, but all the senses—not merely sensual happiness, but intellectual—not merely the happiness of the individual, but of the human family.

First.—Of the times at which this instinct ought not to be gratified. With females it ought not to be gratified until they are seventeen or eighteen years of age, and with males not until they are a year or two older. The reason is, if they refrain until these ages, the passion will hold out the longer, and they will be able to derive much more pleasure from it in after life, than if earlier gratified, especially to any great extent. A due regard to health and happiness also enjoins with most persons, some restraint on this instinct—indeed, at all times, but especially for a few years after the above mentioned ages. It ought not to be rashly gratified at first. Begin temperately, and as the system becomes more mature, and more habituated to the effects naturally produced by the gratification of this instinct, it will bear more without injury. Many young married people, ignorant of the consequences, have debilitated the whole system—the genital system in particular; have impaired their mental energies; have induced consumptive and other diseases; have rendered themselves irritable, unsocial, melancholy; and finally, much impaired, perhaps destroyed, their affections for each other, by an undue gratification of the reproductive instinct. In almost all diseases, if gratified at all, it should be very temperately. It ought not to be gratified during menstruation, as it might prove productive, to the man, of symptoms similar to those of syphilis, but more probably to the woman, of a weakening disease called *fluor albus*. In case of pregnancy a temperate gratification for the first two or three months may be of no injury to the woman or the forthcoming offspring. But it ought to be known that the growth of the *fœtus in utero* may be impaired, and the seeds of future bodily infirmity and mental imbecility of the offspring may be sown, by much indulgence, during utero-gestation or pregnancy, especially where the woman experiences much pleasure in such indulgence.

Having already glanced at some of the bad effects of an undue gratification of this instinct, I have but little more to offer under the head of *Intemperate Degree*. It will be borne in mind that temperance in this thing is not to be decided by numbers, but that it depends on circumstances; and what would be temperance in one, may be intemperance in another. And with respect to an individual, too, what he might enjoy with impunity, were he a labouring man, or a man whose business requires but little mental exercise, would, were he a student, unfit him for the successful prosecution of his studies. Intemperance in the gratification of this instinct has a tendency to lead to intemperance in the use of ardent spirits. The languor, depression of spirits, in some instances, faintness and want of appetite, induced by intemperate gratification, call loudly for some stimulus, and give a relish to spirits. Thus the individual is led to drink. This inflames the blood, the passions, and leads to further indulgence. This again, calls for more spirits; and thus two vicious habits are commenced, which mutually increase each other. Strange as it may appear to those unacquainted with the animal economy, an intemperate indulgence sometimes gives rise to the same disease—so far as the name makes it so—that is frequently cured by a temperate indulgence, viz. nocturnal emissions.

Every young married woman ought to know that the male system is exhausted in a far greater degree than the female, by gratification. It seems indeed, to have but little effect, comparatively, upon some females. But with respect to the male, it has been estimated by *Tissot*, that the loss of one ounce of semen is equal in its effects upon the system to the loss of 40 ounces of blood. As it respects the immediate effects, this estimation, generally speaking, may not be too great. But a man living on a full meat diet, might, doubtless, part with fifty ounces of semen in the course of a year, with far less detriment to the system, than with 2000 ounces of blood. It is a fact, that mode of living, independent of occupation, makes a great difference with respect to what the system will bear. A full meat diet, turtles, oysters, eggs, spirits, wine, &c. certainly promote the secretion of semen, and enable the system to bear its emission. But a cool vegetable and milk diet calms all the fiercer passions, the venereal especially. Most men adopting such a diet as this, will suffer no inconvenience in extending the intervals of their gratification to three or four weeks; on the contrary, they will enjoy clear intellects and a fine flow of spirits. This is the diet for men of literary pursuits, especially the unmarried.

As to the mischievous manner, it consists in the unnatural habit of onanism, or solitary gratification. It is an anti-social and demoralizing habit, which, while it proves no quietus to the mind, impairs the bodily powers, as well as mental, and not unfrequently leads to insanity.

While the gratification of the reproductive instinct, under such circumstances, and in such manner as I have mentioned, leads to bad consequences, a temperate and natural gratification, under proper circumstances, is attended with good—besides the mere attendant pleasure, which alone is enough to recommend such gratification. I admit that human beings might be so constituted that if they had no reproductive instinct to gratify, they might enjoy good health; but being constituted as they are, this instinct cannot be mortified with impunity. It is a fact universally admitted, that unmarried females do not enjoy so much good health, and attain to so great an age as the married; notwithstanding the latter are subject to the diseases and pains incident to child-bearing. A temperate gratification promotes the secretions, and the appetite for food; calms the restless passions; induces pleasant sleep; awakens social feelings, and adds a zest to life which makes one conscious that life is worth preserving.

APPENDIX.

[I here connect with this work, by way of Appendix, the following extracts from an article which appeared in the "Boston Investigator," a paper which, *mirabile dictu*, is so "crazy" as to be open to the investigation of all subjects which mightily concern mankind.]

THE only seeming objection of much weight that can be brought against diffusing a knowledge of checks, is, that it will serve to increase illegal connexions. Now this is exactly the contrary effect of that which those who have diffused such knowledge most confidently believe will arise from it. To diminish such connexions, is indeed *one* of the grand objects of these publications — an object which laws and prisons cannot, or at least do not, accomplish. Why is there so much prostitution in the land? The true answer to the question is not, and never will be—Because the people have become acquainted with certain facts in physiology. It is because there are so many unmarried men and women—men of dissipation and profligacy, owing to their not having married in their younger days and settled down in life. But why are there so many unmarried people in the country? Not because young hearts, when they arrive at the age of maturity, do not desire to marry, but because prudential considerations interfere. The young man thinks I cannot marry yet, I cannot support a family, I must make money first, and think of a matrimonial settlement afterwards. And so it is, that through fear of having a family, before they have made a little head-way in the world, and of being thereby compelled to "tug at the oar of incessant labour throughout their lives," thousands of young men do not marry, but go abroad into the world, and form vicious acquaintances and practices. The truth, then, is this, there is so much of illegal connexion in the land, because the people had not, twenty years ago, that very information which, it would seem, some, doubtless through want of due reflection, are apprehensive will increase this evil. I might quote pages to the point from "Every Woman's Book;" but I fear my communication would be too lengthy. I content myself with a few lines. "But when it has become the custom here as elsewhere to limit the number of children, so that none need have more than they wish, no man will fear to take a wife, all will marry while young; *debauchery will diminish;* while good morals, and religious duties will be promoted."

It has been asked, if a general knowledge of checks would not diminish the general increase of population? I think that such would not be the result in this country until such result would be desirable. In my opinion, the effect would be a good many more families (and on the whole as many births), but not so many overgrown and poverty stricken ones.

It has been said, it is best to let nature take her course. Now in the broadest sense of the word nature, I say so too. In this sense, there is nothing unnatural in the universe. But if we limit the sense of the word nature so as not to include what we mean by art, then is civilized life one continued warfare against nature. It is by art that we subdue the forest; by art we contend against the element; by art we combat the natural tendency of disease, &c.

As to the outrageous slander which here and there one has been heard to utter against the fair sex, in saying that fear of conception is the foundation of their chastity, it must be the sentiment of a "carnal heart," which has been peculiarly unfortunate in its acquaintances. "To the pure all things are pure." Chastity, as well as its opposite, is in a great degree constitutional : and ought in a like degree to be regarded as a physical property, if I may so say, rather than a moral quality. Where the constitution is favourable, a very indifferent degree of moral training is sufficient to secure the virgin without the influence of the above mentioned fear; but where it is the reverse, you may coop up the individual in the narrow dark cage of ignorance and fear, as you will, but still you must watch. An eminent moralist has said, "That chastity which will not bear the light [of Physiology] is scarcely worth preserving." But, verily, I believe there is very little such in the market. What there is naturally short-lived, and, after its demise, the unhappily constituted individual stands in great need of this light to save her from ignominy. What might it not have prevented in the Fall River affair? And if one of two things must happen, either the destruction of fecundity, or the destruction of life, which of the two is the greater evil? In these cases, alone, this light is calculated to do sufficient good to counterbalance all the evil that would arise from it; so that we should have its important advantages to the married, in a political, a domestic, and a medical point of view, as so much clear gain. This of course is my opinion ; but since I have probably reflected more upon the subject than all the persons concerned in my imprisonment put together, until it can be shown that I have not as clear a head and as pure a heart as any of them, I think it entitled to some weight.

PUBLISHERS' PREFACE.

The pamphlet which we now present to the public is one which has been lately prosecuted under Lord Campbell's Act, and which we republish in order to test the right of publication. It was originally written by Charles Knowlton, M. D., whose degree entitles him to be heard with respect on a medical question. It was first published in England, about forty years ago, by James Watson, the gallant Radical who came to London and took up Richard Charlile's work when Carlile was in jail. He sold it unchallenged for many years, approved it, and recommended it. It was printed and published by Messrs. Holyoake and Co., and found its place, with other works of a similar character, in their "Freethought Directory" of 1853, and was thus identified with Freethought literature at the then leading Freethought *depot*. Mr. Austin Holyoake, working in conjunction with Mr. Bradlaugh at the *National Reformer* office, Johnson's Court, printed and published it in his turn, and this well known Freethought advocate, in his "Large or Small Families," selected this pamphlet, together with R. D. Owen's "Moral Physiology" and the "Elements of Social Science," for special recommendation. Mr. Charles Watts, succeeding to Mr. Austin Holyoake's business, continued the sale, and when Mr. Watson died in 1875, he bought the plates of the work (with others) from Mrs. Watson, and continued to advertise and to sell it until December 23, 1876. For the last forty years the book has thus been identified with Freethought, advertised by leading Freethinkers, published under the sanction of their names, and sold in the headquarters of Freethought literature. If during this long period the party has thus—without one word of protest - circulated an indecent work, the less we talk about Freethought morality the better; the work has been largely sold, and if leading Freethinkers have sold it—profiting by the sale— is mere carelessness, few words could be strong enough to brand the indifference which thus scattered obscenity broadcast over the land. The pamphlet has been withdrawn from circulation in consequence of the prosecution instituted against Mr. Charles Watts, but the question of its legality or illegality has not been tried; a plea of "Guilty" was put in by the publisher, and the book, therefore, was not examined, nor was any judgment passed upon it; no jury registered a verdict, and the judge stated that he had not read the work.

We republish this pamphlet, honestly believing that on all questions affecting the happiness of the people, whether they be theological, political, or social, fullest right of free discussion ought to be maintained at all hazards. We do not personally indorse all that Dr. Knowlt says: his "Philosophical Proem" seems to us f of philosophical mistakes, and—as we are neitl of us doctors—we are not prepared to indoi his medical views; but since progress can on be made through discussion, and no discussi is possible where differing opinions are suppre sed, we claim the right to publish all opinion so that the public, enabled to see all sides of question, may have the materials for forming sound judgment.

The alterations made are very slight; the book was badly printed, and errors of spelling and a few clumsy grammatical expressions have beer corrected; the subtitle has been changed, and in one case four lines have been omitted, because they are repeated word for word further on. W have, however, made some additions to th pamphlet, which are in all cases kept disti from the original text. Physiology has m great strides during the past forty years, and considering it right to circulate erroneous ph ology, we submitted the pamphlet to a docto whose accurate knowledge we have the fulle confidence, and who is widely known in all pa of the world as the author of the "Elements Social Science"; the notes signed "G. R." a written by this gentleman. References to oth words are given in foot-notes for the assistan of the reader, if he desires to study up the su ject further.

Old Radicals will remember that Richard Car lile published a work entitled "Every Women': Book," which deals with the same subject and advocates the same object as Dr. Knowlton' pamphlet. R. D. Owen objected to the "styl and tone" of Carlile's "Every Women's Book, as not being in "good taste" and he wrote hi "Moral Physiology" to do in America what Car lile's work work was intended to do in Engla This work of Carlile's was stigmatized as " cent" and "immoral," because it advoca does Dr. Knowlton's, the use of preve checks to population. In striving to carry Carlile's work, we cannot expect to escape Ca lile's reproach; but, whether applauded or co demned, we mean to carry it on, socially as we as politically and theologically.

We believe, with the Rev. Mr. Malthus, tha population has a tendency to increase faste than the means of existence, and that *som* checks must therefore exercise control over pop ulation. The checks now exercised are sem starvation and preventable disease; the enc mous mortality among the infants of the poor one of the checks which now keep down t population. The checks that ought to contr population are scientific, and it is these which advocate. We think it more moral to prevent the conception of children than, after they are born, to murder them by want of food, air, and clothing. We advocate scientific checks to population, because, so long as poor men have large families, pauperism is a necessity, and from pauperism grow crime and disease. The wages which would support the parents and two or three children in comfort and decency is utterly insufficient to maintain a family of twelve or fourteen, and we consider it a crime to bring into the world human beings doomed to misery or to premature death. It is not only the hard-working classes which are concerned in this question. The poor preacher, the struggling man of business, the young professional man, are often made wretched for life by their inordinately large families, and their years are passed in one long battle to live; meanwhile the woman's health is sacrificed and her life embittered from the same cause. To all of these, we point the way of relief and of happiness; for the sake ot these we publish what others fear to issue; and we do it, confident that if we fail the first time, we shall succeed at last, and that the English public will not permit the authorities to stifle a discussion of the most important social question which can influence a nation's welfare.

CHARLES BRADLAUGH.

ANNIE BESANT.

Copyright © 1930 by Cambridge University Press

Reprinted from *J. Hyg.*, **29**, 323–329 (1930)

14

THE

JOURNAL OF HYGIENE

EDITED BY

GEORGE H. F. NUTTALL, M.D., Ph.D., Sc.D., LL.D., F.R.S.

QUICK PROFESSOR OF BIOLOGY, DIRECTOR OF THE MOLTENO INSTITUTE FOR
RESEARCH IN PARASITOLOGY IN THE UNIVERSITY OF CAMBRIDGE

IN CONJUNCTION WITH

JOHN S. HALDANE, C.H., M.D., D.Sc., LL.D., F.R.S.

LATE READER IN PHYSIOLOGY IN THE UNIVERSITY OF OXFORD

SIR CHARLES J. MARTIN, C.M.G., M.D., D.Sc., F.R.S.

PROFESSOR OF EXPERIMENTAL PATHOLOGY IN THE UNIVERSITY OF LONDON,
DIRECTOR OF THE LISTER INSTITUTE, LONDON

J. C. G. LEDINGHAM, C.M.G., M.B., D.Sc., F.R.S.

PROFESSOR OF BACTERIOLOGY IN THE UNIVERSITY OF LONDON,
BACTERIOLOGIST-IN-CHIEF, LISTER INSTITUTE, LONDON

G. S. GRAHAM-SMITH, M.D., F.R.S.

READER IN PREVENTIVE MEDICINE, CAMBRIDGE

MAJOR GREENWOOD, F.R.C.P. (Lond.), F.R.S.

PROFESSOR OF EPIDEMIOLOGY AND VITAL STATISTICS
IN THE UNIVERSITY OF LONDON

VOLUME XXIX. 1929–30

CAMBRIDGE

AT THE UNIVERSITY PRESS

1930

175

THE SPERMICIDAL POWERS OF CHEMICAL CONTRACEPTIVES. I.

INTRODUCTION, AND EXPERIMENTS ON GUINEA-PIG SPERMS.

By JOHN R. BAKER, M.A., D.Phil.

(With Plate II.)

INTRODUCTION.

THE spermicidal powers of the various chemical contraceptives sold to the public have never previously been compared, and no one has been in a position to say that one spermicide is preferable to another. The only literature on the subject consists of the pamphlets issued by the makers of the different pessaries, and these give little or no information on the length of time taken to kill sperms at stated concentrations. The Birth Control Investigation Committee therefore asked me to undertake this investigation. The work was financed by the Committee, and carried out, with Prof. Goodrich's permission, in the Department of Zoology and Comparative Anatomy at Oxford.

It must be understood that in this investigation no observations were made to find whether any of the contraceptives tested have harmful effects upon the vagina or uterus. This question is being studied by other workers under the auspices of the Birth Control Investigation Committee. Some of the makers of the contraceptives studied regard their *germicidal* powers as a recommendation; but this was not considered in this investigation.

Only solid pessaries were investigated, since it seems probable that the semi-liquid ones will be less used owing to their requiring special appliances for their introduction into the vagina. Four contraceptives (quinine, chinosol, semori and speton) were studied in detail. A standard method of comparing the spermicidal powers of chemical contraceptives was elaborated, and by this means two more contraceptives (double-strength quinine and finil) were investigated. New contraceptives can readily be compared with these six by using the standard method of comparison. The standard method will be described in Part II of this report. The characteristics of the six contraceptives studied are given below. Plate II shows what happens when each of these six pessaries is placed in 7·5 c.c. of distilled water in a specimen tube and left for $2\frac{1}{2}$ hours at body temperature.

Quinine. The pessary is shaped like a solid flattened thimble. It weighs 2·08 grm. It is stated by the makers to consist of cocoa-butter and 5 grains of quinine bisulphate. When placed in water at the temperature of the body, the pessary retains its shape unless the tube containing it is shaken (see Plate II). It seems probable that the quinine would take a long time to find its way to all parts of the vagina. Possibly the cocoa-butter itself interferes with the free movement of the sperms with which it comes in contact. Quinine pessaries are manufactured in England.

Chinosol. The pessary is of the same shape and weight as the quinine pessary. It is stated by the makers to consist of cocoa-butter and 3 grains of chinosol. The cocoa-butter melts and floats at the surface of water at the temperature of the body (see Plate II). Chinosol pessaries are manufactured in England.

Semori. The pessary is a tablet weighing 1·04 grm. It is stated by the makers to consist of sodium bicarbonate, tartaric acid, boric acid and "ortho-oxychinolin sulf." When placed in water at the temperature of the body, the pessary at once starts to make a foam of small bubbles. The purpose of the sodium bicarbonate and tartaric acid is presumably to make this foam by the production of carbon dioxide. The foam probably finds its way to all parts of the vagina, and it is thus rendered unlikely that sperms could pass into the uterus without coming into contact with it (unless the end of the penis were introduced into the cervix, which is said sometimes to occur). Semori is manufactured in Germany.

Speton. The pessary is a tablet weighing 1·20 grm. It is stated by the makers to consist of "natrium dichlorylsulfamidbenzoic," "dioxybernstein acid," and sodium bicarbonate, and to give off oxygen in the vagina. When the pessary is placed in water at the temperature of the body, a rather violent effervescence takes place at once, resulting in a foam of large bubbles (presumably of oxygen and perhaps carbon dioxide). The foam occupies a greater space than that formed by the semori and finil pessaries (see Plate II). A large precipitate is formed, which would appear to be rather disadvantageous. Speton is manufactured in Germany.

Double-strength Quinine. This pessary resembles the ordinary quinine pessary in every way, except that it may be presumed to contain 10 instead of 5 grains of the bisulphate. It is manufactured in England.

Finil. The pessary is in the form of a thin tablet. Two are directed to be used at the same time. The weight of the two pessaries is 1·30 grm. The pessary is stated by the makers to consist of "dioxyquinolin sulf.," boric acid, burnt alum, potato-starch, tartaric acid, sodium bicarbonate and dried egg-albumen. The composition of the pessary resembles that of semori, with the addition of alum, starch and egg-albumen. When placed in water at the temperature of the body, a dense foam of small bubbles is formed at once, together with a small precipitate. Finil is manufactured in Germany.

The first necessity in an investigation into the spermicidal effects of chemical contraceptives is that the conditions of the experiments should approximate as closely as possible to the conditions within the vagina. Unfortunately the vaginal fluid is a complex one, formed of the secretions of the labial glands, Bartholin's glands, the vaginal epithelium and the cervical glands, and varies in amount, composition and pH according to whether the woman is sexually aroused and whether she has borne children before. It is clear that a fluid of this sort cannot be exactly reproduced under the conditions of a laboratory investigation.

For this reason, and because in other ways it is impossible to reproduce the actual conditions precisely in the laboratory, it was thought best to perform two series of experiments, as different from one another as could be arranged. Then, if anyone were to criticise one of the series of experiments on the ground that in a certain point the conditions differed materially from vaginal conditions, he could be referred to the other series. One series of experiments was carried out on guinea-pig sperms, the other is being carried out on human sperms. Some critics may object to the use of guinea-pig sperms at all, when the purpose of the experiments is to find out the effect on human sperms, but there are two reasons why they were used in one series. The first is that they are always obtainable at a few moments' notice. The second is that critics might object to general conclusions being drawn from experiments on the sperms of one man; but if it were shown that even guinea-pig sperms behave to the various spermicides in the same way as the human sperms used, then it might reasonably be concluded that the sperms of other men behave like the human sperms used in the experiments.

Although every effort was made to represent vaginal conditions as closely as is possible in glass vessels, yet it must be recognised that the experiments might have had somewhat different results if they could have been carried out in the human vagina.

Before describing the series of experiments on guinea-pig sperms, it will be convenient to mention three features which are common to this series and to the series on human sperms.

(1) *The concentration of the contraceptive.* In man, about 5 c.c. of seminal fluid are passed into the vagina at a single ejaculation. It is very difficult to know how much fluid is already present in the vagina before the ejaculation. This varies very greatly according to the state of sexual excitement of the woman. No records of measurements of the amount of fluid in the vagina exist, but 2·5 c.c. cannot, I think, be very far from the average amount. After ejaculation there are, then, about 7·5 c.c. of fluid. One pessary to 7·5 c.c. of fluid is therefore the standard concentration of contraceptive used in both series of experiments. For brevity, this concentration is termed the "*S*" concentration throughout, and dilutions are termed *S*/10 (one-tenth of a pessary to 7·5 c.c. of fluid) and so on.

(2) *Examination of sperms under the microscope.* It was necessary to have a hot stage for the microscope, in order that the sperms might not become torpid through cold while being examined. For this purpose a constant stream of water at approximately 37° C. was kept running through a hollow microscope stage. The stream of water was produced by a thermostatic heater, working by gas, regulated to a few degrees above 37° to allow for the cooling which takes place during its passage through a rubber tube to the hot stage.

Two or three drops of the fluid containing sperms are placed in a hollow-ground microscopical slide, and covered. The hollow of the slide is sufficiently large to ensure that a large bubble of air is present when only two or three drops of fluid are used, so that there is no danger of the sperms becoming less active from lack of oxygen during their examination. A $\frac{1}{6}$-inch objective is used for examination.

(3) *Estimation of the activity of the sperms.* This is a subject to which I have given a great deal of consideration. After a comparison of the activity

21–2

of a very large number of slides of sperms under all sorts of conditions, I have decided upon the following grades of activity:

III. The majority of the sperms moderately or very active.

II. Ten per cent. of the sperms moderately active, *or* feeble movement in the majority of the sperms, *or* any greater amount of activity that is less than Grade III.

I. Any amount of movement that is less than Grade II (including the slightest movement in a single sperm).

0. No movement whatever observed.

It will be understood that no counts of active and inactive sperms are made, but a general impression is gained by observation of several microscopic fields.

Small differences in activity are shown by the use of the plus sign. Thus II + indicates greater activity than II. But this symbol is used sparingly.

Experiments on Guinea-Pig Sperms.

The experiments in this series are carried out on sperms suspended in a fluid which I have elaborated for the purpose. This fluid, which may be called buffered glucose-saline, is designed to give maximum sperm activity at the temperature of the body. Its composition is as follows:

Acid potassium phosphate	... ...	0·03 grm.	(Dissolve this first.)
Sodium hydrogen phosphate	... ...	0·6 ,,	
Sodium chloride	... ...	0·2 ,,	
Glucose	... ...	3·0 ,,	
Water	... ...	100·0 c.c.	

The standard technique is as follows:

The following are placed in a thermostat at 37° C.: 1 small covered glass capsule containing 17 c.c. of buffered glucose-saline; 2 small covered glass capsules, empty; 1 measuring cylinder; pipettes; hollow-ground microscopical slides and cover-slips.

These remain in the thermostat for 10 minutes or more, to warm up. A male guinea-pig is then killed by a blow on the head, and the tails of both epididymes are removed and placed in the glass capsule containing 17 c.c. of buffered glucose-saline, which has been temporarily removed from the thermostat. The tail of each epididymis is now cut in two and the halves are pressed with forceps to cause the sperms to come out. The fluid is stirred to form an even suspension, and the remains of the epididymes are removed. All this is done rapidly to avoid much cooling. 7·5 c.c. of the suspension is now placed in each of the empty capsules in the thermostat, the warm measuring cylinder and one of the warm pipettes being used. (The remaining 2 c.c. of sperm suspension are thrown away.) Ten minutes or more are now allowed to elapse, in order to be certain that the fluids may have attained the temperature of the thermostat after the slight cooling which occurred during the preparation of the suspensions.

One pessary is now placed in one of the covered glass capsules in the thermostat, the other serving as a control.

Five minutes later both capsules are shaken ten times, the covers being held firmly in position. This is repeated 5 minutes later, and again 5 minutes later. After the third shaking, when the pessary has acted for a quarter of an hour, a microscopical slide of the sperm suspension containing the pessary and another of the control suspension are made, as explained before. Different pipettes are of course used for the two suspensions. The activity of the sperms in each slide is now estimated according to the system of grading explained before, and the result recorded.

It will be observed that in these experiments the concentration of the contraceptive is "S."

Four experiments were made with each spermicide. The results are given in tabular form below.

	Activity of sperms with spermicide at S concentration				Activity of corresponding control sperms			
Quinine	III	II +	III	III	III	III	III +	III
Chinosol	I +	III	III	III +	III	III	III	III
Semori	0	0	0	0	III	III	III	III
Speton	0	0	0	0	III	III	III	III

The conclusion is that semori and speton are far more spermicidal than quinine and chinosol, which have hardly any effect in a quarter of an hour[1].

Note on special technique for speton.

Such a dense precipitate is formed by the speton pessary used at S concentration, that it is impossible to observe the sperms properly under the microscope. A special technique has therefore to be used with speton. In essentials the technique is the same as the standard technique, but it differs in that the pessary is thrown into the fluid and allowed to act for 5 minutes, after which the fluid is filtered and the sperms are introduced into it.

The details of the experiment with the speton pessary are as follows: The following are placed in a thermostat at 37° C.: 1 large covered glass capsule containing 15 c.c. of buffered glucose-saline; 1 small covered glass capsule containing 7·5 of ditto; 1 small covered glass capsule, empty; 1 small glass funnel with glass receptacle and filter-paper; 1 measuring cylinder; pipettes; hollow-ground microscopical slides and cover-slips.

These remain in the thermostat for 10 minutes or more, to warm up. Two speton pessaries are then placed in the capsule containing 15 c.c. of buffered glucose-saline. After 5 minutes the contents of this capsule are shaken and filtered. 7·5 c.c. of the filtrate are pipetted into the empty capsule.

There are now two small capsules in the thermostat, each containing 7·5 c.c. of buffered glucose-saline; one of them contains speton as well in S concentration. These are left for 5 minutes or more to regain the temperature of the thermostat.

A male guinea-pig is next killed by a blow on the head, and tails of both epididymes are removed. Each is divided into two with scissors. One-half of each is placed in each capsule and squeezed with forceps. When the sperms have been pressed out and stirred into an even suspension, the halves of the tails of the epididymes are removed. The suspensions are prepared inside the thermostat, to prevent much loss of heat.

[1] Experiments will be performed to find whether sperms are actually killed, or only temporarily immobilised by the carbon dioxide which is produced by certain contraceptives.

Five minutes after the preparation of the suspensions, both capsules are shaken ten times. From this point onwards the technique is precisely the same as with the other contraceptives. (The three shakings are only given to make the experiment as similar as possible.)

Semori and speton at S concentration are both so lethal to guinea-pig sperms that it is not possible to decide, from the experiments recorded above, whether one of them is more so than the other. A series of experiments with these two spermicides was therefore carried out in precisely the same way as before, except that one-tenth of a pessary (by weight) was used instead of one pessary. At this dilution speton does not make a very dense precipitate, and therefore it was not necessary to use the special technique.

Three experiments were performed with each spermicide. The results are tabulated below:

	Activity of sperms with spermicide at $S/10$ concentration			Activity of corresponding control sperms		
Semori	II	I	II +	III	III	III +
Speton	II +	I	II +	III	III	III +

The table shows that there is no significant difference between the spermicidal powers of semori and speton, and that one-tenth of a pessary of either of these two spermicides is much more effective than a whole pessary of quinine or chinosol.

A series of experiments was performed to find whether the inefficacy of the quinine and chinosol pessaries was due to their not dissolving sufficiently rapidly. In this series the pessary was placed in the fluid 12 hours or more before the sperms were added, and the fluid was shaken from time to time during this period. In this way it was made certain that the spermicides were acting at the full concentration intended by the manufacturer.

The experiments were carried out as follows:

Two pessaries are placed in a stoppered glass phial in the thermostat at 37° with 15 c.c. of buffered glucose-saline. This is left in the thermostat for 12 hours or more, being shaken occasionally during this period.

7·5 c.c. of this fluid are then pipetted into one capsule, and 7·5 c.c. of buffered glucose-saline into another. These are covered and left for 10 minutes or more to warm up.

A sperm-suspension is prepared in each precisely as in the "Special technique for speton" (see p. 327), and from now onwards the technique is the same as in that method.

The results are tabulated below:

	Activity of sperms with spermicide at S concentration, after the spermicide has been allowed to dissolve for 12 hours or more			Activity of corresponding control sperms		
Quinine	III	II +	III	III	III	III +
Chinosol	III	III +	III	III	III	III

The table shows that quinine and chinosol pessaries are ineffective even when they have been allowed to dissolve for 12 hours or more, and that their inefficacy is therefore due to the low spermicidal powers of the quinine and chinosol at the standard concentration.

CONCLUSION.

Experiments on guinea-pig sperms show that one-tenth of a pessary of semori or speton is much more spermicidal than a whole pessary of quinine or chinosol. The latter spermicides, in standard concentration, have little or no effect on guinea-pig sperms in a quarter of an hour. This is due to the small spermicidal powers of the active substances, and not simply to their dissolving slowly out of the cocoa-butter vehicle.

(*MS. received for publication* 10. VIII. 1929.   Ed.)

Reprinted from *J. Hyg.*, **31**, 309–320 (1931)

15

THE
JOURNAL OF HYGIENE

EDITED BY

GEORGE H. F. NUTTALL, M.D., Ph.D., Sc.D., LL.D., F.R.S.

QUICK PROFESSOR OF BIOLOGY, DIRECTOR OF THE MOLTENO INSTITUTE FOR
RESEARCH IN PARASITOLOGY IN THE UNIVERSITY OF CAMBRIDGE

IN CONJUNCTION WITH

JOHN S. HALDANE, C.H., M.D., D.Sc., LL.D., F.R.S.,
Late Reader in Physiology in the University of Oxford.

J. C. G. LEDINGHAM, C.M.G., M.B., D.Sc., F.R.S.,
Professor of Bacteriology in the University of London,
Director of the Lister Institute, London.

G. S. GRAHAM-SMITH, M.D., F.R.S.,
Reader in Preventive Medicine, Cambridge.

MAJOR GREENWOOD, D.Sc., F.R.C.P. (Lond.), F.R.S.,
Professor of Epidemiology and Vital Statistics in the University of London.

PUBLISHED QUARTERLY

CAMBRIDGE UNIVERSITY PRESS
LONDON: FETTER LANE, E.C. 4
ALSO
H. K. LEWIS AND CO. LTD., 136, GOWER STREET, LONDON, W.C. 1
CHICAGO: THE UNIVERSITY OF CHICAGO PRESS
(AGENTS FOR THE UNITED STATES)
BOMBAY, CALCUTTA, MADRAS: MACMILLAN & CO., LTD.
TOKYO: MARUZEN COMPANY, LTD.

Price Twelve Shillings and Sixpence net

1 *July*, 1931

PRINTED IN GREAT BRITAIN

THE SPERMICIDAL POWERS OF CHEMICAL CONTRACEPTIVES.

III. PESSARIES.

By JOHN R. BAKER, M.A., D.Phil.

(University Demonstrator in Zoology, Oxford.)

CONTENTS.

INTRODUCTION.

My first paper (1930) in this series contained a general introduction and an account of a preliminary investigation of a few pessaries with guinea-pig sperms. The second paper (1931) was concerned not with pessaries, but with chemically pure substances, free from any vehicle. In this third paper I return to pessaries. First I describe some experiments performed with guinea-pig sperms in continuation of those reported on in my first paper. I then present an account of a technique for pessaries using human sperms, and of the results obtained with it. Finally, experiments on the foam-producing pessaries in the absence of the foam-producing substances are described. The next paper in the series will deal with more pure substances.

I wish to thank the Hon. Mrs Marjorie Farrer and the Birth Control Investigation Committee once more for continued support. The work described in this paper could not have been performed had not Dr C. P. Blacker given invaluable help in many ways. Prof. E. S. Goodrich, F.R.S., has kindly allowed the whole of this investigation to be carried out in the Department of Zoology and Comparative Anatomy at Oxford. I want to thank him for his interest in the work.

21-2

THE PESSARIES INVESTIGATED.

Some of these were described in the first paper, but it will be convenient to describe them all here, especially as I now have more accurate information as to some of them. The makers of all the pessaries have most kindly communicated the quantitative analyses of them to me, but they do not allow me to make these analyses known to anyone else, except in the case of the quinine and chinosol pessaries.

The qualitative analyses are not secret.

Quinine. The pessary is shaped like a solid flattened thimble. It weighs 2·08 grm. It consists of 0·324 grm. of quinine bisulphate in cocoa-butter. It is made by Messrs Lambert.

Double-strength quinine. This is the same as the quinine pessary, except that it contains 0·648 grm. of quinine bisulphate. It is made by Messrs Lambert.

Chinosol. This is the same as the quinine pessary, except that it contains 0·195 grm. of potassium oxyquinolin sulphate (chinosol) instead of quinine. It is made by Messrs Lambert.

Lactic acid. The pessary is shaped like a solid flattened thimble. It weighs 1·58 grm. It consists of lactic acid in cocoa-butter. It is made by Messrs W. H. Martindale.

Contraps. This is a large spherical pessary weighing 10·9 grm. It consists of magnesium sulphate, lactic acid, quinine bisulphate, glycerine, tragacanth and water. There is no cocoa-butter nor foam-producing substances. It is made by Messrs Docker.

Quinine urea hydrochloride. This is a minute tablet weighing 0·17 grm. It contains only quinine urea hydrochloride and sodium chloride. There is no cocoa-butter nor foam-producing substances. It is made by Messrs Parke, Davis.

Semori. This is a foaming tablet weighing 1·04 grm. It consists of dioxyquinolin sulphate, potassium borotartrate, sodium bicarbonate and tartaric acid. It is made by Messrs Luitpold Werk in Munich.

Speton. This is a foaming tablet weighing 1·20 grm. It consists of sodium dichlorylsulphamidbenzoate, lactose, starch, French chalk, sodium bicarbonate and tartaric acid. It is made by Messrs Temmler in Berlin.

Finil. This is a thin foaming tablet. Two are directed to be used together. The weight of two is 1·30 grm. The constituents are dioxyquinolin sulphate, boric acid, burnt alum, starch, egg albumen, sodium bicarbonate and tartaric acid. Finil is made by the Pharmazeutische Fabrik in Munich.

Monsol. This is a foaming tablet weighing 0·97 grm. It contains powdered quillaia bark, monsol fluid, gum extract, sodium bicarbonate and potassium hydrogen tartrate. Monsol fluid contains substances allied to cresol. This tablet is made by the Mond Staffordshire Refining Co., but is not yet on the market.

EXPERIMENTS WITH GUINEA-PIG SPERMS.

In the first paper in this series it was shown that if a quinine or cocoa-butter pessary is thrown into 7·5 c.c. of guinea-pig sperm suspension at the temperature of the body, and left there for a quarter of an hour, the activity of the sperms is affected little or not at all.

This gave rise to the supposition that the inefficiency of the pessary might be due simply to the slowness of the diffusion of the quinine or chinosol out of the cocoa-butter. Accordingly a series of experiments was performed, in which the pessary was left in glucose-saline solution for 12 hours at the temperature of the body, with occasional shaking, before the introduction of the sperms. As before, one pessary was allowed to 7·5 c.c. of fluid. Although the pessary was of course melted, the sperms were scarcely or not at all affected in a quarter of an hour.

The conclusion reached was that the inefficiency of the pessary was due to the low spermicidal power of quinine bisulphate and chinosol. Since the first paper was written, I have disproved this conclusion, as follows.

A series of experiments was carried out in exactly the same way as in the first series, except that instead of introducing one pessary into 7·5 c.c. of sperm suspension, 0·324 grm. of finely powdered quinine bisulphate or 0·195 grm. of finely powdered chinosol was introduced instead. These are the actual amounts contained in one pessary. The results, which are most remarkable, are recorded below. The activity of the sperms, after a quarter of an hour with the quinine or chinosol, is indicated by a system of grading which is explained at length in my second paper. III indicates that the majority of the sperms were active; 0 indicates that not a single active sperm was seen in ten microscopical fields of a $\frac{1}{6}$ in. objective with No. 2 eyepiece. I, I+, II and II+ indicate intermediate grades of activity. In the experiments recorded below, the control sperms were III or III+ in each experiment.

The results were as follows:

Quinine	0	0	0
Chinosol	0	0	0

Not a single movement in a single sperm was seen in any of the six experiments.

This experiment was performed at S (standard) concentration, *i.e.* in the proportion of one pessary to 7·5 c.c., which is postulated as being the usual amount of fluid in the vagina after coition. The next series of experiments was performed on $S/10$ concentration. The technique was the same, except that 0·032 grm. of quinine bisulphate and 0·02 grm. of chinosol were used instead of the 0·324 grm. and 0·195 grm. respectively. Three experiments were again performed with each pessary, the control sperms being III or III+ in each case. The results were as follows:

Quinine	0	0	0
Chinosol	0	I	I+

This shows that although a pessary of quinine or chinosol has scarcely any or no effect on sperms, even when it has been melted for 12 hours, yet it contains ten times as much quinine as suffices to kill every sperm in a quarter of an hour, or ten times as much chinosol as suffices to kill the great majority of the sperms. I cannot account for this paradoxical result. It would be understandable if quinine bisulphate or chinosol were more soluble in cocoa-butter than in water; but they are quite insoluble in cocoa-butter, and are only suspended in it.

The following table shows the results of all the experiments which have been performed by the standard technique for comparing pessaries, using guinea-pig sperms. Most of these results were recorded in my first paper, but they are all brought together in one place for convenience. The pessaries are arranged in the order of their spermicidal powers. The control sperms were III or III+ in each case. The result of the experiment was not recorded if the control sperms were less active than this.

	At S concentration				At $S/10$ concentration		
Quinine urea hydrochloride	0	0	0	0	I	I	I+
{Semori	0	0	0	0	I	II	II+
{Speton	0	0	0	0	I	II+	II+
Chinosol	I+	III	III	III+	Not tested		
Quinine	II+	III	III	III	Not tested		

EXPERIMENTS WITH HUMAN SPERMS.

Brief description of the technique.

Guinea-pig sperms are extremely convenient to work with, but it was felt to be essential to carry out a series of experiments using human sperms. This was made possible by two men who volunteered as donors. Both men are of young middle age and the fathers of families, so their sperms may be regarded as normal.

In the experiments with human sperms every effort was made to represent actual conditions as closely as possible. The whole experiment was carried out on the scale of one-fifth, in order to economise semen. Thus, instead of trying one pessary to 2·5 c.c. of artificial vaginal fluid and 5 c.c. of semen, which is postulated as being the standard (S) concentration, one-fifth of a pessary was used with 0·5 c.c. of artificial vaginal fluid and 1 c.c. of semen.

The following is a brief description of the technique, for the benefit of those who do not care to follow the detailed description.

0·5 c.c. of artificial vaginal fluid (a neutralised glucose solution) is placed in a glass specimen tube in a damp chamber in a thermostat maintained at the temperature of the body. 1 c.c. of human semen is placed in another tube in the same damp chamber. When the fluids have warmed up, one-fifth of a pessary is thrown into the artificial vaginal fluid. A quarter of an hour later the warm semen is transferred to the same tube as the artificial vaginal fluid and the one-fifth pessary. Half an hour later the sperms are examined under the microscope. The result of the experiment is not recorded unless the control sperms are active (II+, III or III+).

This experiment was performed four or five times with each make of pessary. Those pessaries which were shown by this experiment to be effective were tested again at $S/10$ concentration.

The details of the general technique and of the special techniques required for certain of the pessaries are given below.

Results.

The following is a summary of the results of the experiment. The pessaries are arranged in the order of their spermicidal powers.

	At S concentration					At $S/10$ concentration				
Semori	0	0	0	0		0	0	I	I	I+
Quinine urea hydrochloride	0	0	0	0		0	I	I+	I+	
Monsol	0	0	0	0		I	I	I	I+	
Speton	0	0	0	0		0	I+	II	II	II
{Finil	0	0	0	I		I	I+	I+	II	II
{Chinosol	0	0	0	I						
Double-strength quinine	II+	II+	III	III						
{Quinine	II+	III	III	III	III					
{Lactic acid	II+	III	III	III+						

A complete investigation of contraps was not made, as its very large size introduced difficulties. Only a minute part dissolves when one-fifth of it is placed with 0·5 c.c. of artificial vaginal fluid. In two experiments at S concentration it reduced the activity of the sperms to I. It would have been equally effective at $S/10$ concentration, for the same amount of it would have dissolved.

It seems worth mentioning that the mean amount of semen produced at each ejaculation by one of the donors was 6·7 c.c. This is based on the measurement of 23 ejaculates. The maximum amount was 10·5 c.c. and the minimum 4·5 c.c.

Full description of the technique.

The following is a detailed account of the technique, which may be applied, with the specified modifications, to all pessaries of reasonable size. In order to shorten this account, several references are made to the second paper in this series, in which a very detailed account is given of a somewhat similar technique, for comparing the spermicidal powers of pure substances.

(1) A thermostat is maintained at 37° C. It contains coverslips, pipettes and a damp chamber. The latter, which contains a rack of small specimen tubes, is described and figured in my second paper.

(2) A hot stage, regulated thermostatically to 37° C., is arranged on a microscope.

(3) The average weight of the pessary to be investigated is determined.

(4) One-fifth of a pessary is weighed out, and set aside in a corked specimen tube, sealed with wax, until semen is available.

(5) Some ice and a corked specimen tube are placed in a vacuum flask, the cork of the specimen tube having been impregnated with paraffin wax.

(6) Semen is caught in a rubber sheath at coition.

(7) The contents of the sheath are shortly afterwards transferred to the corked specimen tube, and left within the vacuum flask until required for the experiment.

(8) A neutral fluid, isotonic with mammalian blood, is prepared by adding sufficient 6 per cent. aqueous sodium hydrogen phosphate ($Na_2HPO_4.12H_2O$)

solution to 5·2 per cent. aqueous glucose solution to cause a sample of it to give a yellowish-green colour with the "Universal" Indicator of Messrs British Drug Houses. The amount of phosphate solution required depends on the length of time that the glucose solution has been made up. Since the vaginal fluid is sometimes acid, sometimes neutral and sometimes alkaline, it was thought best to use a neutral fluid. Since the vaginal fluid is a very complicated and variable one, it was obviously impossible to represent its chemical composition accurately in a laboratory investigation.

(9) 0·5 c.c. of this artificial vaginal fluid is transferred with a graduated pipette to each of two test-tubes in the damp chamber, and is left to warm up. One tube is the control tube, the other the experimental tube.

(10) 1 c.c. of semen is transferred with a graduated pipette to each of two other tubes in the damp chamber in the thermostat, and left to warm up. If the semen is stringy, it is difficult to measure 1 c.c. accurately when cold. Under these circumstances it is best to warm the semen slightly before transferring it to the tubes in the damp chamber.

(11) A quarter of an hour later, one-fifth of a pessary of the contraceptive to be investigated is placed in the experimental tube. If necessary it is pushed below the surface of the fluid.

(12) A quarter of an hour later again, the semen from one of the two tubes containing it is transferred with a pipette to the control tube.

(13) Air is bubbled through the contents of the control tube with a pipette. This mixes the fluids and promotes respiration by the sperms.

(14) The contents of the other tube of semen are transferred to the experimental tube.

(15) Air is bubbled through the experimental tube. If the fragment of pessary is caught in the froth, it is pushed down into the fluid again.

(16) The time is recorded as the start of the experiment.

(17) Two hollow-ground microscopical slides are labelled with a grease-pencil. One is labelled *C* (control), the other with letters denoting the name of the pessary under investigation.

(18) Over the grease-pencil lettering on each slide is fixed a blank gummed-paper label, stuck down at one side in such a way that it may be turned back to disclose the grease-pencil lettering. The object of this arrangement is explained in section 24.

(19) The labelled slides are placed in the thermostat.

(20) Ten minutes after the start of the experiment, air is again bubbled through each tube. A clean pipette is of course used for each tube. The repeated bubbling of air through the fluids not only promotes respiration, but also ensures that all the sperms present are acted upon by the spermicide at the same concentration. This is important, for only three drops are examined under the microscope, and inconclusive results would be obtained if it were not certain that the sperms in these three drops were representative of all the sperms in the tube.

(21) Twenty-five minutes after the start of the experiment (section 16), air is again bubbled through the control tube, and with the same pipette three drops of the fluid are transferred to the hollow of the slide marked *C*. (If the fluid does not form readily into drops, an equivalent amount is transferred.)

(22) A coverslip is applied. The slide is left on the floor of the thermostat. Three drops of fluid do not fill the hollow of the slide. A large bubble of air is included below the coverslip, which prevents the sperms from becoming inactive quickly from inability to respire.

(23) The process described in the last section is applied to the contents of the experimental tube and to the slide labelled with the name of the pessary under investigation.

(24) The slides are shuffled together, till the observer does not know which is which. Bias, conscious or unconscious, is thus avoided. The shuffling is particularly valuable when two or three different pessaries are being tested at the same time. (See section 30.)

(25) As exactly as possible half an hour after the start of the experiment (section 16), the slides are removed one by one from the thermostat and examined under the microscope with a $\frac{1}{6}$ in. objective and No. 2 eyepiece, on the hot stage mentioned in section 2. The sperms in the peripheral part of the hollow of the slide are observed. If the sperms in the deep part of the hollow of the slide were examined, a different impression of the percentage active would be likely to be gained. Living human sperms have a marked tendency to apply themselves to surfaces. One may focus a long way up and down in the region of the deep part of the hollow without seeing many active sperms, while crowds of active ones are present in the shallow peripheral part.

(26) The activity of the sperms is recorded on the blank labels on the slides, in accordance with the system of grading which is explained at great length in the second paper. Here it must suffice to say that III indicates that the majority of the sperms are moderately active, II+ indicates that it cannot quickly be decided whether the majority are moderately active or not, and 0 indicates that not a single active sperm was seen in ten microscopical fields of view, while I, I+ and II indicate intermediate degrees of activity.

(27) The blank labels are turned aside to disclose the identity of the slides.

(28) If the control sperms show an activity of II+ or more, the result of the experiment is recorded.

(29) If the control sperms show an activity of less than II+, the result of the experiment is not recorded. It would have been more satisfactory if only those experiments could have been recorded in which the activity of the control sperms was III or III+. Unfortunately this was impossible, as the experiment could not be performed immediately after the ejaculation of semen. Indeed, nearly half of the samples of semen used came through the post.

(30) From one to three contraceptives may be tested at the same time against the same control.

(31) If the pessary forms a sediment which renders it impossible to observe the sperms properly under the microscope, or if it is so small or crumbly that one-fifth of a pessary cannot be separated in one piece, modifications of the technique are employed, which are described below.

(32) If the contraceptive under investigation is not sufficiently spermicidal to reduce the activity of the sperms to 0, the experiment described above is performed four or five times (not counting experiments in which the activity of the control sperms is less than II+).

(33) If the contraceptive under investigation is sufficiently spermicidal to reduce the activity of the sperms to 0 in four consecutive experiments, its efficiency is further tested by carrying out the experiment four or five times, using one-fiftieth of a pessary instead of one-fifth. When one-fiftieth of a pessary is used, the sediment is never great enough to necessitate the use of the modified technique. When one-fiftieth of a pessary is used, the contraceptive is at $S/10$ concentration.

Modification of the technique for pessaries which form a sediment (semori, monsol, finil, speton).

In this modification of the usual technique, the following are placed in the thermostat in addition to the objects mentioned in section 1 of the description of the usual technique:

One glass capsule of about 100 c.c. capacity, with a watch-glass, concave side upwards, for a cover. (A watch-glass is used as a cover, because the foam produced by some pessaries will displace a flat cover. The watch-glass may be weighted if necessary.) One glass funnel with filter-paper and glass receptacle.

The procedure is as usual in other respects up to and including section 8, and then as follows:

(i) 10 c.c. of neutralised glucose solution is placed in the glass capsule. It is left to warm up.

(ii) 0·5 c.c. of neutralised glucose solution is placed in a specimen tube in the damp chamber, and left to warm up. This is the control tube.

(iii) A quarter of an hour after the 10 c.c. of glucose solution were placed in the capsule, 1 c.c. of semen is transferred with a graduated pipette to each of two empty specimen tubes in the damp chamber, and left to warm up.

(iv) Four whole pessaries of the contraceptive under investigation are thrown into the 10 c.c. of glucose solution in the capsule. The capsule is shaken. Four pessaries to 10 c.c. are equivalent to one pessary to 2·5 c.c., which is postulated as being the amount of fluid normally present in the vagina before ejaculation of semen. Much more fluid is taken than will be used, because in the subsequent filtration only a small part of it generally manages to pass the filter. Most is retained in the form of foam. (In the case of finil, eight pessaries are thrown into the capsule instead of four, because two pessaries are directed to be used together at each coition.)

(v) Five minutes later the capsule is shaken again.

(vi) Ten minutes later, when the pessaries have been a quarter of an hour in the fluid, the capsule is shaken again, and the fluid filtered in the warm filter.

(vii) 0·5 c.c. of the filtrate is transferred with a graduated pipette to a tube in the damp chamber. This is the experimental tube. The remainder of the filtrate is discarded.

(viii) The semen from one of the tubes in the damp chamber containing it is transferred with a pipette to the control tube.

(ix) The usual procedure is now adopted, beginning at section 13.

Modification of the technique for the quinine urea hydrochloride pessary.

The quinine urea hydrochloride pessary is so small and powdery that it is not possible to cut off a piece of it exactly one-fifth of the total weight. Its spermicidal power is therefore tested at S concentration as though it were a pessary forming a sediment, since in that technique whole pessaries, not one-fifth pieces, are used. One pessary is dissolved in 2·5 c.c. of neutralised glucose solution at 37° C., and 0·5 c.c. of this is transferred to the experimental tube. The fluid is not filtered, as complete solution takes place.

The same technique is used to test the efficiency of this pessary at $S/10$ concentration, except that one pessary is dissolved in 25 c.c. of neutralised glucose solution. As before, 0·5 c.c. of this solution is transferred to the experimental tube.

This modification of the technique could be applied to any pessary in order to test it at very low concentrations. This would be necessary if any pessary were invented which always killed all sperms at $S/10$ concentration. One would then need to test it at $S/20$ or even $S/100$. This could easily be done by dissolving one pessary in 50 c.c. or 250 c.c. of neutralised glucose solution at 37° C., and transferring 0·5 c.c. of the solution to the experimental tube.

TEST OF FOAMING PESSARIES IN THE ABSENCE OF THE FOAM-PRODUCING SUBSTANCES.

It was felt that foaming pessaries should be tested also without the foam-producing substances, for two reasons. Firstly, there is the possibility that carbon dioxide may only temporarily immobilise sperms. Secondly, if a pessary relies too largely on the carbon dioxide which it produces, it will not be effective unless placed in the vagina at precisely the proper time before the ejaculation of semen.

Guinea-pig sperms were used in this part of the work. Semori, finil and speton were tested, but not monsol. It did not seem worth while in the case of monsol, for this pessary is not yet on the market.

The experiments were carried out as follows.

The essential constituents of the pessary, other than the foam-producers, are dissolved in 0·9 per cent. sodium chloride solution, at the concentration at which they exist when one pessary is dissolved in 2·5 c.c., the postulated amount of vaginal fluid. Unessential constituents, such as French chalk, starch, lactose and egg-albumen, are omitted for the sake of simplicity. A sperm suspension is prepared by squeezing the tails of both epididymides of an adult male guinea-pig in 5 c.c. of B.G.S. (Instructions for the preparation of the fluid called B.G.S. are given in the second paper.) 1 c.c. of this is mixed with 0·5 c.c. of the fluid containing the essential constituents of the pessary, after both have been allowed to warm up for a quarter of an hour. The experiment is disregarded unless the control sperms show an activity of III or III+. In all other respects the experiment is carried out according to the usual technique for pessaries with human sperms.

Finil presents the difficulty that the essential constituents will not dissolve completely at the concentration of one pessary to 2·5 c.c. of 0·9 per cent. sodium chloride solution. It was not necessary, however, to invent a special technique for this pessary, for despite this handicap, it always killed all sperms.

The results were as follows:

Pessaries without foam-producers and unessentials, at *S* concentration.

Semori	0	0	0
Finil	0	0	0
Speton	III	III	III

This proves that, even without foam-producers, semori and finil kill all sperms at *S* concentration. Speton, on the contrary, is without effect if the foam-producers are omitted.

It was decided to test semori and finil at *S*/10 concentration, without foam-producers. The experiments were carried out exactly as before, except that the essential constituents of the pessary, other than foam-producers, were dissolved in 0·9 per cent. sodium chloride solution at the concentration at which they exist when *one-tenth* of a pessary is dissolved in 2·5 c.c.

The control sperms showed an activity of III or III+ in each experiment. The results were as follows:

Pessaries without foam-producers and unessentials, at *S*/10 concentration.

Semori	0	0	0
Finil	I	I	I

This shows that both semori and finil are very spermicidal at *S*/10 concentration even when the foam-producers are omitted. Semori has the advantage both here and in the standard experiment.

It was thought possible that the inefficiency of speton without foam-producers at *S* concentration might be due to the fact that sodium dichloryl-sulphamidbenzoate (the only essential constituent other than foam-producers) is only effective when freshly dissolved. Accordingly the experiment was performed as before, except that the sodium dichlorylsulphamidbenzoate was only dissolved at the last possible moment, 5 minutes before the start of the experiment (*i.e.* 5 minutes before section 16 in the standard technique). This substance dissolves almost immediately. Directly it had dissolved, 0·5 c.c. of the solution was transferred to the experimental tube. It had thus less than 5 minutes in which to warm up instead of a quarter of an hour, but this could not affect the result, as the 1 c.c. of sperm suspension was warmed for the usual quarter of an hour. The control sperms showed an activity of III or III+ in each experiment.

The result was as follows:

Pessary without foam-producers and unessentials, at *S* concentration, dissolved immediately before the experiment.

| Speton | III + | III |

This proves that sodium dichlorylsulphamidbenzoate is not spermicidal even when freshly dissolved, and the spermicidal power of speton is wholly due to its foam-producers.

DISCUSSION.

It is clear that the cocoa-butter pessaries are less effective than the foam-producing ones and the quinine urea hydrochloride pessary, when tested by the techniques described in this paper. Chinosol, the most effective of the cocoa-butter pessaries, is shown by the standard experiments on human sperms to have the same spermicidal power as the least effective of the pessaries not containing cocoa-butter, namely finil.

There is some reason to think that cocoa-butter may have a mechanical effect in actual use, which renders it helpful rather than the reverse. This point is about to be studied under the auspices of the Birth Control Investigation Committee. Nevertheless these experiments show that cocoa-butter prevents the active substances (quinine or chinosol) from acting, in a way that can only be described as astounding. There is plenty of quinine or chinosol in a cocoa-butter pessary, but the cocoa-butter in some way prevents it from affecting sperms, even when the pessary has had 12 hours at the temperature of the body in which to melt and dissolve.

The great spermicidal power of the minute quinine urea hydrochloride pessary is noteworthy. The absence of any foam-producers in this pessary must nevertheless weigh against its use. It is usually placed on the upper (cervical) side of a rubber occlusive pessary.

The complete lack of spermicidal power in the supposedly essential constituent of speton is very remarkable. The pessary as a whole is quite effective, on account of the foam-producers. It is perhaps reasonable, however, to distrust a pessary which relies for spermicidal power wholly on its foam-producers.

Semori emerges from the test as the most effective pessary sold in England. It is effective with or without foam-producers.

SUMMARY.

1. A technique is described for comparing the spermicidal powers of pessaries, using human sperms.

2. Those pessaries which do not contain cocoa-butter are more spermicidal than those that do.

3. Quinine and lactic acid pessaries, in cocoa-butter vehicles, are almost without effect upon sperms.

4. There is more than ten times as much quinine bisulphate in a quinine pessary as suffices to kill all sperms in half an hour, but the cocoa-butter prevents its action in some way which is not at present understood.

5. Semori is the most spermicidal pessary of the nine investigated. Even at one-tenth of the concentration at which it is normally used, it kills every sperm or nearly every sperm in half an hour.

6. Even if the foam-producing substances are omitted, semori remains effective.

7. The minute quinine urea hydrochloride pessary is nearly as effective as semori, but the absence of foam-producing substances in this pessary limits its usefulness.

8. Speton relies for its spermicidal power wholly upon its foam-producing substances. Its supposedly active substance, sodium dichlorylsulphamid-benzoate, is without effect upon sperms.

REFERENCES.

BAKER, J. R. (1930). The spermicidal powers of chemical contraceptives. I. Introduction, and experiments on guinea-pig sperms. *J. Hygiene*, **29**, 323–9.

—— (1931). The spermicidal powers of chemical contraceptives. II. Pure substances. *Ibid.* **31**, 189–214.

(*MS. received for publication* 25. XI. 1930.—Ed.)

POSTSCRIPT. I have recently tested another foaming tablet, called "bircon," by the standard technique with guinea-pig sperms. This tablet weighs 0·64 grm. It consists of zinc sulphocarbolate, chinosol, starch, sodium bicarbonate and tartaric acid. It is made by Messrs Bircon Laboratories in London. The results were as follows:

At S concentration   0   0   0
At $S/10$ concentration 0   0   I

These results should be compared with those for other pessaries given on p. 312 of this paper. Bircon is seen to be more effective than the other pessaries tested: but no experiments have yet been performed to find to what extent it relies upon its foam-producers, nor has it been tested with human sperms.

Reprinted from *J. Amer. Med. Ass.*, **152**, 1037–1041 (1953)

16

COUNCIL ON PHARMACY AND CHEMISTRY

REPORT TO THE COUNCIL

The Council has authorized publication of the following reports. R. T. STORMONT, M.D., *Secretary.*

AN IMPROVED TEST OF SPERMICIDAL ACTIVITY WITHOUT DILUTION OR MIXING

Clarence J. Gamble, M.D.
Milton, Mass.

Comparisons of the clinical effectiveness of contraceptive materials are difficult and subject to large errors because of the unavoidable variations in the correctness and regularity of their use. Attempts to limit observations to those who are regular users are disappointing; many who claim regularity as long as the method is successful may report irregularity of some duration after a pregnancy leads to detailed interrogation. These uncertainties in clinical testing have led to a search for laboratory procedures that may give an indication of clinical efficiency.

SPERMICIDAL TESTS INVOLVING MIXING AND DILUTION

Baker made a careful study of spermicidal powers by mixing equal quantities (0.3 cc.) of semen with physiological salt solutions (0.9% sodium chloride) in which various concentrations of pure substances were dissolved. He determined the lowest concentration of the substance in the final mixture that would immobilize the sperms in human semen in 30 minutes.[1] In testing jellies and suppositories, he and his collaborators mixed 2 gm. of one suppository with 6 cc. of saline and found the greatest dilution of the filtrate that would stop the motion in 30 minutes.[2] He applied these tests to many pure substances and commercial contraceptives.

Voge recommended the study of motion of the sperms after shorter exposures. He measured immobilization times after mixing jellies with equal or double volumes of semen.[3]

To permit the study of many mixtures with the same ejaculate, Brown and Gamble[4] used about 0.04 cc. of semen. They based their comparisons on the period of time required for complete immobilization after thorough mixing. When equal quantities of semen and contraceptive material were mixed (approximating the ratio found in clinical use), the duration

of motility was so brief that distinctions could not be made between the more and the less active mixtures. Therefore, the contraceptive jelly was diluted with 0.9% sodium chloride solution. Final proportions of jelly, 0.9% sodium chloride, and semen of 1:4:5, respectively, gave conveniently distinguishable immobilization times. The recorded time was that of the immobilization of the last discoverable sperm. This method is used as one of the criteria for acceptance of contraceptive materials by the Council on Pharmacy and Chemistry of the American Medical Association.[5]

The "saturation test" of Millman[6] measures the quantity of human semen required in successive additions to 0.05 cc. of jelly to immobilize the sperms within one minute after thorough mixing. For some mixtures, as much as 18 times the volume of the jelly is required. Under the usual clinical conditions this proportion would correspond to an ejaculate of about 90 cc. This is so far beyond the usual quantity that it seems doubtful that differences at such dilutions have clinical significance.

SPERMIDICAL TESTS WITH UNDILUTED CONTRACEPTIVE MATERIALS

Baker, Ranson, and Tynen[2] recognized that the ability to release immobilizing material without stirring and dilution was an important characteristic of a contraceptive mixture. In an experiment termed a diffusion test, the jelly or suppository was smeared over the bottom of a glass capsule and overlaid with 1.25 cc. of human semen. At varying times portions of the latter were removed and examined for motility.

This modification seems a closer approach to postcoital conditions than mixing and dilution. However, the repeated sampling introduces a stirring not present in the vagina, and the procedure gives no indication whether the sample of semen examined comes from the portions in immediate contact with the spermicide or from the higher portions of the fluid.

AN IMPROVED DIFFUSION METHOD

To approximate vaginal conditions, a procedure has been developed in which sperms are observed in semen that is in direct contact with the spermicidal material. For convenience in presentation this will be described in the form considered most desirable. The experiments and reasoning that led to the steps and arbitrary dimensions recommended will be given subsequently.[6a]

Semen, which is secured from young donors by ejaculation into a vial, is stored in an ice bath. It is customarily used for the test one to three hours after production.

Glass tubes of 2 mm. internal diameter and approximately 2 cm. long are prepared. Semen, held in a pipette of the eye dropper variety, is run into the end slightly more than 5 mm.

To secure a part of the contraceptive mixture that has not been affected by evaporation, the first portion (about 2 cc.) of the contents of the flexible metal tube in which it is usually supplied is discarded. The jelly-filled[7] mouth of the tube is placed against the end of the semen column. The latter has been slanted downward at about 45°, making it bulge slightly from the end of the tube to avoid trapping an air bubble between it and the jelly. The jelly is forced into the glass tube for a distance of 10 mm. or more, displacing the semen, which is not allowed to reach the other end of the tube.

To prevent evaporation, paraffin (which melts at about 56 C) is heated to just above the melting point and is swabbed onto each end of the tube. Possible contamination of the semen with jelly from tubes that have been sealed previously is avoided by using one dish of paraffin for the semen ends of the tubes and another for those containing the jelly.

This tube, with another of the same diameter, is placed on a microscope slide and covered with a coverglass; the adjacent surfaces of the latter two have been smeared with microscope immersion oil. The length of the semen column is now measured, using the mechanical stage of the microscope, from the tip of the cone[8] formed by the jelly to the nearest part of the meniscus where air and semen meet. If this is longer than 5.3 mm. or shorter than 4.7 mm., the specimen is discarded.

The tube, in a horizontal position, is obliquely illuminated by a 60 candlepower automobile headlight bulb with a small filament; this light is placed close beyond the tube, and about

Received for publication Oct. 6, 1952.
From the Department of Anatomy of Harvard Medical School.

1. Baker, J. R.: The Chemical Control of Conception, London, Chapman & Hall, Ltd., 1935, p. 44.

2. Baker, J. R.; Ranson, R. M., and Tynen, J.: The Spermicidal Powers of Chemical Contraceptives: Approved Tests, J. Hyg. **37**: 474 (July) 1937.

3. Voge, C. I. B.: The Chemistry and Physics of Contraceptives, London, Butterworth and Co., Ltd., 1933, pp. 80, 100, and 185.

4. Brown, R. L., and Gamble, C. J.: A Method of Testing the Relative Spermicidal Effectiveness of Contraceptives, and Its Application to 10 Commercial Products, Human Fertil. **5**: 97 (Aug.) 1940. Gamble, C. J., and Hamblin, L.: The Spermicidal Times of Contraceptive Jellies and Creams, 1949, report of the Council on Pharmacy and Chemistry, J. A. M. A. **148**: 50 (Jan. 5) 1952.

5. New and Nonofficial Remedies, Philadelphia, J. B. Lippincott Company, 1952, p. xxxii.

6. Millman, N.: A Critical Study of Methods of Measuring Spermicidal Action, Ann. New York Acad. Sc. **54**: 806, 1952.

6a. In November, 1952, Dr. H. Mizuno of Nagoya University, Japan, told the author that he had independently measured and compared spermicidal times under similar conditions. A description in Japanese of his procedure has subsequently been included in the Second Report of the Committee on the Study of Health and Welfare of the Department of Health and Welfare of the Japanese Government, Kyoto, December, 1952.

7. For brevity the word jelly will be used to include jellies, creams, suppositories, and other semisolid contraceptive materials.

8. Friction of the walls of the tube as the jelly is forced in usually results in a cone at the end. The angle at the tip varies, but is usually about 120°. Variations in this angle may result in variations in the surface of the jelly to which the semen is exposed, but these do not appear extreme.

196

45° from the axis of the microscope. The position of the bulb is varied until the best possible view of the sperms is found. To avoid undue heating, the light is turned on (with a foot-pedal) only during moments of observation. A large opening in the microscope stage is convenient.

Motion of the sperms is observed through a 10x objective and 10x eyepiece. While the specimen is not being examined, it is kept in an incubator at 37 C, approximating vaginal temperature.

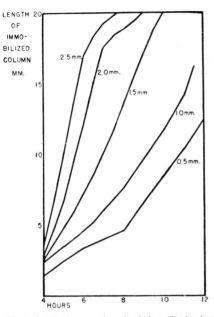

Fig. 1.—Length of semen column in which motility has been abolished compared with time. The semen columns are 20 mm. in length and 2.5, 2, 1.5, 1, and 0.5 mm. in diameter. The curves of the larger diameters are averages of four tubes each; that of the smallest of two tubes. All tubes were filled nearly simultaneously with portions of the same ejaculate and contraceptive material.

The period of time is recorded from the addition of the jelly to the immobilization of the last discoverable sperm that is closer to the jelly than the nearest portion of the meniscus; thus, motion within the angular portion of the semen next to the meniscus is disregarded. The contraceptive material that has the shortest immobilization time as thus determined (using portions of the same ejaculate) is presumed to be the most active.

AGE OF THE EJACULATE

As found in the Brown and Gamble test, the spermicidal time decreases as the ejaculate becomes older. For accurate comparisons, therefore, tubes should be filled at approximately the same time as well as with portions of the same ejaculate.

DIAMETER OF THE SEMEN COLUMN

When the jelly was in contact with the semen in the tube, it was found that the zone in which the sperms were immobilized gradually increased in length. When this rate of increase was compared, using the same brand of jelly and identical semen, but different diameters of tubes, it was found that within the limits tested (0.5 mm. to 2.5 mm.) it was higher in the larger tubes. Results of a typical experiment are given in figure 1. Repeated comparisons of a series of commercial contraceptives showed that their ranking was not significantly altered by changes in the diameter of the tube used.

To reduce the hours needed for observation, a larger tube is desirable, but it makes observation more difficult. To balance these two factors, a tube with a diameter of 2 mm. was chosen.

LENGTH OF THE SEMEN COLUMN

The effect of the length of the column of semen on the rate of immobilization was also explored. It was found that the shorter the column the more rapid the immobilization. Results of a typical experiment are given in figure 2. The ranking of contraceptive mixtures was not significantly dependent upon the length of semen column, provided the same length was used for each material.

Although a decrease in the column length has the advantage of shortening the observation period, it results in greater proportioned errors from variations in length. As a balance between these two factors, a length of 5 mm. was selected.

LENGTH OF THE JELLY COLUMN

If the column of jelly is too short, the toxic materials might be exhausted too early, leading to a longer immobilization time. However, since diffusion in the noncirculating fluid of the jelly is slow, this would not appear to be an important factor. Tests showed no significant difference in immobilization time between columns of the same jelly that were 3 mm. and 10 mm. long. However, lengths of approximately 10 mm. are customarily employed.

END-POINT

The time required for the zone of immobilization to reach any chosen distance from the jelly might be considered to be related to the contraceptive effectiveness of the jelly. Experiments using various distances up to and including the entire length of the column were performed. Results of these tests ranked commercial contraceptive mixtures in approximately the same order as did the other experiments. It was found somewhat easier to determine the time when there were no motile sperms nearer the jelly than the meniscus; consequently this time was chosen for the end-point.

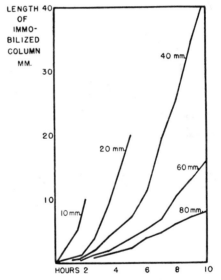

Fig. 2.—Length of semen column in which motility has been abolished compared with time. The semen columns are 1.6 mm. in diameter and 10, 20, 40, 60, and 80 mm. long. Each curve is drawn from a single experimental tube filled nearly simultaneously with the others with portions of the same ejaculate and contraceptive material.

POSITION OF THE SEMEN COLUMN

The position of the tube greatly affects the rate of extension of the zone where the sperms are immobilized. No important differences were found between the rates when the tubes were in the customary horizontal position and when they were 45 or 90° from the horizontal with the semen below the jelly. However, when the tubes were placed vertically with the semen above, immobilization extended less than 1 mm. with even the most active jellies after six or seven hours of observation.

CONVECTION IN THE SEMEN

A flow of sperms and other seminal particles is observed in most of the tubes placed horizontally. This flow is usually toward the jelly in the higher levels of the semen (nearest the objective with the microscope in the customary position) and away from it when the focus is shifted to the lower levels. (A flow in the opposite direction is occasionally observed; at times there is no flow.) The flow appears to be laminar, moving slowly close to the surface; it first increases as the focus is shifted downward, then decreases as the center of the tube is approached. The flow moves more rapidly near the jelly, decreasing toward the other end of the semen column. It often decreases after hours of exposure to the jelly. Difficulties in measuring the depth of the focal plane below the inner surface of the glass have made it impossible to secure accurate comparisons of flows under varying conditions; however, flows as rapid as 1 mm. per minute have been observed.

The findings suggest that the flow is caused by convection. Diffusion of solutes out of the jelly usually makes the semen denser, causing it to sink and to be replaced by less contaminated semen. The spread of the spermicidal ingredients by convection is compatible with the greater rate of extension of the immobilized zone within the larger tubes (fig. 1), because the lesser surface friction of these tubes would allow more rapid circulation.

The theory of convection in the semen also makes understandable the slower rate of decrease of the zone of motility in the longer semen columns (fig. 2). This finding would not be expected if the dissemination resulted from diffusion alone. The entire semen column dilutes the immobilizing materials via circulation, thus delaying their reaching effective concentrations.

This conception also explains the slow spread of immobilization in vertical tubes in which the semen is above the jelly. In this position the lower portions of the semen, made denser by diffusion from the jelly, tend to remain in contact with it, and the toxic materials rise only by the relatively slow process of molecular diffusion. The fact that the immobilization rate is decreased when the semen in the tube is above the jelly would not seem to invalidate the test as an indicator of clinical accomplishment. Cases in which postcoital units of semen are exposed to jelly only on their underside would appear to be extremely rare. All other forms of contact will produce convection.

VARIATIONS IN SEMEN SPECIMENS

When portions of the same ejaculate were utilized in the method described, repeated determinations of spermicidal time showed standard deviations of a single observation of about 12%. In a series of 26 observations using one tube of jelly, with different donors and different ejaculates, the standard deviation of a single measurement was 38% of the average. For the 43 mixtures of 1951 reported in the table, of which all immobilizations were complete before seven hours, the average standard deviation of a single observation was 35% of the corresponding mean. Ejaculates from different donors produced greater variations in test results than the ejaculates from the same donor. The ejaculates from certain donors were consistently above average, whereas those given by others were consistently below average.

While this indicates that several tests with a given material are required to secure an accurate diffusion spermicidal time, single comparisons of two or more preparations tested with the same ejaculate will divide the range of contraceptive mixtures commercially available into a number of groups that are significantly different from each other in spermicidal activity.

SPERMICIDAL RANKING OF SEVENTY COMMERCIAL CONTRACEPTIVES

Semen specimens, secured from eight medical students 21 to 26 years of age, were used to determine the immobilization times of 68 commercial contraceptive preparations secured in 1951 and 2 in 1952. Twenty to 40 materials were compared in each experiment with portions of the same ejaculate, by one or two observers.

The experiments were customarily discontinued after seven hours of exposure of semen to jelly. If motility was still present at this time, the 'distance of the farthest motile sperm from the meniscus at the end of the semen column was recorded. A distance of 5 mm. indicates what motion was seen in the space surrounding the cone that forms at the jelly's tip.

Each commercial preparation was tested six or more times (at least twice by each observer) with semen from five or more different donors. In addition, by preparing the capillary tubes in the order of decreasing spermicidal times, materials of approximately equal activity were tested with portions of the same ejaculate which were of about the same age.

The average of all tests made of a given material is recorded in table 1, except for those preparations that showed motility in one or more tests at the end of seven hours. For these the median value is used. If this exceeded seven hours, the length of the semen column still showing motility is also given.

It seems unwise to commend secret mixtures, since there is no assurance that when these materials are secured in the future they will have the same composition as the samples tested. Materials whose complete formulas are not available, and whose immobilization times were less than 253 minutes (the median of the group) are listed in table 1 as materials A, B, C, and D.

The average standard deviation of 35% indicates that differences between two averages of the six or more observations given in table 1 are significant (less than 1 chance in 20 of being accidental) if they differ by more than 40% of their mean.[9] Since the longest observed times (more than 420 minutes) were more than nine times the shortest (46 minutes), the commercial preparations may be divided into several groups having significantly different spermicidal activities.

For an indication of the reproducibility of the test with different donors, spermicidal times similarly measured in 1950 and 1951, using 39 samples of the same materials with known formulas, are given in the third column of the table. Differences in the two average times for the 22 materials of which the formulas were known to be the same are, on the average, 18% of their means.

EXTRAPOLATION TO CLINICAL CONDITIONS

The spermicidal times from one-half hour to more than seven hours for complete immobilization in the columns of semen 2 mm. in diameter and 5 mm. long are obviously not those anticipated in clinical contraception. Experiments showed that these periods of time decreased to a few minutes as shorter semen columns were tested in tubes whose diameters were 2 mm. In the vagina the entire surface of the droplets is presumably exposed to jelly, which should decrease the time still further. The effective surface of the droplets may be increased by distortion from a spherical shape.

Although the immobilization times under clinical conditions will undoubtedly be much shorter than those given in table 1, the uncertainties regarding the size and shape of the droplets of semen in the vagina after coitus make it impossible to estimate these times with any exactness.

COMPARISONS WITH THE BROWN AND GAMBLE SPERMICIDAL TEST

Spermicidal times of the same samples of commercial contraceptive materials which were determined by the Brown and Gamble method are given in table 2. When ranking by this method is compared with that by the diffusion test (table 1), the correlation is not high. In many instances, mixtures that are more effective after dilution and mixing are less active when access to the sperms is by diffusion out of the jelly or cream and by convection throughout the adjacent semen.

Since the direct and undiluted contact of semen and contraceptive material in the diffusion test more closely imitates clinical conditions than does the Brown and Gamble procedure, it is probable that the diffusion test gives a better

---

9. The relative accuracy of the ranking may be somewhat greater since most of the experiments were arranged to test with the same ejaculate in tubes filled at nearly the same time materials previously found to be adjacent on the scale.

10. Gelatin and agar each showed moderate immobilizing activity.

TABLE 1.—*Diffusion Spermicidal Times*

Material *	1951 Samples, Min.	Length of Semen Column in which Motility Continued, Min.	1949 Samples, Min.	Length of Semen Column in which Motility Continued, Min.
Rice, 30% sodium chloride	27	...	28	...
Material A †	46	...		
Norforms	55	...	...	
Rice, 20% sodium chloride	58	...	46	
D. C. Jelly	71	...	...	
Lactikol Jelly	77	...	...	
Material B †	98	...		
Metakol	100	...	...	
Rice, 10% sodium chloride	101	...	113	
Linton Jelly with Oxyquinoline sulfate	118	...		
Zonitors	122	...	...	
Marvosan Jelly ‡	122	...	118	
Gelaquin 1952	126	...		
Locorol	128	...		
Material C †	130	...	...	
LaSavoy	142	...		
Gelakta 1952	144	...		
Linton Jelly ‡	147	...	216	
Verithol ‡	152	...	118	
Femogene	154	...		
Zylactic Jelly ‡	158	...	214	
L. A. J.	160	...	...	
Bilco Jelly	171	...	...	
Vagagill ‡	175	...	197	
Colagyn ‡	175	...	158	
Cooper Creme Gel ‡	192	...	204	
Koromex Jelly §	199	...	233	
Material D †	201	...		
Uni-Jel	204	...		
Linton Cream ‡	220	...	174	
Lorophyn Jelly	227	...	...	
Warner's Suppository	227	...		
Oxy-Zem ‡	238	...	173	
Gyn-Jel	241	...	...	
Bio-Lab Jelly	243	...		
Vagagill Suppository	246	...		
Uni-Cream	248	...		
Servex	252	...		
Ortho-Gynol Jelly	254	...		
Penetrox Jelly	257	...		
Milex Jelly	260	...		
Arc Creme, Creemoz ‡	263	...	...	...
Cooper Creme §	263	...	261	
Lorophyn Suppository §	278	...	236	
Caprokol ‡	280	...	172	
Lygenes Suppository §	280	...		
Medi-phragm Jelly ‡	283	...	158	
Marvosan Creme §	284	...	221	
Hychex Jel	289	...		
Veritas Kreme §	290	...	284	
Contra Creme §	305	...	302	
Stillman's Jell ‡	309	...	335	
Lygel Jelly §	312	...	311	
Certane Jelly	314	...	247	
Preceptin	323	...		
Lanteen Cream ‡	343	...	362	
Penetrox Creme	346	...		
Eugenic Creme ‡	357	...	406	
Koromex Cream §	372	...	265	
Ramses Jelly §	410	...	420	
Lactikol Creme	411	...		
Hychex Creme	420+	0.3	...	
Arc Jelly, Jellak ‡	420+	1.6	420+	2.8
Pernox Capsule §	420+	1.8	...	
Volpar Paste ‡	420+	2.7	420+	4.4
Murax Jelly ‡	420+	2.9	...	
Certane Creme	420+	2.9	420+	4.3
Lanteen Jelly ‡	420+	3.1	420+	5.0
Nixon Creme ‡	420+	3.1	415	
Bio-Lab Creme	420+	4.0	...	
Milex Creme	420+	4.6	...	
Glyeuthymenol Jelly ‡	420+	5.0	420+	2.2
Ortho-Creme §	420+	5.0	420+	5.0

* Unless otherwise indicated, complete or partial formula is given in addendum.
† Formula unavailable.
‡ Complete or partial formula in J. A. M. A. 148: 50 (Jan. 5) 1952.
§ Formula in New and Nonofficial Remedies, 1951.

indication of the relative clinical effectiveness. A high ranking by both tests will give a "factor of safety," which seems desirable when contraceptive protection is important.

CHEMICAL FORMULAS OF THE MATERIALS TESTED

Each manufacturer was asked for permission to publish the formulas from which the contraceptive mixture was made. The information made available is indicated in table 1. To conserve space the formula is given in the addendum only when it is not available in previous publications. It is to be regretted that 26% are secret mixtures.

A SIMPLE CONTRACEPTIVE JELLY

The apparent convection resulting from increased density of the semen adjacent to the jelly suggested that the circulation of the spermicidal ingredients within the semen might be accelerated by adding a density-producing solute to a jelly. Therefore, sodium chloride was incorporated (with mortar and pestle) in one of the less rapidly immobilizing materials and was found to greatly increase its apparent activity.

TABLE 2.—*Spermicidal Times* by the Method of Brown and Gamble of Contraceptive Jellies and Creams Secured in 1951*

Five Minutes or Less

Arc Jelly, Jellak	Koromex Jelly	Norforms
Bilco Jelly	Lactikol Creme	Ortho-Creme
Bio-Lab Creme	Lactikol Jelly	Ortho-Gynol Jelly
Certane Creme	L.A.J.	Penetrox Jelly
Colagyn	Lanteen Jelly	Preceptin
Contra Creme	Linton Cream	Ramses Jelly
Cooper Creme	Lorophyn Jelly	Vagagill Suppository
D.C. Jelly	Lorophyn Suppository	Veritas Kreme
Eugenic Creme	Lygel Jelly	Zonitors
Femogene	Marvosan Creme	Zylactic Jelly
Hychex Jel	Metakol	
Jellak	Milex Creme	
Koromex Cream	Milex Jelly	

Product	Min.	Product	Min.
Gelakta '52	6	Vagagill	19
Warner's Suppository	6	Certane Jelly	25
Nixon Creme	7	Uni-Jel	30
Bio-Lab Jelly	8	Volpar Paste	33
Lanteen Cream	8	Lygel Suppository	36
Oxy-Zem	8	Arc Creme, Creemoz	51
Verithol	8	LaSavoy	64
Hychex Creme	10	Rice Flour + 30% sodium chloride	92
Pernox Capsule	10	Locorol	100
Caprokol	11	Marvosan Jelly	118
Gelaquin '52	11	Linton Jelly with Oxyquinoline sulphate	137
Cooper Creme Gel	12	Rice Flour + 20% sodium chloride	211
Medi-Phragm	12	Glyeuthymenol Jelly	240+
Penetrox Creme	12	India Gyn-Jel	240+
Warner's Creme	14	Linton Jelly	240+
Uni-Cream	19	Murax Jelly	240+
		Rice Flour + 10% sodium chloride	240+
		Stillman's Jell	240+

* Each time is the median of 5 or more determinations with semen from five different donors.

Because Voge found that 3.4% sodium chloride in a semen mixture immobilized in 10 minutes, it seemed that the action might be caused by this salt's activity. Therefore, various concentrations were added to a 5% tragacanth jelly, a mixture which by itself was found to have little or no immobilizing power. A concentration of 10% sodium chloride in 5% tragacanth was found to immobilize the spermatozoa as well as did nine-tenths of the commercial contraceptives.

The possibility of preparing a homemade spermicidal jelly from a readily obtainable material was investigated. It was found that rice flour and water heated nearly to boiling for 30 minutes in a double boiler, with stirring, produced a jelly with a consistency approximating that of commercial contraceptives when the initial concentration was between 12 and 17% of the water by weight. Wheat and other flours, gelatin, and other jelly-producing substances may also be used; rice flour was chosen for the test with the thought that it would be widely available in countries in which population control is intensely needed.

The immobilizing activities of jellies containing sodium chloride in a concentration of 0.1, 0.2, and 0.3 of the water by weight were tested and found to be among the more active commercial products (table 1).

Such rice flour and salt jellies in which the sodium chloride was 10 and 20% of the water were tested at the Margaret Sanger Research Bureau by three women. Daily vaginal doses of 5 cc. each for 21 days did not cause subjective discomfort or evidence of irritation upon speculum examination.

When the rice flour jelly was kept at room temperature in the laboratory, it usually turned sour in a few days. A jelly made with three times the recommended concentration of rice flour and salt has been found to last weeks at room temperature and to give a satisfactory consistency when diluted with twice its volume of cold water. Stirring for 3 or 4 minutes, followed by a lapse of 15 or more minutes and a slight amount of further stirring, was found to be desirable.

It seems probable that a solution of sodium chloride, of 10% or stronger, will act as an effective spermicide. A rubber or marine sponge, a wad of cotton, or a pad of cloth can hold it in the vagina. It should be inserted before intercourse and retained for a sufficient period thereafter to allow immobilization of the sperm.

SUMMARY

Clinical tests of contraceptive materials are unsatisfactory because of variations in the regularity of their use. Most laboratory tests which have been used to give indications of clinical effectiveness have been based on dilution and complete mixing, neither of which is present to the same extent in clinical use. A method is described for observing the immobilization of sperm in semen in direct contact with undiluted contraceptive jelly, cream, or suppository. Using the test with semen columns 2 mm. in diameter and 5 mm. long, commercial contraceptive preparations have been compared and their rankings are given. It is concluded that density convection within the semen, caused by diffusion into it of ingredients of the contraceptive jelly, is an important process in contraceptive action. A jelly having high spermicidal activity by this test was prepared by heating and stirring together sodium chloride, rice flour, and water.

ADDENDUM

1. Complete quantitative formulas were supplied by the manufacturers for the following products:

	%
Bilco Jelly, 1951	
Cetyl dimethyl benzyl ammonium chloride	0.05
Para-tert, amyl phenol	0.15
Lactic acid	1.0
Glycocoll	0.10
Methyl-p-hydroxybenzoate	0.05
Propyl-p-hydroxybenzoate	0.05
Boric acid	1.0
Glycerin	12.0
Gum tragacanth	1.20
Gum Carob	2.50
Bio-Lab Jelly, 1951	
Phenylmercuric borate	0.017
Oxyquinoline sulfate	0.08
Boric acid	1.00
Glycerin	5.75
Gum tragacanth	4.25
Adjusted with lactic acid to pH 4.5	
D. C. Jelly, 1951	
Chlorothymol	0.015
Paraformaldehyde	0.20
Lactic acid U.S.P. to adjust pH to 3.655	
Propyl-p-hydroxybenzoate	0.20
Glycerin	16.0
Kelcolloid	0.45
Pectinum N.F.	4.0
Femogene, 1951	
Lactic acid	1.0
Oxyquinoline sulfate	0.075
Boric acid	3.0
Glycerin	5.0
Tragacanth	2.0
Disodium phosphate to approximate pH 4.0	
Gelakta, 1952	
Cetyl dimethyl benzyl ammonium chloride	0.1
Para-tert. amyl phenol	0.2
Lactic acid	1.5
Boric acid	1.0
Glycocoll	0.10
Methyl-p-hydroxybenzoate	0.05

	%
Propyl-p-hydroxybenzoate	0.05
Glycerin	12.0
Gum tragacanth	1.20
Gum carob	2.50
Gelaquin, 1952	
Para-tert. amyl phenol	0.1
Oxyquinoline sulfate	0.1
Lactic acid	1.0
Boric acid	1.0
Glycocoll	0.1
Methyl-p-hydroxybenzoate	0.05
Propyl-p-hydroxybenzoate	0.05
Glycerin	15.0
Gum tragacanth	1.2
Gum carob	2.5
Lactikol Creme, 1951	
Glyceryl monoricinoleate	1.50
Sodium lauryl sulfate	0.60
Lactic acid	0.10
p-Triisopropylphenoxyethoxyethanol	1.25
Glycerin	8.0
Glyceryl monostearate	7.50
Stearic acid	15.0
Lactikol Jelly, 1951	
Glyceryl monoricinoleate	1.0
Sodium lauryl sulfate	0.20
Oxyquinoline sulfate	0.05
Lactic acid	1.50
p-Triisopropylphenoxyethoxyethanol	1.25
Butyl-p-hydroxybenzoate	0.02
Glycerin	8.0
Acacia	1.0
Karaya	1.0
Tragacanth	2.70
L. A. J., 1951	
Cetyl dimethyl benzyl ammonium chloride	0.1
Para-tert. amyl phenol	0.15
Lactic acid	1.0
Glycocoll	0.10
Methyl-p-hydroxybenzoate	0.05
Propyl-p-hydroxybenzoate	0.05
Boric acid	1.0

	%
Glycerin	15.0
Tragacanth	0.9
Carob gum	2.25
Starch	5.35
LaSavoy Jelly, 1951	
Chlorothymol	0.01
Lactic acid	2.4
Oxyquinoline sulfate	0.054
Boric acid	0.25
Starch	5.25
Gum tragacanth	1.05
Glycerin	65.8
Linton Jelly Oxyquinoline, 1951	
Formula in reference 4 plus	
Oxyquinoline sulfate	0.1
Locorol, 1951	
Aluminum aceto tartrate	3.125
Oxyquinoline sulfate	0.95
Boric acid	2.345
Glycerin	28.70
Gum tragacanth	1.70
Lorophyn, 1951	
Phenylmercuric acetate	0.05
Polyethylene glycol of monoisooctylphenyl ether	0.3
Methyl-p-hydroxybenzoate	0.05
Sodium borate U.S.P.	8.0
Glycerin	8.0
Calcium carragheen sulfate	0.72
Tragacanth	1.8
Metakol, 1951	
Glyceryl monoricinoleate	1.0
Sodium lauryl sulfate	0.2
p-Triisopropylphenoxypolyethoxyethanol	1.25
Boric acid	3.0
Glycerin	7.0
Gum arabic	0.5
Karaya	1.0
Tragacanth	2.0
Norforms, 1951	
Phenylmercuric acetate	0.02
Benzethonium chloride	0.20
Methyl-p-hydroxybenzoate	0.10
Sorbitan sesquioleate	5.0
Carbowax 1000	11.5
20 dendro palmitic acid	14.68
Ortho-Gynol, 1951	
p-Di-isobutylphenoxypolyethoxyethanol	1.0
Ricinoleic acid	0.70
Oxyquinoline sulfate	0.025
Acetic acid	0.33
Boric acid	3.0
Propyl-p-hydroxybenzoate	0.05
Glycerin	5.0
Acacia	2.0
Tragacanth	3.0

	%
Rice Flour—10% sodium chloride	
Rice Flour	11.3
Sodium chloride	8.06
(the sodium chloride is 10% of the water)	
Rice Flour—20% sodium chloride	
Rice Flour	10.4
Sodium chloride	14.9
(the sodium chloride is 20% of the water)	
Rice Flour—30% sodium chloride	
Rice Flour	9.7
Sodium chloride	20.8
(the sodium chloride is 30% of the water)	
Servex, 1951	
Sodium lauryl sulfate	0.1
p-tert. amylhydroxy benzene	0.15
Boric acid	1.0
Butyl-p-hydroxybenzoate	0.02
Alcohol U.S.P.	5.0
Glycerin	8.0
Uni-Cream, 1951	
Phenylmercuric acetate	0.02
Oxyquinoline benzoate	0.02
Cetyl alcohol	1.0
Boric acid	2.0
Butyl-p-hydroxybenzoate	0.20
Glycerin	5.0
Sorbitan monoleate	5.0
Polyoxyalkalene sorbitan monostearate	3.0
Stearic acid	20.0
Uni-Jel, 1951	
Trioxymethylene	0.04
Dioctyl sodium sulfosuccinate	0.50
Lactic acid	0.09
Sodium oleate	0.67
Trihydroxyethylamine	10.5
Cellulose gum	11.0
Vagakill Suppository, 1951	
Phe-Mer-Nite, a brand of Phenylmercuric nitrate	0.02
Oxyquinoline sulfate	3.85
Acetic acid	3.85
Boric acid	19.2
Cocoa Butter	73.1
Warner's Suppository, 1951	
Oxyquinoline benzoate	0.2
Boric acid	13.9
Salicylic acid	2.8
Lactic acid	0.2
Benzocaine	trace
Cocoa butter white wax	82.9
Zonitors Suppository, 1951	
Stearic acid	0.25
Chloramine-T	2.00
Sodium stearate	6.00
Potassium stearate	2.50

2. For the following products, the available information was limited to the "active ingredients" recorded on the package:

	%		%
Bio-Lab Creme, 1951		**Borax**	....
Phenylmercuric borate	....	Oxyquinoline sulfate	0.08
Oxyquinoline sulfate	....	**Milex Creme, 1951**	
Triethanolamine	....	Glycerol ester of ricinoleic acid	0.50
Stearic acid	....	Sodium lauryl sulfate	0.60
Glycerin	....	Oxyquinoline sulfate	0.02
Propylene glycol monostearate	....	Adjusted with lactic acid to pH 4.5	....
Certane Creme, 1951		**Milex Jelly, 1951**	
Phenylmercuric acetate	0.02	Glycerol ester of ricinoleic acid	0.50
Sodium sulfo dioctyl succinate	....	Oxyquinoline benzoate	0.10
Chlorothymol in a Stearate base	....	Adjusted with lactic acid to pH 4.5	....
Certane Creme, 1949, 1951		**Penetrox Creme, 1951**	
Phenylmercuric acetate	0.02	Glycerol ester of ricinoleic acid	1.50
Boric acid	....	Sodium lauryl sulfate	0.60
Oxyquinoline sulfate	....	Oxyquinoline sulfate	0.02
Sodium sulfo dioctyl succinate	....	Adjusted with lactic acid to pH 4.5	....
Hychex Creme, 1951		**Penetrox Jelly, 1951**	
Phenylmercuric borate	0.0175	Glycerol ester of ricinoleic acid	1.25
Oxyquinoline sulfate	0.08	Oxyquinoline benzoate	0.10
Triethanolamine	....	Adjusted with lactic acid to pH 4.5	....
Stearic acid	....	**Preceptin, 1951**	
Glycerin	....	p-Di-isobutylphenoxypolyethoxyethanol	1.0
Propylene glycol monostearate	....	Ricinoleic acid	1.17
Hychex Jel, 1951			
Phenylmercuric borate	0.0175		
Lactic acid	....		
Boric acid	....		

3. For the following product, the manufacturers gave a quantitative formula which appears complete except for the jelly-forming material:

	%	
Gyn-Jel (Bombay)		
Phenylmercuric nitrate	0.02	In a water-dispersible, self-emulsifying synthetic base ....
Boric acid	2.50	

Reprinted from *J. Amer. Med. Ass.*, **152**, 1042–1043 (1953)

THE POSTCOITAL TEST AS A METHOD OF EVALUATING A CONTRACEPTIVE JELLY

17

Melvin R. Cohen, M.D.
and
Bernard M. Kaye, M.D., Chicago

In the past 20 years, several birth control studies have been made at Mandel Clinic of Michael Reese Hospital, utilizing jelly alone as a contraceptive measure. In 1932 Stein[1] conducted such a study lasting three years, and during the course of the active clinic no pregnancies occurred among the 146 patients in that particular series. Ten years later, Stein, Nielsen, and one of us (M. R. C.)[2] reported on another three year study using the jelly alone. This survey included 231 patients who were interviewed in the clinic over a period lasting from 3 to 36 months. A total of 20 pregnancies could be charged solely to the method utilized in this second series. This study showed that the effectiveness of the method using jelly alone to be an 87.1% reduction in fertility. Since 1942 several reports have been made on the efficiency of the nonmechanical means of contraception, including jelly, cream, and suppositories. The authors of these articles reported that the use of these methods resulted in 85 to 100% reduction in fertility.[3] From a review of the literature of the past 20 years and from our own experience, it is apparent that nonmechanical means can be effective as contraceptive methods.

In the present survey, we utilized what we consider a more scientific and reliable method for testing the efficacy of a specific contraceptive jelly than has been used in former studies. This method is the postcoital examination made after the use of the contraceptive. We feel that this is an effective means of evaluation since spermicidal action was tested at that period of the menstrual cycle when cervical mucus demonstrated greatest receptivity to spermatozoa. The pregnancies that can be charged against a contraceptive per se, eliminating all other factors, can be better estimated by the positive postcoital tests.

The purpose of this study was threefold: (1) to utilize a heretofore untried objective method of evaluating the effect of an experimental jelly on the longevity of spermatozoa, (2) to determine the effect of this jelly upon cervical mucus, and (3) to evaluate this experimental jelly as a contraceptive.*

In our special birth control clinic, 200 patients were instructed in the method using jelly alone. Of these, 158 patients returned to the clinic for at least one visit over a period of 3

From the Department of Obstetrics and Gynecology, Michael Reese Hospital.

1. Dickinson, R. L., and Bryant, L. S.: Control of Conception: An Illustrated Medical Manual, Baltimore, Williams & Wilkins, 1931.

2a. Stein, I. F., and Cohen, M. R.: Jelly Contraceptives; 3-Year Investigation, Am. J. Obst. & Gynec. **41**: 850 (May) 1941.

2b. Stein, I. F.; Cohen, M. R., and Nielsen, R.: Jelly-Alone as Contraceptive Investigation, Human Fertil. **7**: 33 (April) 1942.

3a. Seibels, R. E.: Effectiveness of Simple Contraceptive Method, Human Fertil. **9**: 43 (June) 1944.

3b. Garvin, O. D.: Jelly Alone Vs. Diaphragm and Jelly, ibid. **9**: 73 (Sept.) 1944.

3c. Foster, M. T.: Vaginal Suppositories Vs. Diaphragm and Jelly, ibid. **11**: 123 (Dec.) 1946.

3d. Eastman, N. J., and Seibels, R. E.: Efficacy of the Suppository and of Jelly Alone as Contraceptive Agents, J. A. M. A. **139**: 16 (Jan. 1) 1949.

3e. Eastman, N. J.: Further Observations on the Suppository as a Contraceptive, South. M. J. **42**: 346 (April) 1949.

3f. James, W. F. B.: Study of a Simple Contraceptive Method for Clinic and Private Patients, West. J. Surg. **58**: 197 (April) 1950.

3g. Goldstein, L. Z.: A Vaginal Jelly Alone as a Contraceptive in Postpartum Patient, West. J. Surg. **58**: 708 (Dec.) 1950.

3h. Finkelstein. R.; Guttmacher, A., and Goldberg, R.: A Critical Study of the Efficacy of Jelly as a Contraceptive, Am. J. Obst. & Gynec. **63**: 664 (March) 1952.

3i. Hunter, G. W.; Darner, C. B., and Gillam, J. S.: Ann. New York Acad. Sc. **54**: 825 (May) 1952.

3j. Stromme, W. B., and Rothnem, M. S.: Ann. New York Acad. Sc. **54**: 831 (May) 1952.

* Experimental Jelly "P" was supplied by C.tho Research Foundation.

4. Clift, A. F.: Observations on Certain Rheological Properties of Human Cervical Secretion, Proc. Roy. Soc. Med. **39**: 1 (Nov.) 1945. Cohen, M. R.; Stein, I. F., and Kaye, B. M.: Spinnbarkeit: A Characteristic of Cervical Mucus, Fertil. & Steril. **3**: 201 (May-June) 1952.

to 18 months. The clientele consisted chiefly of postnatal patients and certain women referred because of medical indications. The group consisted of 95% Negro and 5% white women. Thirty-seven patients had used various birth control measures previously. The chief methods employed were diaphragm and jelly (18 patients) and condom (14 patients). Of these patients 9 and 12 respectively stated that the methods had been successful but had been discontinued for personal reasons.

CLINICAL DATA

The patients were interviewed and examined gynecologically before birth control instruction was given. In addition to past medical, surgical, and obstetric history, an inquiry was made regarding previous contraceptive methods and sex habits. A calendar card was issued to each patient with instructions to mark the dates of menses and of coitus. A symbol was to be placed over the date of intercourse, indicating the date on which the clinic contraceptive was used. If no contraceptive was used, the date was to be circled. Each patient was individually instructed in the proper technique as follows. A 5 cc. applicator was to be filled completely with the jelly, inserted into the vagina as high as possible, withdrawn about 1 inch., and the plunger pushed in all the way so as to place the jelly in the upper vagina, close to the cervix. Each patient was cautioned to insert the jelly while lying in a horizontal position, 5 to 10 minutes prior to each coitus. An optional douche was permitted after a minimum of six hours following coitus. Patients were seen within a week after instruction. Whenever possible, the examination was made a few hours after coitus. Examination at this time and at subsequent one to three month intervals included pelvic examination, with particular attention to the study of vaginal and cervical contents. A vaginal speculum was inserted without lubrication, exposing the cervix and the posterior fornix. A small quantity of the vaginal secretion from the posterior fornix was diluted with saline and the smear of this material examined for spermatozoa, leukocytes, trichomonads, and monilia. The cervical mucus at the external os was removed with tissue forceps. After the cervical mucus was removed, a curved glass cannula was inserted into the cervix for aspiration of the endocervical contents. Occasionally, intrauterine samples were aspirated. The cervical mucus was studied macroscopically as to the amount (1 to 4+), viscosity (thin, moderate, or thick), fibrosity *(Spinnbarkeit)*, and flow elasticity. The same specimens were examined microscopically for spermatozoa and leukocytes.

Spinnbarkeit,[4] which is the capacity of the cervical mucus to be drawn into a thread, shows cyclic variations during the menstrual cycle. At the estimated ovulation time, the cervical mucus becomes thin, profuse, glairy, and will show the greatest degree of *Spinnbarkeit* (usually 10 to 20 cm. in length). At this phase of maximum *Spinnbarkeit*, the longevity of spermatozoa is optimal. It is at this time that a contraceptive must be most effective. Therefore, we attempted to test the efficacy of Experimental Jelly "P" at the estimated ovulation time, utilizing *Spinnbarkeit* and the menstrual calendar as the criteria of ovulation.

RESULTS

A total of 289 postcoital tests was performed on the 158 patients. These tests were done 2 to 72 hours postcoitus. Of the 289 postcoital tests, 173 (59.8%) revealed no sperm, 110 (38.1%) examinations showed nonmotile sperm, and motile sperm were found in only 6 (2.1%) examinations (table 1). These positive findings occurred in 5 women, twice in the same patient. Three women stated that they had not followed the exact instructions regarding the technique.

The mucus obtained at the external os after the use of Experimental Jelly "P" was almost invariably thick and plastic and showed a *Spinnbarkeit* of 1 cm. or less. These physical characteristics of cervical mucus are inimical to sperm motility. However, when this thickened mucus was removed with tissue forceps and the endocervix aspirated, the endocervical mucus was found to be consistently characteristic of the phase of the cycle at which it was obtained. In other words, if the jelly itself produced mucus coagulation, this effect was in the zone of contact and did not penetrate to the endocervix.

A total of 200 patients, chiefly postnatal, were instructed in the method using jelly alone. Of the total, 158 patients returned for 1 to 12 follow-up visits. In this group, 30 pregnancies occurred. However, 23 of this group of 30 women admitted to omission of the method, incorrect or inconstant use, or the use of some other contraceptive technique. Eighty-three women were followed for a period extending from 3 to 18 months. Eighteen of these 83 women became pregnant. Of the 18, 3 omitted contraception; 3 admitted to inconstant use of the jelly; 3 failed to follow instructions properly, and 2 switched to another method. Thus, there were 7 pregnancies which might be attributed to failure of the method (table 2).

In computing the pregnancy rate, only those patients who had been followed for at least three months were included. Some patients were seen for the first time shortly before termination of the clinic and others only on their check-up visit one week after instruction. Therefore, the pregnancy rate was computed on the basis of 7 pregnancies out of the group of 83 women who were followed at least three months. The gross pregnancy rate of this group before admission to the clinic was high: 103.15 pregnancies per 100 woman-years of exposure. The corrected rate of jelly failure was 17.46 pregnancies for 100 woman-years of exposure. Therefore, for the method using jelly alone, the reduction in fertility was 83.17%.

Many patients objected to the messiness of the method. Only rarely did they complain of diminished erotic reactions.

COMMENT

The effectiveness of any contraceptive measure depends upon its spermicidal qualities and regularity of use. Through ignorance and the caprice of human nature, any group of patients, private or clinical, will present a certain percentage of failures. Previous clinical studies have shown fairly high percentages of pregnancies with relatively few actually resulting from failure of the method itself. The corrected figures for our clinic compare favorably to those published by Stein,[2b] and Finkelstein.[3b] However, the results of our study are not as favorable as those reported by two other groups of investigators who used Preceptin † in their clinics.[3i,j]

The effectiveness of accepted spermicides in general use has been tested repeatedly in vitro. In this study, the use of an experimental jelly tested in vivo has been reported. The effectiveness in vivo of the jelly can be evaluated by examining vaginal and cervical secretions for living spermatozoa following coitus. In utilizing the postcoital test, we hoped to determine whether the failures resulted from the actual failure of the method as a spermicide or to the human element of possible omission or misapplication of the method.

TABLE 1.—*Positive Postcoital Tests Following Use of Experimental Jelly "P"*

Patient No.	Day of Cycle	Hours Post Coitus	Mucus Amount	Mucus Viscosity	White Blood Cell/ High Power Field	Sperm/ High Power Field	% Motility	Grade	Comment
15	19	13	C* 2+ E† 2+	Moderate Moderate	100 5-10	Occasional 1-2	0 90	0 3	Jelly inserted while in bathroom; patient walked to bed; took douche in a. m.
15	17	12	C 2+ E 2+	Moderate Moderate	50 Occasional	0 Occasional	0 75	0 1, 2	Patient reinstructed in use of jelly but still had positive test
22	18	36	C 1+ E 2+	Thick Moderate	12 6	2 100	0 90	0 4	Jelly inserted while in bathroom; pregnancy followed this exposure
35	21	34	C 2+ E 4+	Thin Thin	25 5-10	2-3 10	0 90	0 3, 2	....
45	62 Lactation	11	C 1+ E 2+	Moderate Thick	25 20	5 3	50 25	1, 3 1	....
70	16	12	C 1+ E 2+	Moderate Moderate	Occasional Occasional	0 2	0 50	0 3	Jelly inserted while in bathroom; took douche in a. m.

* External os of cervix.   † Endocervical canal.

Side-Effects.—The chief complaint against the contraceptive jelly was that of burning during and after its use. A total of 49 persons complained of local burning with the use of the jelly; this included both male and female. Some of these complaints were made by only one partner; in some instances, both partners complained. Twelve women who reported this symptom were found to have monilial vaginitis; when this was

TABLE 2.—*Causes and Number of Pregnancies*

Causes	Number of Pregnancies
Jelly failures	7
Failure to use jelly as directed	3
Inconstant use of jelly	8
Condom failure	2
Omission of all birth control	10
Total	30

treated, the complaint of burning ceased. In 5 patients, monilia-like organisms were found in the absence of any complaints. Some patients reported burning when the jelly was first used, but stated that with continued use the burning sensation disappeared. Because of these side-effects, the formula of Experimental Jelly "P" has been changed to incorporate a new buffer system.

Since the postcoital method is a sampling technique, it is liable to error. There was an incidence of 2.1% positive postcoital tests (motile sperm) in a total of 289 examinations. It is possible that living sperm were present in other cases but were not found by the sampling technique.

SUMMARY

The effectiveness of the method using jelly alone compares favorably with the results published by other investigators who studied similar methods. Experimental Jelly "P" was employed in a group of 158 clinic patients. An 83.17% reduction in fertility resulted. However, acceptance of the method by the patients was poor; less than one-half of the women were reporting to the clinic at the time the study terminated.

Experimental Jelly "P" showed only a superficial coagulating effect upon cervical mucus, and there was no evidence of penetration into the cervical canal.

What was considered a more scientific and reliable method for testing the efficacy of a spermicidal jelly was tried: the in vivo examination of cervical contents following the use of a specific contraceptive. At the conclusion of this study, we were satisfied that the postcoital test is accurate and should be utilized more widely in the evaluation of spermicidal preparations used as contraceptives.

† Preceptin has a different buffer system than Experimental Jelly "P."

Reprinted from *Western J. Surg. Obstet. Gynecol.*, May–June, 144–153 (1963)

Intravaginal Contraceptive Study*

PHASE II. Physiology

(A Direct Test for Protective Potential)

18

VIRGINIA E. JOHNSON
WILLIAM H. MASTERS
ST. LOUIS, MISSOURI

*From the Division of Reproductive Biology,
Department of Obstetrics and Gynecology,
Washington University School of Medicine*

The clinical effectiveness of any intravaginal chemical contraceptive should be established by direct evaluation of the product's spermicidal qualities during its exposure to the normal physiologic demands of active coition and ejaculation. With two exceptions[2,7] there have been no recorded direct attempts to evaluate intravaginal contraceptive materials during or immediately after intercourse.

Heretofore chemical products designed for intravaginal contraceptive usage have been investigated before release for public consumption by the indirect methods of laboratory assay and/or clinical field-trial in order to determine whether they are (a) harmless, (b) effective and (c) aesthetically acceptable.[4] Once medical precedent was established in support of these indirect methods of evaluation, innumerable reports of laboratory testing of individual commercial products flooded the literature.

Theoretical arguments concerning the effectiveness of the various laboratory tests in establishing the clinical spermicidal qualities of any chemical contraceptive product have added further confusion to the problem of interpreting the literature.[1,3,15] In fact, reports of indirect "laboratory assay" technics have reached such unwieldy proportions that MacLeod and his co-workers[8] recently felt it necessary to institute an exhaustive comparison of the in vitro testing techniques for commercial contraceptive products.

The indirect clinical investigative technique of field-trial evaluation also has been so popularized in recent years that results derived from the Pearl formula (pregnancy rate per 100 years of exposure)[16,17] abound in the literature. The basic philosophy of the field-trial "pregnancy failure" evaluation of a contraceptive product is open to ethical question. The investigative technique involves exposing a selected segment of what is considered to be a generally underprivileged population to a new contraceptive product with the implied promise of pregnancy control for those participating in the program. If the product has a high level of contraceptive effectiveness, the "volunteers" are spared a large number of unwanted pregnancies. If not, the investigative conscience can be salved with the obvious fact that the unwanted pregnancies would have occurred anyway, if some form of protection had not been offered. So voluminous has the field-trial literature become that both Hartman[5] and Tietze[18] independently have felt the need for extensive compilation of existing individual product reports.

For the past 2 years a multifaceted investigative program designed to determine the influence of intravaginal physiology upon the anatomic distribution and the contraceptive effectiveness of the diaphragm and of selected commercial spermicidal agents has been conducted by the Division of Reproductive Biology, Washington University School of Medicine. The entire program is based upon the investigative philosophy that direct observation and measurement rather than indirect laboratory or field-trial estimation of spermicidal effectiveness should be demanded of every intravaginal chemical contraceptive before the product is released for public consumption.

The first phase of the research program recorded direct observations of the functional response of the intravaginal diaphragm within the sexually stimulated vaginal barrel and provided information as to the immediate and the delayed intravaginal distribution of impartially selected chemical contraceptives during natural and artificial coition.[6] The second phase has been concerned with results obtained from an investigative technique developed to provide direct clinical measurement of the actual physiologic spermicidal effectiveness of the impartially selected intravaginal chemical contraceptive agents.

During both phases of the investigative

*The investigation received major support from the Frederick Ayer II Foundation. This grant was supplemented by Washington University.

program subject comment related to the aesthetic acceptability of the individual product under investigation was recorded and has been presented in context. No evidence of individual allergic sensitivity to any of the commercial products has been observed in the small study-subject population.

The technique of artificial coitus has been described briefly in the report from the first phase of the research program.[6] The theoretical advantage of investigative control over the normal physiologic responses of the human female to effective sexual stimulation has been suggested in the past [7] and has been established in this study. To avoid repetition, the physiologic advantages of the investigative technique of artificial coitus and the details of subject orientation, so necessary to this research program, will not be reconsidered. Suffice it to say that all female subjects evaluated in the study were experienced in the investigative techniques employed and responded to these forms of sexual stimulation through complete cycles of sexual response.[9-11]

The subject population for Phase II of the contraceptive study is identical with that of Phase I. The 30 individuals described in the first report from this study have been retained for the direct investigation of the physiologic effectiveness of the individual products of intravaginal chemical contraception. The subjects' ages now range from 21 to 43 years, with 16 of the women presently under 30 years of age. Numbers of prior conceptions among individual group members range from 0 to 4 and numbers of children from 0 to 3. Eleven of the female subjects are unmarried, 14 are maintaining an active marital status and the remaining 5 individuals are divorced, separated or widowed.

As in the first phase of the investigative program, subjects were selected arbitrarily to provide clinical representation for normal variations in the structuring of female pelvic anatomy. Pelvic pathology has ranged from a myomatous uterus and advanced cystoceles, urethroceles and rectoceles in the parous subjects to restricted vaginal outlets and a post-abortion, acquired retroversion in the nulliparous subjects.[6]

An investigative technique has been designed to provide direct evaluation of the spermicidal effectiveness of an intravaginal chemical contraceptive agent. The standards of this testing technique are admittedly severe;

so severe, in fact, that no perfect performance was recorded by any of the commercial products tested. All 30 female subjects were exposed to each of the 7 different chemical contraceptives listed in Table II.

Table I

INVESTIGATIVE TECHNIQUE AND GRADING SYSTEM FOR INTRAVAGINAL CHEMICAL CONTRACEPTIVES

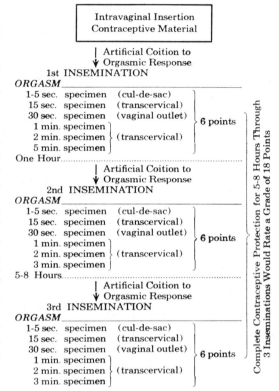

The commercial products were selected impartially at the request of the investigative team by a representative of the National Committee on Maternal Health. These contraceptive products were chosen as representative of the various bases (cream, jelly, foam tablet, suppository and aerosol) which provide the medium for the intravaginal dispersion of the active contraceptive agents. In addition, in an effort to resolve the theoretical argument as to the most effective indirect laboratory test for spermicidal quality, a contraceptive that has scored high in both the mixing and the diffusion tests (Delfen) has been compared to a contraceptive that has scored well on the diffusion test, but poorly in the mixing test (Lanesta).

All subjects were protected from any possibility of pregnancy by the technique of cervical capping.[13] A minimum of 3 days of vaginal control[14] before each investigative session was provided by the subject population.

Each participant read the instructions accompanying the commercial product under investigation and, acting in accord with her interpretation of the directions, inserted the contraceptive material without individual tutoring or physical aid. When a time interval between the insertion of the contraceptive product and the onset of coital activity was requested by the manufacturer, compliance was observed.

Table II

COMPARISON OF PRODUCT CONTRACEPTIVE
EFFECTIVENESS BY POINT SCORING METHOD

Commercial Contraceptive Product	1st Insemi- nation	2nd Insemi- nation	3rd Insemi- nation	Total Points
Delfen Cream	180	180	148	508
Emko Foam	180	180	130	490
Lanesta Gel	170	180	130	480
Lactikol Creme	176	144	100	420
Lactikol Jelly	168	162	61	391
Durafoam Tablets	159	72	3	234
Lorophyn Suppositories	164	56	2	222
Perfect per- formance score	180	180	180	540

After the contraceptive material was introduced into the vagina, each subject engaged in artificial coital activity through a complete cycle of sexual response (Table I). At orgasm a previously examined seminal specimen was injected into the vaginal barrel simulating the male act of ejaculation. A sample of vaginal content was removed immediately (1-5 seconds) from the cul-de-sac. Fifteen seconds after the simulated ejaculation, a specimen of vaginal content was obtained from the transcervical area and at 30 seconds a specimen removed from just within the vaginal outlet. Thereafter, specimens were taken at 1, 2 and 5 minutes from the transcervical depth of the vaginal barrel. All specimens were examined immediately for sperm motility. Even when motile sperm were observed in the initial specimen, all of the regularly scheduled samples were taken and examined in routine manner.

One hour later artificial coition was again

conducted until orgasmic phase sexual response levels were obtained (Table I). A second previously defined seminal specimen was injected into the vaginal barrel during the orgasmic experience. Samples of vaginal content were taken from the same specific areas of the vaginal barrel and in the same time sequence as described in the preceding paragraph.

Finally, from 5 to 8 hours after the initial injection of seminal fluid, artificial intercourse was conducted to orgasmic levels of sexual response and simultaneously a third established seminal specimen was injected into the vaginal barrel (Table I). Again specimens were removed in the same timing sequence and from the same representative areas of the vaginal barrel as previously described.

In order to provide maximum information for every product investigated, the extended 5 to 8 hour evaluation period was subdivided into controlled segments in the following manner. The 30 subjects were separated into 4 groups for the long-range (5 to 8 hour) test of maintained spermicidal effectiveness. Seven of the subjects had the total observation period terminated by final coital activity and insemination at the 5-hour interval. Each of the 7 "5-hour" subjects was checked in similar fashion for all 7 of the products evaluated. Seven more subjects were checked at 6 hours, 7 at the 7-hour interval and the remaining group of 9 subjects went the full 8 hours between the first and last inseminations.

In brief, the direct investigative format is as follows. After the initial intravaginal insertion of an impartially selected, chemical contraceptive product, 3 previously examined fertile seminal specimens were injected over a 5-to-8-hour period. After each insemination, specimens of vaginal content were returned at specific time intervals and from specific areas within the vaginal barrel. All of the specimens of vaginal content were examined immediately for sperm motility.

All subjects were restrained to supine positioning during artificial coition and for the first hour of the observation period (2 inseminations). They were then allowed to move about at will until the last coital and insemination period when female supine positioning was reinstituted. There were several occasions when orgasmic levels of sexual response could not be attained. In these instances, inseminations were instituted after long-maintained plateau phase levels of sexual response had been experienced and it became obvious that an orgasmic phase release of tension was not possible.

The research technique of artificial coition stimulates physiologic responses of the vaginal barrel similar to those produced during normal coital activity. The development of vaginal lubrication levels parallel to those of the subject's normal productivity was insured by direct observation. Since this material serves as a thinning and/or wetting agent for any intravaginal contraceptive material, and also influences vaginal acidity,[10] adequate production of vaginal lubrication must be assured to provide a controlled investigative environment. The normal excitement and plateau phase expansion and elongation of the vaginal barrel developed satisfactorily under direct observation. Wide dissemination of seminal fluid content throughout the vagina was assured with the technique of injecting the specimen at the onset of the female orgasmic phase during the peak of artificial coital activity.

The planned injection of a second seminal specimen (1 hour after the first) and a third specimen (5 to 8 hours after the first) was an investigative attempt to simulate both of the clinical possibilities of a family-unit's return to sexual activity within an hour after prior ejaculation and the not infrequent resumption of sexual activity the morning after a previous night's ejaculation.

Actually, the investigative format described above is a much more severe test of any commercial product's contraceptive effectiveness than the average fertile male could provide in a 5 to 8 hour period. This investigative severity is reflected by the fact that all seminal specimens prior to injection were determined to be within specific limits of fertility, while a normally fertile male might well produce subfertile specimens during second or third ejaculatory opportunities within a 5 to 8 hour period.[12]

All seminal specimens were produced after 3 to 5 days of donor continence. Within 30 minutes after the specimen was available it was evaluated for count, volume, viscosity and initial motility and employed in the investigative program. No sperm specimen was used unless the count was above 60 million per cc. There was a minimum seminal fluid volume requirement of 3 cc. and a demand for at least

75% initial purposeful sperm motility.

It must be emphasized that this clinical test was designed to provide a most severe direct evaluation of contraceptive effectiveness. Not only have initial contraceptive protection rates been established, but the long-range contraceptive effectiveness of the impartially selected commercial products also has been subjected to detailed investigation. When a contraceptive material demonstrates both immediate and long-range protective qualities during repetitive exposure to fertile seminal fluid over a 5 to 8 hour observation period, it is a superior product when compared to a chemical contraceptive that cannot meet these stringent investigative standards.

It also should be emphasized that the initial intravaginal placement of the manufacturer's calculated dosage of the contraceptive material was all that was permitted. Many manufacturers of chemical contraceptive products suggest an additional intravaginal application of their product for every coital opportunity. Since this investigative program was constituted to establish the total long and short range effectiveness of representative contraceptive products chosen impartially from those presently available commercially, additional intravaginal insertions of materials under examination were denied for all products.

The presentation of the data collected during the 7 experimental sessions with each of the 30 subjects creates a major problem. There were 210 clinical experiments, each necessitating from 5 to 8 hours of elapsed time. Each session required 3 seminal specimens of established fertility and 18 individual measurements of the spermicidal effectiveness of the contraceptive product under investigation.

In order to present the essence of the investigative results without the problem of charting compilations, a system of grading of contraceptive effectiveness has been established. As noted in Table I, a score of 1 point has been given for every specimen of intravaginal content that proved all sperm immobilized, under microscopic examination. Thus, for every postinsemination period, a score of 6 points was possible and for an extra 5 to 8 hour investigative session a total of 18 points could be accumulated.

A point score of 18 would indicate that a contraceptive material was still clinically effective 5 to 8 hours after original intravaginal insertion and had sufficient reserve protective potential to inactivate 3 separate fertile seminal specimens. Obviously, if an individual contraceptive material had provided complete protection during short and long range coital exposure with all 30 of the female subjects, a total point score of 540 points could have been amassed. With the figure of 540 representing a perfect score, it has been relatively simple to develop comparisons between a theoretically perfect performance and the actual clinical contraceptive effectiveness of each of the 7 commercial products investigated.

The intravaginal chemical contraceptives have been arranged in order of their total point scores to emphasize their clinical contraceptive effectiveness (Table II). The commercial products have been separated by the demands of the direct testing techniques into 3 obvious levels of contraceptive efficiency. Delfen cream, Emko aerosol and Lanesta gel, in that order, have proved to be excellent protective agents and have scored well, despite the acknowledged severity of the investigative standards. Lactikol creme and Lactikol jelly have returned scores that at best would indicate fair contraceptive protective quality for these products. The Durafoam tablets and Lorophyn suppositories have compiled scores that indicate these contraceptive agents are inadequate to the arbitrary demands of the investigative standards.

The individual contraceptives will be discussed separately. Attention will be directed primarily toward areas of product failure and only secondarily will emphasize successful protective activity.

It is obvious from a survey of Table II that Delfen cream provided complete protection for all 30 of the subjects during both the first and second insemination periods. Thus, a perfect score of 180 points was accumulated for each investigative session.

The area of failure for Delfen was restricted to the delayed (5 to 8 hour) evaluation segment of the study. During this delayed insemination period, 8 out of the total of 30 subjects were not provided complete protection by the product. Subjects A and B showed total failure of contraceptive protection in all specimens taken at the designated time intervals and from the established test areas of the vaginal barrel during the 6 and 8 hour examinations. Two subjects (C and D) when ex-

amined at the 8 hour interval, showed contraceptive protection only in the 5 minute transcervical specimen. One subject (E) evaluated at the 5 hour interval and 1 (F) at the 7 hour interval, demonstrated 2 minute transcervical protection.

Finally, 2 subjects (G and H) in the 6 hour delayed study group returned single positive (motile sperm) samplings of vaginal content, G from the cul-de-sac (1 to 5 seconds) and H from the transcervical vaginal area (15 seconds).

When 1, 2 or 5 minute protection is mentioned, the term signifies failure of contraceptive effectiveness of all specimens of the postcoital vaginal barrel taken before the stated protection time. For example, protection at 5 minutes would mean that only the sixth or last specimen taken from the transcervical area showed immobilized sperm. Protection at 1 minute would mean that the first 3 specimens taken from the cul-de-sac (1 to 5 seconds), the transcervical area (15 seconds) and the vaginal outlet (30 seconds) all showed motile sperm.

In order to explain the occurrence of delayed protection at the 1, 2 or 5 minute time intervals, either of 2 possibilities must be entertained. First, a major portion of the active spermicide(s) may have escaped the vaginal barrel during coital activity prior to ejaculation. In this instance the delayed contraceptive reaction could be attributed to the fact that the minimal retained concentration of the active ingredient(s) necessitated a variable time interval before sperm immobilization could be accomplished. Second, the active spermicide(s) might not have been released from the product's base containment for a variable time interval after coitus and ejaculation. In this situation the seminal fluid actually could aid in dispersion of the active spermicidal agent(s) within the vaginal barrel. Again a time lapse would develop before sperm immobilization was accomplished.

The subject protection failures with Delfen will be used to explain how points are lost from the theoretically perfect score of 180 points for each of the 3 insemination periods. Direct examination of Table II is suggested. Subjects A and B (the total contraceptive failures at 6 and 8 hours) lost 6 points each. Subjects C and D, who demonstrated protection only at the 5 minute sampling interval, lost 5 points apiece. Subjects E and F, attaining protection at 2 minutes, lost 4 points apiece, and the 2 individuals (G and H) who returned single specimens demonstrating a local area of contraceptive failure, only lost 1 point apiece. Thus, out of a possible total of 180 points for the delayed 5 to 8 hour evaluation period, 148 points were accumulated.

The total point score of 508 out of a possible 540 points established Delfen cream as the most effective intravaginal chemical contraceptive of the 7 representative commercial products examined by the direct clinical evaluation technique. Failure area for this product was restricted to a reduction in the product's high level of contraceptive effectiveness during the delayed (5 to 8 hour) investigative sequence. This well may have been the result of wastage of material during the prior coital activity. Although Delfen disseminates rapidly throughout the vaginal barrel, it also spreads widely over the perineum and adheres to the penile shaft during active coition. Therefore, a significant amount of product wastage during successive mounting episodes is inevitable.

Emko foam was the only other intravaginal chemical contraceptive to amass perfect scores during both the first and second insemination periods. During the delayed (5 to 8 hour) examination period, Emko accumulated 130 out of 180 possible points, and ultimately established a total point score of 490 points. Thus Emko fell 18 points behind Delfen in the grading total. This is a small difference in point spread, but it is statistically significant in the evaluation of long-range contraceptive quality.

Emko's listing of protection failures during the delayed (5 to 8 hour) examination period included 2 subjects with complete contraceptive failure, plus 4 subjects who did not demonstrate protection until 5 minutes had elapsed, 3 subjects who developed protection at the 2 minute interval and finally, 1 subject with protection at 1 minute. All of these subjects were in the 7 to 8 hour delayed investigative groups. There were, in addition, 3 more subjects who demonstrated lack of contraceptive coverage in specific local vaginal areas, 1 in the 5 and 2 in the 6 hour groups.

It is apparent from the exhaustive evaluation that Emko is as rapidly and as well-diffused throughout the vaginal barrel and provides just as effective contraceptive protection

during the immediate and the 1 hour insemination periods as Delfen. There is, however, a reduction in the effectiveness of contraceptive protection during the long-range evaluation sequence. The mechanical wastage of this product over perineum and penile shaft during active coition was less than any other chemical contraceptive tested. Therefore, the defect in clinical contraceptive protection obviously could be corrected easily, if a minimal increase in concentration of the active spermicidal agents were added to the present calculated clinical dosage and/or if a minimal increase in the amount of contraceptive material injected intravaginally were added to the present calculated clinical dosage.

Lanesta gel ranked third in clinical effectiveness among the chemical contraceptives investigated. Interestingly, it would have been quite equal to Emko if it had not been for the product's inherent characteristic of slowed diffusion through the vaginal barrel during the first session of artificial coition. Four subjects showed failure in local area coverage: 1 from the vaginal outlet, 1 from the cul-de-sac and 2 from the transcervical area. The 2 subjects who were not protected initially in the transcervical area (15 seconds) did not establish contraceptive protection in this area until after the second coital interlude and, therefore, lost 4 points each as the result of the fact that 4 routine specimens are taken from the transcervical area. Consequently, 10 points were lost by Lanesta during the first insemination period.

As illustrated in Table II, the second episode of artificial coition following an hour's interval accomplished a more effective diffusion of the initial intravaginal dosage of contraceptive material and all subjects demonstrated complete protection during the second insemination period (180 points).

An identical point score to that of Emko (130) was accumulated by Lanesta gel during the delayed (5 to 8 hour) evaluation period. As opposed to either Delfen or Emko, Lanesta did not develop local area protection failures such as in the cul-de-sac or at the vaginal outlet during the delayed observation period. There were, however, 3 complete failures of contraceptive coverage, 1 in each of the 5, 7 and 8 hour investigative groups. Four subjects demonstrated protection at the 5 minute interval and there were 3 subjects showing protection at the 2 minute interval. All subjects with evidence of delayed protection were encountered in the 6 to 8 hour investigative groups.

Direct observation of Lanesta gel during artificial coition showed it to be slower to diffuse throughout the vaginal barrel than either Delfen or Emko. As previously mentioned, this slowed diffusion rate was responsible for the loss of 10 grading points during the first insemination period. However, once total vaginal barrel diffusion of the product was accomplished, protection was more widespread throughout the vaginal barrel (no evidence of immediate local area failure) than was demonstrated by either Emko or Delfen during the delayed observation period.

There is no question but that the active ingredients in Lanesta are severely spermicidal. The fault in this particular product lies in the direction of the excessive viscosity of the base in which the active spermicidal agents are disseminated. The high concentration of failure reports in the last 2 hours of the delayed investigative study suggest that the active spermicidal ingredients were lost during repetitive coital activity. Much of the viscid gel has been observed to adhere to the shaft of the artificial penis, or to spread over subject perineal areas during active coition. This mechanical loss of material was observed to be in excess of Delfen wastage under similar circumstances and far to exceed that of Emko.

Lactikol creme, scoring a total of 420 points, came close to providing complete protection during the first insemination period. There was marked wastage of the creme during the initial episodes of coital activity. One subject demonstrated failure of protection for 2 minutes during the first investigative session and thus accounted for the loss of 4 points during this scoring period. Excessive coital wasteage of the contraceptive creme was demonstrated further by the loss of 36 points in the second insemination period. Product evaluation during the delayed (5 to 8 hour) investigative period accumulated a score of 100 out of a possible 180 points. There were 8 complete failures of any residual contraceptive protection in subjects from each of the 5, 6, 7 and 8 hour investigative groups. In addition, several more subjects demonstrated 2 or 5 minute delayed protection, indicating a low intravaginal concentration of the active contraceptive agents.

The creme base of this product diffuses most effectively after initial injection. However, this particular creme repetitively demonstrated wastage during coital activity. Consequently, a significant amount of the effective contraceptive agent was eliminated mechanically from the vaginal barrel. A total point score of 420 out of a possible 540 points places the Lactikol creme in the moderately successful protective grouping.

Lactikol jelly scoring in the same point range (a total of 391 points) did not have a perfect score in any of the 3 insemination periods. An initial score of 168 out of 180 points during the first postcoital evaluation period was the result of 3 failures of cul-de-sac coverage, 1 in the transcervical area for all 4 routine specimens, and 1 at the vaginal outlet. Finally, there was also 1 failure of protection for a 2 minute interval during the first investigative period.

Marked change in contraceptive protection was apparent during the second insemination period, despite the fact that 162 points were accumulated. The residual jelly was well distributed throughout the vagina at the end of 1 hour and subsequent to the second session of artificial coition. However, body temperature and the activity of the first coital session melted the jelly base and the contraceptive material frequently was observed escaping the vaginal barrel during and immediately following the second coition, even though subjects maintained supine positioning. As the result of this type of material wastage, 3 subjects evidenced complete failure of contraceptive protection during the second investigative period, accounting for the loss of the 18 points.

Material wastage also probably accounts for the very low point score during the 5 to 8 hour observation period, when only 61 out of a possible 180 points were accumulated. There were 12 complete failures of contraceptive coverage in subjects representing each of the 5 to 8 hour investigative groups. In addition, there were several returns of inadequate local vaginal coverage and of protection restricted at the 2 and 5 minute intervals.

Lactikol jelly not only has the inherent difficulty of slowed dissemination during the first coital opportunity, but has the additional distress of melting and being extruded from the vaginal barrel during and subsequent to coital opportunity to such a degree that only a total of 396 points for the 3 insemination periods could be accumulated.

Since both Lactikol creme and jelly contain essentially the same active contraceptive ingredients, it is obvious that the creme base provides a somewhat more effective distributing agent than does the jelly for long-range contraceptive protection. Essentially, both the creme and the jelly were equal in short-term contraceptive protection as evidenced by the combined scores of the first 2 insemination periods (Table II). Neither the Lactikol jelly or creme was as clinically effective under the controlled direct investigative conditions as the 3 products described previously.

The reduced contraceptive protection of either Lactikol creme or jelly may be explained partially by the realization that these products originally were designed for usage in conjunction with the intravaginal diaphragm. Therefore, it must be emphasized that neither product (as presently constituted) provides adequate contraceptive protection, when employed independently of the diaphragm as a contraceptive agent.

The final 2 commercial contraceptive products, Durafoam tablets and Lorophyn suppositories, scored poorly with totals of 234 and 222 points, respectively (Table II). There was no consistent evidence of adequate contraceptive protection either during the initial postcoital study period, or in either of the 2 subsequent periods of investigation. It is obvious that with only 3 and 2 points scored respectively during the delayed (5 to 8 hour) observation period, these 2 products in their present forms do not provide clinically adequate long-range contraceptive protection. A detailed consideration of the multiple subject failures of these products would serve no useful purpose and is avoided here for the sake of brevity.

A clinical difficulty inherent in both of these products is that their bases do not provide for adequate dissemination of contraceptive material throughout the vaginal barrel. There were several instances of complete failure of dissemination of the contraceptive materials in the vaginal barrel during the first postcoital investigative period. Direct examination of the dispersive qualities of both products during active artificial coition demonstrated many areas of unprotected vaginal barrel. There is an additional distress inherent in the present clinical dosage of these products. Frequently,

the material present in either product is insufficient to cover the sexually distended vaginal barrel, even after all of the product base has been dispersed effectively. These 2 commercial contraceptive products must be considered clinically inadequate as evaluated by the severe standards of the direct postcoital test.

DISCUSSION

Inspection of Table II reveals that only the first 2 listed intravaginal chemical contraceptive products provided complete short-range protection for all 30 subjects during the first investigative session of artificial coition and insemination with a seminal specimen of established fertility. These same products (Delfen cream and Emko foam) grouped with Lanesta gel to establish continued protection during the second investigative session, conducted 1 hour after the first insemination. No product was able to return a perfect score during the third or delayed (5 to 8 hour) study segment. Obviously, Delfen provided the best prolonged contraceptive protection during the delayed investigative period with Emko and Lanesta in second place, but far in advance of the rest of the impartially selected commercial products in long-range, clinical contraceptive effectiveness.

The arbitrarily established direct investigative format is admittedly severe. It was designed purposely to describe strengths and limitations of contraceptive effectiveness by direct evaluation rather than to estimate the spermicidal quality of any product by the indirect methods of laboratory assay or of "pregnancy-failure" field-trials.

It may be argued that manufacturers design a product for contraceptive protection during only a single rather than 3 successive coital and ejaculatory sequences. Therefore, any return to coital activity after initial exposure necessitates additional usage of the contraceptive product, as suggested in the instructions contained in the commercial packaging. This argument presumes that all individuals who use the product not only can, but will read the instructions. In addition, it is presumed that the woman in question will follow the instructions faithfully and will remember them correctly even if the set of directions is lost or mislaid. Obviously, any chemical contraceptive product designed with minimal short-term spermicidal qualities is not potentially as effective a clinical contraceptive agent as a product that provides for the normal lack of total public understanding and cooperation by incorporating a significant margin of reserve contraceptive protection in the commercially marketed product.

Regardless of the argument outlined above, there can be no excuse for failure of contraceptive protection of a subject population during an initial coital and male ejaculatory episode. Only Delfen and Emko, under direct intravaginal observation and subsequent to microscopic evaluation of postcoital vaginal specimens established proof of chemical spermicidal effectiveness during the initial evaluation period. While modest corrections in the chemical format of several of the impartially selected commercial products should provide excellent contraceptive protection, the fact remains that as presently constituted, the remaining commercial products do not meet their clinical responsibility as acceptable contraceptive agents when judged by the arbitrary, direct investigative technique described in the body of this paper.

It also should be emphasized at this time that the commercial products evaluated during the 2 year investigative program were selected impartially by a representative of the National Committee for Maternal Health. While they have been adjudged representative of their basic types, they may be assumed in no way to be completely representative of all similar products in spermicidal effectiveness. It remains for other manufacturers to submit their products to some manner of direct investigative format, if adequate evidence of the clinical effectiveness of all intravaginal chemical contraceptive products on the market is to be obtained by the medical profession.

The theoretical argument of the relative value of the laboratory mixing test versus the diffusion test has not been satisfied. Delfen (high score on both mixing and diffusion tests) has been more effective under direct clinical investigation than Lanesta (high score on the diffusion test). The impression remains that this superiority is the result of clinical inadequacy of base material in Lanesta gel rather than an ineffectiveness of the active spermicidal agents. The specific viscosity of Lanesta is at present the fundamental cause of its failure to score more favorably.

The human element in the direct test for spermicidal effectiveness of intravaginal chemical contraceptive products must be considered. Any experimental population limited to 30 subjects, regardless of how representative of female pelvic anatomy their selection might be, is certainly open to question. In this situation the restriction of population size has been a matter of simple economics. Financial support for this investigative program was secured from two impartial sources.* This method of support was followed in an attempt to obviate any suggestion of prejudice that might arise if the investigative program had been underwritten by a pharmaceutical house. The possibility of public health funds to support such an investigative program was not even considered. Thus, while 50 to 100 subjects in the study population would have solved a degree of investigative concern, it is doubtful that a definitive number of subjects could be established which would satisfy all possible criticism.

The human element in the subject population group cannot be equated. For instance, the concerns of aesthetic rejection of an individual product which were discussed at length in the first report[6] were reemphasized in the present study. With 4 exceptions, study-subjects who objected to a particular commercial product during the first year's work also objected to the same product with the repeated evaluations of the second year. Emko foam was the only product that did not elicit vocalized aesthetic distress from the research population. Delfen, with objections from 2 subjects, placed second in this regard. The remainder of the products occasioned multiple vocalized objections such as perineal contamination, dripping, soiling, intravaginal irritation, and so forth. It is quite possible that the objections returned for the remainder of the commercial products would not have been so strong if the aesthetically preferable aerosol-base product had not been available for comparison.

Finally, the delayed (5 to 8 hour) segment of the study emphasized individual variants. For instance, if the first 2 coital sessions were prolonged and resulted in excessive wastage of the contraceptive product from the vaginal barrel, protection levels during the delayed observation session might be less than if the 2 prior artificial coital opportunities had been of short duration. There is no way to control such a

*The investigation received major support from the Frederick Ayer II Foundation. This grant was supplemented by Washington University.

human variant. For that matter, the individual woman frequently may establish similar reaction patterns during repetitive coital exposure.

It is obvious that any direct investigative technique applied to an intravaginal chemical contraceptive does not define adequately potential allergic sensitivities to the product on the restricted basis of exposure to a small study-subject population. Such clinical determinations should be made. However, these results can and should be obtained after prior study-subject exposure establishes that the product in question provides adequate evidence of both short and long-range contraceptive protective quality. It is one thing to request sensitivity evaluation for any intravaginal chemical contraceptive from a statistically significant segment of the population. It is quite another to expose such a "volunteer" segment of the population to unwanted pregnancies in the process. In view of the recently aroused medical interest in adequate product evaluation prior to commercial distribution, the concept of direct clinical testing of the protective potential of any intravaginal chemical contraceptive has been presented.

SUMMARY

The intravaginal chemical contraceptive which provides the largest margin of protection against human error and post-ejaculatory physiologic demand should be judged the most effective product on the commercial market. Such a product should be established as aesthetically acceptable and should contain both long-range and short-range contraceptive protective qualities. Sensitivity to the chemical constituents of any intravaginal contraceptive must be determined by extensive clinical exposure. This final step in product evaluation should be taken only after the above named qualities have been assured. The most effective clinical judgment of the protective potential of any intravaginal chemical contraceptive can and should be established by direct investigation rather than by the presently accepted techniques of indirect estimation.

REFERENCES

1. Brown, R. L. and Gamble, C. J.: Method of Testing Relative Spermicidal Effectiveness of Contraceptives and Its Application to 10 Commercial Products, Hum. Fertil., 5: 97-108, 1940.
2. Cohen, M. R. and Kaye, B. M.: The Postcoital Test as a Method of Evaluating a Contraceptive Jelly, J.A.M.A., 152: 1042-1043, 1953.
3. Gamble, C. J.: An Improved Test of Spermicidal Activity Without Dilution or Mixing, J.A.M.A., 152: 1037-1041, 1953.
4. Guttmacher, A. F. et al.: Methods of Evaluating Spermicidal Agents. Exhibit Leaflet, Planned Parenthood Federation of America, 1959.
5. Hartman, C. G.: Annotated List of Published Reports on Clinical Trials with Contraceptives, Fertil. & Steril., 10: 177-189, 1959.
6. Johnson, V. E. and Masters, W. H.: Intravaginal Contraceptive Study: Phase I. Anatomy, West. J. Surg., Obst. & Gynec., 70: 202-207, 1962.
7. Kaufman, S. A.: Simulated Postcoital Test to Determine Immediate Spermicidal Effect of Cream or Jelly Alone, Fertil. & Steril., 11: 199-209, 1960.
8. MacLeod, J. et al.: In Vitro Assessment of Commercial Contraceptive Jellies and Creams, J.A.M.A., 176: 109-113, 1961.
9. Masters, W. H.: The Sexual Response Cycle of the Human Female. I. Gross Anatomic Considerations, West. J. Surg., Obst. & Gynec., 68: 57-72, 1960.
10. Masters, W. H.: The Sexual Response Cycle of the Human Female. II. Vaginal Lubrication, Ann. New York Acad. Sci., 83: 301-317, 1959.
11. Masters, W. H. and Johnson, V. E.: The Human Female: Anatomy of Sexual Response, Minnesota Med., 43: 31-36, 1960.
12. Masters, W. H. and Lampe, E. H.: Problems of Male Infertility. II. The Effect of Frequent Ejaculation, Fertil. & Steril., 7: 123-127, 1956.
13. Masters, W. H. et al.: The Cervical Cap: An Adjunct in the Treatment of Male Infertility, J.A.M.A., 149: 427-431, 1952.
14. Masters, W. H. and Johnson, V. E.: The Physiology of Vaginal Reproductive Function, West. J. Surg., Obst. & Gynec., 69: 105-120, 1961.
15. Millman, N.: A Critical Study of Methods of Measuring Spermicidal Action, Ann. New York Acad. Sci., 54: 806-823, 1952.
16. Pearl, R.: Conception and Fertility in 2000 Women, Hum. Biol., 4: 363-407, 1932.
17. Pearl, R.: The Natural History of Population, Oxford University Press, New York, 1939.
18. Tietze, C.: The Clinical Effectiveness of Contraceptive Methods, Am. J. Obst. & Gynec., 78: 650-656, 1959.

Washington University School of Medicine

Hot Water

VI

Editor's Comments on Papers 19, 20, and 21

The three papers in this section are probably of interest mostly to physiologists, although at first blush the simplicity of the method would suggest wide appeal.

In 1923, a Japanese physician, N. Fukui, published a paper in the *Japan Medical World* entitled "On a Hitherto Unknown Action of Heat Ray on Testicles." Fukui presented data which show a direct relationship between temperature and the time necessary to cause changes in the testicular cells responsible for production of sperm. His data are not included but he does show a very smooth curve; a bit too smooth for this type of investigation. Nevertheless, the observation that heat in the range 44–48°C can influence sperm production and survival gives rise immediately to the question of whether or not this simple method has value as a contraceptive.

Others were quick to look into this possibility. In 1924, the noted American physiologists, Carl Moore and William Quick, published data that proved what had long been surmised, namely that the scrotum functions as a temperature regulator for the testes. They simply demonstrated that the temperature on the inside of the scrotum is decidedly lower than that of the peritoneal cavity at the same moment. This is an important observation, because it is well established that when the testis is kept at body temperature, as in cases of cryptorchidism, sperm are not produced.

Then in 1927, William C. Young, a zoologist, published an exhaustive study of the influence of high temperature on the testis. He found that when water heated to 46–47°C is run over the guinea pig scrotum for thirty minutes or so, a degeneration of the germinal epithelium begins immediately and continues until the end of about twelve days. He then checked the rodent's ability to reproduce and found a markedly increased rate of sterile matings. Finally, he demonstrated that normal reproductive power is regained and there is no effect on the sexual vigor of the males so treated.

These results would seem to indicate that here is a very simple and effective contraceptive method. However, the reader of these articles will note that although experimentally the rate of sterile matings was increased there were still some productive matings. In addition, the danger of miscarriage, or worse, malformation due to injured sperm, appears to be very real. For these reasons no one has seriously suggested regular hot baths, or a warm scrotal garment for contraceptive purposes. In fact, it has been pointed out that the Japanese have long been addicted to frequent very hot baths, and yet their population growth has obviously not suffered.

Reprinted from *Japan Med. World*, **3**, 27–28 (Jan.–Dec. 1923)

19

ON A HITHERTO UNKNOWN ACTION OF HEAT RAY ON TESTICLES

N. FUKUI, Surgeon-Lieutenant, N. M. C.
Maidzuru

I. Introduction

In 1922, I found that heat ray applied on testicle of rabbit from the surface of scrotum has always selective action on the generative cells, which undergo typical regressive changes. Since then I have studied the action extensively with rabbits and other mammalian animals. The present report includes the consideration of the problem from histological, hygienic and endocrinological sides.

To cause regressive changes in the generative cells only the following three methods are known, namely transplantation of testicle, ligature of vas deferens and application of X-ray. But my cases of heat testicles (for the sake of brevity the testicles which had been applied with heat ray and the generative cells had undergone certain regressive changes are called heat testicles) show more constant and typical changes than those caused by the ligatures or X-ray application. The heat applied is comparatively low, and the lowest is the same as the body temperature of rabbit or 40 C. and the highest is 49 C. Higher temperature than 49 C. is found to be unsuitable for my experiments. It is remarkable that I was able to produce heat testicle with such low temperature.

II. Purpose of My Study of Heat Testicle

1. The cause of descension of testicle into scrotum might be due to the fact that the spermatogenous protein is thermolabile even with body temperature.
2. If the spermatogenous protein is so thermolabile, is there no significance in regard to the problem of human customs, clothes, and habitation as well as of industrial hygiene ?
3. The influence of the results of the heat testicle on the theories of testis endocrinology based on the results of transplantation, ligature and X-ray application, etc.

III. Experiments

The following four kinds of experiments were carried out.

1. Exposure of the scrotum to the sunlight. The exposure was made in clear days in midsummer from 1 p. m. to 3. p. m.

2. Warm water bathing of scrotum. The temperature of water was from 44 C. to 49 C.
3. Warm air bathing of the waist part. The temperature of air was 40 to 44 C.
4. Exposure of the scrotum to arc light.

I have also studied with experimental retained testicle to see the effect of body temperature on its own testicle. The results, however, will be reported in the near future.

IV. Summary

A. Histological study of heat testicle.

Curve of heat testicle : There appears to be a certain definite relation between temperature and time to cause regressive changes in the generative cells. The relation of temperature and the minimal time to produce heat testicle are as follows ;

At 48 C. twenty minutes, at 47 C. half an hour, at 46 C. one hour, at 45 C. two hours and half at 44 C. forty five hours.

The time required at each degree below 44 C. is enormously lengthened, and it requires about one hundred hours at 41 C.

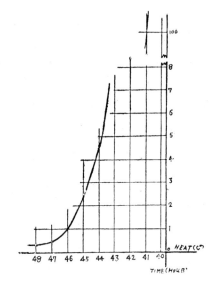

This curve only represents the relation of the temperature and heat to cause a certain histological alteration, and can not naturally be so accurate as determined by physico chemical tests. The relation, however, presents very insteresting equation, thus

$$y = 0.213 + 89 \ e \quad 0.828 \ ^x$$

Thus this curve is peculiar to the heat testicle, and shows an approximate standard to cause heat testicle. I called it provisionally a " curve of heat testicle".

Histological examination of heat testicle shows that a selective destruction of generative cells leaving the supporting cells of the seminiferous tubules (Sertoli's cell). As the canaliculus gradually atrophies, the interstitial and Leydig's cells proliferate. I examined the modes of histological changes with each experiment carried out above the temperature of 44 C. Although there are cretain points peculiar to heat testicle, yet finally the testicle is atrophied, as in the cases of ligatures and X-ray applications. The excess of heat over the curve of heat testicle brings the Sertoli's cells to a partial or complete destruction and if the heat is still higher the interstitial cells are affected. On the other hand, if the temperature or the time remains below the curve, a part or all of the spermatogonies are left intact. I have also investigated the mode of the storing of carmin granules in the heat testicle by making vital stains with lithion-carmin. I observed the histiocytes which entered into the canaliculi of the heat testicle, like that of X-ray testicle, which was found by Mr. Takamori last year.

My experiments showed that epididymis had not been affected by heat.

B. Heat testicle as viewed from preventative medicine

1. Exposure of scrotum to sunlight. When the scrotum of rabbit is exposed to the sunlight in the afternoon from one to three P. M. in July and August, the heat testicle is produced within three hours. If the exposure is made for one hour each day, it requires only four exposures to cause heat testicle. Covering with cotton cloth over the scrotum does not prevent completely.

2. Warm water bathing of scrotum. The total hours are greatly longer to cause a complete heat testicle by subjecting to a certain temperature for each day or with a certain interval for less time than the curve of heat testicle, than subjecting it to the same temperature but with the time of the curve of heat testicle. In the other words, the minimum time to bring about the heat testicle by one continuous application is shorter than the total hours of interrupted applications with the same temperature. It is very important to fix an approximate standard to cause heat testicle by one continuous bath for the people like Japanese who are fond of taking hot water bath. It is found by warm water bathing of rabbit scrotum that the minimum time required for one continuous bathing to cause heat testicle at 44 C. or 45 C. is three hours, while the bath is taken for thirty minutes every day, the total hours to cause the heat testicle being over five hours.

3. When the waist part of rabbit is kept in warm air chamber and the testes is kept at the temperature of 41 C. for nine hours every day a complete heat testicle is produced on the ninth day. Very recently I succeeded in causing heat testicle by subjecting the testes at 40 C.

4. The success of my experiments to cause heat testicle at such a low temperature is vitally important for the further investigation of physiology and pathology of the testes.

5. Exposure of scrotum to arc light. Cotton cloth or lead plate, touching closely to the scrotum can not prevent the action of heat ray, because of their direct conduction of the accumulated heat. It can be avoided by placing a heat absorbent between the source of heat and the scrotum, separating them from each other.

C. Endocrinology of heat testicle.

Rabbit with heat testicles on both sides does not lose its secondary sex characters.

Detailed reports will be made at a later date.

V. Heat Testicles In the Other Mammalian Animals

I have observed the typical heat testicles in dogs, cats, guinea-pigs, rats and goats. The scrotum of rabbit is most convenient for the experiment, but I can say that any testicle in the scrotum can be made heat testicle.

I have a case of a man who had heat testicle. A young man of 22 years old had castration of left testicle with a diagnosis of epididymitis tuberculosa duplex. In the right cauda epididymitis there was an induration and fisture. Scrotum was covered with paraffine with melting point of 60 C. twice a day for one nour. After such treatment having continued for fifty days the fisture disappeared and the induration became smaller. The testicle was very much atrophied, which I think to be heat testicle. Sexual desire came back after the establishment of heat testicle, which had lost until then. A histological examination of a tissue removed from a part of the testicle showed the typical heat testicular pictures histologically.

I wish to take this occasion to pay my respect to Professor Fujinami, head of the Department of Pathology, Kyoto Imperial University. A word of appreciation is due to Professor Hayamai for his kind advices throughout the experiment, and also to Professor Kiyono, whose kindness enables me to obtain carmin for vital stains.

Reprinted from *Amer. J. Physiol.*, **68**, 70–79 (1923)

20

THE SCROTUM AS A TEMPERATURE REGULATOR FOR THE TESTES[1]

CARL R. MOORE AND WM. J. QUICK

From the Hull Zoölogical Laboratory, The University of Chicago

Received for publication December 12, 1923

During the course of the work on sex glands in this laboratory within the last few years, particularly the studies on the testes, we have had forced on our attention the intimate relationship that exists between the scrotum and the testes. Thus in an animal with open inguinal canals (rat, rabbit, guinea pig, etc.) the testes may be periodically drawn into the peritoneal cavity to redescend later into the scrotum; the testes of these animals are normal under such conditions. If, however, the testes are prevented from returning to the scrotum their period of sexual potency is brief indeed. The testes of a guinea pig may be so retained by sewing shut the internal opening of the inguinal canal, by a slight suture of the testis to the peritoneum without closing the canals, or by cutting the very slight mesenterial-like connection of the lower part of the epididymis to the bottom of the scrotal sac, thus allowing the testis to remain free in the peritoneal cavity with the inguinal canals open. Following the latter procedure the testis, in some cases, returns to the scrotum; more often, however, it remains free in the abdomen without adhesions, with its blood vessels, nerve supply and vas deferens intact. Peritoneal retention is rapidly fatal to the generative tissues and in a brief course of time the testis is histologically typical of the naturally occurring cryptorchid or undescended testes such as have been described for the pig, sheep, horse, man and other mammals.

The germinal epithelium of a guinea pig testis is found to be highly disorganized after retention within the peritoneal cavity from five to seven days. Many times the germinal epithelium is so completely degenerate in fifteen to twenty days that the seminiferous tubules have been reduced to a single layer of poorly stained cells occupying a position immediately within the basement membrane. These have usually been considered to be Sertoli cells and not germinal cells in the strict sense, though it appears probable that some of these cells are in reality

---

[1] This investigation has been aided by a grant from the Committee on Sex Research of the National Research Council; grant administered by F. R. Lillie.

70

spermatogonia.   The intertubular tissue usually becomes decidedly prominent after one month; at three or four months' retention within the abdominal cavity the space between the atrophic seminiferous tubules is packed with interstitial cells (Leydig cells).   The testes do not regain functional activity as long as they remain in the peritoneal cavity, but should they return to the scrotum functional activity may be resumed; in animals possessing a scrotal sac the testes may fail to descend, in which case they are always sterile.   The limit of degeneration after which recovery is no longer possible has not been determined, but testes in which the epithelium is reduced to a single layer of cells next the basement membrane have been found to reconstitute normal tubules within a few months after being returned to the scrotum by operative procedures.

The testis-scrotal relationship is again emphasized by a study of testis grafts.   In brief it may be said that out of more than one hundred testis grafts none have been found that contained spermatozoa excepting those that had been transplanted onto the walls of the scrotal sac (tunica vaginalis) and therefore within the scrotum (for further details of this see (2), (3)).   What, then, is the nature of this delicate relationship that exists between the generative part of the testis and the scrotum?

By a process of elimination it appears that the causal factor for degeneration must reside in a differential temperature relationship between the testis and its environment, the environmental temperature being under the control of the scrotum.   Crew (4) has advanced the idea that higher temperatures might account for the aspermatic condition of undescended testes.   Moore (2), (3) has interpreted the results of experimental cryptorchidism on this basis, there being no other factor that would explain the conditions encountered, and Moore and Oslund (5), (6) have gone a considerable way in giving actual proof that the temperature relationship is the correct explanation.

The scrotum is an outpouching of the skin lined by a thin membrane that has been derived from the peritoneum—the tunica vaginalis; in the rodent, in particular, this connection with the peritoneum has not been severed.   The scrotal skin is very thin and well supplied with sweat glands; there is an absence of subcutaneous fat; the muscle layer is extremely thin and the blood vessels of the testis are distributed profusely over its surface.   It is well known that the character of the scrotum varies with different temperatures.   In high temperatures it relaxes to as full a pendent condition as the size will permit whereas in lower temperatures it is contracted, greatly thickened, and the testes are drawn more closely to the body.   Thus on hot days the rat scrotum is relatively huge in size and may protrude considerably in a post-anal position, whereas on cold days it may be so much reduced as to pass unnoticed except on very close examination; indeed the testes on such occasions are more abdominal than scrotal. We see in such an arrangement the physical possibilities of a regulator of temperature and it is on such an assumption that our procedures have been based.

If the scrotum does possess such important regulatory capacities as controlling the environmental temperature of the testes, and the latter depend upon such a control for their well-being, it would appear that proper covering or external insulation from heat loss would cause the germinal cells to degenerate. This has actually been found to hold for the sheep by Moore and Oslund. By secure, though loose, encapsulation of the scrotum in woolen materials for a period of less than three months, the testes were found to have been so seriously affected that spermatozoa were entirely absent; many seminiferous tubules had lost their germinal epithelium and all were in various stages of degeneration; no spermatozoa were present. The type of degeneration was very similar to that found in testes that had only shortly before been forcibly retained within the peritoneal cavity.

Up to this point in the accumulated evidence of the temperature relationships and degeneration, it had merely been assumed that the actual temperature in the scrotum was less than that in the peritoneal cavity, and that the lower scrotal temperature was due to the regulatory capacities of the latter structure. Investigation has proved this assumption to be a reality. We have measured directly, and at the same moment, the peritoneal temperature and the scrotal temperature and find that the scrotal temperature is consistently, indeed without exception, lower than the peritoneal temperature. An account of these observations follows.

Observations. Our investigations have been limited to animals from which we have derived the gradual chain of evidence that has pointed out the physiological relationship existing between the testes and the scrotum: i.e., the guinea pig, rat and rabbit. In each of these animals the inguinal canals are open and ready access is had from the peritoneal cavity into the cavity of the scrotum.

We have been more concerned with relative than with absolute temperatures and have, therefore, employed only simple procedures. To obtain absolute temperatures would involve the use of more complicated procedures and apparatus such as thermo-couples. In brief, our methods have been as follows: The animal was securely fastened to a table; two small abdominal areas were shaved, sterilized and locally anesthetized; apertures of sufficient size to admit the bulb of a relatively sensitive thermometer were made through the body wall and peritoneum, one slightly above the other in the mid-ventral line. We have avoided a general anesthesia as this is known to interfere with the normal heat regulating capacities of the body. For temperature records we employed two 50°C.

thermometers, graduated to one-tenth of a degree. The temperature readings on each thermometer were taken at one or two minute intervals until they were approximately constant for the peritoneum. At the desired moment the lower thermometer, without removing the bulb from the body cavity, was slanted sufficiently for the bulb to pass through the open inguinal canal alongside the testis into the scrotum (saccus vaginalis). Readings of scrotal temperatures and peritoneal temperatures were continued for a few minutes only. The scrotal thermometer was then redrawn into the peritoneal cavity and readings taken until the two thermometers again registered the peritoneal temperature for a short time. We did not prolong the time unnecessarily in order to register the lowest possible temperature in the scrotum. In any observation the animal was off the table within thirty minutes from the beginning of the experiment. At the end, both thermometers were removed, and with a single stitch the apertures in the body wall were closed. In every case the animal recovered from the experiment without any indication of discomfort. Temperature readings of the scrotal thermometer were not only controlled by peritoneal readings on the same thermometer before and after its period in the scrotum, but the upper thermometer as well recorded a control peritoneal temperature throughout the entire observation.

We very soon appreciated the influence of external room temperatures and we have, therefore, carried out the procedures at different room temperatures varying from 37°C. to 14°C.

It was a surprise to find not only such a marked difference between the peritoneal temperature and the scrotal temperature at the same moment but also to find such a great variation of these differences in the different type of animal used for the observation. The white rat gave the greatest difference between the temperatures of the two localities, the rabbit the least, with the guinea pig taking an intermediate position in this respect. In the rat, observed at an external room temperature of 14°C., a difference of 7.5°C. was found to exist between the peritoneal cavity and the cavity of the scrotum. Table 1 is one set of readings taken as recorded in our notebook; other representative observations for the three different animals are expressed in the form of a curve (see figs. 1 and 2). Here the ordinates represent degrees in Centigrade and the abscissae the time of the experiment in minutes; as constructed the curves represent the relative temperatures within the two cavities at the same moment.

It should be emphasized that no exceptions to the above conditions have been found; in each animal observed the scrotal temperature was found to be lower than that of the peritoneal cavity. So far we have not made observations on animals in which the scrotal cavity (saccus vaginalis) was separate from the peritoneal cavity—i.e., with the inguinal canals closed. One would suppose, however, that insofar as the two cavities would be more completely removed from each other, the temperature difference would be even greater than where the open connections exist between them.

DISCUSSION. We believe the observations recorded above complete the chain of evidence, many links of which have only recently been added, that points very definitely to the function of the scrotum as a local regulator of temperature for the testis. Within the peritoneal cavity where the temperature is higher than their normal environmental temperature, the testes rapidly degenerate and do not regain a normal condition as long as they are so situated; if, however, they are returned to the scrotum

TABLE 1

Young adult guinea pig

TIME	DEGREES CENTIGRADE	
	Lower thermometer	Upper thermometer
5:03 p.m.	35.9	35.81
5:05	36.85	36.15
5:07	37.1	37.09
5:09	37.5	37.3
5:11	37.6	37.4
5:13	37.5	38.1
5:15	37.9	37.9
Lower thermometer inserted into scrotum		
5:17	36.85	38.21
5:19	36.1	38.3
5:21	36.1	38.3
Lower thermometer redrawn into peritoneal cavity		
5:23	37.85	38.35
5:25	38.05	38.51
5:27	38.3	38.53
Room temperature	30.85	30.9

even after having lost a vast majority of the generative tissue, they will recover and again produce normal germ cells. So far only scrotal grafts of mammalian testis have proven capable of differentiating spermatozoa. A peculiar testis-scrotal relationship seems necessary for complete germ cell differentiation.

On the other hand, a scrotum insulated externally against loss of heat leads to testicular degeneration. No other explanation for this fact is apparent than on the basis of an interference in the thermo-regulatory function of the scrotum. Furthermore, the proof that higher temperatures are fatal to the generative tissues is given from actual observations on the effect of the local application of higher temperatures to the scrotum (7), (8). Heat applied to the scrotum externally *in one application* pro-

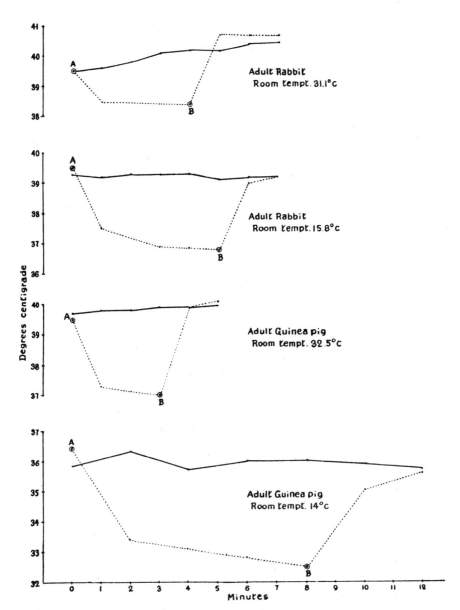

Fig. 1. Graphs showing temperature of peritoneal cavity in comparison with temperature of scrotum in the rabbit and guinea pig, at different room temperatures. In each case (fig. 2 also) the peritoneal cavity temperature (*upper thermometer*) is indicated by a solid line.   At point A, lower thermometer pushed into scrotum alongside testis; decline in temperature indicated by dotted line.   At point B, lower thermometer retracted into peritoneal cavity; temperature increase follows.

duces partial or complete tubular degeneration.   Finally, we have shown
that the actual normal scrotal temperature is appreciably lower than the

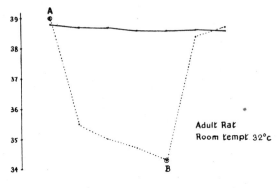

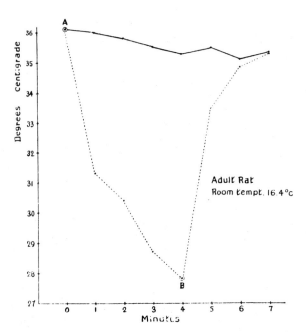

Fig. 2. Graphs showing peritoneal cavity temperature in comparison with scrotal
temperature in the white rat, at different room temperatures. Procedures and
temperature changes indicated as in figure 1.

peritoneal temperature, and that the difference becomes greater as the
external temperature falls.   In nature this is compensated for by scrotal
contraction, thus drawing the testes nearer the body of the animal; a

warmer environment leads to the reverse adjustment and the scrotum becomes more pendent, thinner, and farther removed from the body.

We thus have an explanation on a simple thermo-regulator basis for such conditions of the testes as are found in cryptorchidism (normal or experimental) or the effects that have been reported for vasectomy (9), and for many other conditions causing testicular degeneration. We do not, however, claim to account for all tubular degeneration on this basis for there still remain those conditions such as x-ray treatment, vitamine deficiencies, etc., concerning which evidence is lacking as to temperature phenomena.

We believe also that the evidence is sufficient to assign to the scrotum the function of a temperature regulator for the testes. Cunningham (10, p. 147) has said "Various causes have been suggested for the formation of the scrotum, but no one has ever been able to suggest a use for it." Now that a function has been suggested, if indeed not actually demonstrated for it, in those animals equipped with such a structure, it should be recalled that various graded conditions are found even in its production. The necessity for such a control of temperature must be limited to the mammalian group, as these alone possess a scrotum. Is it not intimately correlated or perhaps indispensably bound up with the entire evolution of the mammalian group?

Several members of the group are able to exist without such a mechanism. The monotremata show no approach to such a condition. Here the reptilian position of the testis is retained; the testes are located in the vicinity of the kidneys. In many forms there is definite indication that the descent of the testis has been a gradual process. In some it has descended into the pelvis and in fact may lie in a small depression—not a real pendent projection—on the anterior abdominal wall (bats, sloth, etc.). Practically all the aquatic mammals lack a scrotum and even such members as the elephant, hyrax and others have not found such a definite structure necessary. A further step in its development is seen in rodents wherein the scrotum is but an outpouching of the peritoneum covered by a thin layer of skin, an open connection with the peritoneal cavity being retained. The final mammalian condition is a complete separation of the saccus vaginalis from peritoneum by closure of the inguinal canals.

In the lower mammals the need for or, if it be so preferred, the adaptation to, the thermo-regulatory capacity of the scrotum, appears either not to exist, or to be compensated for by an inherent difference, perhaps related to actual temperature variations.

The various stages in the development of a definite scrotum may well be associated with the position of the testes in relation to the anterior abdominal wall. Some animals have a somewhat less thick skin of the body wall where the testis rests against it and it is possible that adjustment to temperature may be made in this way. We have observed that a thermometer in the peritoneal cavity with the bulb against the anterior abdominal wall registers an appreciably lower temperature than another one whose bulb is buried in the viscera. A comparison of all mammalian body temperatures, and the extremes of its variation, correlated with the testis and scrotal condition would be extremely interesting. Since we found an appreciably lower peritoneal temperature in contact with the anterior abdominal wall of a rat, there are good grounds for believing that it would be possible to so graft a testis underneath the skin, i.e., outside of the scrotum, that germ cell differentiation might be complete. In subcutaneous grafts of guinea pig testes seminiferous tubules have been found with active spermatogenesis in progress and an epithelium almost normal (see fig. 2, Moore (11) p. 380), but to date no subcutaneous grafts have been observed to contain spermatozoa differentiated in the transplant.

It appears somewhat idle to speculate upon the inherent causes of the production of such a structure as the scrotum, and it is not our particular desire to attempt to account for it upon any specific evolutionary hypothesis. Cunningham (10) has devoted considerable discussion to an explanation of its evolution on a Lamarkian basis. However, the apparent parallelism existing between its gradual acquisition and that of the rise of the female mammalian condition, placental gestation, appears somewhat striking and one could well suppose that the acceptance of an explanation of ·one condition would also serve for the other. In each newly developed characteristic—scrotal origin, and placental gestation— the change has been a gradual one from reptilian to higher mammalian types, with distinct steps easily recognized. Neither condition is indicated in the lowest mammal group, the monotremata. Marsupials present an approach to placentation, and higher groups show graded stages in the perfection of the condition. The birds, in respect to both testicular descent and placenta, are to be excluded entirely from consideration; obviously the testes in this group are not so heat-susceptible as the testes of mammals.

Whatever the conditions may have been that necessitated the origin and development of such a thermo-regulator condition for the testes as appears without question to exist, or whatever its relationship to the evolution of the mammalian group may have been, we are made aware of an extremely interesting, and beautifully correlated mechanism that is not without some practical application from the eugenics point of view.

SUMMARY AND CONCLUSIONS

1. We have demonstrated that the temperature on the inside of the scrotum is decidedly lower than that of the peritoneal cavity at the same moment.

2. The difference in the temperature of the two cavities varies as the external environmental temperature varies.

3. A needed link in the chain of evidence that seminiferous tubule degeneration in cryptorchid testes, natural or experimental, is due to the effects of an abnormally high peritoneal cavity temperature as compared with that of the scrotum or the normal environmental temperature for the testes, has been added.

4. We believe the evidence presented is sufficient to warrant the conclusion that physiologically the scrotum is a local thermo-regulator for the testes, and inferentially we see the possibilities of its having contributed materially to the evolution of the mammalian group.

BIBLIOGRAPHY

(1) MOORE: Anat. Rec., 1923, xxiv, 382.
(2) MOORE: Anat. Rec., 1923, xxv, 142.
(3) MOORE: Science, 1924, 59, 41.
(4) CREW: Journ. Anat., 1922, lvi, 98.
(5) MOORE AND OSLUND: Anat. Rec., 1923, 26, 343. Proc. Soc. Zoöl.
(6) MOORE AND OSLUND: This Journal, 1924, 67, 595.
(7) MOORE AND CHASE: Anat. Rec., 1923, 26, 344. Proc. Soc. Zoöl.
(8) FUKUI: The Japan Medical World, 1923, iii, 27.
(9) OSLUND: This Journal, 1924, 67, 422.
(10) CUNNINGHAM: Hormones and heredity, 1921.
(11) MOORE: Journ. Exper. Zoöl., 1921, xxxiii.

Reprinted from *J. Expt. Zool.*, **49**, 459–462, 489–499 (1927)

21

THE INFLUENCE OF HIGH TEMPERATURE ON THE GUINEA-PIG TESTIS

HISTOLOGICAL CHANGES AND EFFECTS ON REPRODUCTION[1]

WILLIAM C. YOUNG

Hull Zoölogical Laboratory, The University of Chicago

TEN FIGURES

CONTENTS

INTRODUCTION

Adequate demonstration has been given by Prof. Carl R. Moore, of this laboratory, that normal mammalian testes undergo rapid degeneration when they are removed from their normal scrotal position to the abdominal cavity (Moore, '23), and that such testes will regain normal spermatogenetic function only if they are replaced in the scrotum by operative procedure (Moore, '24 a). It has been shown that abdominal temperatures are higher than scrotal temperatures (Moore and Quick, '23, '24), and proof appears conclusive that the degeneration is a consequence of the high temperature. Moore was able, therefore, to ascribe to the scrotum the functional significance of a thermal regulator of testicular temperature. If its regulatory function is masked by insulation (Moore and Oslund, '24), or if hot water is run over the

[1] This work was aided by a grant from the Committee on Sex Research of the National Research Council; grant administered by F. R. Lillie.

459

scrotum (Moore, 24 b; Fukui, '23 a, b), degenerative changes similar to those occurring after abdominal elevation are produced. It is evident, therefore, that germinal epithelium is very sensitive to high temperature.

Although the general features of degenerative changes in the heat-injured testis were familiar, many details of the histological changes, as well as possibilities of recovery of function, had not been determined. In addition, it would be of particular interest to determine the effects of the injury upon the reproductive capacity. This should be accomplished relatively easily by subjecting the animals to a heat treatment that would certainly destroy the germinal tissues wholly or in part, and mating them subsequently and frequently with normal females. Effects of the treatment could then be determined from the outcome of the matings.

The guinea-pig has served as the experimental animal in this study, and the heat was applied by running water, raised a few degrees above that of normal body temperature, over the scrotum. Exposures (time and temperature considered) which appeared optimum in one application were employed. The histological changes and observations on subsequent breeding capacity form the body of this paper. Such a study was suggested by Prof. Carl R. Moore, and I am indebted to him for his supervision, suggestions, and constructive criticism.

MATERIAL AND METHODS

The animals used had been raised in our local animal colony and varied in weight from 525 to 740 grams. Of the ninety males treated, five died before the termination of the experiment. The data forming the basis of this report were obtained from the other eighty-five.

Two methods of bathing the scrota were employed. The first was a slight modification of that used previously by Moore ('24 b). After the fur had been trimmed from the perineal region, the animal to be treated was given a light ether anaesthesia and tied on a board, the ventral surface facing upward. Water at the desired temperature was poured over the surface of the scrotum from a rubber siphon which led from a supply tank with a capacity of 50 liters. A sort of cup was formed around the scrotum by the partly folded hand producing a small reservoir of water about it. The temperature of the water was controlled within a variation of 0.5°C. A second method, somewhat more favorable, was to submerge the scrotum of a slightly anaesthetized animal in a container of warmed water, adequately controlled in temperature. This involved wetting the hind legs and a small part of the ventral posterior surface, but no effect was ever noticed on these parts. The two methods produced equivalent testicular changes, but since the former tended at times to cause a swelling of the penis and to prevent immediate copulation, the latter was employed more frequently.

Exposures of 46° for thirty minutes and 47° for fifteen minutes were found to cause an almost if not complete degeneration and desquamation of germinal epithelium and were employed most frequently.

At varying times after the hot-water application, one testis was removed and preserved for study, and the second allowed to remain for a longer time. This procedure offers several advantages. First, a comparative histological study of two testes removed at different times in the experimental history of an animal can be made. Secondly, twice as many testes in various conditions of change can be studied as would otherwise be possible with the same number of animals. Thirdly, this procedure helps in determining the process and time relationships in degeneration and recovery by enabling the worker to compare the first testis removed by operation with the second removed later at autopsy.

Testes were removed at frequent intervals from one hour until one year after the treatment. The most complete series comprises 105 testes removed 1, 3, 6, 9, 12, 18, 24, 36, and 48 hours, 3, 6, 9, 12, 15, 21, 30, 45, 60, and 75 days, and 3, 4, 6, and 12 months following an exposure of 46° for thirty minutes. From four to twelve testes were removed at each time interval represented from three to sixty days.

All operations were performed under ether anaesthesia and aseptic conditions. An incision was made in the scrotal sac, blood vessels ligated, and the testis and epididymis removed. Not a single case of infection followed any operation, and recovery was immediate in every case. At the time of testis removal, the external appearance of the testis and epididymis was recorded as well as the testis diameter and the presence or absence, relative abundance and condition of sperm in the epididymis.

Testis and epididymis were then dropped into freshly made Bouin's fixative, and within a few minutes divided into three pieces by cross-section to insure better fixation. After dehydration and embedding in paraffin, sections were cut 6 μ in thickness, mounted, and stained, one set with Harris' hematoxylin and eosin and another with iron hematoxylin and orange G. A few testes were sectioned at different levels, but it was soon found that sections through the center of the organ give a satisfactory picture of conditions toward either pole, and the majority of the testes were so sectioned.

Epididymides attached to more than fifty testes removed from one hour until sixty days following the treatment were sectioned and stained with Harris' hematoxylin without a counterstain.

DISCUSSION

Several aspects of the histological changes in the heat-injured guinea-pig testis and effects on reproduction justify further elaboration.

The first concerns the differential susceptibility of cell types—a feature which was conspicuous almost immediately after the treatment and which was noted also by Hart ('22), Fukui ('23 b), and Stieve ('23) following exposure to high temperature, and by numerous other workers who have studied testicular degeneration caused by other factors. Examples are: Mason ('26), following a purified food ration; Siperstein ('21) and Lindsay and Medes ('26), following inanition; Maximow ('99), following injury; Allen ('19) and Arlitt and Wells ('17), following alcohol feeding, and Bergonié and Tribondeau ('04), following x-ray treatments.

It will be recalled, from experiments previously described, that the large primary spermatocytes, secondary spermatocytes, and young spermatids are pycnotic within three hours after the heat treatment. Furthermore, it is only after these cells have fused to form the multinucleated giant cells that other cells are visibly affected. Then, progressing toward the mature sperm, the older spermatids become pycnotic, while subsequently, between eighteen and twenty-four hours, the sperm themselves become altered by apparent condensation. In the opposite direction cells less advanced in their development are likewise found to be increasingly resistant. The early growth stages of primary spermatocytes are more resistant than the large form and the bulk of the spermatogonia most resistant of all. There is, then, a high point of susceptibility centering among the large primary spermatocytes, secondary spermatocytes, and young spermatids, and low points among spermatogonia on one side and spermatozoa on the other.

It is not intended to compare the more resistant cells lying on each side of the apex of susceptibility with one another except to point out that spermatogonia, which, in part at least, are the only cells to retain their normal appearance and position within the testis, are considered to be the most resistant.

An explanation for this differential susceptibility can only be conjectured. The suggestion is made on the basis of work done by Child ('24) that the state of the germ cells at the time of treatment may be of fundamental importance. It will be recalled that, with the exception of a few spermatogonia, the first cells to be affected, namely, the large primary spermatocytes immediately prior to division, the ephemeral secondary spermatocytes, and the newly formed spermatids recently out of mitosis, are probably the most active cells in the testis. It will be recalled, further, that some primary spermatocytes and some spermatids are consistently susceptible, while others are consistently resistant—a condition which can be attributed to differences in state, but not to differences in type. Lastly, the susceptibility becomes lower as spermatozoa are approached in one direction, and the relatively quiescent spermatogonia in the other. There is suggested, therefore, a temperature-susceptibility gradient for developing male germ cells which is related not to the course of germ-cell development, but to the state of the germ cells during their development.

No support, either for the order of germ-cell degeneration given here or for the theory proposed to account for it, is found in other accounts of high temperature effects on the testis. With the exception of the work of Bergonié and Tribondeau ('04) on x-rayed rats and Allen ('19) on alcoholized rats, the same seems to be generally true in accounts of testicular degeneration following injury by other factors. As far as degeneration following heat injury is concerned, one would infer from Stieve's paper that, in the mouse testis, spermatids are the most susceptible cells and spermatogonia the most resistant. Fukui says, with reference to the rabbit: "The generative cells are destroyed gradually by turns from the most differentiated spermatids to the youngest element, spermatogonia," and in another place, "The spermatozoon is the most resistant of all spermatogenous elements against heat." In the absence of the details of their experimental procedure, no definite cause can be assigned for this difference in opinion. It seems possible, however, that the order of germ-cell degeneration given by them can be explained by the condition of the testis at the end of seventy-two hours.

It will be remembered that at this time very few, if any, of the degenerated large primary spermatocytes, secondary spermatocytes, and young spermatids are present in a recognizable condition, the bulk having been apparently chromolyzed and removed. Consequently, the conspicuous forms are pycnotic older spermatids, condensed and normal appearing spermatozoa, primary spermatocytes of the younger and apparently more resistant generation, spermatogonia, and Sertoli cells. It is entirely possible that anyone looking at such a section would conclude the order of degeneration to be spermatids, spermatocytes, spermatogonia and Sertoli cells. Without a complete histological series of testes removed at frequent intervals preceding this time, one would not realize, except perhaps by the conspicuous paucity of cells, that two types of cells had disappeared entirely. It is this condition, therefore, which may explain the order of degeneration given by Fukui and Stieve. The difference is not believed attributable to the animals they used.

A second feature of germ-cell degeneration following the heat treatment concerns the epididymal sperm. The progressive disappearance of sperm from the proximal toward the distal end of this organ, noted by Lawrence and again in this study, has been mentioned. Likewise, the apparent normal reproductive capacity of sperm ejaculated during the first seven days after the heat application has been mentioned. An explanation for these phenomena is suggested by the work of Benoit ('25) and Stigler ('18). The latter, in reviewing literature on the physiology of the epididymis, points out, first, the determination of earlier workers that sperm are activated as they pass through its passages, and, secondly, the assignment of this activating influence to secretory products of the epithelial cells lining the tubule. He concluded that secretions from these cells are protective against heat and that resistance of sperm to heat increases as they pass through the tubule. Evidence for the first conclusion, that epididymal sperm are more resistant to heat than sperm still contained in the testis, comes from an experiment in which sperm from fragments of epididymis and testis were added to slightly alkaline salt solutions and heated. Sperm from the testis became heat rigid at a lower temperature and after a shorter exposure than those from the epididymis. Evidence for his second conclusion, that the resistance of sperm to heat increases as they progress through the epididymis, seems lacking. The theory is interesting in relation to the facts of this study, but its validity must be tested by additional experiments.

The conditions under which recovery of reproductive function takes place and the time required constitute a third feature for discussion. It has already been pointed out that, generally, spermatogonia which survive the heat treatment were found to be the stem cells for an entirely normal appearing epithelium which extends itself gradually throughout the testis. It has been pointed out also that the capacity for fertilization may be regained as early as the fifty-sixth day following the treatment, although, more commonly, this time is about the seventy-fifth day. The conclusion that a new germinal epithelium can arise from spermatogonia surviving a heat treatment is not new, Fukui ('23 b) having made the same observation. But it is clear, from study of the testes from the few animals which did not recover reproductive function within nine months, that there must be prerequisites for recovery other than surviving spermatogonia. As has been indicated, the right testes removed from these animals from one to three months after the treatment each contain a normal epithelium and sperm in a few tubules on one side. No sperm are to be seen in either epididymis. The left testes, removed six months later, show no change from this condition. A few tubules in the same relative location still contain an epithelium with sperm, and no sperm are to be found in the epididymis. It is assumed that excessive tubular atrophy and Sertoli-cell destruction prevented recovery beyond that noted. It is not known what prevented the sperm which were formed during this time from reaching the epididymis and eventually affecting fertilization.

A comparison of the time of the return of spermatogenetic function as determined from these experiments with the time of recovery, estimated previously by Moore ('24 a, '26), is of interest. The latter determined that abdominally confined prepubertal testes will develop a normal germinal epithelium within less than ninety days after return to the scrotum and that abdominally confined adult testes will regenerate a normal epithelium within seventy-four days. In this experiment the capacity for fertilization regained by two males on about the fifty-sixth day after treatment is in close agreement with the histological observation that sperm are again being produced by the forty-fifth day. It would seem likely, therefore, that sperm may become differentiated before seventy-four days in the class of cases with which Moore dealt, as well as following the heat injury by external hot-water applications.

The effect of the heat treatment on reproduction likewise deserves further consideration. The differential susceptibility of different cell types is emphasized by a survey of the breeding records. The production of offspring from sperm present at the time of treatment surely attests to the resistance of these cells. Likewise, the subsequent high percentage of sterile matings is clearly attributable to the complete destruction of the highly susceptible spermatocytes and spermatids from which sperm would normally have developed. Finally, the regained capacity for normal fertilization, traceable to sperm developed from spermatogonia which survived the exposure, can be taken as an indication of the resistance of spermatogonia to heat. At the same time, no cell type seems to have been wholly immune to some effect. The occurrence of sterile matings very soon after the heat treatment demonstrates clearly that sperm are destroyed, and the failure of three animals to recover reproductive function must be attributable to a general destruction of spermatogonia.

The hesitancy to conclude that the pregnancies terminated by abortion and stillbirth are consequences of the heat injury is based chiefly on comparison of individual breeding histories. Apparently anomalous situations are seen to exist when this is done. For example, the succession of abnormal pregnancies in the histories of males nos. 44 and 45 suggest some injury to sperm contained in the epididymis at the time of treatment. The breeding histories of males nos. 77 and 82, on the contrary, would indicate a strong resistance in spite of abnormalities which appeared subsequently in the histories of both animals and in spite of the complete testicular degeneration known to have occurred in the case of male no. 77.

The same anomalous situation is seen to exist with respect to the condition after recovery of reproductive function. The consecutive normal pregnancies toward the end of the breeding histories of males nos. 45, 65, and 61 would indicate that the capacity of spermatogonia to produce normal sperm had not been altered. On the other hand, the records of males nos. 44, 77, and 60 would indicate that sperm developed from spermatogonia which survived the exposure were not normal. If such data are interpreted to indicate that all types of germ cells may be injured in such a way that abnormal pregnancies are caused, it is not understood why an injurious effect of the heat treatment should not have been evident throughout a breeding history as well as during only one part of it. No explanation is suggested by the histological data; in fact, it would seem, from what is known about the condition of testes from these animals at the end stage of degeneration, that male no. 61 would have been more likely to have shown an abnormal reproductive capacity after recovery than any other animal. The situation may be cleared up by experiments planned for the future.

CONCLUSIONS

1. When water heated to 46° or 47° is run over the guinea-pig scrotum for thirty minutes or for fifteen minutes, respectively, a degeneration of the germinal epithelium begins immediately and continues until the end of about twelve days. By this time, a complete evacuation of germinal epithelium, with the exception of some spermatogonia and Sertoli cells, has occurred. The degeneration is characterized by pycnosis and hyperchromatosis followed by a fusion of individual cell types to form multinucleated giant cells. Many degenerating cells chromolyze and are apparently liquefied in situ; others are carried into the epididymis where the same fate is undergone.

2. During this time the order of germ-cell degeneration is observed to be definite. Large primary spermatocytes, secondary spermatocytes, young spermatids, and a few sperma-

togonia are affected first. Subsequently, the older spermatids, spermatozoa within the seminiferous tubules, and early
growth stages of primary spermatocytes are affected. In
cases of severe injury, most of the spermatogonia may be
loosened from their natural position and destroyed. These
cells are considered to be the most resistant of the germinal
elements. Sertoli cells and interstitial cells are considered
to be the most resistant of all testicular elements.

3. The order of germ-cell degeneration is concluded to be
in no relation to the order of germ-cell formation, but, presumably, in relation to their state at the time of treatment;
the more active cells being the first to undergo degenerative
changes.

4. Some epididymal sperm are very resistant to heat injury
and as much as thirty-one days after the treatment are
capable of taking part in fertilizations which are followed by
apparently normal litters. Others seem less resistant, however, for, in less than twenty-four hours after the treatment,
sperm in the proximal end of this organ start to degenerate
and disappear, apparently by liquefaction. Subsequently,
sperm in the more distal portion of the tubule undergo the
same fate. These facts would seem to support the suggestion, not made in this paper, that the epididymis exerts a protective influence on sperm against heat which increases their
resistance to high temperature as they pass through its tubule.

5. Recovery of spermatogenetic function seems dependent
upon the survival of spermatogonia. About the time of complete germ-cell evacuation, the first reconstructive changes
become apparent. The surviving spermatogonia become
active mitotically and are the stem cells for a normal-appear-
ing germinal epithelium, complete in some tubules and producing sperm by the forty-fifth day following the treatment.
The extent of the regenerated area increases gradually until
approximately six months after the treatment, by which time
regeneration is complete throughout the testis, save for those
tubules lining the exposed side which underwent excessive
atrophy.

6. Frequent observed matings of nineteen males used in the histological study, during periods ranging from fifty-six days to one year following the treatment, provided a means of studying the effect of the treatment on reproduction. The breeding histories were observed to be divided into four periods, readily identifiable with histological changes.

7. The most pronounced effect on reproductive capacity was the increase in sterile matings which reached a peak between the forty-fourth and the seventy-fifth day, during which time there was usually an absence or a greatly reduced number of sperm in consequence of the complete destruction of the highly susceptible spermatocytes and spermatids at the time of treatment. The frequency of pregnancies terminated by abortion and stillbirth, which followed matings made subsequent to the tenth day after the treatment and which persisted to a somewhat less extent through the third and fourth months of the average breeding history, may likewise be attributable to the heat injury. Comparison of the individual breeding records casts doubt upon this suggestion, however, and any conclusion must be reserved until this aspect of the problem has received additional attention.

8. Recovery of spermatogenetic function was followed by recovery of reproductive function in sixteen out of nineteen males. The regained capacity for fertilization was characterized by a decrease in the proportion of sterile matings. In three males there was recovery of spermatogenesis in a few tubules, but sperm did not reach the epididymis for some reason which has not been determined. These animals remained permanently sterile.

9. At no time was there any effect on the sexual vigor of any male.

BIBLIOGRAPHY

ALLEN, EZRA 1919 Degeneration in the albino rat testis due to a diet deficient in the water-soluble vitamine, with a comparison of similar degeneration in rats differently treated, and a consideration of the Sertoli tissue. Anat. Rec., vol. 16, pp. 93–112.

ARLITT, ADA H., AND H. GIDEON WELLS 1917 Effect of alcohol on the reproductive tissues. Jour. Exp. Med., vol. 26, pp. 769–778.

THE JOURNAL OF EXPERIMENTAL ZOÖLOGY, VOL. 49, NO. 2

BENOIT, M. JACQUES 1925 Recherches anatomiques, cytologiques et histophysi-
ologiques sur les voies excrétrices du testicule chez les mammifères.
Thèse pour le Doctorat en Médicine. Strasbourg.

BERGONIÉ, J., AND L. TRIBONDEAU 1904 Action des rayons X sur le testicule du
rat blanc. Comptes Rendus des Séances et Mémoirs de la Société de
Biologuie, vol. 57, pp. 592–595.

CHILD, C. M. 1924 Physiological foundations of behavior. Henry Holt &
Company.

FUKUI, N. 1923 a On a hitherto unknown action of heat ray on testicles.
Japan Med. World, vol. 3.

————— 1923 b On the action of heat rays upon the testicle: An histological, hygienic and endocrinological study. Acta Scholae Medicinalis,
Univ. Imp. in Kioto, vol. 6, fasc. II, pp. 225–258.

HART, C. 1922 Beiträge zur biologische Bedeutung der inner-sekretorischen
Organe. II. Mitteilung. Der Einfluss abnormer Aussentemperaturen
auf Schilddrüse und Hoden. Arch. f. gesamte Physiol., Bd. 196,
S. 151–176.

IBSEN, HERMAN L. 1923 An environmental factor causing variation in weight
at birth of guinea-pigs. Proc. Soc. Zoöl., Anat. Rec., vol. 24, p. 413.

IBSEN, HERMAN L., AND LUELLA SCHAUMBERG 1923 Sex ratios in guinea-pigs.
Proc. Soc. Zoöl., Anat. Rec., vol. 24, p. 412.

LAWRENCE, WALTER 1926 The fate of the germinal epithelium of experimental
cryptorchid testes of guinea-pigs. Biol. Bull., vol. 51, pp. 129–152.

LENHOSSÉK, M. v. 1898 Untersuchungen über Spermatogenese. Arch. f. mik.
Anat., Bd. 51, S. 215–318.

LINDSAY, BLANCHE, AND GRACE MEDES 1926 Histological changes in the testis
of the guinea-pig during scurvy and inanition. Am. Jour. Anat.,
vol. 37, pp. 213–235.

MASON, KARL E. 1926 Testicular degeneration in albino rats fed a purified
food ration. Jour. Exp. Zoöl., vol. 45, pp. 159–229.

MAXIMOW, ALEXANDER 1899 Die histologischen Vorgänge bei der Heilung von
Hodenverletzungen und die Regenerationsfähigkeit des Hodengewebes.
Beit. z. path. Anat., Bd. 26, S. 230–316.

MEVES, F. 1899 Über Struktur und Histogenese der Samenfäden des Meer-
schweinchens. Arch. f. mik. Anat. (Bonn), Bd. 54, S. 329–402.

MOORE, CARL R. 1923 On the relationship of the germinal epithelium to the
position of the testis. Proc. Assn. Anat., Anat. Rec., vol. 25, p. 142.

————— 1924 a Properties of the gonads as controllers of somatic and
psychical characteristics. VI. Testicular reactions in experimental
cryptorchidism. Am. Jour. Anat., vol. 34, pp. 269–316.

————— 1924 b VIII. Heat application and testicular degeneration: the
function of the scrotum. Ibid., vol. 34, pp. 337–358.

————— 1926 Scrotal replacement of experimental cryptorchid testes and
the recovery of spermatogenetic function (guinea pig). Biol. Bull.,
vol. 51, pp. 112–128.

MOORE, CARL R., AND ROBT. OSLUND 1924 Experiments on the sheep-testis
cryptorchidism, vasectomy, and scrotal insulation. Am. Jour. Physiol.,
vol. 67, pp. 595–607.

MOORE, CARL R., AND WM. J. QUICK 1923 A comparison of scrotal and peritoneal temperatures. Proc. Soc. Zoöl., Anat. Rec., vol. 26, p. 344.

——— 1924 The scrotum as a temperature regulator for the testes. Am. Jour. Physiol., vol. 68, pp. 70–79.

REGAUD, CL. 1901 Études sur la structure des tubes séminifères et sur la spermatogénèse chez les mammifères. Arch. d'anat. mic., T. 4, pp. 101–155.

SIPERSTEIN, DAVID M. 1921 The effects of acute and chronic inanition upon the development and structure of the testis in the albino rat. Anat. Rec., vol. 20, pp. 355–381.

STIEVE, H. 1923 Der Einfluss höheren Aussentemperatur auf die Keimdrüsen der Hausmaus. Verhand. d. Anat. Gesell., Bd. 57, S. 38–53.

STIGLER, ROBT. 1918 Der Einfluss des Nebenhodens auf die Vitalität der Spermatozoen. Arch. f. gesamte Physiol., Bd. 171, S. 273–282.

STOCKARD, C. R., AND GEORGE N. PAPANICOLAOU 1917 The existence of a typical oestrous cycle in the guinea-pig—with a study of its histological and physiological changes. Am. Jour. Anat., vol. 22, pp. 225–265.

——— 1919 The vaginal closure membrane, copulation and the vaginal plug in the guinea pig, with further consideration of the oestrous rhythm. Biol. Bull., vol. 37, pp. 222–245.

——— 1918 Further studies on the modification of germ-cells in mammals: The effect of alcohol on treated guinea-pigs and their descendants. Jour. Exp. Zoöl., vol. 26, pp. 119–226.

The Vaginal Diaphragm

VII

Editor's Comments on Papers 22 and 23

The development of the vaginal diaphragm again reflects the unique difficulties that the entire field of contraception has experienced. A German physician by the name of Hasse is generally given credit for inventing the diaphragm in about 1882. Actually a Dr. Freidric Wilde did so in 1838. Hasse, apparently fearful that his reputation would be tarnished were he to publish an article concerning contraception, resorted to the pseudonym, W. P. J. Mensinga. In 1882, he published a short monograph in which he described the diaphragm and in the same year he published the article which has been translated for inclusion here. This article, in my opinion, truly sets the flavor of the times, some 90 years ago. Note that the diaphragm is never mentioned. It is referred to as F. S., which stands for facultative sterility, which means voluntary sterility. The author describes, in heart-rending detail, the tragedy of unwanted pregnancies and children. Then he presents case histories to illustrate how, by the use of F. S., tragedy was averted. Few articles document so vividly the need for contraception. The author, Dr. Hasse, then appends a rather startling section in which he presents case histories purporting to show that coitus interruptus causes nothing short of calamity. He lists a variety of horrendous physical and psychological results of this procedure. No one would argue, if his argument were based on facts, that coitus interruptus is the ideal method but, as previously shown, the supposed unhealthy consequences are myths.

The diaphragm caught on, especially in highly developed countries. For years it has been depended upon by educated and relatively affluent women. For really the first time there was a simple method available which transferred control into their hands. It proved effective, could be put in position well ahead of time and left there for a reasonable period. This provided new freedom of action with the consequences stated by Hasse. The diaphragm is still widely used.

An extremely interesting study was reported by Johnson and Masters in 1962. Johnson and Masters have leaped light years forward in the field of sex. Needless to add that even in the enlightened society of today their methods are not wholly condoned. In the paper reproduced here, Johnson and Masters evaluated the effectiveness of the diaphragm using a very impressive direct procedure. They have developed a technique of artificial coitus. This technique permits properly trained women to experience the entire sexual response including multiple orgasms. In addition, the procedure affords direct observation of the vaginal barrel during the sexual cycle. In the study included here, 30 women used vaginal diaphragms and then went through the sexual cycle in three positions, supine, knee-chest, and female-superior. In the latter position, the artificial technique could not be used and men were substituted. They found that in the supine position only once was the diaphragm displaced. This diaphragm maintenance rate was also observed in the knee-chest position, but in the female-superior position there is considerable danger of displacement, especially if there is multiple mounting, as occurs when the penis escapes the vaginal barrel and is reinserted. This is particularly true if the female enjoys multiple orgasms, during which there is considerable vaginal expansion permitting the diaphragm to become loose and subject to displacement. The fact remains, however, that during the 90 years that the diaphragm has been used, a very high success rate in terms of contraception has been the case.

Translation of *Ueber facultative Sterilität* (1882)

Neuwied & Leipzig
1882.
Published by Louis Meuser

22

On Facultative Sterility viewed from the prophylactic and hygienic point of view for general practitioners

DR. C. HASSE

Introduction

The difficulties general practitioners are often forced to cope with remain mostly unknown to clinicians, who are occupied only with disease, while the former deal with the sick human being. Sympathy cannot be presented in abstract form, but it is a valuable attribute in the general practitioner and family adviser. A student can absorb it only if he has had an opportunity to observe his teacher at work outside the university clinic.

The clinician does not come in contact with the more or less important complaints and concerns of daily life. The patient expresses them often only vaguely to his family doctor, who, practically in a position of a confessor, has to consider them as most significant factors.

This is especially true in regard to the confidential consultation and revelation of marital and extramarital relationships. These may be of a pleasant, but are more frequently of a touching, tragic nature.

Taking into consideration the fact that these confessions are rarely motivated by religious reasons, but rather out of need, out of deep inner suffering, in the search for help, for the general practitioner the solution of such problems may be at times easy, at times complicated or even impossible, so that he might have to seek outside help.

True happiness in marriage depends largely on perfect health of both marriage partners, on the best possible psychological and physical harmony in all phases of life. Where this harmony is endangered, both partners suffer, but the consequences are more tragic and long lasting for their children.

If the children are to prosper, there is a duty to preserve, first of all, the life of the wife and mother. This idea has unfortunately not come to a full realization even now, and a large number of examples could be cited to prove it. Suffice it to say that life insurance companies are trying to avoid covering wives in the childbearing age, although this is not specifically stated. But some companies raise their premium considerably until the change of life (climacteric). Others inform the doctors through their agents, in very clear language, that women are preferably not accepted, etc.

The life of a woman has in fact less value. And yet—a wife is a completely equal marriage partner with the same rights to live and work as the husband.

In the orient, where the woman is considered a slave, a larger morbidity and mortality has no practical significance. But in our civilization, where complete equalization is common, a woman should have the same right to existence as a man.

True, the man has to provide the income, which is often difficult, but the woman has to manage it and keep it together. This is, according to her physical and psychological strength, a completely equal burden and can be even more challenging. In addition, the woman bears the burden of reproduction and of early childhood upbringing. These are extraordinary tasks, especially reproduction, which, for lack of experience, cannot be fully understood by men. Since a woman has socially at least the same duties, she must also have the same rights to life, if not more. If necessary, these rights need to be established.

Emancipation efforts by women, generally modest in their disposition, have brought about strange changes of attitude. Compare the old oriental Jewish prayer! "Thank you, o Lord, that I was not made a woman," to: "Lord, I am satisfied to have been made a woman." This is merely a consequence of the utter disproportion in relation to viability found, when comparing the position of the married woman with that of the man.

In the early years of child-rearing, the father is much more dispensible than the mother, and nobody will contradict this fact. The greatest possible protection against sickness and death must be offered to the more endangered mother. Medical skill will have solved this task completely only when, according to the best knowledge, every danger can be kept away from the irreplaceable life, whether these threats are of physical or social origin.

It is truly a difficult, but noble task, to bring philosophical and physiological science into harmony. Unfortunately the particular branches of the general sciences oppose one another. One-sidedness is the common rule because overwhelming amounts of material have to be tackled. Dogmatism and liberalism fight vigorously these days even in the same discipline. But exclusive science suppresses feelings and emotions, so indispensible to the dignity of man.

We all, at least in Germany, are living in an age of conditioned existence, i.e., with the most exactly measured, barest means of existence. Trying to escape this social law would be ridiculous because it is impossible.

If the physician is faced with situations which are rooted in these facts, the "art of medicine" is obligated to cope with them if it wants to retain its reputation. A pious dogmatism cannot be called an art. To subsist upon existing means without endangering life and health, whatever the situation, brings happiness to the family and consequently also to the state. Fortunate are those who can help to bring this about.

To help his fellow man partake of this happiness, to relieve him of worry and sorrow as far as possible is religion—is a commandment of neighborly love.

To care properly in advance for the well being of a family is not a very lucrative goal for the doctor who works for material gain only. But it is one of the most noble and rewarding tasks for the philanthropist.

For him it is a pleasure to have brought peace and happiness into the home. A warm handshake often expresses more than countless words of thanks and compensates for many an injustice, caused variously by envy, avarice or indolence, even if the helper did not receive a material reward for his endeavors.

Most unfortunate are those distressed situations, where also a lack of food prevails, as happens in almost 80 per cent of all cases. Families are especially hard hit if, in addition, they have to preserve a certain façade because of their social class.

For instance, the doctor is called. The woman has hysterical complaints. Her husband tries, in a seemingly loving way, to ease her complaints, but also criticizes her. With effort, he suppresses a certain irritability. To the doctor, the harmony does not appear genuine. Examination of each partner shows that the husband is nervous, sullen and dissatisfied, the woman ailing and thoroughly unhappy. She is ill, physically and psychologically and "cannot bear such life any longer." They are merely living together, and it is obvious that harmony, common endeavor, and inner feelings for each other no longer exist. Life has become drudgery. And still, the outward appearance of the home shows harmony. Three children, aged 3–6, look well fed but not especially clean. The husband's tobacco container stands close to the wife's sewing box, his favorite cup is placed in her spoon cupboard, his pipe hangs casually under her apron on the wall. Real harmony existed earlier. The sensitive wife bears the more obvious share of sorrow in her unhappiness. However, in spite of all the complaints about her husband, a permanent and impressive patience in her remarks cannot be overlooked. This situation appears to be a puzzle, but the trained eye easily detects an evil that can be traced back to a rather natural cause.

Can we find a remedy for a malady by closing our eyes in a snobbish attitude, or is it better and more human to face, with open eyes and without prejudice, the facts as they present themselves, even if they are not ideal?

Many people speak loftily of humanity, but it is unknown to their hearts since it cannot be comprehended by the intellect alone. This is not an intellectual matter, but simply an emotional one. Frequently we find examples of inhumanity and extreme psychological severity clothed in a scientific, correct, faultless approach of the intellect—and why? Because the individual is, for lack of a solid moral foundation, unable to rise above the pitiful baseness of life, above personal considerations, egoistic endeavors, envy, avarice, or to judge the motives of others objectively, and not according to his own righteous, limited point of view.

Without being indiscreet, I would like to show examples of how violence has been done to humanity by applied doctrine. In the *Arch. f. Gyn.*, Vol. XVIII, issue 2, an authority quotes the necessity of an artificial abortion because the woman lacks the strength to bear a child. Still, he does not want to perform a second abortion. We shall not discuss here what abstract science, according to which it may be correct, has to say about this matter. If, however, artificial abortion because of incapability to bear a child shall not be allowed a second time, then it is just as immoral the first

248

time. If a patient under given circumstances and according to the principles of science cannot live without medical help, this help should not be given to him the first time if he may not expect to receive it the second time.

Suppose N. treats a single woman because of incapability to bear a child, induces an abortion (or will he possibly refuse an abortion in this case?) and surely saves her life in this manner. He warns her not to become pregnant again—then loses contact with the patient. Later she returns, married, in great anxiety, with the same problem. He refuses to help, and the woman dies as a result of this pregnancy. Would it not be proper to sue this doctor for homicide through negligence? Is it human not to help a weak human being if you are able to do so? Is it human to say: "You have not obeyed my rules—now I shall let you die in punishment?" Is that humane? Is that merciful? Are the acknowledged teachings of the prophet of Nazareth to be interpreted in such a way?

An opposite situation to this would be the following case: the physician treats a patient with serious gonorrhea, is successful, but warns him seriously to avoid a new infection. The patient nevertheless appears soon for a second time and asks again with confidence for medical help in the same matter. Will the doctor also refuse to treat him? I don't believe so. But where is the difference? In this case, it is probably not even a question of life and death. In the eyes of this doctor, has the health of a man more value than the life of a woman? There is no end to the contradictions. Enough has been said for now: but we will return to this point later.

The studies in the following pages represent the results of 20 years of experience, the great desire to help and to prevent suspected problems from occurring.

The encounter with so much bitter suffering that many patients experience has caused many a doctor to search for remedies that have not been taught but have to be learned if he wants to practice the art of healing, and not just medical science. It is a challenge to find the cause of a lingering illness, to suppress it and prevent premature death of his patient and preserve the uncurtailed happiness of his existence. Many branches of hygiene and prophylaxis have this goal. But the injurious conditions which can be brought about at delivery or in the postnatal condition and through infant feeding have in general found little consideration. A widely practiced, prohibited conception as such is not the doctor's concern. However, where conservation of an individual's life and health is at stake, facultative sterility is certainly indicated.

I. Sad Experiences.

In order to start immediately with the subject matter, a description of experienced cases in private practice may best illustrate the point.

Many physicians are familiar with the terrible scene of a husband breaking down next to the body of his departed wife, who has died in or after childbirth, leaving him and all their children. He reproaches himself bitterly. He accuses himself as the murderer of this beloved being. They—he and his wife—had been warned in time to avoid further pregnancies. They had followed the advice and had abstained, resisted temptation. Finally, they had forgotten themselves and pregnancy resulted.

Now inexorable death had claimed his wife, the dear indispensable mother. Satisfaction of their sexual desires had such a tragic consequence.

Do cases like this happen often? I firmly believe so. I have myself witnessed several instances and recorded them.

1. Mrs. L. O., 40 years old, suffered during her seventh childbirth from sepsis, metritis and pleuritis, and consequently recovered only gradually. However, a chronic endometritis remained. Due to lack of necessary funds it could be treated only insufficiently and was not completely healed. (She was the wife of a small craftsman.) She was medically advised to avoid further pregnancies. For 18 months abstinence was observed. Her physical condition improved gradually, her vitality returned and abstinence was no longer practiced. A new pregnancy started, the woman felt better now than before, aside from occasional abdominal pains. In her eighth month she suddenly died of a brain embolism, which obviously came from the uterus.

It would be superfluous to repeat here the self-reproaches of her husband, father of seven young children.

2. Mrs. B. S., 36 years old, was the wife of a court official. In her 19th year, she had become ill with dysentery, and never fully recovered, in spite of treatment. She married, delivered two children fairly normally. During her third delivery, she suffered a retroperitonitis with abscess formation and consecutive intestinal strictures, which the attending physician considered a consequence of the earlier dysentery. The remaining adhesions played an important role in the development of the postnatal illness. For five to six years his warning to avoid further pregnancies was heeded. The transfer of this couple to a different climate caused an improvement in the sick woman's state of health. She became pregnant again and her well being left nothing to be desired. During delivery, abdominal pains with unappeasable, vigorous vomiting started. The delivery itself was slowed down by weak labor and entanglement of the umbilical cord. This was diagnosed at the second traction. With the help of forceps, the delivery was successfully accomplished. The child lived. The placenta followed quickly and was complete. But this afforded only temporary relief. In the evening, eight hours later, there followed bilious vomiting, violent pains, liquid in the abdomen. Next morning, hematemesis and copious bloody stools set in; the patient collapsed and died. Here we find the same reaction of the morally destroyed husband, who had lived in perfect harmony with his very refined wife.

3. Mrs. H. B., 32 years old, mother of six children, returned home for health reasons from a tropical climate, where they had stayed for several years. The doctor's advice to observe abstinence was hardly kept for six months. The woman was apparently well. Varicose veins developed during the resulting pregnancy, but otherwise she had no complaints. The last week before delivery she felt particularly well. The strong and healthy child was born two weeks early, but the mother suffered from a sudden attack of convulsions. These fits of eclampsia increased in intensity. During one of the attacks, she was catheterized; the urine was dark brown and coagulated over heat. For 20 hours the patient suffered from these continuous convulsions and died as a result.

The husband reproached himself bitterly, as in the other cases. He gradually lost hold of himself and a few years later left his orphans to his relatives.

4. D. L., 31 years old, delicate fair-haired wife of a doctor, of phthisic background, had given birth to two children. In the two following years the couple abstained, and the woman felt relatively well. When a new pregnancy started, clear symptoms of the feared infection could be observed. The patient complained that the pregnancy was beyond her strength. In the 20th week a premature birth resulted, the morbid change in the lung tips increased rapidly, and 14 weeks post partum death followed. The husband reacted with as much distress as in the preceding cases.

5. B. E. was a laborer, 47 years old, father of 14 children. After the 13th child, abstinence had been recommended, because lack of proper care caused many childhood diseases. The warning was not heeded. After the 14th delivery the mother suffered for a long time from peritonitis. The 15th pregnancy resulted in abortion and serious illness of the mother for several months. The household was in debt before, but grew completely dissolute now. The husband drank more heavily than before and he hanged himself in a fit of melancholia. He left a short letter saying that he was unable to support his family any longer and left it to general charity.

6. G. F., 30 years old, a husky healthy laborer, became ill with pleurisy. His wife, a healthy but hard-working woman had delivered their seventh child. He had overworked trying to relieve the labors and burdens of his brave wife. After his recuperation I warned him to avoid further marital relations, because increasing obligations would drain his strength. The woman gladly accepted this admonition, but he replied that as long he had healthy arms, his family would not suffer any need.

A suggestion to take up life insurance was declined for lack of funds. An eighth pregnancy incited the husband again to work harder than usual. He was determined to fight fate. Again the faithful worker, father and husband became ill with pneumonia after his wife's childbed, and his seemingly indestructible vitality was suddenly crushed—he left his wife and children in poverty.

7. Strictly speaking, the following case does not belong here, because the outcome was not fatal. It is, however, important enough.

D. H., 28 years old, wife of a minister, mother of five children, whose father had died of phthisis, had suffered since her first pregnancy from a chronic severe anemia. It had been treated to this point without results. The treatment of an erosion at the orifus uteri was interrupted by the fifth pregnancy. However, the woman did not have any other important complaints. The atrophic fetus was delivered alive and survived for eight weeks. Twelve days post partum a minor sepsis developed, then a protracted course of illness, and finally recuperation followed. The severe anemia was the suspected cause of sepsis. In the absence of lactation it was feared that another pregnancy could follow soon, so abstinence was recommended. A vacation in a favorable climate was taken, but afterwards no attention was paid to the physician's warning to avoid intercourse. A new pregnancy followed. It was a wretched time for the patient's physical condition. Delivery of the baby took place without complications, but the placenta had to be manually removed under the most subtle, antiseptic, precautionary conditions. A heavy after-bleeding was successfully stopped by injection of a hot 2½ per cent carbolic acid solution. Symptoms of a severe sepsis followed on the second day post partum. The condition seemed hopeless. After a very critical eight-month illness the patient was well enough to leave her bed for a short time. Now the woman herself admitted that another pregnancy would be stretching their luck too far.

Every humane expert will agree that the patients in cases 1 and 2 might still be alive today had the pregnancy been avoided. In case 4, without pregnancy life could have been in any case prolonged. In the fifth and sixth cases, the sad consequences could have been avoided. In the seventh case, the family would have never experienced the terrible worries caused by the woman's pregnancy.

These quoted cases should be sufficient to establish a certain prototype. But I would like to add several cases that attract more attention from the purely human, rather than from the scientific point of view.

8. G. G. is a laborer. One evening, his wife, obviously in great distress, brought her husband to me and begged for help: through her fault he had contracted a venereal disease. I questioned her: she herself was not sick. Then she opened her heart to me, because I had known them for years. Since her husband had recuperated from typhus, he had not been able to earn a full living and to care for her and their four living children (four others had died) in the same way as before. Before and after pregnancies, she had often been seriously ill, was at times practically helpless (as was known to me); they could not afford to hire help, the care of her children went beyond her strength. In order not to end in complete poverty, they had consequently agreed that she, the woman, would completely renounce marital relations. Her husband should occasionally find sexual satisfaction some place else. This at least would not be above their means. I could not doubt the truth in this instance, because I knew this brave couple too well. The husband confirmed her story. Proof followed at closer examination. The small, slightly built woman was healthy. The short, frail man suffered from a simple, primary chancre ulcer. From the medical point of view, the treatment of this infection was not particularly difficult. But a man's heart could overflow with pity in view of such a truly social misery. Continuation of this case can be found under No. 22.

9. L. Q., 34 years old, wife of a merchant, had a weak constitution. She became ill with an infection of her lung during her sixth pregnancy. Although delivery followed without incident, the woman was afterwards sent away to rest in a favorable climate because of the rather serious lung infection. She returned relatively well. No symptoms of the disease could be observed. Pregnancy, not at all desirable, did not occur until 1½ years later. Gradually, a new lung infection of greater severity developed. After delivery, it increased so rapidly that the patient soon died of phthisis.

10. C. R., 40 years old, wife of a laborer, apparently a rather strong woman, went through 13 successful pregnancies but had to bottle-feed her babies. Only 4

of the 13 children survived. All the others died early. According to the case history, dyspepsia or its consequences was the cause of death. The 14th pregnancy was interrupted by bleeding in the second week. In spite of treatment pregnancy lasted only eight weeks. Movements of the fetus discontinued. Because of the severe bleeding, which was also treated by me for two weeks, a premature delivery was induced with ergotin. The fetus still showed signs of life. The mother was very weak. She was convinced that she was at the end of her strength. She would rather die than go through the agonies of another pregnancy. No one could argue against that. The couple had stayed poor in spite of hard work and a good income. There had been endless extra expenses because of illness and death. One could ask for what reason 13 children had been born when only 4 survived. The attending physician was the only one who profited from the treatment of the nine deceased children.

11. O. S., 33 years old, a farmer's wife, had scrofula. At 17 years of age she became ill with a severe lung infection. The glands on her neck were quite enlarged, and acute abscesses developed there in different places. The lung infection improved in such a way that calcification and shrinking of the affected area was presumed. Later, she occasionally coughed up small calcified particles.

At 19 years of age, she married a widower several years her senior and became pregnant. The newborn infant was very weak after delivery. The mother became ill with a severe perimetritis, but she recoverd completely from it. The child continued to live but had scrofula. A second pregnancy followed soon without complications, but the mother was unable to nurse the baby. The child survived, became very heavy and fat, but died of a tuberculous meningitis at one year of age. The third child died at nine months from a liver tumor (amyloid degeneration). The fourth child was born with a vitium cordis (the foramen ovale remained open), and it died aged 2½ years. The husband's question as to whether any healthy children could be expected from his wife had to be answered in the negative according to the preceding experiences. Seven years later the husband consulted me because of gonorrhea. To my surprised question as to how this could have happened since he had a much younger, quite good-looking wife, he frankly explained his situation. Since the birth of their last child, he and his wife did not dare to have marital relations any longer, because nothing but sorrow and difficulties resulted. According to mutual agreement, the husband looked elsewhere for satisfaction of his sexual desires.

12. A. K., 29 years old, wife of a coachman, was a strong and healthy girl before she married at age 25. In 3¾ years, four childrn were born. Because of her weakness, the last delivery dragged on very slowly. Extraordinarily heavy bleeding preceded the incomplete expulsion of the placenta, which had to be manually removed. The bleeding had to be arrested with injections of hot aqueous solution of carbolic acid, since the uterus reacted insufficiently to inside and outside friction. It was not surprising to the observer that this poor woman prepared herself for death in view of these manipulations, feeling her strength and perserverance vanish. Her situation went practically beyond the limits of human endurance: to do all her work without any help, to raise her children "in the city," bottle-feed them, constantly care for two infants in the crib while a pregnancy drained her strength, to answer each child's

demand according to its need and finally almost to bleed to death. In her misery, she did not look her young age, but had more the appearance of a care-worn woman of 40. Another pregnancy could easily end fatally, if she could not be relieved of her incumbent household and childcare obligations—and who would be ready to do this?

13. R. V. K., 28 years old, wife of a captain with a pleasant personality, was a young girl, vigorous and sturdy. The first pregnancy ended in miscarriage; a long illness followed. The next four or five pregnancies were discontinued by miscarriage in the 21st to 22nd week. Constitutional defects on either side had to be excuded. Cause of death of the fetus was adiposis of the placenta. The patient also suffered from severe migraine, especially during menstruation. Meanwhile, a chronic endometritis had been treated elsewhere over a longer period of time and she had been repeatedly sent away to a spa. The author also treated her for awhile, seemingly with success, requesting abstinence from the couple. This demand had earlier also been observed for different time periods. But now a new pregnancy set in during treatment. The local extrauterine treatment was continued for another few weeks. The patient passed the critical 22nd week. Fetal movements, which earlier had started in the 20th week, but gradually stopped afterwards, this time developed to full strength. It seemed as if circulatory conditions in the placenta remained undisturbed. But this happy condition did not last long. In the 26th week, while feeling in prime shape, the patient passed away suddenly from a brain embolism. There can be no doubt that the tendency to adiposis was the reason for this sad ending. Prevention of pregnancy could have saved this life and would have permitted full recuperation. The husband fell into a condition of acute insanity, and later melancholia.

14. B. H., 38 years old, a laborer, was an alert, lively young man ten years before. His wife also had a neat, sturdy, healthy appearance. The couple had three healthy children. Now he suffered from a bronchitis, seemed indolent, neglected, sullen and dissatisfied. He was especially unhappy that he had to wait five hours for my visit after he had called me—his longtime physician—even though he lived far outside the city. Soon afterwards his wife, who nursed her eighth living child (two had been miscarried) fell ill from exhaustion. She looked considerably older than her 37 years. The necessary remedies and medications were obtained and used with some success. But the real cause of this family's decay was obviously lack of adequate nourishment. The couple was urgently warned to avoid further pregnancies, even to prevent it. The woman agreed. But the man, previously so industrious, intelligent, but now indolent, mentally tired (he was never a drinker), simply remarked that this was not necessary, that additional children would still be welcome; even if he should perish because of his children it would not matter. Public welfare would have to step in and take care of them, so they could grow up without his support.

The woman listened quietly to these remarks; she was used to grief, maybe she even felt like her husband.

That even the finest and bravest people could fall into such moral indolence through hunger and need should deeply distress the philanthropist.

In the preceding pages, I have cited cases of people and situations from different

254

strata of society. Included were people of very good, mediocre or poor educational backgrounds—refined or coarser personalities. Some were defeated by circumstances in spite of their strength of character, others were weak and suffered the same fate. One irrefutable certainty is clearly indicated by the quoted examples: How can one forbid that kind of cohabitation, which, as such, is morally justified and harmless—in order to prevent later fatalities? To give such reasoning a scientific impression is historical, physiological, moral nonsense.

Such regulations are, on the one hand, based on unreliable information; on the other hand, they are plainly contrary to nature and consequently not permissible. It is impossible and inhuman to implement this prohibition.

Impregnaton may, on the other hand, be prevented because it is possible and human.

It is not surprising that others differ in their opinion concerning this matter, and that they get carried away in a "holy rage" against their opponents. But they cannot deny the naked truth.

It is not clear to me how the authority mentioned above could object to all the facts. He will have to recognize them if he is consistent. It should surely be assumed that he is also genuinely interested in the well being, health and life of every person, regardless of sex.

It is absolutely necessary to have a clear idea on how to reach that goal and then to choose a way that would prove to be most certainly successful and would exclude the incalculable human inclinations. Practical success is the best proof and defies all dogmatism and doctrine. I hope to present that view convincingly in the following cases. All the abovementioned contradictions can simply be avoided through FACULTATIVE STERILITY.

II. Happy Results

15. F. J., 34 years old, wife of a laborer, fell ill with exudative peritonitis after her first pregnancy. Lack of proper care in the beginning and deficient rest later on prevented the desired, positive results after intensive treatment. A new pregnancy and miscarriage occurred. Five or six additional miscarriages followed, accompanied by rather threatening symptoms. During the treatment of the chronic endometritis a three-month abstinence was demanded and observed. Considerable improvement in the patient's state of health was obtained by local treatment. This improvement was also quite obvious in the appearance of the earlier rather depressed woman. New pregnancies followed, but ended 12 to 14 times in miscarriages, at least five times in one year! The morally and physically weakened woman became weary of life, but vehemently refused abstinence. "She would rather sacrifice herself and die than again reject her husband."

F. S. was ordered to ban all danger of pregnancy from the affected uterus. The patient lived 13 months according to medical regulations and recuperated considerably. She became rather careless and a new pregnancy resulted immediately. The critical 9th to 11th weeks passed without complications, pregnancy and delivery took an undisturbed course to the joy of all persons involved.

16. F. G., 39 years old, wife of a baker, was sterile in the first years of marriage.

After dilatation of the uterus she became pregnant. Because of failure of lactation, six pregnancies followed in quick succession. The whole family situation was completely changed by these circumstances, and by recurring illnesses. The increasingly difficult burden of childrearing exhausted the strength of the otherwise sturdy woman in such a way that further pregnancies had to be forbidden after the birth of the sixth child. During her last confinement a mild infection of a lung occurred. The patient herself felt that her strength would soon be exhausted. She was constantly worried and afraid about her offspring's future. Through F. S. she again became composed, and under appropriate treatment the threatening symptoms vanished. Her energy increased considerably in the course of a year. It is the greatest wish of the patient to be able to remain in that happy condition.

17. The following case is analogous to the previous one. F. S., the careworn, haggard, life-weary wife of a laborer, was previously an orderly, industrious woman. She had become depressed and disorderly: however hard she tried, it seemed impossible for her to cope successfully with her household and seven young children. F. S. changed this predicament. In the course of a year, the woman was animated with new courage and vitality. She herself, her surroundings, and especially her children benefited greatly by that change. Her husband, already on the road to self-destruction, was saved from dipsomania.

18. S. H., 39 years old, wife of an artisan, was very anemic. The youngest of her eight children was four years old. The household situation had grown to be difficult; frequent childhood diseases occurred; then she suffered a miscarriage with very heavy bleeding. Her life was seriously endangered for several days. Upon improvement of her condition, her first remark was that she would ask God for her children's sake to spare her from another pregnancy, otherwise she would have to die. When she heard that her request could be granted, she gladly accepted F. S. It is hardly possible to describe the gratitude of this simple couple. The woman experienced a new wave of vitality and assurance in presence of physical and mental rest and the absence of the ever-present, exhausting fears of earlier years. The husband remarked to me: "My wife, who had patiently suffered and had already renounced all joy in life, who was tired of living, became young again. She manages the whole household with renewed, youthful energy to everybody's satisfaction. Now I hope we can grow old together. God bless the good work you did for us."

19. B. E., 32 years old, wife of a civil servant with a very low income (no chance of promotion) consulted me with hysterical complaints. She confessed, with tears in her eyes, that she had given birth to three children in the first four years of her marriage, which she had conceived each time at the first cohabitation. She was scared by this fact on the one hand and by the warnings of an older friend in a similar situation on the other. A larger number of children and a not very conscientious husband had caused this friend great trials and deep grief. With his small salary, B. E.'s husband was by no means able to support additional children unless he became dishonest (his profession provided plenty of opportunity for it). For nine years she had tried to avoid pregnancy and the couple had contented themselves with coitus interruptus or masturbation. She feared that her present complaints as well as her

husband's melancholia were connected with their unfortunate situation. She begged me for help in their distress. An existing ailment of the uterus was treated. Finally, F. S. was ordered. Mental agonies were eliminated, and even a year later husband and wife thanked me repeatedly with tears in their eyes. Even the worried, tense expression had vanished from the beautiful, intelligent face of the woman.

20. G. R., 26 years old, wife of a subordinate revenue official, had a tender constitution. Her father and a younger brother had died of phthisis. She had five children and suffered from lack of milk after each delivery. The patient exhausted herself completely with the care of her children, since she was financially not in a position to keep a servant. Especially when her children came down with a disease, she was constantly wet from perspiration. Gradually appearing sleeplessness caused mental unrest and early morning perspiration. The doctor's occasional request for greater efficiency called forth a stream of tears as an expression of her inability. F. S. was arranged for and set the patient greatly at ease. It gave her a moral lift, which had undeniably a favorable influence on the health of her children. The patient found new delight in her existing tasks and did not have to fear new and greater burdens, so that she herself felt young again and looked with new courage to the future. "You were a real savior in my need," were her sincere words.

21. B. L., 34 years old, wife of a physician, was a healthy, vigorous, stocky person. One uncle had suffered from melancholy and committed suicide. An aunt had fallen ill three times during pregnancy, so that she later had to be placed in an institution. During her change of life, she repeatedly became sick in the same manner and finally died in an insane asylum.

Another aunt suffered from dysmenorrhea, which degenerated into melancholia. She also died in a mental institution. The patient's mother was, during her last two pregnancies, more or less mentally ill, but recuperated completely under favorable circumstances.

B. L.'s first pregnancy was prematurely interrupted by a severe shock; the fetus died six weeks before delivery. The second pregnancy took a normal course, but to the woman's great disappointment she suffered from failure of lactation. The third time, pregnancy was again interrupted, as in the first instance, by a heavy blow to the abdomen in an accident. She carried a dead fetus for eight weeks. After the fourth successful pregnancy, again no milk. The child died a year later in an accident. The mother experienced intense physical excitement. The fifth pregnancy progressed normally for the fetus, but serious symptoms of a psychological disturbance in the mother became obvious. F. S. was ordered, which eliminated forever the patient's fear of a new pregnancy.

The peculiarities of her character diminished in the course of three years and this had an advantageous effect on everybody concerned.

22. (Continuation of case 8) The very unhappy couple that came to me because of their predicament gratefully accepted treatment and F. S. Now the youngest child thrived under the doubled care of her appeased mother.

But in his third year, the child became ill with pneumonia and passed away. In their grief over this loss and in view of the wife's, just as well as the husband's,

257

improved state of health, they strongly yearned for a new baby. They decided no longer to pay attention to the doctor's order. These facts and the certainty of a new pregnancy became known to me by chance sometime later. Happiness and contentment again prevailed in this home. How much misery had they been spared!

23. G. H. H., 30 years old, wife of a retired man, was of tender constitution. She had given birth to four children. The first delivery was very difficult. According to the history, an ailment of the uterus had remained but did not cause great trouble. During the second pregnancy, unpleasant hysterical attacks occurred. Consequently, treatment of the uterine condition was successfully undertaken. Renewed severe hysterical complaints started during the third pregnancy and were treated for the patient's relief as far as her condition permitted it. Successful treatment took place after delivery, and complete recuperation was achieved. The hysterical illness recurred to a threatening extent during the fourth pregnancy (severe mental derangement for hours at a time). The patient's constitution was considerably weakened. Treatment at this point could only be palliative. After delivery, her former state of health was soon restored. However, consideration was given to the fact that this patient's mother had suffered from neurasthenia and eventually died of tuberculosis. F. S. was accepted as the proper answer. The family had been deeply worried about the patient's emaciated, exhausted condition and feared that her mother's fate might also befall her. But in the course of two years, she recuperated extraordinarily. Only brief hysterical attacks occurred in increasingly milder form. Her general health condition improved constantly, so that she looked rosy and vigorous again. She insisted that she could not bear another pregnancy, and it would be impossible to contradict her outright.

24. V. J., 26 years old, wife of a mechanic, had suffered since early adolescence from persistent chlorosis (her mother suffered from a syphilitic floating spleen). V. J. had passed through many illnesses, and her whole constitution was extraordinarily tender and delicate. At 21 years of age, she married and soon expected a child. After delivery she struggled with a serious mastitis and then recuperated only gradually, became pregnant again, and could later nurse her baby for a short time. A third and a fourth pregnancy occurred. Then a miscarriage weakened her delicate health extremely. Her deep distress, her sleepless nights, interrupted by crying, her fears for herself and her children's future obviously diminished the physical and psychological strength of this poor, suffering woman. Without doubt she would not be able to bear such a life for very long. Restorative remedies, which her health insurance company granted, could not have permanent success. She had to be lifted up and strengthened spiritually, and F. S. was the only logical answer. The effect was marvelous. She soon found enough strength, courage and energy to cope with her complicated situation. She was, in her own words, happy to work, so long as she felt that she carried out her duties and would be able to continue to do so in the future. In other words, before long, the depressed woman, weary of life, again showed her former vivacious, pure character. Her repugnant, bitter smile of despair had changed to the happy and confident expression of earlier years.

25. J. V., 35 years old, a bookbinder, had a weak constitution. He was a reliable

and faithful worker and provided a good income. His family grew fast—he already had five children—and he felt it necessary to start a business of his own in order to increase his earning possibilities. For lack of funds, he rented a damp, dark apartment. In this vulnerable situation he contracted articular rheumatism and endocarditis, and had to be hospitalized. During a measles epidemic, his children fell ill with pneumonia and one died. His pregnant wife developed varicose ulcers on her legs and was unable to work. Even though he searched for and later on found somewhat better accommodations, a vitium cordis remained and decreased forever his working ability. Delivery took place in their former damp quarters without medical assistance. The woman lost a great deal of weight and seemed to be permanently weakened. Her ulcers, already healed, broke open again after a period of time. It was obvious that additional pregnancies could prove disastrous for this family. F. S. was gladly accepted. The couple found new courage to cope with all their difficulties. The physical condition of parents and children improved considerably.

26. N. A., 38 years old, wife of a shoemaker, was a small, slightly built woman. She had a difficult miscarriage and needed medical assistance. According to the record, she had given birth to eight children. Most probably after her fourth delivery, she contracted an ailment of the uterus which was never properly examined and was only treated with sedatives. After that time she constantly suffered from back pains, was always very weak and miserable, and unable to take proper care of her household.

The present, ninth pregnancy was interrupted by a miscarriage with heavy bleeding. The patient gave the impression of a totally wretched, barely viable person. The inner labium was hard, protruding, completely eroded. The outer labium was puffed up and likewise eroded. The uterus and the left enlarged ovary were very sensitive. F. S. was considered and accepted after brief successful treatment. When the youngest child died from dyspepsia, intestinal infection and rickets, the patient experienced a short setback, but recovered quickly, especially since she felt newly encouraged to take unrestrained care of her loved ones.

Conclusion

The "happy experiences" represent a choice from a large number of similar occurrences. The different character of the story in each case should be sufficient to establish a certain prototype for the indication of F. S. Since these cases are not merely of medical interest, but touch in a special way a moral issue, we asked the opinion of a minister. He emphasized the highly moral value of facultative sterility, which to this point has brought unexpected blessings into the family. But he also insisted that F. S. would have to remain in the hands of the professional, which is self-explanatory and not otherwise possible. The patients in question submitted willingly to medical supervision, since the most important values—life and health—were at stake. In regard to the physical as well as to the psychological health of all concerned, including not only the patients, but their whole families, the eminently favorable results in the quoted, individualized case histories of the last section cannot be denied. And they serve to clarify the hygienic and prophylactic importance of F. S. Only the physician, especially the gynecologist, can arrange for it.

F. S. has to be strongly pressed from the prophylactic, private and social-hygienic points of view, as all of the quoted cases prove. Life and well being of the parties rank higher than production of new individuals.

Consequently, medical advice should not include a warning of new conception without recommendation of F. S., because abstinence in marriage *per se* is against nature and therefore not permissible.

Each physician who feels responsible for the physical and mental well being of his patients should therefore help prevent further pregnancies, if in his human and professional judgment they could prove to be disastrous for the family. A mere warning is inhuman, since it is impossible to curb human instincts effectively and forever.

As other remedies can be prescribed, it should be possible as well to forbid conception, if this is scientifically and humanly indicated—be it to cure or to prevent sickness and death. If for scientific reasons on one hand, and humanitarian on the other, abortion, sterilization, and artificial insemination have found an accepted place in therapy, then the absolutely harmless F. S. should find ready recognition among the gynecological-therapeutic remedies.

From the above-mentioned material it should be possible to derive some

INDICATIONS

for F. S., to which more could certainly be added.

I. Permanently: in case of incapacity to bear children, well-founded fear of tuberculosis and mental disease and other pathological changes as a consequence of pregnancy and delivery.

II. For a longer, undetermined period of time: in case of syphilis and other constitutional diseases, until recovery occurs (to prevent unhealthy descendants). After recovery from acute infections of the reproductive organs; after sepsis, until a complete restoration has been achieved; during chronic conditions of the uterus. Additional indications in this category could be: morbidity and mortality of children, caused by insufficient nutrition as a consequence of their parents' overwhelming responsibilities.

III. For a definite period of time (at least 18 months): in case of failure of lactation; here nature has deprived the mother of the ability to nurse her child. The care of a bottle-fed infant is by far more difficult and strenuous—and the occurrence of gastric disturbances more likely—than when the baby is breast-fed. Complications for the mother could arise because of insufficient rest.

III. Calamities

Even though the purpose of this study seems now to have been accomplished, I have to add a third set of observations, which rarely come to light. But I am convinced that they could be noted in a multitude of instances. I am referring to the matter of "being careful," which by now promises to become a national calamity. Everybody knows it and knows about it, but does not talk about it, especially in the presence of a physician. And yet, this fact is of such eminent physiological and psychological importance that it has to be faced realistically. Exercitant Conjuges Congressum retrahendo ante Ejaculationem (coitus interruptus).

Again, case histories will best illustrate the consequences of such practices. However, I want to relate only a few, since so many cases resemble each other.

It stands to reason that the information was given by the patient in full confidence and with an ardent desire for relief, even though the patient himself often had no idea about the nature and cause of his complaints. The practice itself, however, is considered as absolutely harmless, because "so many do it" . . . .

There may be unsatisfactory, or unreleased sexual fluctuation of the uterus, caused by dreams and pollution-like sensations, which induces sometime later—on the following day—a mechanical discharge of the blood vessels through contraction of the uterus *in toto* (since the vasomotor contraction is more or less weakened or paralyzed by the inevitable psychic depression through disappointment). These contractions generally cause cramps of the uterus and back pains. Such observations can often be made soon after miscarriage or three to five weeks post partum (the blood vessels are at that time in a more or less atonic state), and especially often after coitus interruptus. When the contractility of the uterus is finally reduced by this repeated procedure, a chronic condition of active hyperemia of the uterus with its various consequences follows.

For the woman, coitus interruptus has the following consequences: for the time being, the whole apparatus becomes actively hyperemic through the genital irritation. The uterus, however, remains quiet, since the hyperemia is not released by psychic satisfaction. This condition has to become a chronic one through frequent repetition. The necessary consequences are uterine congestion, uterine catarrh, formation of mucus, edema and swelling of the portio, corrosion of the orifice, and hypermenorrhea; in other cases, hysterical fits, convulsions, bladder cramps, migraine, apparent gastric disorders, etc. Sexual apathy and aversion to the formerly beloved husband are not uncommon.

Symptoms in the more sturdy male might not appear as soon, but are otherwise almost identical: passive hyperemia of the reproductive organs, varicocele, hemorrhoids, bladder spasms, constant moisture on the skin and the surroundings of the genitalia, great sensitivity, vexation with feverish activity (the characteristic of our times). All of these conditions can develop into symptoms of pure hysteria with various types of irradiating pains and nervous complaints.

27. This case refers to a history mentioned before.

D. Q., 35 years old, factory owner, was slender, of slight build, with a passionate character, father of three children, the oldest one six, the youngest one three. He suffered from intensive irritability which was exacerbated by hemorrhoids, accompanying a severe urge to urinate. Corresponding treatment with sedatives by a colleague and, later, applied hydrotherapy were without success. On the contrary, a state of absolute hysteria gradually developed. Local examination shed little light on the situation. It seemed that the area surrounding the neck of the bladder was more sensitive to the catheter than usual, and the mucous membranes of the rectum were lax. There was redness around the anus and the scrotum because of constantly present moisture. Even though the symptoms were supposedly identical with an affection of the genital apparatus, nothing definite could be diagnosed. Apparent improvement suddenly gave way to the outbreak of very unpleasant symptoms.

In the meantime, this patient's wife, a slightly built, emaciated woman, also fell ill with hysterical troubles. I was consulted because of hypermenorrhea and temporary leukorrhea. Miscarriage as a possible cause of these conditions was vehemently denied, since it would be "impossible." Upon questioning, she answered, that they were "too careful, because her husband could not bear to see her suffer so much again. She did not want to die prematurely and leave her children motherless, as had happened in her family." Lack of food was denied, but it posed, in fact, a problem.

Local examination revealed tuberous dilatation, easy bleeding, edematous tissue, chronic hyperemia, ulceration—in general a flabby, atonic genital apparatus. The woman's remarks revealed the cause of his and her ailments. F. S. was immediately ordered, with proper local and general treatment for both partners. After a short period of time, quite splendid results became obvious. Even though they both could be occasionally provoked to act hysterically for certain external reasons, these fits were in comparison very mild. Their emotional disturbances, which to the doctor's despair were not an openly discussed dilemma, subdued in time. Husband and wife had found each other again.

28. O. J., 26 years old, a minor official's wife of pale, delicate appearance, became a widow and married a widower with a child as old as her own. During her second gestation, she suffered from ulceration of the portio with consecutive hysterical complaints, from which she completely recovered only after delivery. Her general state of health improved rapidly. After more than a year, I heard the complaint that the woman suffered from severe abdominal pains after sexual intercourse. Examination revealed, indeed, hyperemia and erosion of the portio, but the symptoms were not serious enough to justify the "uterine spasms." A very close examination brought to light the fact that the couple was "always very careful" in order to avoid another early pregnancy for economic reasons.

29. A. R., 45 years old, a bookbinder, consulted me because of gastralgia. A hemorrhoidal condition was apparently the reason for his complaints. He suffered from dizziness, unpleasant sweating and moisture around the anus, pains or feelings of tension in the chorda. Treatment showed only slow, incomplete success.

His delicately built wife, 36 years old, had suffered from many illnesses and a coxitis in younger years, after which she was severely lame. She lived through difficult pregnancies and had given birth to three children. At the deliveries, medical help was necessary because of her one-sided, flat pelvis. Her tender health was impaired. (Her father had died of pulmonary tuberculosis.) She was warned to avoid further pregnancies. Later on, a slight erosion and fluor albus were temporarily and successfully treated. Leukorrhea occurred repeatedly, but no other treatment besides lukewarm injections of salt water was applied. Recently, she had suffered from a minor hysterical fit. Close examination revealed that they had always "been very careful" and had been able to avoid conception. Thus, the cause of the husband's and wife's illnesses could be fully explained. The woman gratefully accepted F. S. "for her husband's sake."

30. R. V. K., 36 years old, tall, slender, the wife of an official, had in her younger days been treated for ovaritis, which had not been recognized as such. Consequently, she had suffered from severe hysteria. At 19 years of age she married. Her three pregnancies were accompanied by frequent hysterical paroxysms. That was 12 years ago. Partly because of this condition and partly because of a long-lasting pleuritic affection, she had been warned to avoid further pregnancies. She did not become pregnant. But since then, she again often suffered hysterical attacks. Hyperemia of the portio, fluor albus, erosions of the orifice were at various times accompanied by convulsions, apparent gastric disorders, hypermenorrhea, bladder spasms and back pains. All these symptoms occurred very suddenly and without an externally detectable cause. Response to general and local treatment was always quick and satisfactory. The couple had always "been very careful," which was definitely the cause of the hysterical symptoms.

31. D. E., 30 years old, the owner of a printing business, suffered as a student from heart palpitations and other nervous disorders (onanism?) without discovery of a material cause. The symptoms vanished after he got married, but they returned in an aggravated form soon after the birth of his child. The entire clinical picture was that of a melancholic hysteria. After his wife stopped nursing her child, this quite vigorous woman suffered from fluor albus, erosion of the portio, hypermenorrhea and migraine. No other pregnancies followed, since they were "very careful." Economic worries presented also a problem in this case, even if it did no seem so. The afflictions of this couple could easily be traced to their "carefulness."

32. L. R., 31 years old, wife of a merchant with a pleasant, soft, compliant disposition, fell ill during her fifth pregnancy with septic pleuritis, and was seriously ill for a long perod of time. Afterwards, a chronic endometritis, fluor albus and ulceration of the portio remained and were accompanied by general hysterical symptoms. Her timid wish not to become pregnant soon was not granted for long. Treatment was interrupted by a sixth pregnancy. The patient was quite ill during the whole period of time. Her strength was exhausted. Delivery was accomplished without medical help, but dragged on very slowly (ergotin). In any case, the fetus was born healthy, but suffered later from anemia and rickets. A very slow recovery followed. Treatment of the uterine ailment as well as of a starting furunculosis of the labia majora was resumed. The couple was strictly warned to avoid conception but did not follow this advice for long. The seventh pregnancy was again a wretched one and it was discontinued by a premature delivery in the 26th week. When finally an eighth pregnancy started and was terminated by a complicated miscarriage, pregnancy was at last downright forbidden and the use of the condom recommended. This device was used for a period of time. The woman recovered under corrresponding treatment. But the condom was rejected as very disagreeable. "My husband is reasonable, he is careful," were the woman's words. For false modesty, she refused to accept F. S.

After intercourse frequent back pains and abdominal pains occurred. Edematous swellings of the portio and vagina with hysterical headaches and vomiting were successfully treated, but recurred frequently. The woman heroically endured all this. She was merely joyful about the fact, that her five-year-old child remained the youngest and she herself stayed alive for her family. Gradually, however, her husband became nervous, irritable, easily annoyed and feverishly busy. Discord of the genital nervous system occurred. A cause other than coitus interruptus could not be established. Finally, F. S. was accepted and a definite improvement in the condition of both partners achieved.

The keen observer, who is not only interested in temporary morbidity, but also in the ethical relationships of the family, will be able to add hundreds of pertinent cases to these cited.

It is remarkable that this "carefulness" is being practiced mainly by the more educated strata of society, because it presupposes higher intelligence and control over the willpower and the instincts. In the lower classes, it is rarely or not at all used. There, more indolence can be observed.

This conflict between reason and emotion, between the mind and the instincts implies that ultimately nobody, neither man nor woman, can escape the inevitable consequences of hysteria and its related affections. Sooner or later morbid conditions appear. This procedure—"carefulness"—certainly constitutes one of the reasons for the general contemporary nervousness.

At the end, I state the following thesis, established in the preceding pages:

> "Where life, well-being and the health of the mother appear to be endangered by additional pregnancies—regardless of secondary circumstances—it is the duty of the philanthropist to forbid conception and allow FACULTATIVE STERILITY to take place."

Mens ingenua Deo grata.

Reprinted from *Western J. Surg. Obstet. Gynecol.*, July–Aug., 202–207 (1962)

Intravaginal Contraceptive Study

Phase I. Anatomy*

23

VIRGINIA E. JOHNSON
WILLIAM H. MASTERS
ST. LOUIS, MISSOURI

From the Division of Reproductive Biology, Department of Obstetrics and Gynecology, Washington University School of Medicine

Attempts to evaluate the clinical effectiveness of techniques designed for contraceptive protection have brought into focus the reluctance of earlier research to examine directly the intravaginal function of the various contraceptive methods. Neither the vaginal diaphragm nor any of the multiple chemical products designed for intravaginal conception control have been observed objectively during periods of sexual response. As a result of the failure of medical research to approach this fundamental clinical problem directly, the indirect techniques of *in vitro* testing and of field-trial evaluation have dominated the literature in spite of their obvious limitations.

Only 2 direct attempts to investigate intravaginal contraceptive physiology have been recorded. These pioneer efforts were published by Cohen and Kaye[1] in 1953, and by Kaufman[2] in 1960. The details of the experimental techniques were presented and the considered inadequacies of physiologic control were emphasized. Present investigative effort has profited from these suggestions.

The investigative program, designed to evaluate the intravaginal clinical function of the diaphragm and of selected chemical contraceptive agents, has been divided into 2 separate phases. The first phase, described in this paper, records the functional anatomy of the intravaginal diaphragm during artificial coitus, together with direct observations of intravaginal distribution of selected chemical contraceptives, also observed during artificial coitus. The second phase of this investigation will present results of tests designed to provide estimates of the intravaginal spermicidal effectiveness of various chemical contraceptive agents.

A research technique of artificial coitus, originally designed to aid in the evaluation of the sexual response of a female subject population, has been developed by the Division of Reproduc-

tive Biology, Washington University School of Medicine. The application of this technique has been restricted primarily to a well-established basic science program of investigation into the fundamentals of the human female's total cycle of sexual response. The inadequacies of physiologic control described by Kaufman,[2] such as lack of effective sexual stimulation, vaginal lubrication production, female orgasmic response, and so forth, have been overcome by the research technique of artificial coitus. In addition, this procedure affords direct observation of the vaginal barrel during the entire female sexual response cycle. These cycles are, at present, also being recorded by colored motion picture photography.

With such a technic available, brief clinical experiments have been designed to investigate the intravaginal causes for diaphragm conception control failure, together with an evaluation of the physiologic intravaginal distribution of selected chemical contraceptive agents during coitus.

The vaginal diaphragms used in the experimental sessions were purchased on the open market. Individual female subjects were fitted by use of intravaginal fitting rings with diaphragms considered to be of correct size on the basis of clinical experience. Both coiled and flat spring diaphragms were employed. The chemical contraceptives evaluated were selected at the authors' request by Dr. Christopher Tietze, Director of Research of the National Committee on Maternal Health, and included 2 creams (A and B), a jelly, an aerosol foam, a foam tablet and a suppository. Since these products were selected as representative of the several general types of chemical contraceptives, and since our investigation offers no basis for comparison of the selected products with others of the same type, the materials will not be identified here.

The first requisite for the female subject population of the Division of Reproductive Biology is that the individuals be sexually mature and capable of orgasmic response, either during coitus or after manipulative stimulation. The female subjects used in Phase I of the intravaginal contraceptive study totaled 30 in number. Extensive Kinsey-type[3] sex histories were recorded for all members of the group. The subjects' ages range from 20 to 42 years, with 18 of the subjects under 30; the numbers of their pregnancies, from 0 to 4; the numbers of children, from 0 to 3 (Table I). Eleven of the female subjects are unmarried; 14 subjects are maintaining an active marital status; the remaining 5 subjects are divorced, separated or widowed.

Variation in anatomic status of the pelvic viscera of the research population also has been

---

*This investigation was supported by a research grant from the Frederick Ayer II Foundation.

considered of significant moment to this project. Therefore, detailed pelvic evaluations have been conducted on all subjects and are recorded as follows: Of the 16 subjects who have never had children (Para 0), 14 present essentially normal pelves. One Para 0 subject (the Gravida II) has severe broad ligament lacerations and an acquired

Table I

DISTRIBUTION OF FEMALE SUBJECTS BY NUMBER OF PREGNANCIES AND CHILDREN

No.	Number of Children				
Pregnancies	0	1	2	3	Total
0	12	....	....	....	12
1	3	6	....	....	9
2	1	1	4	....	6
3	....	....	....	2	2
4	....	....	....	1	1
Total	16	7	4	3	30

(secondary) 3° retroversion, possibly occasioned by a criminal abortion procedure (vaginal packing). One Para 0 subject has a congenital retroversion of the uterus.

Among the 7 subjects who have had 1 child (Para I), 5 have essentially normal pelves, with good perineal support, minimal cervical involvement and anteriorly placed uteri within essentially normal limits as to size and mobility. Two Para I subjects have acquired (secondary) uterine retroversion, one of the 2° and the other of the 3° variety. In both cases the uteri are enlarged to about twice the normal size and are somewhat soft. One of these subjects also has a severely lacerated external cervical os.

Two of the 4 subjects with 2 children (Para II) have essentially normal female pelves, although there is a demonstrable relaxation of the vaginal barrel. The remaining 2 of the Para II subjects present the following pelvic pathology: One has a moderate cystocele and rectocele, while the other has a moderate cystourethrocele and an advanced rectocele. Both of these individuals also have chronic cervical erosion.

The 3 subjects with 3 children (Para III) were especially selected for this project. These subjects have poor perineal support, with cystoceles, urethroceles and rectoceles of moderate severity. One of the group has a severe acquired (secondary) uterine retroversion, with bilateral lacerations of broad ligament support. A second member of this group has a myomatous uterus which is estimated to be 2 to 3 times normal size. The third subject has moderate uterine descensus. In addition, she is also distressed with advanced pelvic and labial varicosities.

The first phase of the intravaginal contraceptive study has been divided into 3 parts: (I) the subject conditioning program, (II) the intravaginal diaphragm function study and (III) the intravaginal chemical contraceptive distribution study. The details of these investigations will be presented in order.

I. *Subject Conditioning Program.* As previously stated, all members of the experimental subject population are sexually mature individuals, capable of orgasmic response, either during coitus or from manipulative stimulation. However, the technique of artificial coitus necessitates conditioning of these individuals to assure definitive research results. In every instance, all 30 members of the subject population assigned to this clinical experiment underwent 3 separate sessions to establish familiarity with and effective sexual response to the artificial coital technique. At least once during these sessions, all 30 subjects developed a completely effective "orgasmic phase" sexual response.

Although all subjects established definitive orgasmic pattern responses by the end of the third session, most of the women were able to accomplish this degree of sexual tension release during the first or second session. For the sake of conditioning uniformity, however, three sessions were insisted upon, regardless of the early effectiveness of the individual subject's sexual response to the experimental technique. The observed production of vaginal lubrication was considered to be within the individual subject's normal limits.

Direct observation of the vagina (made possible by the artificial coital technique) demonstrated the usual anatomic response of expansion of the inner two-thirds of the vaginal barrel and the development of an orgasmic platform in the outer one-third of the vaginal barrel as the sexual cycle developed. The cervices and uteri of all subjects, with the exception of those with the previously described retroverted positioning, follow the normal pattern of elevation into the false pelvis during "plateau phase" response, further expanding the inner portion of the vaginal barrel.[4-7]

II. *Diaphragm Function Study.* The diaphragm function study comprised direct observation of 30 female subjects in each of 3 basic coital positions (supine, female-superior and knee-chest). In addition, a fourth observation series consisting of individually selected combinations of coital positions was developed to record the results of multiple mounting. All coital activity was conducted with the aid of the artificial penis, with the exception of the female-superior positioning, which necessitated a male partner. Since each of the subjects was evaluated through all 4 of the selected coital techniques, 120 experimental sessions were devoted to the diaphragm conception control study.

Several anatomic problems, closely related to all of the coital positions investigated, will be covered by a preliminary general discussion. The results of the observations from the 30 experimental sessions with each position will be condensed into brief but specific discussions of the theoretical causes for failure of diaphragm conception control. In this manner, both general and specific concerns of each coital position will be emphasized and, thus, may be more easily described for patients seeking contraceptive consultation.

In general consideration, it should be emphasized that a firm nulliparous-type of perineum has an obvious advantage in retaining any diaphragm in its retropubic placement, since there is a tendency for the diaphragm to fall from behind the symphysis in the parous vagina, particularly when there is poor perineal support. When there is loss of correct diaphragm positioning, it usually occurs secondarily to the "excitement phase" expansion of the inner two-thirds of the vagina during mounting sexual tension.

The longer the excitement and/or plateau phases of sexual response are maintained, the more the anteroposterior and the lateral wall expansion develop in the inner vaginal barrel. As a consequence, a diaphragm that was fitted to correct size in the sexually unstimulated state will often lose close contact with the walls of the expanded vaginal barrel. In addition, the diaphragm frequently slips from side to side within the vaginal canal (away from its midline placement) when the female pelvis is driven strongly against the shaft of the penis. The more violent the pelvic thrust by either the male or female partner, the more frequent the tipping of the diaphragm at this advanced stage of the sexual response cycle.

It should also be noted that there is usually more expansion of the parous than the nulliparous vaginal barrel. This expansive ability may well be the result of parous separation of the relatively constrictive perivaginal fascia in the midline, both anteriorly and posteriorly. Thus, the basic concern in diaphragm fitting should focus on the parity of the patient and the size selected should be the largest that can be tolerated.

When a woman has a retroverted uterus (whether the malpositioning is congenital or acquired), the usual transcervical lateral wall expansion occurs during increasing sexual tension, but uterine elevation does not occur. Con-

sequently, the expansion of the vaginal barrel in the anteroposterior vaginal axis is greatly restricted. However, due to the filling of the cul-de-sac by a retroverted uterus (particularly the enlarged corpus of an acquired retroversion) there is a tendency to fit such an individual with too small a diaphragm. In this instance, even the anatomically restricted cul-de-sac expansion will allow the diaphragm to fall from behind the symphysis.

Other factors which contribute to the possible loss of correct diaphragm placement are rimming of the diaphragm with contraceptive jelly and/or the excessive production of vaginal lubrication. Vaginal lubrication is usually produced in greater than necessary amounts only by long-maintained sessions of sexual stimulation. Occasionally, however, excessive lubrication production is an individual characteristic.

A. *Female Supine Position.* The correctly placed vaginal diaphragm has the best chance of providing anatomic protection against conception when the female maintains a supine position. There was only one instance in this coital position when a diaphragm was totally displaced from its previously correct midline location during the 30 directly observed complete sexual response cycles. The diaphragm was dislodged from its firm retropubic placement during the excitement phase expansion of the inner two-thirds of the vaginal barrel. A rather extended plateau phase further increased the expansion of the parous vagina (a Para III subject), until the diaphragm was moving freely with penile thrust. A severe orgasmic phase response with accompanying strong pelvic thrust trapped the diaphragm against the left vaginal wall. Upon the removal of the artificial penis during the resolution phase, the cervix was observed to be completely exposed to the content of a theoretical ejaculation.

B. *Knee-Chest Position.* Correct diaphragm placement is maintained in the knee-chest position almost as well as in the female supine position. When the inner two-thirds of the vaginal barrel undergoes excitement phase expansion, there is the usual tendency for the diaphragm to slip into either of the lateral vaginal fornices. This tendency is of negligible consequence in the nulliparous individual. In 2 instances (both parous subjects) the diaphragm was observed to lose the normal retropubic placement during an extended period of coital activity and ultimately became encased behind the cervix. In one instance this occurred just prior to and in the other during an actual orgasmic phase experience.

It should be pointed out, however, that both women had enjoyed multiple orgasmic reactions: one, 2 times, and the other 3 times, during the particular observation period. Consequently, both subjects developed markedly distended inner vaginal barrels, and the shift of the diaphragm behind the cervix was accomplished only after the first orgasmic phase experience. Diaphragm protection would have been provided during any male ejaculatory experience that had occurred during the initial orgasmic sequence. There is the theoretical concern, however, that seminal fluid deposited during the female's first orgasmic phase could obtain easy access to the external cervical os, when the diaphragm slipped from correct positioning during a later stage of the female's multiple orgasmic response. In addition, had repeated male coital activity developed, or had male ejaculatory control been possible until the second female orgasmic response, conception could obviously have occurred.

There is always the risk in the knee-chest position of inserting the penis in front of the diaphragm ring, between the diaphragm and the anterior vaginal wall. If the actual mounting process is controlled by the female partner, correct penile placement can be assured. In essence, if particular care is taken during penile insertion in the knee-chest position, diaphragm protection is as assured as in the female-supine position.

C. *The female-superior position* is second only to a multiple mounting occasion as the greatest cause for diaphragm displacement and potential contraceptive failure. Again, it is necessary for the female subject to be well-stimulated sexually, with the resultant wide distention of the inner two-thirds of the vaginal barrel. In 2 instances in the 30 directly observed coital engagements employing the female-superior position, the penis was inadvertently placed between the diaphragm ring and the anterior vaginal wall at the initial mounting episode. Since this was the only position in which male subjects were used, all experimental teams were checked for penile positioning immediately after every mounting episode.

Further complications were observed 5 more times in this observation series. In 3 instances, when the penis was inadvertently lost from the vaginal barrel during coital activity and remounting occurred, the hastily reinstated penis was placed between the diaphragm and the anterior vaginal wall. On 2 occasions, the diaphragms were completely dislodged from cervical protection placement during female orgasmic response, and were retrieved in one case from the anterior fornix, and in the other from the lateral vaginal wall.

It is obvious that these situations represented potential opportunities at failure of diaphragm conception control. Thus, in the female-superior position, penile placement during the initial or any subsequent mounting attempts should be carefully checked by the coital unit using a diaphragm for conception control. Although the number of the research group is admittedly limited, it is still of clinical concern that out of 30 observed copulations in the female-superior position, there were 7 obvious possibilities for diaphragm conception control failure.

D. *Multiple Mounting.* During normal coital activity, the problem of multiple mounting is most frequently encountered at the height of sexual tension response. With the deep thrust and quick withdrawal of the penis, as the male approaches ejaculation, the penis frequently escapes the vaginal barrel. With the hurried remounting that usually occurs during these sexually demanding circumstances, it is quite possible to reinsert the penis in front of, rather than behind, the diaphragm circle. This mistake obviously can be made by either the sexually demanding male or the sexually demanding female member of the coital team.

The greatest difficulty in maintaining proper dia-

phragm positioning for cervical protection has been observed during episodes of multiple mounting, regardless of coital position. When a woman is well-stimulated sexually (orgasmic response to a first mounting opportunity), the diaphragm frequently drops from behind the symphysis as the penis is withdrawn. With return to effective sexual stimulation, followed by remounting, the penis may easily be reinserted between the diaphragm and the anterior vaginal wall (particularly if the remounting is hurried).

In order to evaluate this problem, all 30 subjects were directed to achieve multiple orgasmic response in a variety of coital positions of their own choosing. Repetitive mounting with position variation (during which vaginal barrel observation was constantly maintained) continued until the subjects had totally satisfied their individual sexual demand. Eight of the subjects reintroduced the penis between the anterior vaginal wall and the diaphragm during the multiple mounting opportunities. Again, this complication particularly applied to the parous individual, since the penile insertion between the diaphragm and the anterior vaginal wall occurred only twice in nulliparous subjects.

As further indication of the potential danger of the multiple mounting process, it is interesting to recall that the most frequent diaphragm placement failure in the female-superior positioning also occurred when remounting was necessary during coital activity.

III. *Intravaginal Chemical Contraceptive Distribution Study.* The study of the intravaginal distribution of chemical contraceptives covers 6 chemical contraceptives, selected as previously described. Each of the 30 subjects, after a minimum of 48 hours continence, was observed through complete cycles of sexual response in artificial coitus, with each of the 6 contraceptive materials. Prior to sexual stimulation, the subjects read the directions accompanying the contraceptive material and introduced these agents into the vagina according to their individual interpretation of the directions. When the manufacturer suggested a time lapse between contraceptive insertion and coital activity, this request was observed.

During observed coital activity, only 2 of the 6 products (Cream A and aerosol foam) demonstrated widespread immediate distribution along the vaginal walls and in the pericervical and the cervical canal areas. Immediate distribution is defined as complete coverage of the total vaginal barrel, as observed with the first thrust of the penis. Cream A provided vaginal wall coverage for a matter of hours, even after repeated mounting episodes. The foam also maintained coverage of the cervical canal and was well-situated in the vaginal rugal pattern after repeated mountings. There was a tendency toward wastage of Cream A by excessive coverage of the penile shaft, while the aerosol foam provided relatively little penile shaft coverage, and was better contained within the vaginal barrel.

From an aesthetic point of view, 2 of the subjects complained of postcoital vaginal dripping subsequent to insertion of Cream A. There were no postcoital complaints after the intravaginal applications of aerosol foam.

Cream B was next in the order of facility of distribution. However, several thrusts of the penis were necessary to accomplish total vaginal barrel distribution for this product. In addition, the shaft of the penis was always heavily covered with the contraceptive material when withdrawn, providing significant material wastage.

From an aesthetic point of view, 11 of the subjects complained of the marked tendency of Cream B to lather the entire female perineum, and even the inner aspect of the thighs during coitus. This tendency becomes particularly apparent if coital connection is maintained for several minutes and the female subject is carried through a complete sexual response cycle.

The jelly distributed poorly under direct observation. Frequently, there were large concentrations of this material which could be identified on the posterior, lateral or anterior vaginal walls. These isolated areas of jelly concentration were observed almost as frequently as the instances of successful vaginal barrel distribution. The cul-de-sac, for instance, might be well-covered, but there would be little or no jelly in the anterior vaginal barrel. Frequently, the reverse occurred. If the jelly had been initially placed near the vaginal outlet, there might be reasonably good distribution in the outer half of the vagina, and the cul-de-sac observed to be completely free of contraceptive material.

With long continued coital activity, the jelly assumes a more liquid consistency, through the influence of body heat, the dilution of vaginal lubrication or mechanical friction. Good vaginal wall coverage is then accomplished, but there is marked drainage and dripping from the vaginal outlet as the artificial penis is removed after the subject's orgasmic response. Five subjects complained of this perineal contamination.

The basic disadvantage encountered with the jelly is that the vaginal distribution of the product is patchy unless significant periods of pre-mounting sex-play are conducted. In all probability, most of the failures with this material occur when the male partner ejaculates shortly after initial vaginal penetration before widespread distribution of the jelly can occur.

The foam tablets reacted with marked individual variation among the 30 subjects. In some instances, there was a well-established foam reaction, particularly if the subjects were carried through a total orgasmic cycle. In other words, if clinically adequate vaginal lubrication was produced, the foaming process was significantly encouraged.

In 9 of the subjects, there was very little foaming of the tablets after vaginal placement, despite the prescribed moistening of the tablet prior to insertion. Small portions of the tablet were observed on the posterior or lateral vaginal walls subsequent to the mounting process with no apparent contraceptive coverage of the cervix or the cul-de-sac. If the male partner should ejaculate shortly after vaginal penetration, there would be very little coverage of the cervical os in the situation described above. While it is obviously true that the seminal pool will increase the foaming activity of the tablets, it is also true that the cervical canal may be exposed to the seminal pool before effective contraceptive control can be established with this particular technique.

An additional complaint, subjective in nature, has been recorded for the foam tablet. When the product foamed actively in the intravaginal environment before mounting was accomplished, 7 of the subjects complained of an irritative reaction to the foaming process. Complaints of itching, a sensation of heat and general vaginal irritation were voluntarily contributed by the subjects.

The suppositories also dissolved slowly when observed in the intravaginal environment. A patchy, localized distribution of this material was frequently directly observed during artificial coital activity. Either long-maintained precoital sex play or an extended pre-ejaculatory mounting process was necessary before adequate dissolution of the product could be assured. There were 4 occasions when undissolved suppository material was observed concentrated in a small localized site on the vaginal walls after extended coital activity. In addition, there were several observed instances when the suppository in a completely dissolved state did not cover the entire vaginal barrel. This shortage of material was observed to occur more frequently in the parous than the nulliparous vaginal barrel.

Aesthetic objections to the suppository were reported. When adequately dissolved, the material dripped and drained freely over the perineum, not only postcoitally, but during actual coital activity. Eleven of the subjects objected to the product on these grounds.

The second phase of the intravaginal contraceptive study is now in progress. Seven intravaginal chemical contraceptive agents are in process of evaluation by direct postcoital sampling of vaginal content to determine sperm survival. Recordings of the immediacy and the duration of intravaginal contraceptive performance will be reported for each product.

SUMMARY

Thirty female subjects from the research population of the Division of Reproductive Biology, Washington University School of Medicine, have been observed directly during artificial and actual coitus in attempts to record intravaginal anatomic causes for failure of diaphragm conception control. In addition, 6 chemical contraceptives have been evaluated during artificial coitus to record intravaginal distribution information for each product. Aesthetic objections to the chemical contraceptives also have been noted. The results of all observations are reported in context.

REFERENCES

1. Cohen, M. R. and Kaye, B. M.: The Postcoital Test as a Method of Evaluating a Contraceptive Jelly, J.A.M.A., 152: 1042-1043, 1953.
2. Kaufman, S. A.: Simulated Postcoital Test to Determine Immediate Spermicidal Effect of Cream or Jelly Alone, Fertil. & Steril., 11:199-209, 1960.
3. Kinsey, A. C. et al.: The Sexual Behavior of the Human Female, W. B. Saunders Co., Philadelphia, 1953.
4. Masters, W. H.: The Sexual Response Cycle of the Human Female. I. Gross Anatomic Considerations, West. J. Surg., Obst. & Gynec., 68:57-72, 1960.
5. Masters, W. H.: The Sexual Response Cycle of the Human Female, II. Vaginal Lubrication, Ann. N. Y. Acad. Sci., 83: 301-317, 1959.
6. Masters, W. H. and Johnson, V. E.: The Human Female: Anatomy of Sexual Response, Minnesota Med., 43:31-36, 1960.
7. Masters, W. H. and Johnson, V. E.: The Physiology of Vaginal Reproductive Function, West. J. Surg., Obst. & Gynec., 69:105-120, 1961.

Female Sterilization

VIII

Editor's Comments on Papers 24 Through 27

Castration has been known and practiced since antiquity. Accordingly, the observation that removal of the gonads prevents conception is very old. However, the observation was also made that castration is accompanied by more than simple sterilization. In addition, in the woman at least, it is a major operation. Consequently, there has been a continuing search for a simple method that would render the subject sterile without disrupting the normal sexual activity. In this section, female sterilization will be considered; in the next, male sterilization.

In 1834, an English obstetrician, James Blundell, M.D., suggested sectioning of the fallopian tubes for this purpose. The paragraph in his textbook, *The Principles and Practice of Obstetricy* makes delightful reading and is reproduced here. He states ". . .that the shortest way to avoid the necessity of operation, would be the abstinence altogether from intercourse with the other sex. The most solid resolution, however, may sometimes thaw; and when a woman is married, she may be placed under those circumstances in which it is not very easy to adhere to this advice, her life perhaps falling a sacrifice to her neglect." He is, of course, speaking of cases in which pregnancy would threaten the patient's life. He suggests that the fallopian tubes be cut and a portion of each tube removed.

This suggestion was followed, but with a surprising failure rate. In 1916, an American physician, Robert Dickinson, published a curious paper entitled "Simple Sterilization of Women by Cautery Stricture at the Intra-Uterine Tubal Openings, Compared with Other Methods." He not only discusses the matter at hand but ranges into a discussion of various contraceptive methods, objections to sterilization of the husband, and objections to sterilization of the wife. Several statements are made which seem odd as late as 1916. He says that "Since the gratification is mostly on the part of the man (because of the present lack of premarital teaching and post-marital training and the dread of pregnancy always present) it is up to the man to accept the handicap—such as the cover. And the selfish man refuses." He goes on to discuss vasectomy and states that "no man has been found willing to submit to the operation. . . ." As for sterilization of women he insists that "[n]o man of fine feeling would ask his wife to submit herself to such a risk, even with powerful physical impulses on her side." But he does make an astonishingly prophetic prediction: "I make bold to voice the belief that we shall eventually adopt, as a means of security, the unintermittent wearing of some very simple Y-shaped device, entirely intra-uterine, easily placed or removed. . . ."

Dickinson then describes what he calls a simple sterilization procedure. It involves passing a tube through the uterine canal until it reaches the cornu. A cautery is pushed through the tube until the electrode lies in the cornu. The area is then burned so that a stricure develops. He claims this causes little discomfort, but he offers no data concerning its effectiveness as a contraceptive method. Simple or not, the procedure seems to have disappeared.

The key publications in this field are by Madlener, Pomeroy, and Irving. But rather than reproduce these papers, which are primarily concerned with surgical technique, I have selected a comprehensive review of all the methods of Allan Garb, M.D. Therein is to be found a brief historical review and an excellent comparison of the various methods. The fundamental problem seems to be to sever, crush and/or tie the tubes and to do so in a manner that prevents reestablishment of a pathway for the sperm and the ovum. The author reviews almost 30,000 cases and calculates an overall failure rate of 0.71 per cent. The Madlener procedure has the highest failure rate; the Irving method by far the lowest, being very close to foolproof.

In short, there is now a surgical technique for practically absolute prevention of conception, but this involves a major operation and there is the even more serious objection that it is not an easily reversible procedure, if indeed it is reversible at all. Accordingly, other technqiues have been sought. In an article included here, Drs. Neumann and Frick suggest the use of tantalum clips to occlude the tubes. Their animal experiments suggest that the method is effective and after removal of the clips the tubes regain their patency. In addition, they propose a procedure to put the clips in place by means of an instrument that is introduced through the vagina to the so-called cul-de-sac, where the instrument's sharp end punctures the tissues to enter the abdominal cavity. The clips are then attached to the fallopian tubes.

Reprinted from *The Principles and Practices of Obstetricy*, 360 (1834)

24

THE

PRINCIPLES AND PRACTICE

OF

OBSTETRICY,

AS AT PRESENT TAUGHT,

By JAMES BLUNDELL, M.D.

PROFESSOR OF OBSTETRICY AT GUY'S HOSPITAL.

In Five Parts:

I. THE ANATOMY OF THE FEMALE SYSTEM.—II. THE PHYSIOLOGY OF THE FEMALE SYSTEM.—III. THE SIGNS AND DISEASES OF PREGNANCY.—IV. THE ART OF DELIVERY.—V. THE AFTER-MANAGEMENT OF THE PUERPERAL STATE, THE DISEASES OF PUERPERAL WOMEN, AND STRICTURES ON THE DISEASES OF INFANTS.

———

TO WHICH ARE ADDED, NOTES AND ILLUSTRATIONS.

———

By THOMAS CASTLE, M.D., F.L.S.

MEMBER OF TRINITY COLLEGE, CAMBRIDGE, ETC., ETC.

WASHINGTON:

STEREOTYPED AND PUBLISHED BY DUFF GREEN.

· · · · ·

1834.

If the pelvis be contracted in so high a degree, that parturition, by the natural passages, is impossible, I need scarcely tell you, that the shortest way to avoid the necessity of the operation, would be by abstinence altogether from intercourse with the other sex. The most solid resolution, however, may sometimes thaw; and when a woman is married, she may be placed under those circumstances in which it is not very easy to adhere to this advice, her life perhaps falling a sacrifice to her neglect. My friend Dr. Hull, of Manchester, once transmitted me the case of a woman whose pelvis was contracted in a high degree; she knew her situation, remained in a state of abstinence many years, but afterwards became pregnant and died. Now is there any mode in which, when the obstruction of the pelvis is insuperable, the formation of a fœtus may be prevented? In my opinion there is; for if a woman were in that condition, in which delivery could not take place by the natural passage, provided she distrusted the circumstances in which she was placed, I would advise an incision of an inch in length in the linea alba above the symphysis pubis; I would advise further, that the fallopian tube on either side should be drawn up to this aperture; and, lastly, I would advise, that a portion of the tube should be removed, an operation easily performed, when the woman would, for ever after, be sterile.

Reprinted from *Surg. Gynecol. Obstet.*, **23**, 203–214 (1916)

SIMPLE STERILIZATION OF WOMEN BY CAUTERY STRICTURE AT THE INTRA–UTERINE TUBAL OPENINGS, COMPARED WITH OTHER METHODS[1]

25

ROBERT L. DICKINSON, F.A.C.S., Brooklyn, New York

SUMMARY

CONTRACEPTIVE measures are difficult to establish as the invariable rule because of their handicaps, the self-control demanded under emotional stress, and a degree of uncertainty accompanying each procedure. Section of the vas deferens, though simple, is not accepted by the male, and mere ligature cuts through. Also, of the pair, he is not the one who requires safeguarding. Ovarian shrinkage by X-ray is neither sure nor is its duration determined. Chemical slough stricture inside the upper uterine angles as advised by Froriep in 1850 was given up, but is worthy of new study. The various operations on the fallopian tubes involve opening the abdominal cavity from above or below, which is never justifiable for this purpose alone, while most of the women for whom it is indicated are poor subjects for operation. Moreover, operations call for the hospital and weeks of disability and may be followed by dragging adhesions; and there is a small percentage of danger to life. The only outlook for a simple and sure method, and that without risk or loss of time and with but little pain, seems to be through closure of the tube, where it enters the uterus, by a stricture produced as the result of a burn with the fine-tipped cautery electrode, a procedure simple enough to be done in the office. Of course all sterilizing measures are predicated on childbearing, in any given instance, being a grave risk to life or productive of permanent ill health.

Steps of procedure. Time selected, 7 to 10 days after period (for least vascularity and thickness of lining).

Location. Hospital, if the patient is sensitive; office, usually.

Technique.

(1) Loose clothing, empty bladder.

(2) Lithotomy posture (or Sims).

(3) Bimanual examination.

(4) Sims speculum, tenaculum in cervix.

(5) Injection of 5 to 10 minims 10 per cent novocaine adrenalin solution into uterus with Skene intra-uterine pipette and pressure; also application to vaginal cervix and vagina, as anæsthesia controls. After 10 minutes and due bleaching proceed to—

(6) Test the shape and length of cavity by ordinary uterine sound; this length noted.

(7) Slide on cautery sound goes to same measure.

(8) Burn of some spot on external os, with slight pressure, until wire tip is buried, to serve as a cautery control. Note time needed.

(9) If cervix is hard, burying of tip in an anæsthetized place on the vaginal wall as control. Note of required time.

(10) Cautery sound passed to cornu; held there, without pressure, the same length of time as needed to bury wire tip in cervix or vagina, with same amount of current.

(11) Repeated on opposite side.

(12) Watching slough and scar form on cervix or vagina. When firmly contracted, one may be able to test the tubes for patency by the Cary method — injecting a silver solution into the uterus under pressure, and securing an X-ray shadow of the distended uterine cavity, and also of the tubes, if they are open.

STERILIZATION OF WOMEN

A bare outline of the various procedures follows:

(a) By opening the abdomen; (b) by intra-uterine treatment.

(a) *By opening abdominal cavity.* (1) *Removal of the ovaries* is inexcusable if the ovaries are sound, as disturbances of sudden climacteric and sexual apathy result. This method has been abandoned.

(2) *Removal of the uterus*, leaving ovaries and feelings intact, is unwarranted except

---

[1] Read before joint session of the Chicago Gynecological Society and the Chicago Medical Society, February 16, 1916. (For discussion see p. 234.)

in case of tumor, uncontrollable bleeding, or bad prolapse.

(3) *Removal of the tubes* together with wedge at cornu is certain, but must be delicately done not to damage ovarian circulation with resultant shrinkages. It is not easily done in vaginal operations.

(4) *Exsection of portion of tubes.* (a) Of wedge at cornu, only. This is certain, but more surgery than in *b* and *c*. (b) With burial of proximal end under peritoneum; no pregnancies reported following it. (c) Simple removal of piece (best with proximal ligature only). This is practically certain, as only two pregnancies are known to have followed.

(5) *Ligature of tube*, single or double; some pregnancies follow — in women and lower animals. Any kind of tubal ligation or removal of a section (except into cornu) has resulted in an open end (42 per cent) and has occasionally been followed by restoration of continuity, but pregnancies following any tubal operation are infrequent enough to be curiosities. Any tubal ligatures may result in hydrosalpinx (although abdominal end of tube is wide open) as shown in animal experiments and in human beings.

(6) *Tubal ampullæ fastened into vagina* — on occasion of vaginal cœliotomy — has been rarely tried; in my patient, tenderness at these openings persisted.

(b) *By intra-uterine treatment.* (1) Obliteration of the whole uterine cavity by steaming (atmocausis) is difficult to control and has been abandoned.

(2) Atresia produced at entry of tube into the cavity of the body of the uterus by (a) chemical corrosion slough, circular scar closure; (b) cautery burn, slough, circular stricture—action on selected spots, area of damage readily kept within limits.

That there is a field for study and for better methods than we have had is shown by the difficulties with all other ways of safeguarding the woman to whom pregnancy means serious risk to life or health.

OBJECTIONS TO CONTRACEPTIVE METHODS

Unless we believe in asceticism, with marriage as a brother-and-sister relation, we must instruct patients in methods of birth-control.

The difficulty concerning these several methods, whether withdrawal, vaginal suppositories, womb veil, or stem, after-douche, or male cover, is that where most needed they are likely to be least used, and for two reasons; the forethought involved, the watchfulness never to be caught off guard, the self-control and unselfish consideration for the mate, are demanded of a man, a woman, or a pair swept away by passion; and, further, they are required of the rough workman or dull peasant. This is a big task in training, particularly as we must ask most of the least intelligent if we desire to breed up and not down. Always spontaneity of caress is to be coupled with preparedness; the enchantment with a measure of fearfulness.

Since the gratification is mostly on the part of the man (because of the present lack of premarital teaching and post-marital training and the dread of pregnancy always present) it is up to the man to accept the handicap — such as the cover. And the selfish man refuses.

After very considerable experience with solid, cylindrical, wholly intra-uterine stems (for anteflexion and for premature menopause, placed so that they may remain continuously for years) I make bold to voice the belief that we shall eventually adopt, as a means of security, the unintermittent wearing of some very simple Y-shaped device, entirely intra-uterine, easily placed or removed, while for temporary guarding we shall chiefly trust to the cover, tested and lubricated.

OBJECTIONS TO STERILIZATION OF HUSBAND

Let us pass by the question of defective and diseased males that should be sterilized. Let us grant for the sake of argument the general claim that since the male receives most gratification (in some cases all the pleasure and all the recurrent desire) therefore all the preventives should be his. Nevertheless one may yet hope to be able to suggest without offense that there is a basis for a scientific or legal stand to the following effect. Of the pair, since the woman is the one who needs safeguarding, the paralysis of the man's procreative (as distinguished from his copulative) ability is beside the mark and is attacking the wrong end of the problem in the married.

A claim may also be made for immunity from sterilization on the part of the husband which he could hardly, with good grace, voice himself; namely, the possibility of future marriage and the desire for progeny from such marriage. This reasoning would apply particularly when the wife is an invalid — less to her who has overborne.

For the male there is a relatively uncomplicated method of sterilization with slight loss of structure or of time. Vasectomy, or the removal of a piece of the conduit above the testicle, as it runs close under the skin of the scrotum, by the use of local anæsthesia, has become a standardized procedure and has been accepted by the laws of several states for the sterilization of the defective and the criminally insane. For the man who desires a method which would permit of resumption of function, should he care to have children later, reuniting of the cut ends has been proposed (or else simple ligation of the duct). Through a small incision in the scrotal skin the vas deferens is brought to the surface. A fine silk or linen ligature or silver wire is passed about it and drawn snugly enough to obliterate the caliber of the duct but with intention not to cut it through. The ends of the ligature are cut close, the duct dropped back, and the skin closed. The ligature becomes encysted. A test made of the semen shows all other elements, and unaltered bulk, but no spermatozoa. If at some subsequent time it is desired to resume this capability for fertilization, the wound can be reopened and the little ligature cut off. But experiment has shown that, as with other ligatures, with mucous lining in apposition with mucous lining, and particularly with pressure from behind, it is difficult or impossible to shut off a canal.

While criminals can be forced to submit to the operation it does not prevent their living a loose sexual life. It may indeed foster such license, since cohabitation is safeguarded from the danger of impregnation. But it does prevent the degenerate and the criminal thus treated from propagating their kind. The trouble with either operation, as one sees it in practice, is that although many a husband comes begging for a sure means of prevention after he has produced four or five children, or because of his wife's tuberculosis or Bright's disease, yet no man has been found willing to submit to the operation in this writer's experience and in that of many others.

As to the uncertainty of ligation of the vas deferens, all the data bearing on the difficulty or improbability of closing a duct by muco-mucous apposition would apply; also no ligature except silver wire will last. Fraenkel's animal experiments have an interesting bearing. Silk, if too thick, suppurates; if too thin, absorbs. Thick silk tied with moderate pressure cuts into the canal of the fallopian tube of rabbits. In 4 cases, with silk, the canal was found broken into in 15 to 20 days. In 8 cases using thick silk, the lumen was present within 23 to 90 days. There were experiments on 26 rabbits on a tube 1 to 2 mm. in thickness and therefore comparable to the vas deferens. In some few cases Fraenkel cut the tube or cut out sections of it or even used the cautery, yet he could not close the canal except in rare instances. With these various methods, 42 per cent of these fallopian tubes stayed open. In more than one-half of his ligated tubes the ligature worked in far enough to open the lumen, there being no difference between thick and thin silk; the opening into the peritoneal cavity occurring under the knot or opposite it. Once, plain catgut was found present at 157 days and once silk absorbed in 14 days. He suggests silver wire or silkworm as a more permanent ligature. In one case No. 14 iron dyed silk had cut across the tube and lay all outside it, the re-established tube with its lumen perfect, the ligature and its knot intact and encapsulated.

That simple removal of a piece of the vas may not suffice is shown by the following instances. In two cases Fraenkel cut a gap out of the fallopian tube of the rabbit 1½ cm. long, yet these tubes remade themselves perfectly macroscopically and microscopically. With double ligature and simple section

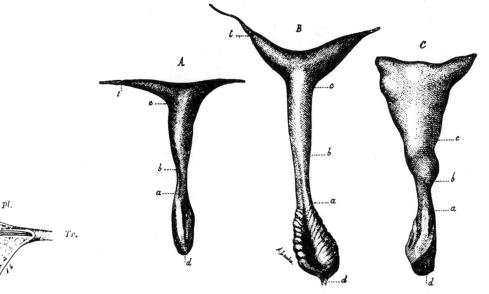

Fig. 1. Orifice of the tube open and spread out to show the longitudinal folds (Guyon). Virgin uterus.

Fig. 2. Casts of the uterine cavity (natural size), after Guyon. A, Cast of uterine cavity of virgin 17 years old; c, cornu of uterus; cb, inferior segment of body; ba, isthmus; ad, cervix; t, tubes, slight narrowing at the point of junction of their cavity with that of the body. B, Cast, nullipara 42 years old. The same letters for the same parts. The horns are longer and the superior segment more developed. C, Cast of cavity of uterus of multipara (same organ as Fig. 5) triangular form of cavity of body; enlargement and deformity of the uterine horns.

no restoration occurred. In animals there is easier regeneration of organs than in man: yet Zweifel's woman showed just such reconstructive power in her tube. Double ligature and a simple cut across would seem to be indicated. This would facilitate a reuniting later, if such were desired, though success is doubtful.

OBJECTIONS TO OPERATIVE STERILIZATION OF WOMAN

Every laparotomy involves a certain percentage of risk, however simple the procedure undertaken inside the abdomen. There is always the possibility of bowel adhesion or of omental drag, and these adhesions may give more or less discomfort. There can hardly be more than one answer to the question whether a method with any death-rate at all — small as that rate may be — and possible complications afterward, is justifiable when done largely for the safeguarding of sexual gratification on the part of husband and wife. No man of fine feeling would ask his wife to submit herself to such a risk, even with

powerful physical impulses on her side. Nor is it to be forgotten that a laparotomy, even a simple one, involves from one to three weeks in bed, and even with a cross incision like the Pfannenstiel, with its hidden scar, care needs to be taken for some months on account of the possibility of hernia.

For the sterilization of women all the procedures, save one, have involved entering the peritoneal cavity through an abdominal incision or through a vaginal incision. In either case the tubes are tied, or else tied and cut and one end of each buried. Or the tubes are removed. Removal of the tube is so likely to disturb ovarian circulation, and so prolongs the operation, that the most popular method is double ligature and burying the proximal ends. Ligature with section without burying has resulted in some cases in a reopening of the tied tube and pregnancy has followed. It is said to be possible to restore a tube by approximating the cut ends or by insertion of the cut end into the uterine cavity. It should be made clear, however, that success under these conditions is problematical.

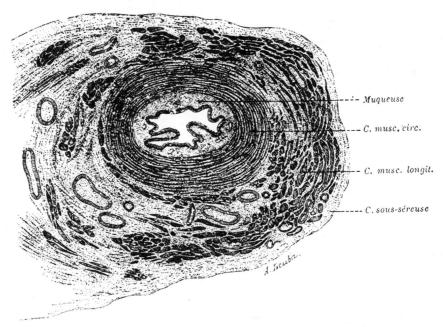

--:-- Muqueuse

--- C. musc. circ.

--- C. musc. longit.

---- C. sous-séreuse

Fig. 3. Transverse section of the tube near the uterine orifice (Orthman).

Strictures produced at the uterine cornu call for certain preliminary considerations, anatomical and pathological.

ANATOMY

Testut states that the inner opening of the tube scarce permits the introduction of a boar's bristle. Poirier and Charpy say "the ostium uterinum measures about one millimeter in diameter and is impossible to catheterize in the living [Floeckinger's case excepted and accepted] and even difficult to see in the dead, and is often closed by very thin mucus" (Fig. 1).

"In the nullipara one sees in the incised organ that the intramural segment, analogous to the uterine cornu of animals, resembles a funnel (Fig. 1) opening toward the cavity of the uterus. The narrowest part of the tubal canal (which is the ostium uterinum in the multipara) is found in the nullipara some millimeters further and not exactly at the superolateral part of the cavity of the uterus" (Richard). While most of our sterilizing is done for the multipara, it will thus be seen that for the non-parous uterus a smaller tip and greater care are needed, lest we place the stricture too low and leave blood from

menstruating membrane to back up behind it. Guyon's casts show the differences (Fig. 2).

"The mucous coat," says Testut, "lines the muscular coat of the tube and adheres to it entirely without a connective-tissue layer between. There is scant folding in the interstitial section. In the intervals of the folds the mucous membrane measures 0.1 mm. to 0.2 mm. in thickness" (Fig. 3).

Our deliberate inquiry has, however, chiefly or only to do with the mucosa of the cavity of the uterus at a point as far into the angle as we can penetrate with a blunted tip without force. To quote Testut further, "the mucous membrane of the body of the uterus adheres intimately to the muscular coat beneath it; but it is very friable and consequently alters easily. Its thickness at the middle of the uterus, where it attains its maximum, is 1 to 2 mm.; from there it diminishes gradually in passing toward the superior angles. At the level of the entrance of the tubes it is hardly 0.5 millimeter."

"The thickness of the walls of the uterus, elsewhere in the corpus averaging 10 to 15 mm., is at the opening of the tubes only 8 mm. (Sappey) . . . . The width of the transverse diameter is 25 mm. between the tubes.

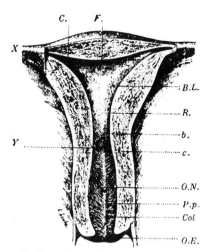

Fig. 4. Cavity of uterus of virgin, posterior surface natural size. *pp*. Palma plicatæ clearly defined, *O.N.*, Nabothian glands (Guyon, Rieffel).

. . . . The uterine cavity of the multipara has a triangular shape like that of the nullipara but less regular . . . . According to Guyon, Hageman, and Mauclaire this cavity becomes enlarged (or at least the uterine horns descend, in a sense, so that if from the extremity of the horns of the uterus one draws (in a virgin) a straight line to the internal os (Fig. 4, XY) one will have nearly the form of the cavity of the multipara (Fig. 5): the uterine horn has not disappeared but widened or enlarged."

CLOSURE OF THE INNER END OF THE TUBE BY DISEASE

All the authorities agree that in hydrosalpinx or pyosalpinx obliteration of the lumen of the tube at the uterine end practically does not occur (Albers, Reymond, Landau). Closure is produced only in a mechanical way, by kinking. Atresia (absence of any opening) by the shut-down of a scar (*narbige Einziehung*) or adhesion (*Verwachsung*) is rare (Fromme and Heynemann, Veit's *Handbuch*).

There is an ample literature well illustrated for the closure of the fimbriated ends of the tube, but only a paragraph or a sentence given by each writer concerning the pathology, macroscopic or microscopic, of the inner end of the tube. A reasonable search found no picture of a section of a sacto-salpinx that cut through fundus and interstitial and uterine

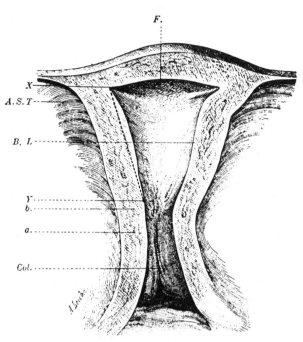

Fig. 5. Cavity of the uterus of a multipara; natural size. Triangular form of the body; folds of the tube radiating in the superolateral angles; double column of the palma plicatæ (Guyon).

portions of the tube and its sac. Our total find is one diagram of Reymond's that does not take in the cornu. Microscopic sections exhibit the kinked tube, where the lumen is shown two or three times in the same slide. In practice the pathologist's contention is borne out by authentic but most uncommon cases, beginning with Frank's in 1840, in which the tube empties its contents into the uterus. The anatomic proof was furnished by Rokitansky and Klob.

CLOSURE OF THE TUBE BY LIGATURE

The classic experiments are Fraenkel's, embracing 33 operations on 26 rabbits. The tubes of the higher mammals are very like the human, histologically. Those of the rabbit are 1 to 2 mm. thick. He found that notwithstanding favorably placed strands and tight ligatures one does not often succeed in interrupting the lumen of the canal of the tube. Whether with section or with ligature, tight or loose, thick or thin, of catgut, or silk, or rubber, atresias were accidental and rare. Forty per cent of the canals stood open into

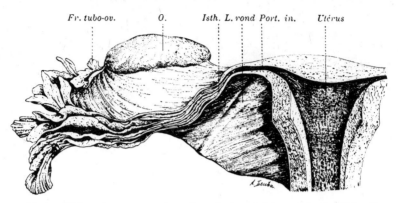

Fr. tubo-ov.   O.   Isth. L. rond Port. in.   Utérus

Fig. 6. Right tube cut open throughout its length in a multipara (Richard).

the peritoneal cavity, and a ligature could cut through and the canal repair itself. In two of the cases the cutting away of a section 1.5 cm. long resulted in a re-established channel. He was not able to use the hot wire to cauterize the lining because the caliber was too narrow. Ten to fifteen per cent of his ligated tubes ended in hydrosalpinx, though the ampulla was open. He counsels omission of a ligature on the cut end of the distal portion if section is done. For sterilization Fraenkel recommends removal of a wedge at the cornu and favors removal of the whole tube with the wedge. The reopening of the tube coincides with general operative experience in part, since, rather as curiosities, a small number of pregnancies have been reported after ligation or amputation of the tubes.

EXPERIMENTAL CLOSURE BY CAUTERY

Experiments upon animals to test cautery stricture are unsatisfactory because of the bicornate uterus, with the tube a continuation of the uterus, there being no cornu as it exists in the human uterus. Their uterine musculature is so thin, compared with the bulging thickness of the human uterine wall near the cornu that it is not possible to make adequate comparison. The only advantage in animal experimentation is that the abdomen can be opened and the action of the cautery observed through these thin-walled structures. One difficulty with observations on the ape consists in the high cost of all the larger monkeys. Therefore our preliminary studies will

be mainly restricted to the application of this method to patients with reasonably symmetrical uteri which will subsequently require to be taken out for the hæmorrhages of the menopause; that is, the persistent bleeding of arteriosclerosis or chronic metritis which is not relieved by curetting. I made this test also with a small fibroid uterus, but on one side the cautery tip ran up beneath a submucous fibroid and lodged there (Fig. 7). The test cannot well be made in the operating room after curetting has been done because of the oozing but on such a menorrhagic uterus, in which one has failed with curetting, the experiment may harmlessly precede removal to train one for actual cases where it is indicated. In the office it should be done, for such practice, at some time a few weeks before hysterectomy, so that the scar would have been formed and could be studied in section and it should not be done at such a brief time preceding operation that suppuration is under way at the time of removal.

Is there danger of the *cautery tip puncturing* the uterine wall? In experiments with a newly killed animal it is seen that as far as the intestinal wall goes there is not a great deal of difference between ten seconds and twenty seconds application of the heat. If five seconds application of the tip at a given heat will result in an eschar involving the whole mucous membrane, then twenty-five seconds is needed to produce perforation of the entire intestinal wall. This field of double the necessary exposure gives us a wide margin of safety. Moreover one takes care

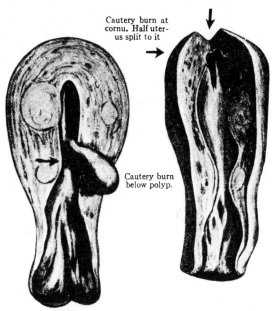

Cautery burn at cornu. Half uterus split to it

Cautery burn below polyp.

Fig. 7. Sketch of uterus in which the blunt or dome-tipped cautery-sound produced burns, preceding hysterectomy, as a demonstration of this method. Misapplied on one side — under polyp.

that no pressure is exerted in applying our heat and thus we further safeguard its application.

As shown by the researches of Hitchman and Adler, the mucous membrane of the uterine cavity is two or three times as thick during the six or seven days preceding the beginning of menstruation as during the resting stage. Therefore this is a time to be avoided. For three or four days after the cessation of menstruation, however, bleeding is so readily produced on contact that these days also should be avoided. The best time therefore will be from the seventh to the fourteenth day following the cessation of the flow.

CATHETERIZATION OF THE FALLOPIAN TUBES

W. Tyler Smith in 1849 speaks confidently of passing a fine whalebone guide through a silver directing tube which, fitting the curves of the cavity, leads the fishbone to the horn of the uterus and so beyond. "The fallopian angle of the uterine cavity is so acute, and the internal surface so smooth and dense in this situation that it is almost impossible for the whalebone fiber to miss the tube . . . . It is

necessary to have two silver tubes or catheters, one for the left, the other for the right" with "the curve of the uterine sound . . . . and an additional lateral curve at the extremity, turning toward the fallopian tube . . . . not as large as the uterine sound . . . . The bougie is very flexible at the extremity." Further study of this abandoned procedure is worth undertaking (Fig. 8).

STRICTURE BY CHEMICAL ACTION

The attempt to treat diseases of the endometrium and hæmorrhage by strong corrosive agents brought out a considerable literature in both French and German. The ultimate sweeping condemnation of the severer methods has an important bearing on our particular problem. Such destruction of the lining of the uterus occurred that obliteration of the cavity resulted, in part or in whole; or vicious stenosis followed, shutting off parts of the uterus and blocking up menstrual flow or suppressing it entirely. The reports demonstrate the power and effectiveness of these agents, which, hurtful in excess and when applied to a large area, may well do the work we require if properly limited and controlled. For instance Rielander (*Veit's Handbuch*, 226) did four hysterectomies 15 to 30 hours after chemical intra-uterine treatment (iodine, colloidal silver, formalin). The mucous membrane after 30 per cent formalin in alcoholic solution was sloughing in 24 hours, and after 50 per cent formalin in watery solution necrosed throughout, where cauterized. Crayons of 50 per cent zinc chlorid in the uterus, or the stick of fused silver nitrate left hours in the cervix — even with its thick lining — have produced complete obliteration. Of course such severe and painful measures thus applied are to be condemned. They may even lead to threatening hæmorrhage, from deep sloughing, as in the cases of Duehrrsen and Duvelius. With these brief references to a large subject we pass on, merely drawing attention to the familiar partial closures of the vagina from cohesion of surfaces bared of their linings, and these in a canal subject to more motion than the uterine walls.

Froriep, in 1850, proposed a limitation of this chemical action in order thus to pro-

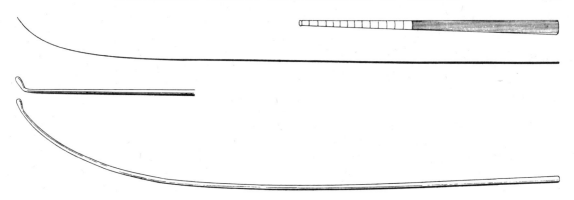

Fig. 8.   Front and side views of the fallopian catheter.   The first showing the uterovaginal curve; the second, the fallopian curve of the instrument.   The other figures represent the whalebone bougie and the handle (scale unknown). (Tyler Smith.)

duce a limited slough and a stricture located in the tip of the horn of the uterus. ˙ He seems to have received little attention. The procedure consists herein: The speculum is introduced and "the conductor (Leitungs-rohr) is passed through the os uteri up to the uterine opening of the tube and through this is pushed a sound tipped with nitrate of silver and so the circumference of the tubal opening is changed into a slough by deep cauterization." The same process is carried out on the other side, and "then the casting off of the two sloughs is watched."

"This casting off will take place (by analogy with cauterization of the bladder opening) in about 7 days, and there is the greatest possibility that, as no excretory flow keeps the way open, the complete adhesion (Ver-wachsung) has already occurred, as soon as the casting off of the slough has taken place. That the closure is perfect may be ascertained with sureness 8 days later by introducing the whalebone sound of Dr. Tyler Smith by which one may convince himself that the tubal lumen toward the uterus is passable. If this should be the case on one side, naturally the procedure must be repeated." He goes on to say that this cauterization is not dangerous, as it is the practice to produce such cauteriz-ing with much deeper reaching injury to cure endometritis when the caustic agent must be applied through the speculum and when it is accomplished without consciousness on the part of the patient and many times without any marked reaction.

STRICTURE BY INTRA–UTERINE CAUTERY
ELECTRODE

A method is submitted, simple and without danger, and heretofore only published by me in a discussion. It involves a moderate de-gree of gynecological dexterity and also some familiarity with the use of the electric cautery. It may be carried out in fifteen minutes in any office properly equipped.

The procedure consists in the production of a complete closure at the point where the fallopian tube enters the uterine cavity. The stricture is caused by scar shrinkage following the burn and the slough produced by the application of heat through a cautery tip the size of the point of the ordinary uterine sound on an instrument resembling a uterine sound, or by the use of the ordinary nasal electrode.

My evolution of this method has been as follows: Hunner has advocated the treat-ment of endotrachelitis by the use of the Paquelin tip. While simple and superficial involvements do best under silver salts or iodine, when one encounters a cervix chron-ically everted, eroded, and markedly granular, there is no method inducing such quick and permanent healing as the use of the heated wire. Take, for instance, the woman who has had one or two children and, as a result, has suffered considerable laceration of the cervix with subsequent outrolling and raw-ness. She desires other children. Mean-while the cervix has to be put into order. If it is repaired or amputated subsequent

284

delivery will almost always tear it open again. Or there are cases in which the disease is on a sufficiently small area of the cervix so that, once healed, there would be no need of doing an inversion operation. The smallest sized tip that is used in the nose is applied in a point-puncture fashion or in longitudinal stripes, the burn going through the thickened mucous membrane. This may or may not have been preceded by the use of adrenalin novocaine applied to surfaces freed from all mucus. The method is a painful one without cocaine. One more successful use of this means in endotrachelitis I have developed; namely, in aggravated cervical catarrh. The cervical canal is solidly blocked with clear mucus, very tenacious and often large in quantity. In such cases one can spend several minutes in twisting strips of gauze into the canal before the half drachm of tenacious mucus has been entangled and is gradually withdrawn. Then we have a cavity which would hold the tip of the finger provided it could pass the narrowed external os. It had been my habit to treat these by scraping the gristly lining of this cervical canal with the small, sharp curette, which rasps as if on the back of Brussels carpet. If one fails under such conditions, the ordinary cautery wire tip of small size is laid along this area in stripes; or the tiny dome, its end the size of the ordinary uterine sound, is employed.

These matters have been developed in some detail because anyone who would carry out the method which I advocate in this paper would have an advantage in being accustomed to the use of the cautery under the above conditions, and would feel himself at home when this little dome or tip is slipped far out of sight up into the angle of the uterus. Previous experience shows just what heat will produce a given amount of slough.

DETAILS OF PROCEDURE

The steps are as follows: A suitable case is chosen. The patient has no submucous fibroid or cancer or any other disease which would necessitate a hysterectomy, or any disease which would necessitate opening the abdomen, for in either of these cases

hysterectomy or ligation of the tube would be clearly indicated rather than this method. Lying on the table with clothing loosened and bladder empty, in the lateroprone posture, and the Sims speculum in place, with the perfect illumination of the head light, or the forehead mirror, in a darkened room, a single tenaculum seizes the anterior lip of the cervix and steadies it. The canal being clean and open, 5 to 10 minims of novocaine (10 per cent) in adrenalin solution are injected through a Skene pipette and held under pressure a few seconds. Ten minutes are allowed for anæsthesia. Then the canal is wiped with Churchill's tincture or pure carbolic acid. Next the ordinary uterine sound, with the ordinary curve, and surely sterile, is passed into the uterus and to the fundus. It turns gently sidewise to outline the cavity of the uterus and find the cornu, and an exact note is made of the distance. We will say from the external os this is 2.5 inches. A clear mental picture is made of each cornu and the distance apart of the two angles. The sound is withdrawn. The cautery sound (which is of the same size) is bent to conform in shape to the uterine sound and has its slide pushed up until there is exposed exactly 2.5 inches of the farther end. This sound bears on its tip a little spiral or dulled point of platinum wire which will become incandescent. The switch is thrown and the platinum wire heated up as a test that it is working. Then against the cervical mucous membrane, in plain sight, the platinum tip is placed. The current is turned on. A count is made of the number of seconds required to burn into the tissues a sufficient distance to bury the platinum wire. This will then be the correct time, under ordinary circumstances, for the cornu. If the cervical tissue is dense from chronic inflammation a part of the vaginal wall may furnish the control test. It will have been previously bleached with novocaine-adrenalin. Now the tip is allowed to cool and this sound is passed into the uterus and finds the cornu as previously determined. Then the current is turned on for the number of seconds that have been found necessary to produce the burying effect at the cervix, care being taken

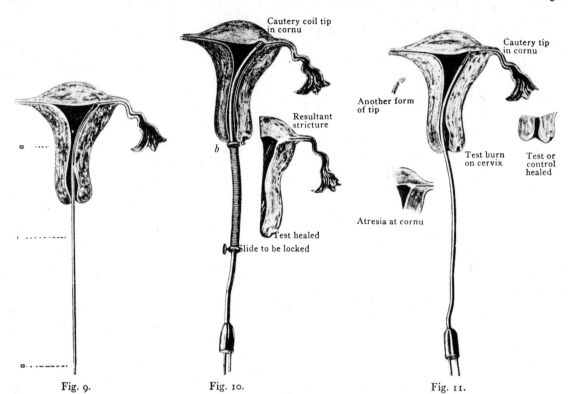

Fig. 9.   Fig. 10.   Fig. 11.

Fig. 9. Sterilization by chemical cauterization, showing metal or bent wood rod tipped with caustic. The rod may run in the catheter.

Fig. 10. Sterilization by cautery stricture with dome tip on uterine sound. This collar (*b*) prevents tip en-tering beyond previously determined depth. (*a*) Test cautery.

Fig. 11. Sterilization by cautery stricture with fine cautery electrode.

to exert no pressure more than is necessary to hold the cautery sound in place. The other cornu may be done at the same time or at a second session. The patient may lie down a bit or go home in some comfortable way and be quiet at home that afternoon and evening. If she has discomfort next day she should be quiet for that day and two or three thereafter. The reaction is usually no more than that of an ordinary intra-uterine application. A little bloody dis-charge may occur then or some days later, and the next period may be a little uncomfort-able. There occurs on the cervix a slough and then a clean granulating wound that within two or three weeks is healed over. The cervix condition gives a guide to what is going on inside. At the end of three or four months the presence of a stricture and the closure of the tube may be ascertained by the X-ray method of William H. Cary of Brooklyn.

Strict indications must be worked out for each case. This goes without saying. The presence of physical conditions—like extreme deformity of the pelvis, or of disease, such as chronic Bright's, or of disability, such as idiocy, epilepsy or confirmed insanity or of criminality — these are presupposed. The more difficult decisions are in the case of women apparently permanently neurasthenic from severe labors or who have had to have several pregnancies interrupted. In any case written consents of husband and wife (or of the parents of an idiot) and signed agree-ments of physician and specialist should safe-guard this measure.

Objections. The objections to cautery stricture will probably lie in unskilled at-tempts. An insufficient cauterization will not produce atresia (complete closure). Ad-hesions of the uterine walls lower than the angle will do what the old chemical corrosives did and may back up menstrual blood behind the spot acted on. Local hæmatometra or even hæmatosalpinx may result from such imperfect technique. By analogy with experimental ligatures of tubes on animals hydrosalpinx may follow this procedure even with tubes wide open at their flaring ends. Such hydrosalpinx has been of mild degree. The main trouble of course lies in the difficulty of knowing whether one has succeeded and whether assurance can be given so positively that the pair can omit contraceptive measures. Wherefore, until experience with removed uteri or freedom from pregnancy proves the procedure right we cannot be sure of it, unless, possibly, we can refine Tyler Smith's tubal catheter or perfect Cary's shadows.

In the case of defectives the simplicity of the procedure makes it worthy of trial even if we cannot guarantee all attempts.

REFERENCES

ALBERS, J. F. H. Erlaeuterung zu dem Atlasse der pathologische Anatomie, 1862.

BANDL. Pitha-Billroth, Chirurgie iv, 1879, v, 1.

BILLROTH, TH. Handbuch der Frauenkrankheiten, 1877, xi, 24 (refers to Smith and Froriep).

CARY, WILLIAM H. Note on determination of patency of the fallopian tubes by the use of collargol and X-ray shadow. Am. J. Obst., N. Y., 1914, lxix, No. 3.

DOEDERLEIN. Veit's Handbuch der Gynaekologie, 1907, ii, 226.

DOEDERLEIN and KROENIG. Operative Gynaekologie, 1912, p. 340.

DUMONTPALLIER. Traitément local de l'endometrite chronique. Gaz. d. hôp. 1889, lxii, 605.

FRAENKEL, L. Experimente zur Herbeifuehrung der Unwegsamkeit der Eileiter. Arch. f. Gynaekologie, 1889, lviii, 374.

FROMME and HEYNEMANN. Veit's Handbuch der Gynaekologie, 1910, v, 131.

FRORIEP, R. Zur Vorbeugung der Nothwendigkeit des Kaiserschnitts und der Perforation. Notiz. a. d. Geb. d. Natur-und Heilk., 1849.

HENNIG, C. Die Krankheiten der Eileiter und der Tubarschwangerschaft fuer praektische Aerzte dargestellt, mit 18 Holzschnitten, 1876. Vollstaendigste Literatur. (Reference given by Winckel. Not available.)

HUNNER, G. L. The treatment of leucorrhœa with the actual cautery. J. Am. M. Ass., 1906, Jan. 20.

KLOB, J. M. Pathologische Anatomie der Weiblichen Sexualorgane, 1864.

LANDAU. Les salpingites, 1892 (small monograph). Arch. de tocol. et de gynéc., Par., 1892, xix, 936; J. de méd., chir., et pharmacol., Brux., 1892, i, 181.

MARTIN, A. Krankheiten der Weiblichen Adnexorgane, 1895, i, 54 (refers to Froriep).

POIRIER et CHARPY. Traité d'anatomie humaine, 1907, v, 411, 436.

REYMOND, EMILE. Contribution a l'etude de la bacteriologie et de l'anatomie pathologique des salpingo-ovarites, 1895.

SMITH, W. TYLER. New method of treating sterility by the removal of obstructions of the fallopian tubes. Lancet, Lond., 1849, p. 529.

TESTUT. Traité d'anatomie humaine, 1895, p. 566.

WALDEYER, W. Das Becken, 1899, p. 505.

WINCKEL, F. Die Pathologie der weiblichen Sexualorgane, 1881. Gives literature.

Reprinted from *Obstet. Gynecol. Surv.*, **12**, 291–305 (Feb. 1957)

Review

26   A REVIEW OF TUBAL STERILIZATION FAILURES

ALLAN E. GARB

Department of Obstetrics and Gynecology, State University of New York, Downstate Medical Center and the Kings County Hospital, Brooklyn, N. Y.

Fallopian tubal sterilization is a common practice. At least 29,500 cases are reported in the literature, and this, of course, is only a small fraction of the actual number of tubal sterilizations performed. That pregnancy can occur after tubal sterilization is well known. However, the *incidence* of such recurrence is generally not known, and various figures are often quoted for such recurrences which contradict each other. It is the purpose of this paper to attempt to summarize a large portion of the literature on this matter and to bring up to date a numerical figure which represents the actual incidence of failure of tubal sterilization.

Dickinson and Gamble, listing an extensive bibliography on all types of technics used in sterilization, state that "combinations and variants on methods of approach, of resection of the fallopian tubes, of crushing and of burying and of cautery, have put into the literature at least 3,500 titles covering some 43 procedures for obstructing the oviducts." The reports concerning failures of sterilization are much less numerous, and from time to time various authors have attempted to bring the literature up to date by summarizing these reports. In attempting to condense the summaries this paper will confine itself only to those pregnancies resulting from failures of tubal sterilization.

HISTORICAL REVIEW

Historically sterilization of the female has been of interest to the medical profession since first contemplated by Hippocrates as a means of eliminating hereditary perpetuation of the insane. Von Blundell is credited with the initial written suggestion of tubal sterilization in his textbook, published in 1834. The method he suggested was total resection but he wrote that simple division might successfully prevent pregnancy. Froriep, in 1850, suggested the creation of a chemical slough stricture in the upper uterine angles to prevent pregnancy. This was the forerunner of the recent suggestions for failure in a case of tubal ligation. Between 1880 and 1910 a wide variety of procedures was carried out with uniformly poor results. In 1898 and 1899 many failures were encountered by Ries, Fraenkel and Aftergeld. A report by Leonard in 1913 emphasized the high incidence of failure of all methods of sterilization. An extensive report by Nuernberger in 1917 described 36 methods of tubal sterilization and concluded that salpingectomy or cornual resection was the best. He found that the major part of the failures was due to sutures insufficiently secured or too snugly tied. Madlener's publication in 1919 received widespread acclamation in this country and in Germany and introduced a popular technic for tubal sterilization. Williams, in 1921, reviewed 44 cases at the Johns Hopkins Hospital.

291

Many new technics were developed from 1920 to 1940. Up to 1926 Müller cited 793 cases of tubal sterilization operations with 34 known failures. In 1926 and again in 1932 Madlener reported on two series with no failures, with his technic, though others reported failures. Von Graff reviewed the subject up to 1938. He collected 4,279 Madlener sterilizations with 19 known failures, wherein he made a critical analysis of the failures. He concluded that the failures resulted from not adhering to Madlener's exact technic. Dippel, in 1940, studied five Madlener failures and demonstrated two cases of endosalpingiosis. Lazard, in 1940, reviewed the entire subject and stated that "of the tubal sterilization procedures the Madlener type is the safest." However, Lazard felt that because ectopic pregnancies occurred and that fatalities due to infection, embolism, intestinal adhesions and obstruction had been reported (he mentions five deaths) following tubal procedures, hysterectomy is the surest and safest method of sterilization. He concluded: "At best, tubal sterilization procedures leave a functionless organ, potent only for future pathology." In 1933 and 1939 Lull reported extensively upon the method introduced by Pomeroy, stating that in his clinic the method had given exceptionally fine results. His careful analysis of the reported failures of the Pomeroy method confirms the importance of exactly adhering to the technic. His papers offer "proof" that Pomeroy's technic is the simplest and safest of the tubal type sterilization.

In 1946 Knight compared the results of the Pomeroy operation with the published statistics on the Madlener method. He concluded that the 0.31% failure in the Pomeroy operation was better than the 0.6% average failure in a large series of the Madlener type. Knight reported that up to 1946 more than one hundred methods of tubal sterilizations had been described, including knotting of the tubes. The majority of these operations are minor variations on one or two basic themes. All have resulted in a variable number of failures. Carrington, Burlington and Bullitt found references to three patients in whom pregnancy occurred after removal of most of the uterus, and a fourth in whom it occurred after a bilateral salpingectomy accompanied by resection of a wedge from the uterus. Schultze observed pregnancy after total resection of both tubes and amputation of the fundus. Liepman reported it after supravaginal hysterectomy. McMillan and Dunn reported two pregnancies in the same patient after supravaginal hysterectomy with excision of all of one tube and ovary and part of the other tube. Lasch reported pregnancy in a woman who had both tubes, wedges from the uterine cornus and one ovary removed. Stringer, in 1932, reported an instance of congenital absence of the left fallopian tube with removal of the right ovary for torsion of a cyst with subsequent intra-uterine pregnancy. Stringer cited this as an example of "transmigration of the ovum." In 1933 Polak said "pregnancy has occurred after all methods of tubal sterilization, hysterectomy and bilateral salpingo-oophorectomy. The only certain method of preventing conception is the complete removal of ovaries, tubes and uterus." As late as 195: Thomas stated "panhysterectomy is to be preferred to tubectomy for preven ception insurance because there are no failures and, more importantly, there i no chance for subsequent development of serious uterine disease. With repr(

duction completed the uterus contributes nothing; in fact, the womb is then a potential liability."

STERILIZATION PROCEDURES

The various tubal sterilization procedures can be classified in several ways: as therapeutic, voluntary or statutory; as uterine, ovarian, or tubal; as inguinal route, vaginal route or abdominal route; as postpartum, postcesarean or post-laparotomy; as tubal ligation, tubal resection, cornual resection or total salpingectomy; or combinations of all these. Generally, however, tubal operations are classified according to the author, the operative technic or combinations of the two. McNeil and Webb, in 1948, made a questionnaire study of the most common sterilization operations used in the United States. Their conclusions are as follows:

(1) The Pomeroy method is the most frequently used following cesarean section and with laparotomy.

(2) The Madlener technic is the second most popular method used after cesarean section.

(3) Cornual resection is the second most popular method with laparotomy.

(4) Hysterectomy is chosen when uterine disease exists.

Other operations are salpingectomy, defundation, modified Irving sterilization and the Aldridge method of temporary surgical sterilization. Most of the remaining operations are minor variations of those mentioned. By far the most prevalent reports in the literature concern the Madlener and Pomeroy methods. Most of the older literature concerns the former and the more recent concerns the latter. A brief description of the most common tubal sterilization (bilateral) procedures follows.

(1) *Pomeroy operation:* The base of a loop of tube is tied with catgut and the loop together with the subadjacent mesosalpinx is excised distal to the point of ligation. The ligature is absorbed and the two severed ends of the tube have a tendency later to diverge from one another. The principle of the method is ligation and resection.

(2) *Madlener operation*: A loop of tube is grasped with forceps and crushed at its base with a broad clamp. Each arm of the loop is ligated with a nonabsorbable suture at the point of crushing. The principle of the method is crushing and ligation.

(3) *Cornual resection*: The tube is ligated one centimeter from the cornu. The tube is freed from the mesosalpinx and a suture is placed about the cornual branch of the uterine vessels. The tube is excised at the cornu and the cornual wound is closed. The broad ligament is split and the cut end of the tube is buried between the leaves. The round and broad ligaments are brought over the cornu for peritonization and further protection.

(4) *Modified Irving operation*: The tubes are cut and the proximal ends are buried within a pocket of the uterine wall. The broad ligament is closed and the distal end of the tube is buried in the broad ligament (optional).

STERILIZATION FAILURES

In 1946, Knight collected the following series of Madlener sterilizations and failures:

Author	Year	Number of Cases	Number of Failures	Percentage
Von Graff...............	Lit. to 1938	4,279	19	0.44
Neubauer................	1938	83	2	2.40
Adair and Brown........	1939	50	0	0
Lazard..................	1940	117	1	0.85
Dippel.................	1940	101	5	4.90
Hewitt and Whitley......	1940	100	0	0
Brennecke..............	1941	23	0	0
Pfeutze.................	1941	165	3	1.90
Thornton...............	1941	3	0	0
Mays and Dilworth.......	1941	29	0	0
Lock...................	1942	2	0	0
Totals...............		4,952	30	0.6

Dieckmann and Hauser, in 1948, added 912 sterilization cases, the great majority of which were of the Madlener type. They reported 33 Madlener failures (3.6%). Other earlier reports concerning the Madlener method not included in the two studies mentioned are Madlener's own study in 1919 of 89 cases without failure. In 1932 Madlener again reported on a total of 166 cases operated upon in 22 years without a known failure. Gianella, in 1933, collected 604 cases (using a slight modification of the Madlener technic) with one failure. Rubovitz and Kobak reported Madlener failures in 5.3%, and Darner in 8.2%. Schultze collected 32 instances of failure and added two of his own in an unrecorded number of Madlener operations.

Knight also reported on a series of Pomeroy sterilizations and failures. The breakdown follows:

Author	Year	Number of Cases	Number of Failures	Percentage
Lull....................	1940	812	0	0
Thornton...............	1941	219	0	0
Lock...................	1942	57	2	3.5
Sloane.................	1944	174	1	0.6
Totals...		1,262	3	0.31

In Knight's collected series, the incidence of failure for the Pomeroy procedure (0.31%) is about half that for the Madlener (0.6%). In addition to the above data Bishop and Nelms, using the method of Pomeroy, reported 319 cases without failure. In 1947 Nelms and Doyle reported 404 cases with one failure (a ruptured ectopic pregnancy) and Lull and Mitchell, in 1950, reported on a total of 1,550 Pomeroy sterilizations with four failures (0.25%). Boyson and

McRae, reporting in 1949 on 19 cases of Pomeroy tubal sterilization through the vagina, cite a failure in one case (5.2%). Fox reported on 50 Pomeroy sterilizations with one failure (2%).

Reports on failures following sterilization by the cornual resection technic are not nearly so numerous as those for the Madlener and Pomeroy methods. Nuernberger, in 1917, estimated the incidence of failure of cornual resection to be about 7.7%. Knight reported on 42 cornual resections (1946) with no failures. Boyson and McRae reported on 11 cornual resections performed through the vagina (1919) with four failures (36.4%). Rotten (1955) reported five failures (4.76%) in 105 cornual resection operations from January, 1942, to September, 1954.

Reports of failure in the Irving modification sterilization operation are extremely rare. In 1950, Irving reported on the results of 814 patients sterilized by this method between the years 1916 and 1949 at the Boston Lying-In Hospital. He cited no failures. In November, 1956, Prystowsky and Eastman reported (by personal correspondence) the first Irving technic failure ever encountered in their long and extensive experience.

Numerous tabulations on several sterilization technics with failures have been recorded. On the obstetrical service at Sloane Hospital for Women between January, 1934, and January, 1944, 233 tubal sterilizations were performed. As reported by Knight (and mentioned before in this paper) 174 or 75% were Pomeroy resections, 42 or 18% cornual resections with no failures, and 14 or 7% segmental resections with or without burial of the stumps with one failure. All sterilizations were performed at the time of cesarean section in conjunction with hysterectomy or as puerperal procedures. Irving summarized all operation for sterilization on the public wards of the Boston Lying-In Hospital from 1916 to 1949. Irving's report (1950) covers 645 operations reported by Fox in 1940 and 461 cases operated upon since. The total number of operations for sterilization was 1,106. The summary follows:

Type of Sterilization Operation	Number of Cases	Number of Failures	Percentage
Bilateral Irving	814	0	
Bilateral Pomeroy	118	2	1.7
Unilateral Irving combined with other methods	12	0	
Unilateral Pomeroy combined with other methods	3	0	
Hysterectomy	93	0	
Wedge-shape excision	50	0	
Oophorectomy	6	0	
Salpingectomy	5	0	
Ligation of tubes	3	0	
Defundation of uterus	2	0	
Totals	1,106	2	0.18

Lee, Randall and Keettel, in 1951, reported on 1,169 operations on the fallopian tubes at the University Hospitals of Iowa (1926–1948) "for the primary purpose of producing sterilization." Tubal sterilization was the only operative procedure performed in 502 cases. In the remaining 667 instances some other surgical procedure was included. A summary follows:

Type of Sterilization Operation	Number of of Cases	Number of Failures	Percentage
Madlener (abdominal)	⎰544	⎰4	⎰0.7
Madlener (abdominal with cesarean sec.)	⎨194	⎨4	⎨2.0
Madlener (vaginal)	⎱377 (1,115)	⎱4 (Madlener)	⎱1.1
Cornual resection (abdominal)	40	0	
Cornual resection (vaginal)	7	0	
Pomeroy (abdominal)	3	0	
Salpingectomy	3	0	
Defundation	1	0	
Totals	1,169	12	1.0

In 1954 Weinbaum and Javert reported on the sterilization of 643 female patients at the New York Hospital over a twenty year period (1932–1952). Their results are summarized below:

Type of Sterilization Operation	Number of Cases		Failure	Percentage
	Obstetrical	Gynecological		
Madlener	33	6		
Pomeroy	110	23		
Madlener-Pomeroy	218	37	1	
Irving	31	5		
Aldridge	0	1		
Cornual resection	20	9		
Cornual purse-string	7	1		
Ligation, section, peritonealization	38	10		
Ligation, section and overlapping	16	1		
Ligation only	6	3	1	
Ligation, clamping, resection	7	2		
Ligation, section	8	1		
Salpingectomy	1	2		
Mixed tubal	9	9		
Subtotal hysterectomy	11	0		
Total hysterectomy	1	0		
Authors' technic (modified Taussig-Madlener-Pomeroy)	10	0		
Insufficient data	6	1		
Totals	532	111	2	0.4

In an extraordinarily well-documented and complete paper, Prystowsky and Eastman reported, in 1955, on 1,830 puerperal tubal sterilizations performed at Johns Hopkins Hospital between June 1, 1936 and December 31, 1950. In answer to a questionnaire, a follow-up of 1,022 (55%) patients was obtained, and 17 failures (1.7%) were reported. In four of these the pregnancy was tubal. The break-down follows:

Type of Sterilization Operation	Number of Cases		Failure	Percentage
Pomeroy				
Puerperal sterilization	1,022		3	.29 ⎱
At cesarean section or hysterotomy	400 ⎱ 1,478		7	1.75 ⎰ .7
6 or more weeks postpartum or never pregnant.	56 ⎰			
Irving	206			
Madlener	41		3	7.32
Cornual excision	27			
Atypical operation	18		1	5.55
Salpingectomy	5			
Other	55	⎰only one⎱ tube ⎱ligated⎰	3	5.45
Totals	1,830 (follow-up of 1,022 cases)		17 (of 1,022 cases followed)	1.7

In the 1,022 early puerperal sterilizations by the Pomeroy technic there were three known failures, a ratio of 1:340 operations, whereas in 400 cases in which the Pomeroy procedure accompanied cesarean section or hysterotomy, there were seven known failures, a ratio of 1:57 operations. Of the few failures culminating in ectopic pregnancies, two were after puerperal Pomeroy ligation, one after a Madlener operation, and one after an atypical silk technic. One ectopic pregnancy terminated fatally. In addition, two women died from pulmonary embolism, a death rate of 0.3% in 1,022 puerperal Pomeroy sterilizations.

Isolated reports of sterilization failures are sprinkled throughout the literature. Some do not mention the operative procedure used; many do not record the number of cases surveyed and others do not give their source of reference. Furthermore, it is probable that many of the earlier reported failures were included in mass surveys by later authors. In some cases the references are not available and are of little value but are mentioned for purposes of completeness. Müller cited 793 cases of tubal sterilization (including 511 Madlener) operations (up to 1926) with 34 known failures. Jaroschka (1931) reported 194 consecutive cases of partial resection and peritonealization of stumps with no known failures. Mayer reported in 1936 that "several hundred" tubal sterilization operations had been performed at the New York Mt. Sinai Hospital with only three known failures. The method used was "modification of the technic of Hans and Kohler who tie off a loop of the tube," and in addition, a resection of the "redundant portion of the loop." Aldridge, in 1934, reported on one case of temporary surgical sterilization with subsequent pregnancy. The Aldridge method employs the burial of the fimbric ends of the tubes beneath the peritoneum of the broad ligament. Eighteen cases of pregnancy have even been reported following ligation of the ovarian vessels and the inferior vena cava as a method of control in thromboembolic disease (Collins, Batson, 1954). Gilbert, in 1950, reported on the Rincon method of sterilization in 1,284 cases at the Ryder Memorial Hospital in Puerto Rico, with two failures. He believed the average failure rate was one in every 98 cases, or about one per cent. Price in Zurich (1935) reported eight failures in 1,500 cases, (operative technic not known). Greggerson reported two failures in 98 cases (technic not known). Curth, in 1939, reported on 1,000 Madlener and Menge operations with one failure after cornual resection. Doederlein, in 1934, reported a 4.5% failure rate (technic not known). Lutz and Kellogg have each reported one Pomeroy failure. Farerh (Zurich, 1936) reported 9,393 sterilization operations with one failure in 200. Gobble, in 1955, reported on a five year survey of 533 tubal ligations (1948–1952) in North Carolina but did not mention reports of failures. Ross and Farber, in 1953, reported a tubal sterilization failure with ruptured tubal pregnancy complicating a therapeutic pneumoperitoneum. Recently numerous reports from France on isolated cases of tubal sterilization failure have been reported by Gaujoux, Milliez, James, Leconte and others.

In addition, many reports have appeared on intra-uterine cautery sterilization with subsequent failures, but the subject is not included within the scope of this paper.

DISCUSSION

The causes of failure following tubal sterilizations are many. Carrington, Burlington and Bullitt (1943) demonstrated the formation of a patent, epithelium-lined fibrous cord 20 mm. long that connected the separated ends of the divided oviduct after an attempted tubal sterilization. They concluded that "operations on the flexible part of the oviduct appear to have about 5% failures. Resections of the cornua appear much more certain of success." Dieckmann and Hauser (1948) noting 33 failures in their 912 Madlener cases (3.6%), blamed their high percentage of failures on the fact that the senior residents and not the attending physicians performed most of the tubal operations. They noted that the minimum period between tubal ligation and subsequent pregnancy had been two months, the maximum 39 months. The fertility of this group of patients ranged from a minimum of two pregnancies to a maximum of nine, the average being 4.1. The youngest patient at the time of tubal ligation in whom a failure occurred was 20 years, the oldest 43 years, and the average age was 28.3 years. Failures could be ascribed to either mistaken identity (one case) where the round ligament was ligated, or to cases where the tubes were ligated but the lumen re-established, presumably as a result of an excessive constriction of the ligature which had either sheared or completely severed the tube. Bachman (1954) reported that total salpingectomy is occasionally followed by abdominal pregnancy. Whether partial or complete, it carries the risk of interference with ovarian blood supply and is attended by up to 5% incidence of ovarian cysts within five years. Weinbaum and Javert (1954) reported that failures occur more frequently after postpartum operations on the midportion of the tube, which is one reason for choosing the narrow isthmic portion. Failures, they stated, are usually the result of recanalization, utero-tuboperitoneal fistulas or faulty technic resulting in ligating the round ligament.

Most authors report few failures following the Pomeroy method of sterilization. Lull and Mitchell (1950) ascribe two of the four failures in their series of 1,550 cases to poor technic in which the Pomeroy method was not followed explicitly. Boysen and McRae (1949) emphasize that a majority of the sterilizations reported in the literature were done on the pregnant or puerperal uterus. They suggest that the conditions and changes resulting from pregnancy may be a factor in many of the failures and that failure is not entirely due to the technic used. Dieckmann and Hauser, who reported the highest percentage of failures in their 24-hour postpartum cases, support this view. Dippel, in 1940, in a critical analysis of five failures of the Madlener technic, was able at subsequent laparotomy to demonstrate by several sections of the operation sites that failures were due to tuboperitoneal fistula or canalization of the damaged lumina. One patient had a very early pregnancy at the time of Madlener sterilization. Nelms and Doyle reported complications, in a Pomeroy sterilization, of one intestinal obstruction and a secondary hemorrhage from slipping of the ligature. Lee, Randall and Keettel (1951) state that vaginal sterilization has the same incidence of failure as the abdominal but is technically more difficult. The Irving modification operation is sometimes troublesome to perform and has found very limited favor, according to Bennet (1953). Gilbert states that the Irving and cornual excision operations are both time-consuming and have caused much bleeding at operation. Knight stated that an important cause of failure in many reported cases was faulty surgical technic. Sampson demonstrated the great propensity of tubal epithelium to regenerate and recanalize adjacent tissue following injury. The tubal epithelium, according to Sampson, shows a striking exception to healing of operative wounds among other hollow viscera because of its ability to sprout new invading cells which grow into detours beyond the channel (endosalpingiosis).

Rubovitz and Kobak and Dippel demonstrated the occurrence of the biologic phenomenon which Sampson called endosalpingiosis. These authors have demonstrated the presence of tuboperitoneal fistulas and canalization of mesosalpinx following the Madlener operation. The mechanical factors concerned in the carefully studied failures seem to be related to the use of non-absorbable suture material which is notorious for its ability to cut through both devitalized and normal tissue. "It appears, then," Knight stated, "that the Madlener operation may be justly criticized as unsound from both the mechanical and biologic aspects." Many authors agree, and statistics in this paper reveal, there is a relatively high incidence of failure in the Madlener operation.

Cornual resection does not appear to be as popular today as it was formerly. The failures of this procedure have been due apparently to small hematomas and foreign body reactions resulting in one or more fistulas communicating with the peritoneal cavity and lined by tubal epithelium. Burial of one or both tubal stumps following a segmented resection has not been found to be foolproof. Sampson believes that this refinement increases the blood supply to the injured tubal epithelium and thus abets the rapid regeneration of the tubal epithelium with the formation of fistulas. In 1955 Rotten reported 105 cornual resection operations, listing the five failures (4.76 %) in time intervals of two to 53 months following operation. Three sterilizations were performed at the time of cesarean section, and two were done within 24 hours after delivery. In three cases the cause of failure was undetermined but in two cases there was recanalization or fistula formation. Rotten summarized the causes of failure as follows: (1) errors in technic with incomplete ligation; (2) errors in identification, such as ligation of round ligament (occurring most commonly when surgery was performed through the vaginal route); (3) use of non-absorbable ligatures and undue tension which can facilitate the formation of a new canal; (4) the tendency toward endometrial proliferation through breakdown of suture lines and fistula formation to produce new uterine openings; (5) the uncertainty in some types of loop resections and ligations that the size of the loop is correct and more than just the serosa of the tube is included; and (6) performance of the sterilization procedure of ligation and resection postpartum when the incidence of failure is greater than when done during some gynecological operation. In all types of tubal sterilizations the majority of failures become manifest within three to six months after the original procedure. However, a latent period for as long as ten years has been recorded in the German literature. Prystowsky and Eastman emphasize a striking finding in their series of 1,830 cases in "the extreme length of the period that sometimes intervenes between tubal sterilization and pregnancy, this interval being 90 months in one of the cases and over 56 months in two others." These authors deduce that, when judging the merits of a particular sterilization procedure, "many years must elapse before an accurate evaluation can be made."

Dickerson reported that in 1950 sterilization operations of wide variety show an average of one reopening in 200 closures. Spontaneous reopening of the uterine tubes falls into three classes: one group ends in a uterine pregnancy; one group ends in a tubal pregnancy and one shows a tubo-peritoneal fistula. Dickerson reported that of 19 pregnancies after Madlener's operation about half were extra-uterine. Most authors now conclude that due to a higher number of failures than was felt justified, the Madlener technic is not nearly so popular as it was formerly. However, Dieckmann and Hauser still believe, as of 1948, that the Madlener is "the simplest and safest surgical procedure and can be performed at the time of a gynecologic operation, at the time of cesarean section, at the time of interruption of pregnancy by the abdominal route or as the 24-hour procedure advocated by our clinic." The majority of authors now agree with Knight that the Pomeroy sterilization is a "safe, simple, sure and rapid procedure." The reported failures of this operation are much fewer than for the Madlener, and the Pomeroy sterilization avoids mechanical and biologic hazards inherent in other types of tubal sterilization. However, Prystowsky and Eastman reported in 1955 on the high incidence of sterilization failure when the Pomeroy operation was done at the time of cesarean section or hysterotomy (1:57) as compared with a much lower rate (1:340) in the "puerperal sterilization" group. These authors state that "although we have no explanation for this surprising difference, we have been sufficiently impressed by it to abandon the Pomeroy procedure at cesarean section and hysterotomy in favor of the Irving technic. Moreover, in view of the two ectopic pregnancies that occurred after the Pomeroy operation, one of which was fatal, it is our opinion that the Irving technic is probably preferable in all cases unless haste is mandatory." In addition to the death from ectopic pregnancy, two women died from pulmonary embolism, a death rate of 0.3% in 1,022 puerperal Pomeroy sterilizations. Prystowsky and Eastman conclude that "the Pomeroy operation, therefore, is not an innocuous procedure but carries definite risks both immediate and remote."

CONCLUSIONS

Tabulations of the statistics recorded in this paper follow. The first compilation is of all tubal sterilization procedures and failures reported regardless of method of operation (Madlener, Pomeroy, Irving, cornual resection or others) but does not include the isolated individual reported failures.

Author	Year	Operation	No. of Cases	No. of Failures	Percentage
Nuernberger	1917	Cornual resection	?	?	7.7†
Müller	1926	?	793	34	4.3*
Bishop, Nelms	1930	Pomeroy	319	0	0
Jaroschka	1931	?	194	0	0*
Madlener	1932	Madlener	166	0	0
Gianella	1933	Madlener	604	1	0.17
Rubovitz, Kobak	1934	Madlener	?	?	5.3‡
Doederlein	1934	?	?	?	4.5†
Price	1935	?	1,500	8	.53*
Farerh	1936	?	9,393	47 (approx.)	0.5*
Mayer	1936	?	"several hundred"	3	?†
Greggerson	1938	?	89	2	2.3*
Curth	1939	?	1,000	1	0.01*
Fox	1940	Pomeroy	50	1	2.0
Darner	?	Madlener	?	?	8.2†
Darner	?	Pomeroy	141	0	0
Schultze	?	Madlener	?	34	?†
Knight	1946	Pomeroy-Madlener	6,214	33	0.53
Nelms, Doyle	1947	Pomeroy	404	1	0.25
Dieckmann, Hauser	1948	Madlener	912	33	3.6
Boyson, McRae	1949	Pomeroy-cornual	30	5	16.6
Irving	1950	Several resection methods	1,106	2	0.18
Gilbert	1950	?	1,284	2	0.16*
Lull, Mitchell	1950	Pomeroy	1,550	4	0.25
Lee, Randall, Keettel	1951	Several methods	1,169	12	1.0
Weinbaum, Javert	1954	Several methods	643	2	0.4
Rotten	1955	Cornual resection	105	5	4.76
Prystowsky, Eastman	1955	Several methods	1,830	17	0.93
Totals			29,496	210	0.71

* Used in totals, but reliability questionable
† Not used in totals because data incomplete
‡ Considers fistulas as "failures" in spite of rarity of pregnancy

These over-all tabulations are broken down into five main groups according to the operative procedure, that is, Madlener, Pomeroy, cornual resection, Irving modification and all those not included in the first four procedures mentioned.

Operation	Author	Year	No. of Cases	No. of Failures	Percentage
Madlener	Madlener	1932	166	0	0
"	Gianella	1933	604	1	0.17
"	Rubovitz-Kobak	1934	?	?	5.3‡
"	Darner	?	?	?	8.2†
"	Schultze	?	?	34	?†
"	Knight	1946	4,952	30	0.67
"	Dieckmann-Hauser	1948	912	33	3.6
"	Lee-Randall-Keettel	1951	1,115	12	1.1
"	Weinbaum-Javert	1954	39	0	0
"	Prystowsky-Eastman	1955	41	3	7.32
	Totals.............		7,829 (plus)	113 (plus)	1.44
Pomeroy	Bishop-Nelms	1930	319	0	0
"	Darner	?	141	0	0
"	Fox	1940	50	1	2.0
"	Knight	1946	1,262	3	0.31
"	Nelms-Doyle	1947	404	1	0.25
"	Boysen-McRae	1949	19	1	5.2
"	Irving	1950	118	2	1.7
"	Lull-Mitchell	1950	1,550	4	0.25
"	Lee-Randall-Keettel	1951	3	0	0
"	Weinbaum-Javert	1954	133	0	0
"	Prystowsky-Eastman	1955	1,478	10	0.68
	Totals.............		5,477	22	0.40
Cornual resect.	Nuernberger	1917	?	?	7.7†
" "	Knight	1946	42	0	0
" "	Boysen-McRae	1949	11	4	36.4
" "	Irving	1950	50	0	0
" "	Lee-Randall-Keettel	1951	47	0	0
" "	Weinbaum-Javert	1954	29	0	0
" "	Rotten	1955	105	5	4.76
" "	Prystowsky-Eastman	1955	27	0	0
	Totals.............		311	9	2.89
Irving modification	Irving	1950	814	0	0
" "	Weinbaum-Javert	1954	36	0	0
" "	Prystowsky-Eastman	1955	206	0	0
	Totals.............		1,056	0	0

Summarized, the final tabulations are:

Operation	No. of Cases	No. of Failures	Percentage
All procedures............	29,496	210	0.71
Madlener................	7,829	113	1.44
Pomeroy.................	5,477	22	0.40
Cornual resection.........	311	9	2.89
Irving modification........	1,056	0	0
Others..................	14,823	66	0.45

"Others" in the above tabulation is the difference between "all procedures" and the four major procedures. This group contains unreliable and incomplete data, minor variations of the major procedures and major procedures which are not listed as such.

It is most important to interpret these final statistics correctly. They are based only upon the reported cases the author was able to "dig up," and surely the total of 29,496 sterilizations of all types does not begin to approach even a small fraction of the actual sterilizations performed. Almost half of this figure (14,249) is from a period before 1946. Many of the statistics before that date are based upon "approximate" of "estimated" calculations. Many of the newer reports may contain data from the old reports, thus duplicating results. Furthermore, much of the literature is written in a foreign language, especially German, and most of these report cases before 1936 and are now unobtainable in any American library. In addition, most of these early reported cases cannot be broken down into the various sterilization technics. This is significant because the largest series reported (Farerh, 9,393 cases) falls into this group. There are nearly 100 modifications of the major sterilization technics, and a case may be listed under a heading which does not really fit the operative technic employed. Also, though tubal failures are still reported, the incidence since 1940 is much less than before 1940. Therefore, an over-all evaluation of the literature from 1917 on would be very misleading. Hence, to be most accurate, operations and failures reported in patients after 1940 should form the basis for any vital statistics on tubal sterilization failures.

The only statistics of present value are those given on the Madlener and Pomeroy operation failures. The data on cornual resection and Irving modification procedures are not sufficient to be of statistical significance as yet as compared with the other procedures, although the rarity of failures in the Irving technic is very impressive. The over-all incidence of failure, 0.71%, is not too meaningful in that much of the data are old and unreliable. The statistics given for failures in the Madlener (1.44%) and Pomeroy (0.40%) procedures are of significance, however, because the data upon which these figures are based are in most instances recent (1946 and on) and have been reliably reported.

SUMMARY

An historical review of tubal sterilization failures is given, and reports of failures by various authors have been tabulated in order to arrive at significant and "quotable" figures. A total of 29,496 cases recorded from 1917 to the present have given an incidence of tubal sterilization failures of 0.71 % from all types of operations. Seven thousand eight hundred twenty-nine recorded Madlener operations have resulted in 1.44 % failures. There were 0.40 % failures in 5,477 Pomeroy operations. The latter sterilization technic is currently the operation of choice, according to most authors, although the Irving operation is rapidly gaining recognition inasmuch as no failures are reported in 1,056 recorded cases, although Prystowsky and Eastman have recently found one Irving failure, not officially reported at the writing of this paper.

219 East 19 Street   *New York City*

REFERENCES

1. KENT, G. B.: Normal pregnancy following ligation of the fallopian tubes, Indianapolis M. J., *20:* 266, 1917.
2. DAVIDSON, H. A.: Pregnancy following double ligation of both fallopian tubes: Second cesarean section, South. M. J. *16:* 881, 1952.
3. MAXWELL, J. P.: Pregnancy after multiple ligature with section of the fallopian tubes, Chinese Med. J., *48:* 748, 1934.
4. MAXWELL, J. P.: Pregnancy after ligature of the fallopian tubes or persisting after curettage, Chinese Med. J., *43:* 1120, 1929.
5. ALDRIDGE, A. H.: Temporary surgical sterilization with subsequent pregnancy, Am. J. Obst. and Gynec., *27:* 741, 1934.
6. MAYER, M. D.: Pregnancy after bilateral tubal ligation, J. Mt. Sinai Hosp., *3:* 85, 1936.
7. DIPPEL, A. L.: Tubal sterilization by the Madlener method: A critical analysis of failures, Surg., Gynec. and Obst., *71:* 94, 1940.
8. FOX, F. H.: A comparison of the Irving and Pomeroy methods of tubal sterilization, Surg., Gynec. and Obst., *71:* 462, 1940.
9. CARRINGTON, G. L., BURLINGTON, N. C., AND BULLITT, J. B.: Pregnancy after tubal sterilization, Am. J. Obst. and Gynec., *45:* 892, 1943.
10. KNIGHT, R. V. D.: Tubal sterilization, Am. J. Obst. and Gynec., *51:* 201, 1946.
11. NcNEIL, R. J. AND WEBB, A. N.: The present status of female sterilization technics in the United States, California Med., *69:* 39, 1948.
12. DIECKMANN, W. J. AND HAUSER, E. B.: Pregnancy following tubal sterilization, Am. J. Obst. and Gynec., *55:* 308, 1948.
13. BOYSEN, H. AND McRAE, L. A.: Tubal sterilization through the vagina, Am. J. Obst. and Gynec., *58:* 488, 1949.
14. DICKINSON, R. L.: Technics of Conception Control, The Williams & Wilkins Company, Baltimore, 1950.
15. DICKINSON, R. L. AND GAMBLE, C. J.: Human Sterilization: Techniques of Permanent Conception Control, Waverly Press, Inc. 1950.
16. GILBERT, C. R. A.: Rincon method of sterilization, Am. J. Surg., *80:* 345, 1950.
17. IRVING, F. C.: Tubal sterilization, Am. J. Obst. and Gynec., *60:* 1101, 1950.
18. LULL, C. B. AND MITCHELL, R. M.: The Pomeroy method of sterilization, Am. J. Obst. and Gynec., *59:* 1118, 1950.
19. LEE, J. G., RANDALL, J. H. AND KEETTEL, W. C.: Tubal sterilization: A review of 1,169 cases, Am. J. Obst. and Gynec., *62:* 568, 1951.
20. COFRESI, E.: Realidad Poblacional de Puerto Rico, San Juan, Pan American Book Stores, 1951.
21. BENNET, E. T.: A modified Pomeroy sterilization, J. Maine M. A., *44:* 314, 1953.
22. COLLINS J. H. AND BATSON, H. W. K.: Pregnancy subsequent to ligation of ovarian vessels and the inferior vena cava, Am. J. Obst. and Gynec., *67:* 1202, 1954.

23. Weinbaum, J. A. and Javert, C. T.: Sterilization at the New York Hospital over a twenty year period, 1932–1952, West. J. Surg., *62:* 95, 1954.
24. Bachman, L.: Tubal sterilization in the human female, Hawaii Med. J., *13:* 264, 1954.
25. Ross, Joseph and Farber, Jason E.: Tubal sterilization failure with ruptured tubal pregnancy, West. J. Surg., *61:* 12, 1953.
26. Gobble, F. L. Jr. et al.: A five year survey of tubal ligations, North Carolina M. J., *16:* 133–6, 1955.
27. Lazard, E. M.: Sterilization procedures on women, West. J. Surg., *48:* 294–299, 1940.
28. Thomas, Walter L.: Prevenception insurance: Panhysterectomy versus tubectomy: South. M. J., *46:* 787–791, 1953.
29. Stringer, S. W.: External migration of an ovum in a case of congenital absence of fallopian tube, New York J. Med., *52:* 1443, 1952.
30. Allen, Edward: The Vaginal Approach in Gynec. Surgery, The Surgical Clinics of North America, *33:* 1, 193–207, 1953.
31. Milliez, P. et al: Sterilization et Grossesse, Bulletins et Memoirs de la Societe Medicale des Hospitaux de Paris, *71:* (1–2), 55–58, 1955.
32. Borch-Madsen, P.: Fire Tilfgelde af Graviditet efter Tidligere Vaginal Sterilization (Four cases of pregnancy after early trans-vaginal sterilization), Ugesk. laegr., *117:* 1279–81, 1955.
33. Gaujoux, E. and Gaujoux, J.: Une Observation de Grossesse apres sterilization, Bulletin de la Federation des Societes de Gynecologie et d'Obstetrique de Langue Francaise, *7:* 60–1, 1955.
34. James, M.: Une Grossesse Inattendue, Comptes Rendus de la Societe Francaise de Gynecologie, Paris, *25:* 258–263, 1955.
35. Leconte des Floris, H.: L'Illusoire Ecrasement Tubaire (unreliable crushing of fallopian tubes), Comptes Rendus de la Societe Francaise de Gynecologie, Paris, *25:* 252–4, 1955.
36. Rotten, G. N.: Failure in sterilization, West. J. Surg., *63:* 146–150, 1955.
37. Darner, Charles B.: Lancet, *68:* 118–120, 1948.
38. Fairbanks, E. J.: New England Obst. and Gynec. Soc., *5:* 17–25, 1951.
39. Prystowsky, H. and Eastman, N. J.: Puerperal tubal sterilization. Report of 1,830 cases, J.A.M.A., *158:* 463–467, 1955.
40. Prystowsky, Harry: Personal Correspondence, November 21, 1956.
41. Zangemeister, W.: Intrauterine Gravidetät nach beiderseitig operierter Tubengravidita. Zentralbl. Gynäk., *54:* 718, 1930.
42. Nizza, M.: La sterilizzazione della donna del punto di vista clinico e medico-legale. Su di un caso di gravidanza dopo sterilizzazione tubarico. Arch. di antropol. crim., *53:* 59–176, 1933.
43. Bittencourt, J.: Ainda sobre "gravidez topica apos ligadura das trompas". Rev. med. de Pernambuco, *4:* 247–253, 1934.
44. Schultze, K. W.: Schwangerschaft nach Tubernsterilisation. Zentralbl. Gynäk., *61:* 1683–1692, 1937.
45. Cuizza, T.: Su di un caso do gravidanza insorta dopo sterilizzazione tubarica temporanea. (Pregnancy years after temporary tubal sterilization). Ginecologia, *4:* 473–79 1938.
46. Müller, F.: Schwangerschaft nach sterilisierender operation. Zentralbl. Gynäk., *64:* 1010–12, 1940.

Reprinted from *Amer. J. Obstet. Gynecol.*, **81**, 803–805 (1961)

Occlusion of the Fallopian tubes
with tantalum clips

27

H. H. NEUMANN, M.D.

HENRY CLAY FRICK, II, M.D.

New York, New York

SINCE the blocking of the Fallopian tubes halts fertility with a minimum of disturbance of the physiology of the reproductive tract, many such methods have been in common practice for almost a century.[1] In the experiments to be described, we attempted to substitute for the various ligature materials tantalum or silver clips. If such clips would effectively occlude the Fallopian tubes they may offer some practical advantages, inasmuch as they may be inserted with the aid of a stapler under culdoscopy and thus make it a fairly speedy, perhaps ambulatory, procedure: furthermore, since a rather narrow segment of the tubes is occluded, without resection of tissue, the possibility exists that after removal of the clips patency may be restored. Evans,[2] who had applied clips on the Fallopian tubes, considered the possibility of a reversibility of the procedure; if this would be demonstrated, the procedure may be regarded as a contraceptive method, rather than sterilization.

Experimental study on the effects of metal clips on the Fallopian tubes

On 8 monkeys (5 rhesus and 3 baboons), clips made from tantalum or silver were applied to the medial portions of the tubes. One clip was applied to each tube with two exceptions, when 2 clips were applied at a distance of about 10 mm. The width of the clips was 2 mm.

On the monkeys, these clips were applied during laparotomies. After varying lengths of time from 1 to 7 months, the peritoneum of the animals was reopened. The clips were removed and the abdomen closed; after periods of from 1 to 5 months, under a third laparotomy, the tubes were removed and examined histologically.

The observations which we describe later in detail can be reviewed as follows:

None of the clips seemed to produce slough or a noticeable local tissue reaction. Several weeks after insertion, they appeared to be covered by a thin, transparent lining. The effectiveness of the tubal occlusion after application of the clips was observed histologically. After removal of the clips, we observed a tendency toward restoration of tubal patency; however, there were exceptions. On the two tubes on which 2 clamps had been applied, the lumen remained occluded during the time of observation. In some other tubes which had only one clip applied, fibrosis seemed to persist after removal of the clips; they appeared occluded histologically at least for the period of time of observation (Table I). No conclusion was reached as to the particular suitability of silver versus tantalum.

From the Department of Obstetrics and Gynecology, College of Physicians and Surgeons, Columbia University.

This study was aided by a grant from the Population Council.

Incidentally, clips scattered at random in the peritoneal cavity of baboons did not seem to cause any morbidity.

Development of an instrument for human application

The stapling instrument which is presently under clinical trial contains, apart from the telescope and light, a freely moveable arc to seize and clutch the tube under direct vision and to lead it between the jaws of the clamp; and the clamp itself, a modified Oliva-Crona forceps. The instrument is inserted into the cul-de-sac through a cannula, elliptic in cross-section, with diameters of 9 and 12 mm., with Decker's[3] technique of culdoscopy.

Motions of the grasping arc are controlled from the handle, which also permits straightening of the instrument in order to with-

draw it safely from the pelvis without catching other organs. The clips are about 3 mm. in width and 9 mm. in length, with a ribbed inner surface; some of the clips we used are winged, which facilitates their reopening (Fig. 1).

Comment

From the described experiments, it appeared that metal clips blocking the Fallopian tubes can be applied effectively and without causing discernible inflammatory reactions. Of 18 clips applied, 2 were found to have slipped off the tissue; both had been roughly prepared and hand filed and had somewhat sharp cutting edges. All of the smooth-edged machine-prepared clips had remained in the places of their application.

When 2 clips were applied to a tube, a hydrosalpinx developed between the blocks;

Table I. Results of application and removal of metal clips on the patency of the Fallopian tube

Animal	Weight (Kg.)	Duration of block with clip (months)	Length of observation after removal of clips (months)	Tube	Histologic observations on tubes
Rhesus	4.5	6		Left Right	Both tubes effectively occluded*
Baboon	12.5	6	5½	Left	Lumen recovering, mucosa damaged†
				Right	Mucosa recovered
Baboon	6	7	3	Left	Tube patent, apparently normal
				Right	Fibrotic changes, closed lumen
Baboon	2.5	4	3	Left	Tube patent
				Right	Tube occluded
Rhesus	12	Both tubes occluded; the animal died before recovery could be observed			
Rhesus	5	4	3	Left	Hydrosalpinx (2 clips had been inserted)‡
				Right	Tube histologically normal
Rhesus	4	1	4	Left	Tube occluded
				Right	Tubal mucosa recovering
Rhesus	5	4	4	Left	Tube patent, normal mucosa
				Right	Tube patent, normal mucosa

*The sections were made after removal of the clips, in order to establish the effectiveness of tubal occlusion.

†Two clips had been attached to the left tube, which had not recovered. One clip, however, was found loosely connected to the tissue. Further reference to this fact is made in the discussion.

‡Three months after removal of the 2 clips, the hydrosalpinx was much reduced, the tube appeared patent, though with an abnormal mucosa.

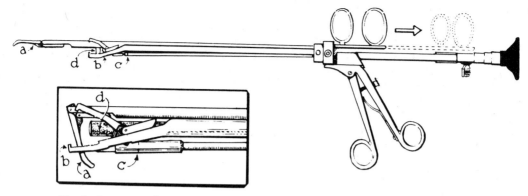

Fig. 1. Instrument for the application of tubal clips under culdoscopy. (Tubal clamp manufactured by American Cystoscope Makers, Pelham, New York.) Instrument shown without cannula. *Inset:* a, grasping arc, b, open clamp, clips not inserted, c and d, optical components.

this, while not a surprising finding, confirmed effective occlusion of the tubes, which was otherwise demonstrated histologically.

As to the restoration of patency, the results were not uniform; more than half of the tubes seemed patent again, while others remained occluded and fibrotic or appeared in various stages of recovery. If only about half the tubes are definitely patent after several months, the percentage of animals thus provided with at least one functioning tube is much higher.

The anatomy of the tube and the other pelvic organs in the experimental animals, particularly the baboon, appears very similar to that of the human reproductive organs and quite different from the narrow tortuous oviduct of the cat and dog. It remains to be observed clinically how far the findings apply to humans over much longer periods of time.

The method of suspending fertility with tubal staples is likely to have a higher rate of failure than, for instance, the Pomeroy procedure,[4] and would not be a substitute for it where sterilization is medically strictly indicated.

The application of clips may be preferable to the common methods of tube ligation if reversibility were a factor, and particularly if it would lend itself to rapid mass application as a hospital outpatient procedure, by means of culdoscopy in countries where overpopulation has become a pressing problem and contraceptive methods as a repetitive procedure requiring individual persistence are unlikely to succeed. If sufficiently simplified, the method may be useful as a public health measure in areas where the need for it is coupled with legal and religious tolerance toward such a procedure.

Summary

The Fallopian tubes of 8 baboons and rhesus monkeys were occluded with tantalum and silver clips. There was no evidence of sloughing or tissue irritation.

Upon removal of the clips after varying periods of time, tubal patency seemed restored in about half the tubes after several additional months, others seemed in the process of recovery, and some showed fibrotic changes that made recovery even after longer periods seem doubtful. The probability that animals may be provided with at least one patent tube some time after the removal of the clips appears high.

An instrument is described for the occlusion of the Fallopian tubes with tantalum staples under culdoscopy. This instrument is presently under clinical trial.

If the simian findings apply to the human Fallopian tubes, the insertion of tantalum staples through the cul-de-sac may offer a useful procedure of controlling fertility.

Male Sterilization

IX

___

Editor's Comments on Papers 28 Through 31

Castration of men has been performed throughout history for several purposes. As guardians of the royal harem, eunuchs were in demand for obvious reasons. This procedure not only eradicated their interest in the property being guarded but, when castration was carried out early in life, the eunuch would usually grow tall and present an imposing appearance. Castration was also resorted to in order to prevent the young male soprano voice from changing. Many operatic roles were written for "castrati." Castration has also been suggested, and sometimes used, as "treatment" for sexual offenders. But the concept of performing vasectomy apparently did not seriously arise until early in the 20th century. Vasectomy, of course, would not serve for keepers of the harem, for the opera, or for male sexual offenders. For sterilization, though, it has obvious appeal because it is a simple operation, is effective when properly done, and it should not interfere with sexual drive or performance.

In 1909, a Dr. William Belfield published an article in a rather obscure journal that is reproduced here. He urges "vasectomy for criminals, feeble-minded, and otherwise defective descendants of the famous Jukes criminal. . . ." Belfield points out that castration will probably never secure legal sanction for this purpose and he considers vasectomy preferable to permanent confinement. He points out that vasectomy is less serious than the extraction of a tooth and goes on to recite interesting legislation of the times designed to authorize the sterilization of confirmed criminals, idiots, imbeciles, and rapists. Dr. Belfield states that vasectomy is both practicable and unobjectionable, but that it is still generally unknown. He does not even suggest that it could be used as a generalized contraceptive measure.

If we now leap ahead 60 years to 1969 we find that vasectomy is being used throughout the world to limit population, particularly in India. And in the article by Dr. Sekhon, a professor of surgery in India, there is concern only for the development of better technique so that the operation can be done faster, easier, and with better results.

308

The next article, in which the legal and medical aspects of vasectomy are explored, is co-authored by a lawyer and a physician. Although the article was published in 1959 it sounds as though it might have been written in 1859. But then the law often lags behind by that interval of time. The question seems to be whether or not vasectomy is legal and not contrary to public policy. The conclusion would appear to be that sterilization is permissible for a variety of causes but not simply because the individual concerned desires an effective birth control method. The authors state that "...we do not advocate sterilizations of convenience for contraceptive purposes alone...." They state that "Connecticut, Kansas, Montana, and Utah ... prohibit sterilizations not performed under the eugenic law or on grounds of medical necessity...." The question is whether sterilization constitutes the crime of mayhem. They cite a 1934 case in which the court said: "It (vasectomy) does not render the patient impotent or unable to 'fight for the king,' as was the case in mayhem or maiming. We therefore hold that under the circumstances of this case the contract to perform sterilization was not void as against public policy, nor was the performance of the operation illegal on that account." And a British court held that, "Sterilization has no effect upon mental or muscular vigour and so should not be held to be a maim." But the authors cite a 1954 decision which insists that "if, however, there is no just cause or excuse for an operation, it is unlawful even though the man consents to it...." This court goes on to state: "Take a case where a sterilization operation is done so as to enable a man to have the pleasure of sexual intercourse without shouldering the responsibilities attaching to it. The operation is then plainly injurious to the public interest. It is degrading to the man himself. It is injurious to his wife and to any woman whom he may marry, to say nothing of the way it opens to licentiousness; and, unlike contraceptives, it allows no room for a change of mind on either side. It is illegal, even though the man consents to it...." This in 1954! So the authors conclude that medically it is a fine procedure for prevention of pregnancy. Legally it is unlikely that a court would hold a sterilization of convenience to constitute mayhem although it might find some other basis of criminal liability.

The objection that "it allows no room for a change of mind of either side" is being answered by operations for re-anastomosis, as indicated in the next paper, published in England but from an Indian hospital.

The behavioral consequences of vasectomy have been extensively studied. One of the better papers on this subject was published by Drs. Hodgers and Ziegler in 1968. To be sure, there are a few men who react to their psychological disadvantage as a result of vasectomy, but for the overwhelming majority there is absolutely no change in their response, in the frequency of intercourse, or in their extramarital activities. On the other hand, the problem of birth control is resolved and this, in most instances, constitutes a big plus.

Recently two rather unexpected results of vasectomy have been noted. In the first place, alert entrepreneurs are establishing commercially successful sperm banks for those contemplating vasectomy. Anticipating surgery, the man simply deposits an adequate semen sample and should he later change his mind about reproducing he can withdraw his deposit. The second report, by John B. Henry, M.D., suggests that as a result of the absorption of the sperm trapped in the proximal part of the vas deferens there may be immunological consequences. This report remains to be verified and expanded.

Reprinted from *The Chicago Med. Recorder*, **31**, 219–222 (1909)

28

THE

CHICAGO MEDICAL

RECORDER

VOL. XXXI.

JANUARY-DECEMBER, 1909

———

CHICAGO:
THE MEDICAL RECORDER PUB. CO.
PULLMAN BUILDING.

310

THE STERILIZATION OF CRIMINALS AND OTHER DEFECTIVES BY VASECTOMY.

WILLIAM T. BELFIELD, M. D.

The urgent necessity for restricting the procreation of natural criminals and other irresponsible parasites on society, is securing popular recognition. To this end various impotent or impracticable methods have been proposed, and even incorporated into the statutes of several states. Thus Minnesota, Connecticut, Kansas, Michigan and Ohio forbid the marriage of feeble-minded, epileptic and insane women under the age of 45 years. But since marriage is nowhere essential to procreation, least of all among the mentally defective, such laws—even if rigorously enforced—would not efficiently restrain the breeding of irresponsibles. For example, of the thousand criminal, feeble-minded and otherwise defective descendants of the famous Jukes criminal, many were born out of wedlock.

It is obvious that a measure which shall effectively prevent procreation by the mentally defective, must appeal not to their feeble minds but to their bodies; they must be made physically incapable of procreation.

How shall this be accomplished? Three methods have been proposed—castration, colonization, vasectomy.

1. Sterilization of the male criminal by castration, though often discussed, will probably never secure legal sanction, because it destroys the subject's sexual power; for while different men worship different gods, all men worship the same goddess, Venus.

2. Colonization—the confinement of the mentally defective in colonies where access to the other sex should be impossible—has been often suggested as a bar to their propagation, though only by those who have never considered vasectomy. Thus at a recent discussion before the Physicians' Club of Chicago, an eminent speaker advocated colonization for preventing the breeding of human derelicts. When this gentleman's attention was subsequently called to the value of vasectomy to this end, he frankly endorsed it in these words: "This method of arresting the production of criminals is, I am bound to believe, one of the coming blessings to humanity."

3. Vasectomy sterilizes a man without the slightest impairment of his sexual power or pleasure. It merely closes the minute canals through which the fertilizing elements of the male—the spermatozoa —must pass from the testes to the organs which secrete the bulk of the seminal fluid and deposit it in the genital canal of the female.

The absence of the spermatozoa from this fluid does not impair the mechanism of erection and ejaculation. This is abundantly proven by the robust sexual health of thousands of men who have been unwittingly sterilized through bilateral epididymitis, and who never suspect that their procreative functions are not perfectly normal until their marriages prove barren; they are potent, but not fertile. That vasectomy itself is equally harmless to sexuality is shown by the experience of those upon whom it has been performed; among these, within my personal knowledge, are married men who chose this means, rather than criminal abortion, to prevent the transmission to offspring of their own hereditary taints, such as insanity and syphilis.

Vasectomy is an office operation; it is performed in a few minutes under cocaine anaesthesia, through a skin cut half an inch long; it entails no wound infection, no confinement to bed; it is less serious than the extraction of a tooth.

The prevention of procreation by male defectives through vasectomy is not an iridescent dream. In March, 1907, the Indiana legislature passed a bill authorizing the sterilization of "confirmed criminals, idiots, imbeciles and rapists" in the state institutions of Indiana. In the prison at Jeffersonville over 800 convicts have been sterilized, some by authority of the state, but over 200 of them at their own request. This voluntary submission to sterilization by hundreds of convicts, removes the only conceivable opposition to this method of protecting society—namely, the sentimental.

In February, 1909, the Oregon legislature passed a duplicate of the Indiana bill, adding a definition of "confirmed criminals" as contained in the bill. This term "shall be deemed to apply to and include all persons serving a third term in any penitentiary or penal institution upon conviction of a felony."

As yet only Indiana and Oregon have actually passed such a law, though the subject has been broached elsewhere. Thus Gov. Sheldon, in his last message to the Nebraska legislature, recommended the consideration of a similar measure; and his successor, Gov. Shellenberger, writes that he will bring this matter before the proper legislative committee.

For obvious reasons this measure seems worthy of national attention. That the unrestrained procreation of their own kind by criminals, feeble-minded and other defectives should cease, is already recognized. But no plan other than vasectomy is both practicable and unobjectionable; and the vasectomy method is still generally unknown. For example, a leading Chicago daily recently discussed editorially the merits and demerits of colonization as a means for restricting the breeding of criminals, but failed to mention the Indiana plan—doubtless because it had never been brought to the editorial attention.

Illinois carefully rears all its defectives—criminals, imbeciles, epileptics, etc.—at the public expense in costly and ever multiplying infirmaries—and this is right. But Illinois has never placed the slightest restraint upon propagation by these same defectives, and this is wrong. The average man, so soon as convinced that vasectomy is a trifling operation, and that it does not impair sexual pleasure, heartily approves this method of race suicide for criminals and other defectives, because of the obvious advantages to the community; the sentimentalist, who places unselfish love for the defective above the safety of his family from burglar and rapist, should be reminded that the greatest kindness that can be shown to the as yet unbegotten offspring of the feeble-minded of all kinds, is to help them to remain unbegotten.

It would seem that our profession can in no other way render a greater service to the community with less effort, than by educating the public to an understanding of the sterilization by vasectomy of confirmed criminals and other defectives. This we can do individually and collectively. An official recommendation of the Indiana law by county and state societies to their respective legislatures might help some; but influential laymen who will buttonhole their respective legislative representatives, and insist that such a bill must be passed, will accomplish far more.

A copy of the Indiana bill adopted two years ago, is appended:

Preamble.—Whereas, Heredity plays a most important part in the transmission of crime, idiocy and imbecility:

Therefore, Be it enacted by the General Assembly of the State of Indiana that on and after the passage of this act it shall be compulsory for each and every institution in the state, entrusted with the care of confirmed criminals, idiots, rapists and imbeciles, to appoint upon its staff, in addition to the regular institutional physician, two (2) skilled surgeons of recognized ability, whose duty it shall be, in conjunction with the chief physician of the institution, to examine the mental and physical condition of such inmates as are recommended by the institutional physician and board of managers. If, in the judgment of this committee of experts and the board of managers, procreation is inadvisable and there is no probability of improvement of the mental condition of the inmate, it shall be lawful for the surgeons to perform such operation for the prevention of procreation as shall be decided safest and most effective. But this operation shall not be performed except in cases that have been pronounced unimprovable: Provided, That in no case shall the consultation fee be more than three ($3.00) dollars to each expert, to be paid out of the funds appropriated for the maintenance of such institution.

This Indiana law has been recommended for public consideration by the directors of the Chicago Physicians' Club, and of the Chicago Society of Social Hygiene.

100 STATE STREET.

Reprinted from *Indian J. Med. Res.*, **58**, 1433–1442 (1970)

Percutaneous Vasectomy
A Comparative Study Using A New Instrument
And Technique

G. S. Sekhon

*Professor of Surgery and Head of the Department of Clinical Surgery
Medical College   Rohtak*

29

Received for publication September 9 1969

An instrument for percutaneous vasectomy (vasectome) has been devised. It enables the vas to be encircled and divided by a diathermy snare wire introduced through a special needle. The vas may, thus, be divided at one place (single-cut) or more than one place—Double-cut, Triple-cut. Instead of diathermy division, the vas may also be prolapsed, through a small stab (Pin-hole vasectomy) using another new instrument—a Skin-protector—in conjunction with the vasectome. The prolapsed vas is then divided and ligated by one of the conventional methods. Seventy cases were submitted to vasectomy by various techniques, including conventional vasectomies. Forty-two cases could be followed up to 6 months. Single-cut procedure failed to achieve azoospermia in two cases. All the other cases were sperm free up to 6 months, irrespective of the technique used. Amongst the successful procedures, bilateral diathermy division of the vas at 2 places 5 mm apart (Double-cut), is the procedure of choice, because of the fewer complications, shortest time taken and the smallest quantity of local anaesthetic drug required. The per-cutaneous nature of operation is particularly well suited to the field conditions, where the degree of asepsis achieved may be questionable. Lack of stitches and permission to enjoy a regular post-operative bath are added advantages.

Introduction

A number of complaints and complications attributable directly or indirectly to vasectomy have been reported from time to time by many workers (Ohri **et al** 1958, Phadke 1962 and Sinha **et al** 1969). With a view to ensure fewer complications and a greater mass appeal, a new instrument and technique have been developed, which enable diathermy division of the vas, per-cutaneously with satisfactory results.

The instrument consists of a vasectomy needle (I), a needle holder (II) and a pull-through needle (III)—an extra-long sewing machine type of needle. The vasectomy needle (I) is a No. 15 injection needle, bent into a U shape in its proximal half. The upper ends of the U bend are drilled, to allow the pull-through needle to be pushed through or withdrawn from the vasectomy needle. While the handle of the instrument is held in the hand, the thumb manipulates the pull-through needle, through the agency of the knob **K**.

1

Vasectomy technique (Diagram 'A') :   The vas is carefully rolled under the scrotal skin, so that there is very little extra-vasal tissue around it.   It is held in place between the thumb and the index finger of the left hand (Fig 1).   One to 2 ml of 2% xylocaine solution containing adrenalin is infilterated into the tissues around the vas.   With the instrument held in the right hand, the distal half (straight half) of the vasectomy needle is pushed through the scrotal tissues just behind the vas, so that the latter forms a loop across the distal half of the vasectomy needle, covered over by a narrow bridge of skin. This fact is confirmed by the surgeon and the assistant by palpating the vas across the needle at **P** (Fig 2).

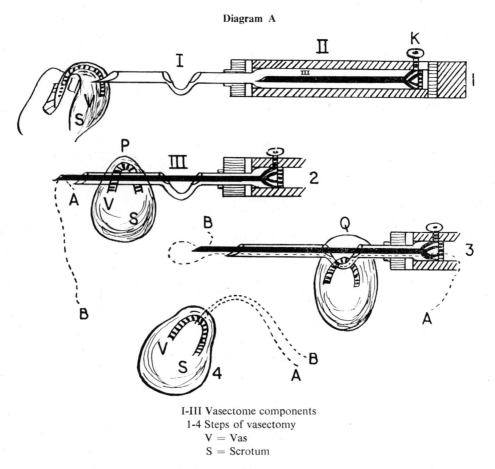

Diagram A

I-III Vasectome components
1-4 Steps of vasectomy
V = Vas
S = Scrotum

Now the tip of the pull-through needle III is advanced beyond the tip of the vasectomy needle, by pushing the knob **K** with the thumb.   The eye of the pull-through needle is threaded with steel wire S.W.G. 30 to 34.   This end **A** of the steel wire is withdrawn by backward pull of the thumb on the knob **K**.   The vasectomy needle **I** is now pushed further, so that the vas comes to rest across the bottom of the **U** bend, while the bridge of skin covers its open upper end. The knob **K** is again manipulated forwards, so that the pull-through needle, this time, passes in front of the vas. This fact is also confirmed by the surgeon and the assistant, by not being able to feel the vas across the body of the pull through needle bridging the open end of the **U** bend at **Q** (Fig 3), since the vas this time lies behind it. The other end of the steel wire **B** is then threaded into the eye of the pull-through needle, and the same is again withdrawn, of course, this time in front of the vas. The two ends of the steel wire are now pulled upon, so that the initial wide sweep of the wire beyond the tip of the vasectomy needle is withdrawn, to encircle the vas in the **U** bend only. The instrument is finally withdrawn completely, by sliding it over the double folded steel wire, emerging through a single skin puncture (Fig 4). The fact, that the vas is really hooked up under the scrotal skin by the wire loop is also confirmed by palpating for the vas at this stage.

The wire ends are then threaded through a polythene tube or a narrow slot on the side of a piece of non-conducting plastic sheet. The purpose behind this is to prevent spreading out of the two limbs of the wire loop emerging from the scrotum. While the non-conducting material is held firmly against the scrotal skin, a gentle traction is maintained on a haemostat holding the double folded steel wire near its ends. The wire or the haemostat is now touched with a diathermy coagulation point. Thus, having coagulated and divided the vas, with a minimal of extra-vasal tissues, the wire loop jumps out of the scrotum, through an invisible skin burn.

When attempting more than one diathermy cut for each vas (two is the rule), the additional wire loops are passed 5 mm apart around the vas, before it is actually divided. The presence of a previous loop facilitates the insertion of a fresh one, by keeping the vas anchored under the skin.

Skin-protector for pin-hole vasectomy (Diagram B) : While awaiting assessment of the results of percutaneous vasectomies by the diathermy technique, another instrument was added to the equipment, to enable the delivery of the vas and its subsequent division and ligation under direct vision, through a small skin stab incision. For this purpose, all the preliminary steps involved in passing the wire around the vas with the help of a **vasectome** are the same, except that, instead of dividing the vas by diathermy current, the wire ends are threaded through a narrow hole in a metallic plate ('Skin-protector') and fastened on to the screws **X** and **Y**. The wire when tightened, by turning the screw knobs, helps to prolapse, a tiny knuckle of scrotal skin, with vas underneath it. Stab incision in the overlying skin and gentle teasing of the tissues, brings the vas into view. Then, it is not difficult, to pull out a length of vas, from its loose fascial sheath. The vas is dealt with, by any of the conventional methods of division and ligation (Hanley 1968 and Pugh **et al** 1969). The steel wire is finally withdrawn and the Skin-protector discarded. The scrotal skin on either side of the vas is lifted up, thus, helping the divided and ligated vas to sink back into the scrotum, leaving only a small skin puncture, which does not need a stitch.

In either case, the skin punctures are sealed off with Tinct. Benzoin Co. A suspensory bandage is worn for a week and hard labour is prohibited during the period. The use of analgesics and sulpha drugs is advised for three days. The person can start taking bath from the very next morning. Semen is tested after 3 months. The use of contraceptives is continued, till the semen is declared sperm free.

Diagram B

Skin-protector

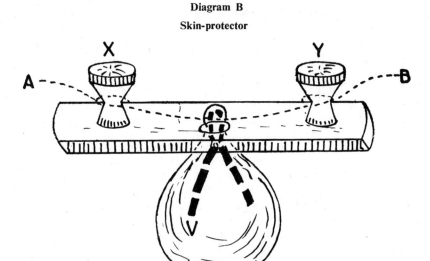

Material and Methods

Seventy cases were submitted to vasectomy by different techniques described above, as well as, by the conventional scrotal incision, from February 1969 to January 1970. Of these, only 42 cases attended regularly for the follow-up and will be discussed in detail, while the remaining 28 cases could not be contacted. The cases were divided into two main groups :—

Group I : Per-cutaneous vasectomies using diathermy snare :

    1. Single-cut (each side) ....10 cases

    2. Double-cut (each side)   ....10 cases

    3. Triple-cut (each side) .... 2 cases

Group II : Vasectomy through a scrotal incision :

    1. 'Pin-hole' vasectomy ('Mini-cut') ....10 cases
            3-4 mm incision

    2. Vasectomy using conventional incision ....10 cases
            1-2 cm with skin stitches

Total = 42 cases

The cases were contacted one week after the operation and then after 3 and 6 months, as well as at any time they wished to consult for any advice. Semen examination was carried out after 3 and 6 months for all the Group I cases. If a case failed to show azoospermia by that time, the semen examination was repeated after 10 months. Group II '1' cases have been due for semen examination only once i.e. after 3 months, while the Group II '2' cases operated by different surgeons by the conventional techniques were contacted for interrogation only once, i.e. 6 months to a year after the operation, when their semen was also examined. At the time of follow-up the cases were particularly interrogated for pain and the scrotum was examined for swelling or infection.

Discussion

It will be quite evident from Table I that the Single-cut diathermy vasectomy is not at all a satisfactory procedure, because the method has failed completely or early recanalization has occurred in case Nos. 6 and 8, as evidenced by a normal semen picture, even at the end of a period of 10 months. Again, case Nos. 2 and 5 showed oligospermia with more or less constant counts between 14 and 20 million sperms per ml. This may be due to bilateral stenosis of the vas at the site of diathermy division, very much allied to the healing of any tube by stricture formation, following trauma, such as, the ureter, urethra, bile ducts, etc. ; or it may be the result of complete occlusion of the vas on one side and stenosis on the other. On the other hand the case No 10 revealed a falling count and was azoospermic when tested after 10 months. The slow progress in this case is probably attributable to fewer ejaculations during the period, as he was away from the family most of the time. Whether the two cases showing oligospermia had a low count before operation would be difficult to say, but as their youngest children were 3 years and one year old respectively, it may be assumed that they had normal counts before. Incidentally, such hypo-fertility counts have been reported by Kothari **et al** (1967), using nylon bristles as Intra-vasal-contraceptive devices (IVCD). However, we feel that azoospermia and not oligospermia should be the aim, because oligospermia may mean disappearing sperms, following a successful vasectomy, or reappearing sperms following spontaneous recanalization of the vas.

Table I. Single-cut vasectomy

Case No.	Name	Date of vasectomy	Follow-up features					Semen examination				
			Pain	Swelling	Infection	Weeks	Result	Weeks	Result	Weeks	Result
1	O.P.	2.4.69	—	—	—	20	—	26	—		
2	M.L.	2.5.69	—	—	—	20	±	24	±	40	±
3	B.	23.5.69	—	—	—	16	—	25	—		
4	K.S.	26.5.69	—	—	—	10	—	25	—		
5	*R.S.	27.5.69	—	—	—	12	±	27	±	40	±
6	M.R.	3.6.69	—	—	—	16	+	26	+	40	+
7	P.L.	10.6.69	—	—	—	12	—	25	—		
8	R.D.	17.6.69	+	+	—	18	+	24	+	40	+
9	N.R.	19.6.69	—	+	—	12	—	24	—		
10	N.B.	20.6 69	—	—	—	20	±	28	±	41	—

Follow-up features : + = Mild   Semen : + = Normal count
               — = Absent   — = Azoospermia
                                           ± = Oligospermia
* = Reported increased sexual desire after vasectomy

In contrast to the Single-cut technique, all the other methods appear to be quite satisfactory in achieving the   objective.   There being no special advantage of the Triple-cut procedure (Table III), over the Double-cut (Table II), the Triple-cut technique with unnecessary additional trauma resulting in more pain and swelling, was, therefore, abandoned quite early during the study thereby submitting only two cases for the same.

Table II.   Double-cut vasectomy

Case No.	Name	Date of vasectomy	Follow-up feature			Semen examination			
			Pain	Swelling	Infection	Weeks	Result	Weeks	Result
1	R.C.	13.9.69	—	—	—	20	—	24	—
2	P.C.	18.9.69	—	—	—	14	—	28	—
3	P.S.	21.9.69	—	—	—	22	—	26	—
4	S.S.	23.9.69	—	—	—	16	—	28	—
5	M.P.	22.9.69	—	—	—	12	—	25	—
6	O.P.	28.9.69	—	—	—	14	—	25	—*
7	H.M.	29.9.69	—	—	—	13	—	28	—
8	J.B.	18.10.69	—	—	—	15	—	27	—
9	R.B.	24.10.69	+	+	—	11	—	24	—
10	L.N.	27.10.69	+	+	—	18	—	24	—

Follow-up features :   +   =   Mild   Semen :   —   =   Azoospermia
　　　　　　　　　　　 —   =   Absent

*Vasectomy done 2 years before by open method, with ligation and division of the vas somewhere else, had recanalized resulting in normal semen picture and further pregnancy in the family

Table III.   Triple-cut vasectomy

Case No.	Name	Date of vasectomy	Follow-up features			Semen examination			
			Pain	Swelling	Infection	Weeks	Result	Weeks	Result
1	R.C.	30.10.69	+	+	—	12	—	24	—
2	P.R.	30.10.60	+	+	—	14	—	24	—

Follow-up features :   +   =   Mild   Semen :   —   =   Azoospermia
　　　　　　　　　　　 —   =   Absent

Despite the fact, that the series is rather small, but the trend indicates, that the chances of infection, following the use of a diathermy snare technique, in contrast to open vasectomies (Tables IV and V case Nos. 6 and 8 Table IV and case No. 10 Table V), will always be remote, because a burn when inflicted is always sterile.   There is no handling of the tissues by the surgeon's hands in the per-cutaneous techniques, which is particularly advantageous, while performing vasectomies under field conditions, with greater chances of local infection, including the dangerous post-operative tetanus.

Although the **Pin-hole** vasectomy cases have not been followed for a sufficiently long time (Table IV), but the results can be anticipated to fall in line with those obtained by the conventional vasectomy techniques, using longer skin incisions (Table V), since the procedure is essentially the same, i.e. division and ligation of the vas under direct vision. However, the chances of a local swelling and haematoma appear to be slightly more, following **Pin-hole** vasectomies (Table IV). This is probably, because of the better haemostasis achieved while operating through longer incision in conventional vasectomies and reduced haemorrhage while diathermy snare is being used for dividing the vas in others.

Table IV. 'Pin-hole' vasectomy

Case No.	Name	Date of vasectomy	Follow-up features			Semen examination	
			Pain	Swelling	Infection	Weeks	Result
1	A.N.	18.12.69	—	—	—	16	—
2	M.R.	20.12.69	—	—	—	20	—
3	R.K.	9.1.70	+	+	—	13	—
4	S.N.	10.1.70	—	—	—	12	—
5	J.R.	17.1.70	—	—	—	12	—
6	S.L.	18.1.70	+++	+++	+++	14	—
7	R.N.	18.1.70	—	—	—	14	—
8	B.S.	20.1.70	+	+	+	12	—
9	R.S.	24.1.70	—	—	—	13	—
10	R.D.	28.1.70	—	—	—	12	—

Follow-up features : + = Mild   Semen : — = No sperms
                    +++ = Severe   — = Absent

Table V. Conventional vasectomy (1-2 cm incision)

Case No.	Name	Date of vasectomy	Follow-up features			Semen examination	
			Pain	Swelling	Infection	Weeks	Result
1	P.C.	22. 2.69	—	+	—	48	—
2	D.C.	15. 4.69	—	—	—	47	—
3	S.R.	25. 4.69	+	+	—	40	—
4	A.S.	29. 5.69	—	—	—	41	—
5	A.D.	28. 7.69	—	—	—	31	—
6	B.S.	23. 8.69	—	—	—	27	—
7	S.R.	6. 9.69	—	—	—	28	—
8	M.L.	18. 9.69	—	—	—	25	—
9	R.D.	23.10.69	—	—	—	25	—
10	N.L.	25.10.69	+++	+++	+++	24	—

Follow-up features : + = Mild   Semen : — = Azoospermia
                    +++ = Moderately severe   — = Absent

Table VI offers a comparison of various procedures. The failure of the Single-cut and no added advantage of the Triple-cut over the Double-cut procedures has already been discussed. While the chances of a palpable nodule and hyper-aesthesia are evenly distributed, that of local infection are definitely more following the con-ventional procedures and **Pin-hole** vasectomies.

Table VI.   Comparison of different methods

Procedure	Average time for isolation of vas and local anaesthesia in minutes	Average operation time in minutes	Average total time in minutes	Average quantity xylocaine ml	Complications	Order of preference by masses
Per-cutaneous :						
1. Single-cut*	5	3	8	3	Failed operation	
2. Double-cut†	6	4	10	4	+	**First**
3. Triple-cut	7	5	12	5	++·	First
Open operations :						
1. Pin-hole (Mini-cut)	5	15	20	4	++	Second
2. Conventional technique (1-2 cm cut)	2·5	7·5	10	6	++	Third

* Single-cut   —   Failed operation, because semen positive in some of the cases
† Double-cut   —   Procedure of choice, because of successful outcome, shortest average total time, smallest quantity of local anaesthetic drug required and first preference by masses, because of its per-cutaneous nature post-operative comfort and fewer complications

Complications :   +   =   Few   ++   =   More

Although nothing can be said at this stage, about the late spontaneous recanaliza-tion of the vas, but since sufficient time has elapsed (more than 6 months) for the firm sealing of the vas ends by scar tissue, after the diathermy procedures, the chances must be quite remote, in any case, not more than those following the open division and ligation of the vas.

It may be pointed out, that the possibility of missing the vas during per-cutaneous procedures is merely theoretical, since at every stage of the operation, the location of the vas at the right place is confirmed by the surgeon and his critical assis-tant.   In some of the cases at least, even the divided ends of the vas can be palpated at the end of the operation.   In any case, it has not been missed in 50 prostate cases vasectomized by the diathermy snare technique at the time of first stage of prosta-tectomy, in whom the divided vas was subsequently exposed and confirmed at the time of the second stage of prostatectomy.

The chances of injury to the testicular artery by the blind diathermy technique must be quite rare, because, the testicular artery is located a little farther away from the vas, in a separate leash of veins of the pampiniform plexus.   Moreover, the bend of the vasectomy needle is not large enough, to accommodate too many structures along with the vas.   Even if worst comes to worst, still the testicular atrophy need not follow, because of a rich collateral circulation (Koontz 1965). Moreover, the chances of same thing being repeated on the other side, and again the collateral circulation not keeping pace, cannot be anything but hypothetical, especially when it is realised, that in the diathermy snare technique, the trauma due to mal-handling of the surrounding tissues does not occur, which is quite in contrast to the rough handling occasionally witnessed, during open procedures, while searching for a missed vas or a slipped vas. It is probably for this reason that a haematoma following an open operation is not unknown (Hanley 1968). We fully subscribe to Hanley's views, that if a haematoma does develop, then the treatment of choice is early incision and drainage and not aspiration of haematoma. In this series of 42 cases, followed up for a sufficiently long time, none of the cases showed any evidence of testicular atrophy, or diminished testicular sensation or a diminished sexual desire, though, the last has been reported from time to time for vasectomies performed by open method.

The real safeguard against complications following diathermy snare vasectomies, is the inclusion of minimal extra-vasal tissue in the diathermy loop. This is achieved by gently rolling the vas under the skin, using the index fingers and thumbs of both the hands, before injecting local anaesthetic solution. In case of difficulty, this is facilitated, if the gloves are removed temporarily during the manoeuvre. On still other occasions holding the vas between the thumb and index finger of one hand and transfixing it with a hypodermic needle pushed just behind it does the job. In any case, the time and labour spent in achieving this objective of including the minimal extra-vasal tissue is worthwhile, because the rest of the procedure is quite simple and easy. The difficulties met with in the early cases pass off as more and more experience is gained. The problem is frequently faced in cases having a short, thick cord and a small thick walled scrotum. The presence of a hydrocele or a hernia may be considered contra-indications for the percutaneous technique, although, we have succeeded in a case of each, after reducing the hernia and tapping the hydrocele.

Half a dozen cases vasectomized by different techniques reported a certain degree of hyper-aesthesia, during the early post-operative period. This is probably due to back pressure following blockage of the divided vas and may partly account for the increased sexual desire at least for some of the cases. In our opinion, in some of the cases it may be due to an irritable focus being set up in the lower cord centres (Sekhon et al 1970), while in others it is certainly the result of sense of security against having unmanageable families.

Some of the incidental observations made during the course of present study are worth recording. The largest number of cases (22) submitted to vasectomy between 30-35 years age. The maximum number of couples (14) had undergone the operation after having 4 children. Majority had two or three male children before agreeing for vasectomy. Only one case had one male child before getting operated. As far as the educational status of our cases is concerned, they can be evenly distributed into four groups of non-educated, primary education, matric and above. The presence of a few teachers, doctors and lawyers in our series is in contrast to their conspicuous absence, in the large series reported by Sinha **et al** (1969) from a similar urban population of Lucknow.

Conclusions

In the end it may be concluded, that the Double-cut diathermy snare vasectomy is the procedure of choice and hence the final answer to the problem and should be given wider field trials. It is superior to the conventional vasectomy, because of its minor nature, freedom from encumbrances of large dressings and subsequent removal of stitches. The closed nature of the diathermy burn with no handling of tissues and no need for introducing foreign bodies, such as sutures and ligatures, naturally accounts for the remote chances of infection and hence its particular suitability while working under field conditions. The freedom to have a regular bath after the operation is an added advantage to those living in tropical countries. No wonder, more and more persons are volunteering and wish to be submitted to the diathermy division of the vas, with our new instrument—the Vasectome.

Acknowledgment

The author is thankful to Dr. Harbans Lal and Dr. & Mrs Inderjit Singh of the Family Planning and Research Centre, Rohtak, for their keen interest and cooperation in referring the cases for the study. Thanks are no less due to the members of the staff of the Clinical Surgery Department for the motivation and submitting some of their very close relatives for the various procedures.

References

Hanley, G.H. 1968. Vasectomy for male sterilization. **Lancet ii, 207-209.**

Koontz, A.R. 1965. Atrophy of the testicle as a surgical risk. **Surg Gynec Obstet 120, 511-513,**

Kothari, M.L. and Pardnani, D.S. 1967. Temporary sterilization of the male by intra-vasal contraceptive device (IVCD). **Indian J Surg 29, 357-363.**

Ohri, B.B. and Jhaver, P.S. 1958. Clinical use of vasectomy for male sterilization. **Indian J Surg 20, 280-284.**

Phadke, G.M. 1962. Vasectomy. Directorate of Health Services, Ministry of Health, Government of India.

Pugh, R.C.B. Path, F.C. and Hanley, H.G. 1969. Spontaneous recanalization of the vas deferens. **Brit J Urol 41, 340-347.**

Sekhon, G.S. and Sekhon, M.S. 1970. Vasectomy : Newer techniques. **Punjab Med J 19, 271-277.**

Sinha, S.N. Jain, P.C. and Parsad, B.G. 1969. A socio-medical study of ubran sterilized males in Lucknow. **J Indian Med Ass 53, 134-141.**

Reprinted from *J. Urol.*, **81**, 259–263 (1959)

THE LEGAL AND MEDICAL ASPECTS OF VASECTOMY

RICHARD C. DONNELLY, J.S.D. AND WILLIAM L. F. FERBER

30

In January 1958 an article was published in this Journal by Dr. Charles Rieser entitled "Vasectomy: Medical and Legal Aspects." The authors disagree with some major tenets and conclusions advanced by Dr. Rieser, and wish to place before the medical profession their point of view.

The authors' interest in sterilization has been stimulated by The Human Betterment Association of America, a philanthropic organization which concerns itself with the medical, legal and sociologic facts concerning sterilization. The opinions expressed in this article are concurred in by the lawyers, physicians, demographers and sociologists who, with the authors, form The Medical and Scientific Committee of The Human Betterment Association.

We fully agree with Dr. Rieser that a sterilization performed pursuant to one of the 28 state statutes, whose constitutionality has been upheld, involves no criminal or civil liability for the physician. Indeed, the statutes usually provide specifically that participants shall not "be liable either civilly or criminally." Incidentally, Dr. Rieser is in error when he states in his table 1 that Texas prohibits all sterilizations. This error, however, is corrected in the text where he points out that sterilizations are prohibited only in "state or similar type hospitals." It should also be pointed out that the Texas prohibition is based upon an administrative interpretation of an ambiguous statute rather than a court decision.

In view of this area of agreement with Dr. Rieser, we shall focus primarily upon non-institutional sterilizations done as a therapeutic measure. No state specifically forbids therapeutic sterilizations. Indeed, four states affirmatively authorize the operation in cases of "medical necessity" (Connecticut, Kansas, Montana, and Utah). It is also common practice for eugenic

Accepted for publication August 4, 1958.

Note by editor. Dr. Donnelly is professor of law, Yale Law School, New Haven, Conn. Dr. Ferber is director of urology, Elmhurst General Hospital, New York, N. Y. and assistant attending urologist, the Mount Sinai Hospital, New York, N. Y.

sterilization laws to contain the following provision:

"Nothing in this act shall be construed so as to prevent the medical or surgical treatment for sound therapeutic reasons of any person in this State, by a physician or surgeon licensed by this State, which treatment may incidentally involve the nullification or destruction of the reproductive functions."

It is our contention that in states not specifically permitting therapeutic sterilizations the courts would look with favor upon such an operation if a physician should become involved in a legal proceeding when the sterilization was performed on solid medical grounds. For example, in the case of *Christensen v. Thornby*,[1] the Minnesota Supreme Court held that vasectomy of a healthy husband to protect his wife from a dangerous pregnancy was not against public policy. The decision stated:

"We are not here confronted with the question of public policy as applied to sterilization where no medical necessity is involved. Aside from the statutes in the few states that have prohibited it, we find no judicial or legislative announcement of public policy against the practice of sterilization. Certainly, even in those states with the statutory prohibition, the exception of medical necessity would justify a physician in performing the operation here alleged . . . We therefore hold that under the circumstances of this case the contract to perform sterilization was not void as against public policy nor was the performance of the operation illegal on that account."

Numerous analogies from other fields of the law point the same way. For instance, the Federal Statutes prohibiting the transportation of contraceptives and contraceptive information make no exception in favor of physicians. Nevertheless, the Federal Courts in a host of cases have held that the statutes do not prevent "the carriage by mail of things which might intelligently be employed by conscientious and competent physicians for the purpose of saving life or promoting the well-being of their patients."[2] In practical

[1] 192 Minn. 123, 255 N.W. 620 (1934).
[2] United States v. One Package, 86 Feb. 2d 737 (2d Cir. 1936).

essence these decisions have invalidated the Federal contraceptive statutes, thus making free distribution of contraceptive advice and materials no longer a Federal offense. And the United States District Court for the Southern District of New York recently applied the same principles to so-called obscene matter.[3]

One of the most dramatic cases raising similar issues was the English case of *R. v. Bourne*.[4] A girl of 14 had been shockingly raped by a number of soldiers and became pregnant. Her medical advisers decided that for the sake of her physical and mental health the pregnancy should be terminated and they appealed to Dr. Alec Bourne, a distinguished English gynecologist, to perform the operation. The governing English statute on abortion made no exception for therapeutic abortions. Dr. Bourne not only consented to act but announced publicly that he would make a test case of the matter. As a result, he was brought to trial. The judge's direction to the jury, which resulted in Dr. Bourne's acquittal, is a striking vindication of the legal view that the defence of necessity applies not only to the common law but also to statutory crimes. Mr. Justice Macnaghten not only read into the abortion statute an exception for "preserving the life of the mother" but gave "life" a qualitative interpretation. He said:

"If the doctor is of opinion, on reasonable grounds and with adequate knowledge, that the probable consequence of the continuance of the pregnancy will be to make the woman a physical or mental wreck, the jury are quite entitled to take the view that the doctor who, under those circumstances and in that honest belief, operates, is operating for the purpose of preserving the life of the mother."

If therapeutic sterilizations are legal and not contrary to public policy, what are the indications for such an operation? We feel that physicians have been too timid and cautious in not taking a strong stand for a broad and humane interpretation of such terms as "medical necessity" and "sound therapeutic reasons." It is our position that a physician may safely perform a sterilization on therapeutic grounds when, in his opinion, parenthood at any future time would be a threat to the patient's physical or mental health and well-being, providing certain procedures— to be mentioned later—are followed. A complete list of therapeutic indications cannot be spelled out since each case must be individually evaluated. Nevertheless, some of the indications are as follows:

1) Afflictions of an hereditary nature involving previous offspring of a marriage or in some instances the involvement of one or both actual or potential parents, afflictions such as Huntington's chorea; chondrodystrophy; hemophilia; Friedreich's ataxia; Schilder's disease; gargoylism; phenylpyruvia; amaurotic familial idiocy; Lawrence-Moon-Biedl syndrome; Niemann-Pick's disease; cerebral symmetrical diplegia; cystic fibrosis of the pancreas, etc.

2) Conditions which are aggravated by repeated pregnancies, such as chronic hypertensive vascular disease, advanced cardiac changes, isoimmunization due to RH blood factor having resulted in previous lethal fetal involvement, severe varicosities, etc.

3) Physical, mental or emotional defect which may seriously impair the patient's functioning as an adequate parent and/or which causes the physician to conclude that parenthood, at any future time, would be hazardous.

4) Multiparity to a degree affecting adversely the patient's health or well-being.

It is our contention that when sterilization is indicated in the marital situation it makes no difference from a legal point of view whether it is the wife or the husband who is sterilized. In other words, a vasectomy may be performed on the husband when a medical contraindication to pregnancy exists in his wife. This position is supported by the Minnesota case of *Christensen v. Thornby*.[5] The court said:

"Plaintiff was married and presumably would remain married to his present wife, who had been competently advised of the danger of further pregnancy. The operation of sterilization upon a man is a simple one, accompanied by very slight hazard, whereas that upon a woman is more serious and requires a greater degree of skill on the part of the physician. It entails hospitalization. It is frequently performed upon women who habitually miscarry or abort. So far as progeny is concerned, the results to this married couple would be the same were effective sterilization performed upon either. Therefore, in our opinion, it was entirely justifiable for them to take the simpler and less dangerous alternative and have the husband sterilized. Such an operation does not impair, but frequently improves, the health and vigor of the patient. Except for his inability to have children, he is in every respect as capable physically and mentally as before."

The experience of the medical author confirms the observations of the court. Vasectomy is indeed a simple surgical procedure. It is rarely followed by any postoperative complication.

[3] United States v. 31 Photographs, 156 Fed. Supp. 350 (S.D.N.Y. 1957).
[4] (1938) 3 All E.R. 615.

[5] Footnote 1, *supra*.

Libido and potency are in no way reduced. On the contrary potency may be enhanced by the removal of fear of pregnancy. It should also be noted that the procedure is surgically reversible in many instances where pregnancy is subsequently desired. It is well recognized that spermatogenesis persists after vas resection. There have been many reported instances of successful vasovasotomy followed by pregnancy.

We also agree with Dr. Rieser that vasectomy is medically indicated when there is the possibility of postoperative epididymitis following prostatic surgery.

When sterilization is indicated, we believe that the following procedure should be followed:

1) *With Respect to All Patients.*
a) When, in the opinion of the examining physician, an operation is indicated, a written opinion should be rendered stating the indications warranting it.
b) Before any sterilization operation is performed, the written consent of the patient, and spouse if there be one, should be obtained.
c) When anything in the patient's history or behavior during the interview raises any question concerning his capacity to consent to the operation, there should be a psychiatric examination and determination concerning his capacity.

2) *With Respect to Minors and Incompetent Persons.* Minors may not be deemed capable of legally effective consent to a sterilization operation. Furthermore, an incompetent person may not understand the nature and consequences of the operation and may be otherwise not competent to consent to its performance. In such cases, the sterilization may still be performed after following these steps:
a) There should be a written medical finding that the condition indicating the advisability of sterilization is a permanent one, not likely to improve to the point where sterilization would no longer be indicated. In the case of the sterilization of an incompetent person under the age of 21, added precaution should be taken to determine this to the greatest possible degree of certainty.
b) There should be an additional written finding that the condition which renders the patient incapable of consent to the operation will probably not improve to the point where the patient at a future time will be legally competent to consent, if this be the case.
c) A physician's report recommending sterilization of a minor, or of an incompetent, or other person not capable of legal consent who might later improve to the point of being competent to consent to the operation, should indicate why it is deemed advisable not to postpone the operation until the patient reaches 21,

becomes competent or proves to be permanently incompetent.
d) The written consent of the parent, guardian or other person responsible for the patient's care and support should be obtained in addition to the written consent of the patient. If the minor or incompetent is a ward of a probate or other court, the court's approval should also be obtained.

Although we do not advocate sterilizations of convenience for contraceptive purposes alone, we feel it is worthwhile to consider briefly the legal aspects of sterilization on such grounds. The central issue is whether the patient can validly consent to the operation, assuming he is mentally capable of doing so. It sould be noted first that consent is never a defense in an action against a physician based on his negligent or incompetent performance of an operation. Secondly, consent would be no defense to a criminal prosecution based on a statute specifically forbidding the operation. Thus, in Connecticut, Kansas, Montana, and Utah, which prohibit sterilizations not performed under the eugenic law or on grounds of medical necessity, consent to a sterilization of convenience would probably be no defense to a criminal prosecution.

There has been much speculation as to whether sterilization constitutes the crime of mayhem. If so, consent would probably not be a defense to a criminal prosecution. In *Christensen v. Thornby*,[6] although involving a therapeutic sterilization, the court stated:

"It [vasectomy] does not render the patient impotent or unable to 'fight for the king', as was the case in mayhem or maiming. We therefore hold that under the circumstances of this case the contract to perform sterilization was not void as against public policy, nor was the performance of the operation illegal on that account."

Perhaps the strongest refutation of the argument that a sterilization, even one of convenience, is mayhem is that of Professor Glanville Williams, the distinguished English jurist, in his recent book, "The Sanctity of Life and the Criminal Law." Williams says:

It is sometimes said that a person cannot effectively consent to the commission of a maim (mayhem) upon himself, and the question then resolves itself into whether sterilization is a maim. In principle, a maim was some injury that lessened a person's ability to fight and defend himself, such as cutting off a hand or even knocking out a tooth (which would impair his power to bite an adver-

[6] Footnote 1, *supra.*

327

sary); and castration was also held to be a maim, because it was thought to diminish bodily vigour or courage. Sterilization has no effect upon mental or muscular vigour and so should not be held to be a maim. Also, vasectomy is not a maim because the legal meaning of a maim (as contrasted with a wound) is that it is permanent; the possibility of a reversal operation means that the prosecution cannot prove that vasectomy is permanent. Again, the law of maim seems historically to have no application to women. Even if all these difficulties are surmounted, it may be questioned whether the antiquated law of maim affords a satisfactory basis for a conclusion as to the defence of consent. It seems unlikely that a person would today commit a criminal offence by having his teeth extracted without adequate reason."

A decision that sterilization is not a maiming does not end the difficulty. The general policy of the particular state toward birth control generally, the religious affiliations of the judge, the fact that most judges are males and males seem to have a stronger instinctive reaction against sterilization than females, are factors that leave the question of criminal liability for sterilizations of convenience uncertain. In the recent English divorce case of *Bravery v. Bravery*,[7] the husband had been sterilized solely as a contraceptive measure. Lord Justice Denning, in a dissenting opinion took occasion to say, though it was in no way necessary for the decision, that a sterilization of convenience even with the consent of the wife is a criminal offense. He said:

"An ordinary surgical operation, which is done for the sake of a man's health, with his consent, is, of course, perfectly lawful because there is just cause for it. If, however, there is no just cause or excuse for an operation, it is unlawful even though the man consents to it . . . Likewise, with a sterilization operation. When it is done with the man's consent for a just cause, it is quite lawful, as, for instance, when it is done to prevent the transmission of an hereditary disease; but when it is done without just cause or excuse, it is unlawful, even though the man consents to it. Take a case where a sterilization operation is done so as to enable a man to have the pleasure of sexual intercourse without shouldering the responsibilities attaching to it. The operation then is plainly injurious to the public interest. It is degrading to the man himself. It is injurious to his wife and to any woman whom he may marry, to say nothing of the way it opens to licentiousness; and, unlike contraceptives, it allows no room for a change of mind on either side. It is illegal, even though the man consents to it . . .

Those cases under the criminal law have a bearing on the problem now before the court, because the divorce law, like the criminal law, has to have

regard to the public interest, and consent should not be an absolute bar in all cases. If a husband undergoes an operation for sterilization without just cause or excuse, he strikes at the very root of the marriage relationship. The divorce courts should not countenance such an operation any more than the criminal courts. It is severe cruelty. Even assuming that the wife, when young and inexperienced, consented to it, sne ought not to be bound by it when in later years she suffers in health on account of it, especially when she was not warned that it might affect her health."

Under this view of Lord Justice Denning, a physician who sterilized a husband "without just cause or excuse" would be criminally liable whether or not the wife consented. However, the two judges constituting a majority in the *Bravery* case expressly disassociated themselves from the views of Denning. They did feel that if a husband has himself sterilized "without good medical reason" and without his wife's consent it would "be a grave offence to her which could without difficulty be shown to be a cruel act" and hence a ground of divorce. The majority judges also felt inclined to "draw attention to the obviously grave potentialities of such an operation for the parties to a marriage." It is not clear whether the majority would impose criminal liability on a physician when there are no medical reasons for the operation and when the wife does not consent since in the *Bravery* case the wife had known of her husband's plans to have the operation and made no affirmative objection to it although she did not formally consent. Furthermore, the majority found that the operation "took a relatively minor place among the wife's complaints."

With respect to the divorce problem, a similar American case is *Kreyling v. Kreyling*,[8] where the wife brought suit for divorce alleging desertion on the ground that the defendant husband had refused to have intercourse with her for a period of two years unless he used a contraceptive device. In awarding the divorce the New Jersey court said:

"Where both husband and wife willingly indulge in birth prevention no legal problem arises, the matter being solely one for the individual consciences of the parties, honestly formed according to their religious and moral beliefs. Where, however, as the evidence in the instant case shows, one of the parties, the defendant, solely for his own personal selfish convenience, or, as he puts it, so that he may enjoy the luxuries of life, insists upon contraception to prevent his wife from becoming a mother, he being the active agent in the

---

[7] (1954) 1 W.L.R. 1169; (1954) 3 All E.R. 59.

[8] 20 N.J. Misc. 52, 23 Atl.2d 800 (1942).

use of the contraceptive device over her continued protests and against her will, it must be said that such conduct persisted in willfully, obstinately and continually for two years is cause for divorce on the ground of desertion."

By a parity of reasoning the New Jersey court might very well hold that if a husband is sterilized for nontherapeutic reasons and without his wife's consent his conduct would be a ground for divorce.

Dr. Rieser indicates in his article that a physician who performs a vasectomy might encounter legal difficulties if the wife later becomes pregnant because of "spontaneous reanastomosis of the vas deferens." This was precisely the situation before the Minnesota Supreme Court in *Christensen v. Thornby*.[9] There the defendant physician had performed a vasectomy upon the plaintiff to protect the health of his wife. The wife later became pregnant and survived the birth. Suit was brought against the doctor for breach of contract plus damages for anxiety and attendant birth expenses. There was no allegation of negligence, lack of skill, or malpractice. The court held for the doctor on the grounds that the operation was not contrary to public policy and that there had been no misrepresentation, fraud or deceit on the part of the physician. Since the plaintiff was "blessed with the fatherhood of another child" he sustained no damages.

With regard to this problem of recanalization, it has been the experience of the medical author that the technique employed may determine the incidence of recanalization. He removes at least three centimeters of vas. The proximal cut end is tied with nonabsorbable suture material and a layer of fascia is interposed between the proximal and distal cut ends. He has performed 14 vas resections for sterilization during the past 18 months. Twelve were done under local procaine anesthesia. Seminal fluids were examined repeatedly after operation in each instance until complete azoospermia was noted. In no case were spermatozoa found eight weeks after vasectomy and in five instances they were absent after two weeks. In any event, it is imperative that semen analysis be repeated until no spermatozoa are found.

LEGAL CONCLUSIONS

A sterilization performed pursuant to a state sterilization statute involves no criminal or civil liability for the physician.

[9] Footnote 1, *supra*.

A therapeutic sterilization performed to protect the patient's physical or mental health and well being is lawful.

When sterilization is therapeutically indicated in the marital situation it makes no difference from a legal point of view whether it is the wife or the husband who is sterilized.

Before any sterilization is performed, the written consent of the patient and spouse, if there be one, should be obtained. If the patient is a minor or an incompetent the written consent of the parent, guardian or other person responsible for the patient's care and support should also be obtained.

In states specifically forbidding sterilizations for nontherapeutic reasons, the consent of the patient would not be a defense to a criminal prosecution.

It is unlikely that a court would hold a sterilization of convenience to constitute mayhem although it might find some other basis of criminal liability. Whether consent would be a defense would depend on how serious the court considered the offense.

A sterilization of convenience of one party to a marriage without the consent of the other would be a ground for divorce and might subject the operating physician to civil liability.

If both partners to a marriage consent to a sterilization of convenience, the physician should not be held civilly liable.

If a wife becomes pregnant and has a child after the sterilization of her husband—to which she consented—it is doubtful whether there is any civil liability on the part of the physician.

In all of the above situations it is assumed that the operation was performed competently and without negligence. Consent is never a defense in an action against a physician based on his negligent or incompetent performance of an operation.

MEDICAL CONCLUSIONS

Vasectomy is a logical procedure for the prevention of pregnancy.

Repeated semen analysis should be made until complete azoospermia is present.

The incidence of recanalization can be reduced by careful operative technique.

The procedure can be reversible in a good percentage of the cases.

Reprinted from *Brit. J. Urol.*, **42**, 340–343 (1970)

A SIMPLE TECHNIQUE OF RE-ANASTOMOSIS AFTER VASECTOMY

31

By K. C. MEHTA, M.S., and P. S. RAMANI, M.S.

B.Y.L. Nair Charitable Hospital, Bombay 8, India

THE wider use of vasectomy as one of the methods of family planning is likely to bring in its wake an increasing demand for re-anastomosis, though in only a small percentage of individuals.

This paper is based on an experience of 26 restorative operations. In the first 3 cases end-to-end anastomosis of the vas (O'Conor, 1948), was carried out, but we were soon convinced that side-to-side anastomosis would be better (6 cases) in preventing post-operative stenosis. Further, during re-operation on a failed case from our initial series, we found extensive fibrosis replacing the vas at the site of anastomosis. We believed that this was due to avascular necrosis of the vas

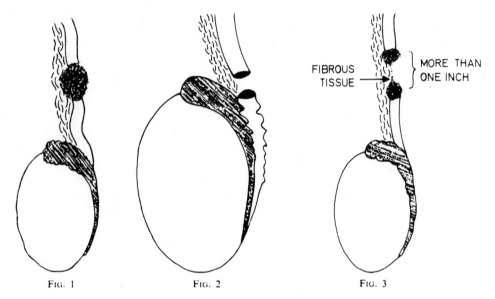

FIBROUS TISSUE

MORE THAN ONE INCH

FIG. 1   FIG. 2   FIG. 3

Different appearances of cut ends of vas as seen at operation.

as a result of interference of blood supply due to excessive mobilisation. Like the ureter, a mobilised vas, when divided transversely undergoes avascular necrosis (Swinney and Hammersley, 1963).

Thus the present technique of side-to-side anastomosis without mobilisation of the vas was evolved and used in 17 consecutive cases.

Reasons for Re-anastomosis.—The indications for re-anastomosis were remarriage, death of a male child or children, desire to have more children and for psychological reasons. In this series vasectomy was performed on 5 patients who had no children, 2 of whom were not even married. In 2 patients there had been accidental injury to the vas during operations for hydrocele and inguinal hernia. Three patients were re-operated on for failure of the initial re-anastomosis. The interval between vasectomy and re-anastomosis varied from 3 months to 4 years.

Pre-operative Evaluation.—Pre-operative evaluation of the scar, the spermatic cord, the vas. the epididymes and testes was helpful in planning the operation. There was no dilatation of the

340

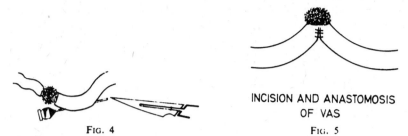

INCISION AND ANASTOMOSIS
OF VAS

Fɪɢ. 4   Fɪɢ. 5

Fig. 4.—Method of incision of proximal and distal ends of vas. For details see text.

Fig. 5.—Anastomosis of the two incised ends.

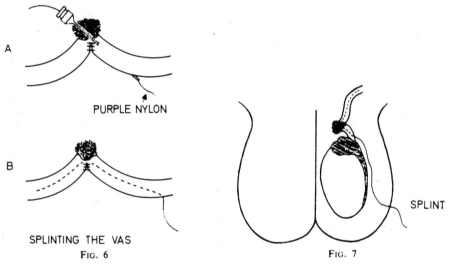

A

PURPLE NYLON

B

SPLINT

SPLINTING THE VAS
Fɪɢ. 6   Fɪɢ. 7

Fig. 6.—A and B, Method of splinting the vas with purple nylon. The splint is threaded
into the vas through the lumen of a syringe needle.

Fig. 7.—Splint in position at the end of the operation.

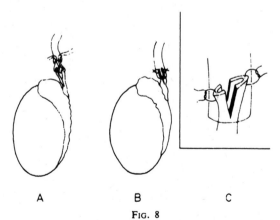

A   B   C

Fɪɢ. 8

A, B and C, Methods of anastomosis when vasectomy is
performed near the narrow convoluted part of the vas. For
details see text. Figure 8, C is a magnified view showing
details of anastomosis.

proximal vas (Phadke and Phadke, 1967) but in the majority the epididymes showed enlargemer .
The testes did not show any variation from the normal except for partial atrophy on one side 1
2 patients in whom the anastomosis had been attempted elsewhere. The different appearances f
the cut ends of the vas as seen at operation are shown in Figures 1, 2 and 3.

Technique of Operation.—Fourteen patients were operated on under spinal anæsthesia and
the remaining 3 under general anæsthesia. The average time taken for operation was 75 minutes.
A vertical upper scrotal 2-inch long incision is made. An upward extension of this incision to the
external inguinal ring is occasionally necessary. The cord is delivered and the cut ends of the vas
surrounded by a small fibrous mass are identified. Mobilisation of the vas either from the cord
or from the fibrous mass is unnecessary as this is associated with risk of injury to its blood supply
and that of the testes. The normal-looking vas just proximal and distal to the fibrous mass is
incised transversely until the lumen is entered, care being taken not to transect the vas completely.
A 24 gauge B.D. needle is passed into the lumen and brought out through the wall about 3 mm.
away. A fine pointed knife is engaged in the bevel of the needle and the vas is incised longitudinally as the needle is withdrawn (Fig. 4).

If the operation is done less than a year after vasectomy milky fluid oozes out through the
proximal end. This fluid must be washed away with normal saline to prevent formation of a
sperm granuloma (Lyons *et al.*, 1967). Normal saline, 2-3 ml., is injected into the distal cut end
to ascertain its patency.

The 2 incised ends are anastomosed side-to-side with 2-3 posterior and 2-3 anterior interrupted stitches (Fig. 5). These stitches are passed through partial thickness of the wall without
entering the lumen and the knots are tied on the outer side. A purple nylon splint (Campbell,
1963) is introduced before inserting the anterior stitches (Fig. 6). Nylon, 5/0, on a atraumatic
needle is used for anastomosis. One or two stay stitches are taken through the soft tissues around
the vas. The cord is replaced, the end of the nylon splint is brought out through the scrotal wall
and the incision is closed in layers (Fig. 7).

When vasectomy has been performed near the narrow convoluted part of the vas, a new
technique is used instead of standard epididymovasostomy. The cut ends are separated from the
fibrous mass carefully without extensive mobilisation. The proximal cut end is incised on each
side longitudinally for a distance of about 2 mm., thus creating 2 split flaps. Then the 2 split ends
are drawn into the lumen of the distal vas. A stitch is placed at the edge of each split flap. Each
end of this stitch is brought out through the wall of the distal vas at a distance of about 2 mm. and
a knot is tied on the outer side (Fig. 8, A, B and C). This technique was used unilaterally on 3
occasions. Since 2 of these 3 patients had nearly normal semen analysis following the operation
the technique is presumed to be successful.

Post-operative Mamagement.—Complete rest in bed is advised for a week. The nylon splint
is removed along with the skin stitches on the seventh day. Broad spectrum antibiotics and anti-
inflammatory agents, indomethacine (Indocid-M.S.D.) or oxyphenbutazone (Tanderil-Geigy)
are administered routinely. Prednisolone (30 mg. daily) is given orally for a week after healing of
the wound. Semen analysis is carried out after 3 weeks and repeated when necessary.

Results.—The appearance of spermatozoa in the semen suggests a successful result, though
the count may not return to normal for 3 to 6 months. If there are no sperms after 3 months the
operation is considered to be a failure. In our experience, none of the failures ever showed
spermatozoa after 3 months. Of the last 17 operations only 2 failed.

CONCLUSIONS

Vasectomy is reversible in the majority, if anastomosis is carried out meticulously. The
reasons for failure are infection, hæmatoma, injury to the blood supply of the vas and testis

blocked lumen and faulty technique. Avascular necrosis of the vas due to extensive mobilisation leading to fibrosis is in our opinion a major cause of failure.

Fibrosis, hæmatoma and injury to the blood supply of the vas and testis can all be prevented by the technique described here.

We thank the Dean, T.N. Medical College, for permission to use the records of some of the patients.

Addendum:—Since the submission of this article for publication, 5 more side-to-side anastomoses of the vas have been carried out, with success in all.

REFERENCES

CAMPBELL, M. F. (1963). " Urology ", Vol. 1, p. 678. Philadelphia: Saunders.

GLASSY, F. J. and MOSTOFI, F. K. (1956). Spermatic granuloma of epididymis. *American Journal of Clinical Pathology*, **26**, 1303-1313.

LYONS, R. C., PETRE, J. H. and CHUL NAM LEE (1967). Spermatic granuloma of epididymis. *Journal of Urology*, **97**, 320-323.

O'CONOR, V. J. (1948). Anastomosis of vas deferens after purposeful division for sterility. *Journal of the American Medical Association*, **136**, 162-163.

PHADKE, G. M. and PHADKE, A. G. (1967). Experiences in reanastomosis of vas deferens. *Journal of Urology*, **97**, 888-890.

SCHMIDT, S. S. (1956). Anastomosis of vas deferens. An experimental study. *Journal of Urology*, **75**, 300-304.

SUNDERASIVARAO, D. (1955). Spermatozoal granuloma of epididymis. *Journal of Pathology and Bacteriology*, **69**, 324-326.

SWINNEY, J. and HAMMERSLEY, D. P. (1963). " A Handbook of Operative Urological Surgery ", p. 67. Edinburgh: Livingstone.

Intrauterine Devices

X

Editor's Comments on Papers 32 Through 36

The idea of fitting something into the uterus in order to prevent conception, or at least to frustrate implantation of the fertilized ovum in the uterus, is very old. Throughout history a variety of devices have been placed within the uterus or in a position to block the entrance into the uterus. Most of these were designed to prevent entrance of the sperm, although a German physician, R. Richter, reported that the presence of silkworm gut in the uterine cavity prevented pregnancy. He apparently did not follow up on this observation because little attention was paid to it until Ernest Graefenberg of Berlin exploited the idea.

Greafenberg published his first study of the intrauterine devices in 1928 in a German journal. In 1930 he was asked to present his findings and conclusions at the Seventh International Birth Control Conference held in Zurich. Those proceedings were published in English in 1931. Dr. Graefenberg's contribution to that publication is reproduced here. This is a comprehensive report in which he first distinguishes between intrauterine devices and those that were formerly used which, as he says, are intrauterine in name only because most of the device lies in the vagina and is merely attached to the uterus in order to provide a mechanical obstruction to the entrance of sperm.

Graefenberg first used silkowrm gut but soon changed to silver rings. These he found stay in place better and can be more easily examined and removed. He observes that the normal menstrual cycle is maintained and that the ring may be left in place for a year or more, although he does admit that in some cases there is bleeding for a few days after insertion, there may be some pain, and a few women can never tolerate the device.

Having reported on the technique and the advantages and effectiveness, he then addresses himself to the means by which the ring prevents pregnancy, and after considering many possibilities admits that he really does not know. In this discussion he makes a very fine distinction. He thinks that the ring does not prevent fertilization of the ovum but that the fertilized ovum is prevented by the device from becoming embedded in the uterine wall. This, he goes on to say, is not abortion because by definition, at least by his definition, in order to abort the ovum must be first be embedded in the uterus. Thus he concludes that the device functions by "expulsion of the possibly fertilized ovum."

Dr. Graefenberg then addresses himself to the various objections that have been raised by others. First he cautions that the ring should not be placed in a woman that is already pregnant and to avoid this it should only be inserted immediately after menstruation. Second, he shows that the ring does not cause permanent sterility; as soon as it is removed, patients conceive. And third, he finds absolutely no evidence that the device results in malignant growths.

Finally, there is the admission that the method is not 100 percent reliable; with the silver ring his failure rate is 1.6 per cent. He offers several reasons for these failures.

As we have already seen, the field of contraception has always been interwoven with philosophy, psychology, and theology. Even as late as 1930, Dr. Graefenberg found it necessary to maintain that tradition. He first points out that the attitude of gynecologists toward intrauterine methods has been uniformly unfavorable. Then he goes on to state that ". . . we must think first of the woman in connection with any contraceptive method. Every method that affects the man is doomed to failure, for the man must be balked in his pleasure, whereas the woman is always the one to suffer. By freeing the woman from the need of making troublesome preparations, we favorably influence her sexual reactions. There can be no better way to combat the wide-spread frigidity among women and other neurotic conditions than by providing them with a protection against pregnancy."

But, as Graefenberg said, the attitude toward intrauterine methods was unfavorable, not because there was any evidence that the method was either unsafe or ineffective but simply because world authorities, almost completely without reason, opposed it. This was particularly true in the United States. And not until the Editors of the *American Journal of Obstetrics and Gynecology* in 1959 invited Dr. W. Oppenheimer of Jerusalem to write a review article on the Graefenberg ring method did this opposition begin to give ground. In his article, which is reproduced here, Oppenheimer quickly points out that he has used the ring in more than 1,000 cases, finds it effective, has never seen any ill effects, that it can stay in place at least 12 months, and following removal, normal pregnancy can quickly occur.

In the same year (1959) Dr. Ishihama published a similar review in the *Yokohama Medical Bulletin*. He too found the ring highly effective and without side-effects.

The Oppenheimer and the Ishihama papers, at long last, demolished enough of the opposition to the method that extensive experience could be gotten, modifications made, and rational evaluations undertaken. Two leaders in this effort in the United States have been Drs. Jack Lippes and Lazar Margulies. Their contributions are reproduced in this section. Lippes not only reports his extensive experience but goes on to discuss the use of a polyethylene loop in place of the silver ring. Margulies devised polyethylene spirals. Both proved to have advantages. The final word is, apparently, still not in. But without doubt the acceptance of the intrauterine device has increased rapidly since 1959 and continues to do so. The remaining problem seems to be expulsion of the device by some women and, particularly in nulliparous patients, discomfort. For those who retain the device and suffer no discomfort, a better method is hard to imagine.

Reprinted from *Proc. Seventh Intern. Birth Control Conf.: The Practice of Contraception*, 33–47 (1931)

32

THE PRACTICE

OF

CONTRACEPTION

AN INTERNATIONAL SYMPOSIUM AND SURVEY

EDITED BY

MARGARET SANGER

AND

HANNAH M. STONE, M.D.

WITH A FOREWORD

BY

ROBERT L. DICKINSON, M.D.

———————

From THE PROCEEDINGS OF
THE SEVENTH INTERNATIONAL
BIRTH CONTROL CONFERENCE
Zurich, Switzerland, September, 1930

———————

BALTIMORE
THE WILLIAMS & WILKINS COMPANY
1931

SECTION 2. INTRAUTERINE METHODS

AN INTRAUTERINE CONTRACEPTIVE METHOD

By Dr. Ernst Graefenberg

Berlin

I have the honour to present to you a brief account of the contraceptive method I have been using, and beg to be excused if I repeat much that I have already said in public on the subject upon other occasions.

Before going into details, I must once more emphasize that the contraceptive method I am using is entirely an intrauterine one. This method cannot be compared with other methods in use which are frequently called intrauterine. You know many of these methods, which, however, are only intrauterine in name, because part of the device either remains in the region of the cervical canal, or in most cases is fixed outside the cervix, that is in the vagina.

I will only mention the collar button pessary with the long neck, the Sterilett, as well as the Pust pessaries in which a glass knob lies outside the outer edge of the cervix. I lay much stress upon the fact that in the method which I recommend no part of the device projects beyond the inner edge of the cervix. Only thus can the bacteria from the lower sexual organs be prevented from being introduced into the bacteria-free cavity of the uterus.

I again stress the need for distinguishing between methods lest we classify totally different methods under the same heading. Dr. Pust's method is not intrauterine either. If we want to build the best possible foundation for future research, we must distinguish between the purely intrauterine methods and the mixed intrauterine methods.

Formerly I used the silk-worm gut star. This silk-worm gut is the product of the glands of the silk-worm and is commercially obtainable in a prepared durable form.

33

The silk-worm method is not new. In its first form it had, however, the same disadvantage as the methods to which I have just referred because one of the silk ends of the star projected through the cervical canal into the vagina; this was primarily designed to facilitate its subsequent removal from the uterus. This method was also a vagino-cervical method; but I soon gave it up. Aside from the risk of bacterial invasion the method had the further disadvantage that the pointed ends of the star were uncomfortable for the man. I therefore took special care to see that the silk star lay completely within the cavity of the uterus, and did not project into the cervical canal. A strand of ordinary silk-worm thread was cut in three parts, and the parts tied with the finest silver wire in the form of a star. The end of each part of the star was knotted or polished and smoothly fused to prevent any risk of injury. Silver wire was selected because silk could not be felt by the probe introduced into the uterus, whereas the silver wire gives a definitely metallic sensation when touched. This is most important when ascertaining whether the star has been properly placed or when attempting to remove it. The wire also shows clearly on X-ray plates, which is valuable in doubtful cases.

Later I gave up the use of the silk-worm gut star because I had a series of failures. The star was compressed by uterine contractions and was expelled with uterine cramps. I now use it only in cases of inelastic narrow cervix with inelastic folds, which make the insertion of the ring difficult, and only allow the passage of the smallest instrument. In these cases the danger of expulsion is also smaller. For these reasons I gave up using the star in favor of the ring.

In order to overcome the possibility of its slipping out, I rolled the silk-worm into a ring, and twisted silver wire round it to hold it in shape. Here again the silver wire has the advantage that it can be easily felt and its position ascertained. This ring is comparatively stiff and cannot so easily be expelled by uterine contractions. The circular shape also has the advantage that superficial scratching of the mucous membrane and bleeding is less likely to occur.

Later I gave up the use of silk-worm entirely, and replaced it

FIG. 5. Intrauterine silver rings, three different sizes.

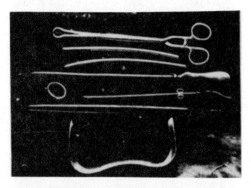

FIG. 6. Instruments required for introducing the silver ring.

FIG. 7. Forked instrument for the introduction of the ring.

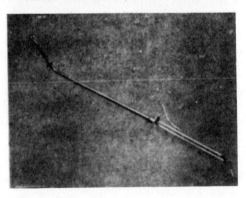

FIG. 8. Hooked instrument for the removal of the ring.

by rings made of silver or gold wire, twisted spirally and prepared by a manufacturer. These spiral rings have a smooth surface, and are more easily felt with a probe than the silk-worm and wire ring, and are particularly visible on X-ray plates.

These spiral rings are obtainable in various sizes and may easily be sterilized by boiling (Fig. 5). Their pliability allows them to be passed through the cervical canal in the form of an oval, and they return to their original circular shape within the uterus. When selecting the size, care must be taken not to prescribe so large a ring that the lower edge remains within the region of the cervical canal. On the other hand, it must not be so small that it does not properly fill the cavity of the uterus. In my experience a silver ring of 1.75 centimeter diameter is most suitable for tne average sized uterus. Too large a ring can easily project into the cervical canal, causing pain and a sanguineous discharge, and can gradually be forced outwards by the movements of the uterus. Even when the ring is not completely expelled by uterine contractions so that it is left with the larger part projecting into the cervical canal, it causes discomfort and, what is more serious, does not prevent conception.

It is not a difficult matter for any doctor who has experience in gynaecological examination and technique to insert a silver ring into the uterus. But I must repeat my warning that this is not a method to be used casually by any doctor who has no gynaecological experience. Not every physician is capable of using it. If I am an oculist I do not treat women's diseases, and a specialist on parasitic diseases would not be able to do so either. A certain amount of gynaecological experience is absolutely essential. The method can be learned, however, just as every medical student learns to curette a uterus, but one must have adequate previous experience before applying the method.

Naturally, as is the case of all intrauterine work the importance of asepsis cannot be too much emphasized. All instruments must be boiled, and the silver ring must be ready, attached to the instrument with which it is to be inserted (Fig. 6). At the same time the next size larger and the next size smaller rings must be prepared and sterilized so that it is possible to change the size at the last minute. The introducer is in the form of a uterine sound, the upper end of which is shaped like a fork. (Fig. 7). The ring is hung upon the fork, and is held uppermost when using the introducer. In cases of retroflexion, the inserting fork must naturally be turned round for insertion, and the ring must also be fixed accordingly. I will explain better with some lantern-slides.

Here you will see the cervix being exposed by means of a vaginal speculum. The os is then washed with a piece of cotton-wool soaked in a disinfectant, and the outer lip held up with a hooked forceps (Fig. 9). I use the Krupp forceps because these pinch the tissues of the cervix least. By means of a uterine sound (4 mm.) the position and size of the uterus, as well as the width and elasticity of the cervical canal is then ascertained (Fig. 10). It is best for the physician himself to hold the forceps, so that he may himself notice the details when inserting the sound. The sound is used particularly to determine the size of the uterus, because the ring must be placed in the cavity of this body. At the same time the sound indicates the length of the cervical canal, which is also most important in estimating the exact size of the uterine cavity. Sometimes it is difficult to insert the sound on account of projecting folds of the cervical mucous membrane, a condition which is especially found in cases of hypoplastic uterus. This difficulty can generally be overcome by stretching the cervical canal with the aid of two Hegar dilators, size 5 and 6 (Fig. 11). When a No. 6 has passed the cervical canal, then the silver ring can also be passed through with the introducer (Fig. 12). While passing the cervical canal the ring becomes oval in shape, but as soon as it has been passed into the uterus it returns to its original circular form. It is most important that the introducer should be pushed upwards till it reaches the dome of the uterus. When it is withdrawn, the ring is pulled off the fork by contact with the walls of the uterus.

The method is practically painless and an anaesthetic is rarely necessary. In cases of very sensitive women, with a narrow cervical canal and especially with pronounced projection of the plicae palmatae, I sometimes give a whiff of ethyl chloride. Local anaesthetics are not suitable for such women, because they find the preparatory injection too painful.

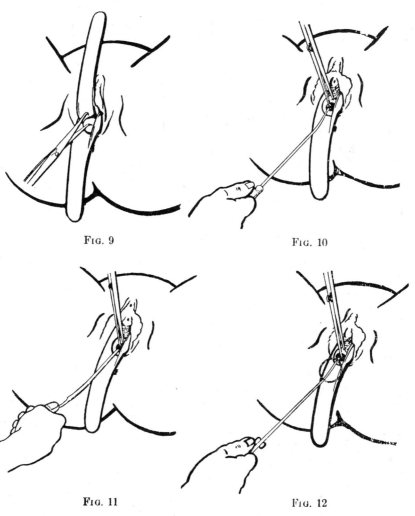

FIG. 9

FIG. 10

FIG. 11

FIG. 12

FIG. 9. The cervix is exposed and the outer lip held up with a hooked forceps.

FIG. 10. A uterine sound is introduced to ascertain the position and size of the uterus and the width and elasticity of the cervical canal.

FIG. 11. The cervical canal is stretched with a Hegar dilator.

FIG. 12. The silver ring is introduced.

The removal of the ring is equally simple. After exposing the os, the outer lip is again grasped with the forceps. The physician then takes a sound and feels for the metal ring, and then he pulls it out with a long thin polypus forceps, or with a specially designed hooked instrument which has recently been placed on the market (Fig. 8).

Formerly, I used to remove and re-insert the silkworm or silver ring after one year. Now I only examine the patient to see that the generative organs are in good condition, and that the ring is in the correct position. In this connection I act upon the principle of *quieta non movere*. The insertion of a sound shows whether the ring is correctly placed or not, and the patient may also be X-rayed, if desired.

The insertion of the ring is followed by slight bleeding for the first few days. It is easily understood that superficial lesions of the mucous membrane may occur during the introduction of the ring. These lesions ooze blood and mucus until the epithelial layer has grown again. Frequently uterine contractions also occur, giving rise to discomfort similar to menstrual pains. The dilatation itself causes some pain, which can last for several hours, but the contractions soon cease, and there is no further sensitiveness after one or two days.

It is most important to watch the patient's temperature, because bacteria may penetrate through the lesions in the uterine mucosa. The patient's temperature should therefore be taken regularly for the first three days. I examine my patients at the end of the first week, and after the first menstruation. The first examination is important so that the presence of any inflammation may be determined in time, and the second because the first menstruation following the insertion is often accompanied by very heavy bleeding and the ring might be expelled at this time. The presence of the ring may, therefore, be verified at this examination. Later the risk of losing it is less, and the patient then waits a year before returning for a re-examination.

The patient should be warned that the first menstruations may be longer and more profuse. The period of menstruation is longer because it begins slowly, the first traces of blood being noticed a few days before the actual menstruation begins. The real menstruation starts at the right time, it is only that a certain amount of sanguineous secretion appears a few days before the menses, that is during the premenstrual period.

The explanation for this peculiar condition is obtained by the aid of the microscope. The foreign body in the uterine cavity causes a change in the mucous membrane. There is no disturbance of the physiological rhythm of proliferation and regeneration of the membrane, the processes are only intensified. This naturally applies also to the premenstrual mucous membrane, which exhibits an increased functional activity and resembles the pre-pregnant mucous membrane. The premenstrual mucous membrane is normally very similar to the pregestational membrane, and this similarity is still more marked in the case of a uterus containing a ring. Here the mucous membrane becomes much thicker and hyperaemic, I would call it a hyper-decidua. As such, it can naturally begin to bleed before the date for menstruation. This heightened functional activity may also cause bleeding at the end of the ovulation period, that is, in the middle of the menstrual cycle. It can also give rise to bleeding after intercourse. I am inclined to believe that the gold ring causes less hypersecretion and bleeding than the silver ring.

These symptoms occur only during the first weeks, later the patient has no further trouble. Only if these symptoms persist should the ring be removed and then reinserted after a certain length of time. Since I have observed that all troublesome symptoms usually disappear in a short time, I have avoided changing the ring at the end of a year. I have been supported in this by the fact that quite a considerable number of women who, contrary to my instructions, did not return to me for a re-examination until years afterwards, have been entirely free from all discomfort.

What exactly is the physiological action of this intrauterine method? At the beginning I thought that a chronic but harmless inflammation of the mucous membrane had been set up by the presence of the foreign body and that it was impossible for the ovum to imbed itself in the changed mucosa. Careful and thorough microscopic examinations of the mucous membrane, in which I was assisted by Professor Robert Meyer, of Berlin, however, showed no signs of such inflammation. On the other hand, a hyper-decidual change of the mucosa was always observed (Fig. 13.) Russian authorities have also described this condition, although they regard the change as pathological. This is not correct because similar slides are obtained during the normal menstrual period. The same observers have also made accurate tests of the uterine secretion and its pH concentration. This was found to be remarkably increased, and regarded as the cause of the contraceptive action. It was thought that the sperms were killed by this high pH concentration. This cannot be correct, because the occurrence of cases of pregnancy both inside and outside of the uterus does not agree with this hypothesis. I believe that the mechanical changes in the mucous membrane in the form of a hyper-decidua are the cause of the temporary sterility. Whereas normally the decidua forms only after the ovum has become imbedded, and can then protect itself from all outside harm, now the condition of the uterus prevents the ovum from imbedding itself. In accordance with this theory, the spermatozoa are not killed, nor is the fertilization of the ovum by the sperm prevented, it is only that it is impossible for the ovum to imbed itself in the mucous membrane. It is therefore incorrect to speak of a monthly early abortion. The essential condition for an abortion is the previous embedding of the ovum, and this is exactly what is prevented by the ring. These processes can only be compared with normal menstruation. If normal menstruation is regarded as the expulsion of an unfertilized ovum, then the process which results when a ring has been inserted can only be considered as the expulsion of a possibly fertilized ovum.

This is not mere sophistry, and I think that we can entirely disregard the theory of an abortion since the ovum does not imbed itself.

When discussing the possibility of inserting the ring, we must investigate the contraindications more closely. I must emphasize the observation that a 100 per cent reliable method would be ideal but that perhaps it will never be discovered. You all know that even surgical methods for the prevention of conception through

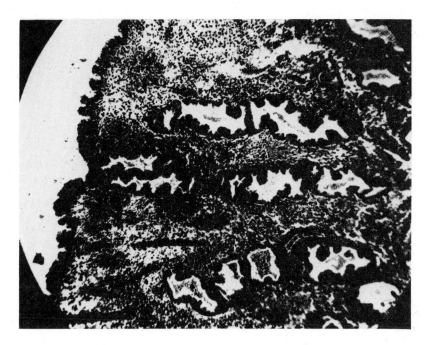

FIG. 13. Microcopic section of uterine scrapings from a woman who had worn a silver ring.

ligation of the fallopian tubes, or the spermatic cord, are not 100 per cent reliable. It is the tragic fate of biological methods that they sometimes fail. We must be prepared for failures, but we must see that no harm comes to those who seek our advice.

It must therefore not be forgotten that this method is not suitable for all women. It cannot be used in cases of inflammation or infection of the pelvic organs. Therefore a thorough examination of the patient is essential. This must be made by a physician who has had experience in gynaecological diagnosis. The examination should include a test of the genital secretions, and the determination of the condition of the uterus and adnexa. The patient's medical history will be found useful in this connection. In cases of former pelvic inflammation, special care must be taken because any intrauterine manipulation may cause a relapse of the inflammation. It is particularly dangerous to overlook any symptoms of gonorrhoea, because this condition, as is well known, has a special tendency to spread.

We were told that gonorrhoea is dying out. On the contrary, a marked increase may be observed, which is most deplorable. As long as the uterus is free from irritation and clean, there is no danger in using this method. If there is any trace of gonoccocci, however, these may spread upwards through the manipulation and cause serious complications.

Special care must be taken with patients who have had gonorrhoea. If I can find no gonococci, I try a blood fixation test which is an excellent way of ascertaining the presence of gonorrhoea in doubtful cases. If the blood-test is positive, I never insert a ring. The patient must also be examined for any changes in the adnexa which may have been caused by a former gonorrhoea. These are not always a contra-indication. The blood-test will be found useful here, too, to show the state of things, and avoid long explanations on the part of the patient.

Gonorrhoea may also be acquired after the ring has been inserted. I have seen numerous cases where the patients became acutely ill with severe symptoms. In such cases the ring must be removed at once, and the symptoms will then subside.

Gonorrhoea is not the only danger to be guarded against.

Other types of bacteria and changes in the uterine and vaginal secretions are also important from the point of view of indications and counter-indications. We have prepared a special 'scale of cleanliness' of the genital secretions according to the number and kind of bacteria they contain, the figures 1, 2, 3, 4 being used to indicate ascending degrees of impurity. A discharge in which there are many pus corpuscles we regard as a bad secretion. Such a discharge is dangerous, and tends to cause inflammation if a ring is inserted. If the secretion is not clean, I strongly advise to treat the catarrh first, and then to insert the ring.

A simple cervical catarrh, without hyperaemia, is a long and drawn out affair and difficult to clear up completely. A ring, however, may be inserted without the fear of aggravating the disease, nor is there any danger that the ring will cause an increase in the discharge.

The question has also been raised as to the possibility of the ring in itself causing a cervical catarrh, which would produce a discharge. This is only a theoretical possibility when the ring does not lie in the uterine cavity but reaches down into the cervical canal, for, as you are all aware, the lining of the uterine cavity is not a mucous membrane at all, the actual mucus secreting cells are only to be found in the cervical canal, so that it is only irritation of the cervical canal that can cause a discharge.

Since I have at various times inserted a ring when the patient was already pregnant, either because she had not told me that she had missed her period, or because menstruation was imminent and she was already pregnant, I advise that the ring be inserted immediately after menstruation.

It must also be noted that the ring should not be inserted in cases where there is a profuse menstrual flow, which is frequently due to changes in the uterus. These may easily be aggravated by the presence of a foreign body. In themselves, such changes are not a contra-indication, provided they are non-inflammatory in character. It is not always possible however, to insert the ring in cases of prolapse of the uterus and vagina.

Another most important question; if the ring is worn for a long time, can it cause permanent sterility so that pregnancy becomes impossible after removal of the ring? Our object is to induce a temporary sterility, and not a permanent one. I have had numerous cases in which the patient became pregnant immediately after removal of the ring, once, in fact, contrary to her desire.

I have not seen any cases of permanent damage to the uterine mucosa or to the uterine muscles. In cases where the mucous membrane of the uterus reacted more violently, all symptoms disappeared when the ring was removed.

An underdeveloped uterus is not a contra-indication. Can a hypoplastic, infantile uterus bear the presence of a foreign body? According to my experiences with the Sterilett method, the foreign body stimulates growth, for I have had numerous cases of women with hypoplastic organs, suffering from dysmenorrhoea, where the latter symptom disappeared after the insertion of the foreign body. The organ proceeded to develop normally, and regular menstruation was established.

The Russian, Lourié, raised a very serious objection to this method, suggesting that malignant growths may be caused by the presence of a foreign body in the uterus. He based his opinion upon the observation that intrauterine devices cause a change in the epithelial layer of the uterine mucous membrane. These changes are similar to those frequently found in the early stages of carcinoma. It is obvious that if we accept this theory, we can only speak of cancer of the cavity of the uterus. Carcinoma of the cavity, however, occurs very rarely, because cervical cancers have very little tendency to turn into carcinoma of the body. The other danger, that a cancer might develop in the cervical cavity is far greater. In all my ten years experience, however, I have never seen anything of the kind. Among my records, which are by no means meagre, I have seen no case of cancer in women wearing a ring although many of my patients have reached the age at which cancer usually occurs. Such a possibility is also fairly remote because the mucous membrane in which a growth might occur is thrown off every month, and replaced by a new one.

Our method, too, is not 100 per cent reliable. I gave up using the silk-worm star method because I had a large number of failures. The star was either expelled, or else, it lay too high in the uterine cavity, so that a large part of the uterus remained unprotected and imbedding was possible. I therefore took up the ring method. Here, too, however, I have observed several failures. The first question is how a pregnancy is possible with a foreign body in the uterus. We have been taught that in case of pregnancy, the least interference can cause an abortion, and that therefore nothing must ever be done even to the external genitalia for fear of inducing an abortion. We are also taught that a sound is the most dangerous instrument in connection with abortions. On the other hand I would like to point out that sounding a gravid uterus actually rarely leads to an abortion. It is most difficult to induce an abortion by the use of a sound, particularly during the first eight weeks. I do not know of a single case of abortion caused in this manner. You may judge from this how extraordinarily resistant the uterus is. Even advanced pregnancies have been examined, without causing the uterus to abort.

How are the cases of failure to be explained? In the majority of cases, the ring was not in the right position; it was in the cervical canal, for it can happen, if the cervical canal is wide and stretched, more particularly in the case of a multipara, that the ring slips out entirely or else is expelled partially into the cervical canal. Patients are not always aware of the loss of the ring, because it may be forced out with an excessive flow at menstruation. Loss of the ring, however, is often due also to the choice of the wrong size, the ring being too small and not filling the uterine cavity, so that the pre-menstrual reaction or the pre-gravid reaction was not strong enough entirely to prevent the ovum from imbedding. You will ask how it is that women who have borne no children do not retain the ring. I had a proof of this a few days ago. It concerned the wife of a colleague (when things do not turn out properly, it is always in connection with a colleague) I had fitted her with a ring, and yet she became pregnant. During the curettage, which became necessary, it appeared that the inner os was completely open; I was able to insert a Hegar dilator No. 12 without causing pain. Think of this and then of women who have had three or four abortions. The inner os must be so stretched that a complete closure of the uterus must be quite impossible. The ring lay too deep down and provided no protection. If pregnancy had actually taken place, I do not think it right to leave the ring in position. Since the removal, however, is always accompanied by bleeding, I advise curetting at the same time.

If one is to judge by the medical literature, the attitude of gynaecologists towards the question of intrauterine methods of contraception is uniformly unfavourable. Accounts of inflammatory changes following the use of such methods, are also found in the literature. If the cases in question are, however, more thoroughly analysed, it will almost always be found that they do not deal with our real intrauterine method, but with methods involving stiff parts lying in the cervical canal or even sticking out into the vagina. They are almost always cases of utero-vaginal foreign bodies, which form a means of communication between the vagina which always contains bacteria, and the cavity of the uterus which is free from them. There is the risk of infecting the uterus in the use of all such methods. Even the most recent publication of Von Tietze in the Deutschen Medizinischer Wochenschrift, No. 31, 1930, deals exclusively with vaginal-cervical stem pessaries, in spite of the fact that his title to the article refers to the harmful effects of the use of intrauterine pessaries. These are all methods of which I am not in favor. When estimating the value of these publications, careful distinction should be made between our purely intrauterine method, and those which apply both to the vagina and the cervix.

In conclusion, I will give a summary of my results. In the course of my private practice during recent years I have fitted the following number of patients with intrauterine devices.

400 with silk worm stars
1100 with silk worm rings
600 with silver rings

These figures apply to the total number of women and include duplicate cases.

I have had 3.1 per cent of failures with the use of the silkworm method and only 1.6 per cent with the use of the silver ring.

This figure could be still further reduced if a chemical method could be used in combination with the ring. I agree with Dr. Leunbach's suggestion that perhaps a suppository or tablet should also be inserted, or that a post-coital douche be advised. I consider this important because the presence of the ring does not prevent a fertilised ovum from imbedding itself in some extra-uterine place. I must emphasize that is is possible for an extra-uterine pregnancy to occur in women who are wearing a silver ring.

May I repeat, too, that this method is not suitable for every doctor, nor is it suitable for every woman. We must differentiate very carefully between individual cases. I am therefore very glad that this discussion is taking place, because it may throw new light upon this intrauterine method and perhaps you may be led to regard the method more favorably than seems to be the case at present. This is important because we must think first of the woman in connection with any contraceptive method. Every method that affects the man is doomed to failure, for the man must not be balked in his pleasure, whereas the woman is always the one to suffer. We must also remember, however, that many women are lazy and stupid, and take no interest in protecting themselves. All these points must be taken into consideration. Then there are also the women who are indifferent, who are not in a position to make the necessary preparations, and do not want to go to a physician. There are women who become psycho-neurotic if they have no method available that makes them independent of the doctor. By freeing the woman from the need of making troublesome preparations, we favorably influence her sexual reactions. There can be no better way to combat the wide-spread frigidity among women and other neurotic conditions than by providing them with a protection against pregnancy. I am in agreement with the psychiatrists who advise the use of such a protection in cases of women suffering from neuroses in which the sexual life plays a part.

From what I have told you, you will see that, provided it is harmless, this method should be studied further. You will certainly be able to do much with it. The important point is that it must not be regarded as the only method; every physician must select the method that in his opinion is the right one for the individual patient.

Copyright © 1959 by the C. V. Mosby Company

Reprinted from *Amer. J. Obstet. Gynecol.*, **78**, 446–454 (1959)

33

IN 1929 Graefenberg reported for the first time the celebrated ring which bears his name and which has subsequently been the center of great dispute among gynecologists all over the world. Graefenberg's motive was contraception, and he claimed for his device both safety and effectiveness.

However, the reception accorded this invention was from the start stormy in the extreme. At the seventh International Congress for Birth Control (1930), Pankow, Hammerschlag, Küster, Adler, and Frei all expressed opposition to this innovation—although not one of these distinguished gentlemen had ever had any experience of his own with the ring! On the other hand, Norman Haire of London, who had had experience with the ring, staunchly defended it.

Much of the opposition—to the dispassionate historian's view of today—apparently arose from the unfortunate experiences with the earlier intrauterine devices, such as Pust's pessary. The previous instruments, however, had included extensions which protruded through the cervix into the vagina.

Nevertheless, the opposition won the day, at least in the United States. Thus the Greenhill and the Curtis texts mention the method only to condemn it. The Crossen volume does not even mention it. To all intents and purposes, this technique has disappeared in this country. Therefore, in seeking a re-evaluation of the Graefenberg ring, the Editors have turned to a foreign country, and Dr. W. Oppenheimer, Director of the Department of Gynecology and Obstetrics at the Shaare Zedek Hospital in Jerusalem, has responded with this account of his experiences with this technique.

The Editors must perforce point out that the publication of this re-evaluation does not constitute an official or a personal endorsement on their parts of the Graefenberg ring as a contraceptive technique. We will not repeat the error of the first vehement critics, so, not having personal experience with the method, we must remain objective. We can speak neither for nor against it, and Dr. Oppenheimer is more than able to speak persuasively for himself.

PREVENTION OF PREGNANCY BY THE GRAEFENBERG RING METHOD

A Re-Evaluation After 28 Years' Experience

W. OPPENHEIMER, M.D., F.I.C.S., JERUSALEM, ISRAEL

(From the Department of Gynecology and Obstetrics, Shaare Zedek Hospital)

AT A time when so many countries are overpopulated, the prevention of pregnancy has become a consideration of increasing importance. The medical or eugenic indication for the interruption of pregnancy is recognized in many parts of Europe and America, while in Japan and India, for example, it has become an official instrument of population policy. Since there is some danger in the interruption of pregnancy, a method of preventing pregnancy, which would be free from risk, has become a problem of the first order.

For the past 70 years, since Mensinga[1] introduced the "Dutch Cap," a soft vaginal rubber pessary with a spiral elastic rim, this pessary, with its several variants—such as Ramses, Matrisalus, and Diaphragma—has found general acceptance despite the fact that it has some disadvantages. The manipulation of introducing the cap shortly before intercourse hinders many women from experiencing orgasm and may lead to nervous disturbances. Moreover, in cases where the anterior vaginal wall has descended, as well as in cases of retroversion of the uterus, the method frequently fails. Its safety is approximately 95 per cent. The hard cervical caps, which were introduced during the twenties and then commonly used in Central Europe, have a great many ill effects—erosions, secretion retained in the cap which gives off offensive odor, and hypertrophy of the vaginal mucosa around the rim of the cap. These hard caps are therefore regarded as unsanitary. The "safe period" method has proved too uncertain. Under the circumstances it is understandable that there should be a universal search for a better and safer method to prevent pregnancy.

It is for that very reason, and because I believe the Graefenberg ring is an excellent method, which, while discussed in the overheated atmosphere of the early thirties, could not be considered objectively, that I am bringing up the question again. The ring in my own experience and in that of other reliable gynecologists has shown better results than any other method and has proved to be absolutely harmless. Nobody doubts that there is a possibility of infection, as in every intrauterine procedure, if one does not work with all the care and asepsis necessary.

Since 1930 I have inserted the Graefenberg ring 866 times. Since the beginning of writing this re-evaluation another 150 rings have been inserted. On the basis of my findings I consider it far superior to other preventive methods for the following reasons:

1. I have never, in more than 1,000 cases, seen any illness caused by it.
2. It yields far better results than the soft rubber caps.
3. It can be applied also (a) where the patient refuses the soft rubber cap for psychosexual reasons, (b) in cases of descensus of the anterior vaginal wall, and (c) in cases of retroflexion of the uterus.
4. It is inserted by the physician only once in 12 months.
5. It does not cause sterility subsequent to its removal and patients can then become pregnant just as quickly as women who have never worn a ring.

During the first 2 to 3 years I used the Graefenberg silver ring and then switched over to the silkworm gut ring. I fasten a piece of silver wire to hang from the ring so that the presence of the ring can be ascertained by x-ray examination.

Technique of the Method

The silkworm gut ring (which I shall call the silk ring) is usually inserted 3 to 4 days after the end of the menstrual period, and removed 9 to 12 months later, a day or 2 before the beginning of menstruation. Prior to the insertion of the ring the patient is carefully examined and swabs are taken from the cervix and urethra. Patients with any kind of inflammation and those with suspected genital tuberculosis are excluded and so are patients with severe bleeding caused by submucous fibroma, endometriosis interna, and hyperplasia glandularis cystica.

For the actual insertion of the ring all the instruments have to be sterilized. One needs, apart from the normal gynecological instruments, a special instrument to insert the ring which I shall describe below. The silk ring consists of 3 or 4 intertwined threads of silkworm gut each 14 cm. long with a knot at either end. In order to avoid any cracking of the silk threads while they are being intertwined, I soften them in warm water prior to knotting the ends and making the ring; this is to ensure that the end points or a cracked thread will not pierce the uterine wall. The silver wire attached to the ring should be 0.2 mm. thick. The instrument for inserting the ring is a thin hollow sound slightly bent at the upper end like a normal uterine sound; 0.5 cm. from its point the sound has a notch. The ring is fixed into this notch by means of a thin metal rod passing through the sound. In order to do this the ring is gripped by the anatomical forceps in such a manner that all the silk threads are placed one alongside the other so that the metal rod can pass over the threads and fix them into the notch of the sound (Fig. 1). After iodization of the cervix and vagina

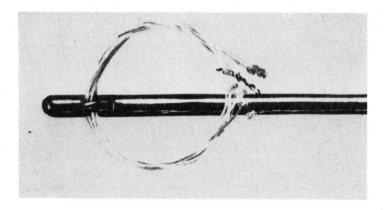

Fig. 1.—Part of the instrument for introducing the ring, showing the mechanism for fixing the ring.

and seizure of the cervix with the tenaculum forceps, the instrument carrying the ring is introduced into the uterine cavity like a uterine sound. Then the rod which passes through the instrument is withdrawn a few centimeters, thereby releasing the ring. The ring remains in the cavum uteri and the instrument is removed from the uterus slowly and carefully with slight rotatory movements. The whole process is practically painless and lasts only a few minutes; the actual insertion takes 3 to 4 seconds at the most.

The removal of the ring also takes only a few seconds. For this I use an instrument resembling a crochet hook but rounded at the top. After grasping the cervix with the tenaculum forceps the instrument is passed into the fundus uteri and when withdrawn it easily hooks onto the ring. I avoid removal and insertion—that is, changing the ring—in one session, in order to give the uterine mucosa a chance to rest for a few days.

Statistics

During the years 1930-1957 I have equipped 329 women with 866 rings, effecting one to 20 insertions per case (Table I).

TABLE I

SES	NO. OF INSERTIONS	NO. OF CASES	NO. OF INSERTIONS
	1	1	11
	2	2	12
3	3	2	13
,5	4	1	14
14	5	1	15
8	6	1	16
5	7	1	17
3	8	1	19
1	9	1	20
2	10		

Advantages of the Method

The most outstanding quality of the ring method is its absolute harmlessness. In 866 insertions I have never seen any kind of inflammation or infection whatever, even in the presulfa and preantibiotic era. Moreover I have not had to use any antibiotic or sulfa preparation in any of the 866 insertions.

If earlier literature reports cases of all kinds of inflammation and even death then this may be accounted for in the following ways: (1) the method was not applied properly and aseptically; (2) the ring was inserted in cases of latent or unrecognized infection; (3) the patients were subsequently infected with gonorrhea or other disease; (4) upon failure or after the ring had dropped out, an illegal abortion had been carried out by an unpracticed or irresponsible person.

The second advantage of the method is its effectiveness. I have experienced 2 failures in 150 insertions of silver rings, i.e., 1.3 per cent; and 20 failures in all insertions, silver rings and silk rings, i.e., 2.4 per cent. But if we consider that the total of the 866 rings were in situ for an aggregate period of 793 years, i.e., 10,309 cycles, we arrive at one gravidity in 515 cycles or about 40 years. The rubber cap, on the other hand, shows 5 per cent failures; i.e., 5 failures in 100 cycles and 25 failures in about 40 years. The Graefenberg ring is thus 25 times as safe as the rubber cap. No other method offers such a high degree of safety. In a number of cases the ring has dropped out unnoticed. In 9 of my cases the ring was found in the vagina either by me during the follow-up examination or by the patient herself. In another 21 cases I found the end of one thread just visible in the os externum, i.e., the ring had slipped forward but was not yet outside the os and could be replaced by another ring in time to prevent conception. We know nothing definite as to what causes the ring to slip out of the uterine cavity. Possible causes are: (1) the ring is too large; (2) the uterus is too sensitive and therefore ejects the ring; (3) the internal os is too wide open and the ring therefore slips down gradually; (4) contraction of the uterus during orgasm leads to ejection of the ring; (5) the ring was left too long in water after sterilization and thereby became too soft so that during insertion it was compressed in the cervical canal and did not regain its original shape.

It is to be assumed that the silk ring is less liable to cause contractions than the silver ring, since of my 866 rings, approximately 700 of which were silk rings, only 5 per cent slipped forward as against 20 per cent of the silver rings inserted by Norman Haire and 17 per cent of those inserted by Leunbach.[2] Three years ago I changed the silk ring to a form similar to the silver ring by intertwining the threads 3 times instead of twice and by using 4 instead of 3 threads. Since that time no case of pregnancy or of dropping out or of slipping forward has occurred. In spite of that I would advise 2 to 3 control examinations after insertion of the ring. Occasional failures are possible even when the ring is properly in position; in the few such cases observed by me, pregnancy and delivery were normal. In one of these cases an x-ray revealed the ring to be in utero 6 weeks after delivery and it was easily removed 2 months after confinement. In 2 of my cases where there was amenorrhea without pregnancy I checked the ring by x-ray and was thus able to reassure these patients. The patients continued to wear the ring and menstrual periods reappeared.

It is interesting to note that the ring does not become less efficacious by habitual wearing; on the contrary I have never observed a failure after the third or fourth insertion. On the other hand as soon as another pregnancy was desired it occurred spontaneously without any treatment and only a short time after removal of the ring. I have never had to treat for secondary sterility any ring-wearer who had become pregnant before without previous treatment.

I have given up using the ring in nulliparas for contraception because in such cases it is rejected more frequently than in parous women. I have found that after abdominal cesarean section, in cases where, except for a narrow edge, the os externum has expanded but has not visibly torn, the ring can easily be inserted and keeps well in place.

Perforation during insertion of the ring appears to be very rare. The only case which I know of was reported by Murphy.[3] In this case there was a complete perforation of the lateral uterine wall and the silver ring was lodged in the right parametrium. The patient became pregnant and after x-ray had shown the ring to be outside the uterus, it was removed by laparotomy and the pregnancy continued undisturbed.

In ring-wearers who became pregnant and had spontaneous abortions, Stefko[4] frequently found deformities of the fetus and the placenta which he ascribed to the ring; but Mall[5, 6, 7] and Keibel and Mall[8] had already discovered 70 per cent of abnormalities of the ovum during the first month, and 50 per cent during the first and second months of pregnancy in cases of spontaneous abortion among patients who did not wear a ring. Hertig,[9] Rock,[10] and their co-workers[11, 12, 13] found in 1,000 cases of spontaneous abortion 61.7 per cent of abnormal ova, and hydatidiform degeneration of the chorionic villi in two thirds of these cases. Corner[14] found similar results in other mammals, especially in the pig. Stefko's view is also contradicted by my own experience and that of other writers; neither the babies who had been carried to term by ring-wearers nor the respective placentas showed any deformity. Despite his interesting investigations, Stefko's conclusions have thus been completely disproved. There is therefore no justification whatever for interrupting pregnancies occurring with the ring in situ for fear of fetal deformity. I have never observed extrauterine pregnancy as a consequence of the ring.

If we consider that in the presulfa and the prepenicillin era over 50 per cent of all gynecological diseases were of an inflammatory character and that more than 50 per cent of gynecological operations, at least in large Central European cities, were for the remedy of inflammatory diseases and their consequences, we can fully appreciate the remarkable harmlessness of a correctly performed insertion of the silk ring and what it means that in over 1,000 insertions I have never observed a resultant inflammation or extrauterine pregnancy.

Sterility after wearing the ring has not occurred in any of my cases. A great many women had the ring changed time after time for many years, and some, despite my warnings, wore the same ring for 2 to 4 years without any complications. In no case was treatment for sterility required in order to induce a pregnancy. In many cases pregnancy occurred in the first month after removal of the ring, in others after 2 to 4 months, and in 2 cases after

6 months. Many of my patients wore the ring between several pregnancies, which always occurred spontaneously whenever desired. All pregnancies went to term.

In the early stages of wearing the ring the patients occasionally have increased and prolonged bleedings, very rarely also slight bleedings between the menstrual periods. Patients who have been warned against the method by a third party are especially prone to complain at first; however, these symptoms practically always disappear when the patient is given sufficient confidence. There is often a slight brownish discharge a day or two before and after the menses. It is important therefore to inform the patient about this fact prior to insertion. Removal of the ring because of increased bleeding is rarely necessary. I have done it in only 2 cases, in which the ring was introduced 8 weeks after confinement, when perhaps the uterus was not yet fully involuted.

It is interesting to note that sometimes the reverse happens; the menses are shortened and severe and lengthy menstruations become completely cured and normalized by the ring. This occurred in those cases in which the prolonged bleedings have a psychological basis.

All experience tends to disprove the allegation that the Graefenberg ring occasions tumors:

1. I have never observed cancer of the uterus (cervix or corpus) in any of the ring-wearers, although many of them have worn the ring for 10 to 20 years (one for 28 years). Theoretically, cancer of the uterus in wearers of the silk ring is as little to be expected as cancer of the stomach or intestines after an operation, involving the use of silk thread, on these organs.

2. Among my patients who had worn the ring there were only 2 cases of ovarian tumors, one a dermoid and the other a cystoma simplex; that is to say, the occurrence of ovarian tumors is not higher than in those who are not ring-wearers.

3. There has been no endometriosis interna or externa following the use of the ring.

4. Myoma in ring-wearers has been observed by me in 7 cases. In one of them the patient had already had an operation with enucleation of multiple myomas a few years before the first ring had been inserted. She had later had a parametrically developed cervical myoma which in pregnancy blocked the entry of the fetal head into the pelvis minor so that she had to be delivered by cesarean section. Since then, although the patient started wearing the ring after that birth and has worn it now for several years, the fibroid has shrunk continually. This case therefore has to be deducted from the 7 myoma cases. The remaining 6 cases include several which, in all probability, were not caused by the intrauterine ring. In one of these cases I did not discover the fibroid until 6 years after the last ring had been removed. But even if we reckon 6 cases of myoma in 329 ring-wearers, this is a proportion definitely within normal limits.

So far, I have carried out 10 test curettages immediately upon removal of the ring. They were examined at the Pathological Institute of the Hebrew University and Hadassah Medical School, Jerusalem, and they showed no signs of endometritis or any other pathological changes. This agrees with the results of the examinations carried out by Robert Meyer and some British pathologists.

The cause of the effectiveness of the ring has not yet been established. We have to think of several possibilities. There might be the formation of a deciduoma which can be produced by mechanical, chemical and electrical methods. It was first produced by Loeb[15] in 1907 in experiments with guinea pigs and rabbits and later by other research workers[16-25] in other animals and finally by Eichner[26] in human beings. It is interesting to note that a number of scientists pulled a loop of silk thread, as a mechanical stimulus, through the cavum uteri of the animal in order to produce a deciduoma without relating it to contraception, just as Graefenberg did in his contraceptive device without relating it to deciduoma.

In earlier literature it was suggested that the ring works by causing a change in the pH content in the uterine cavity, or, as Graefenberg maintained, by an early overdevelopment of the secretory phase of the uterine mucosa which might prevent the settling of the ovum. Norman Haire[30] on one occasion expressed the opinion that the ovum might settle on the ring itself, and, on another occasion, that the ring as such might produce increased alkalinity of the mucosa corporis which would kill the sperma and thus prevent pregnancy. Carleton,[27] in experimenting with rats, found atrophy of the uterine mucosa in the parts where the ring touched the uterine wall, and believed this to be the cause of sterility. This latter conjecture is very unlikely since the ring touches only a small sector of the uterine mucosa and the fertilized ovum has an opportunity of settling in many other places. I, myself, thought also that a trail of cervical mucous which became attached to the ring might remain after the introduction of the latter through the cervix, changing the alkalinity of the cavum. However, in a case where I amputated the uterus with the ring in situ, such a connection between the ring and the cervical mucous could not be observed. Another explanation, which occurred to Bloch,[28] Director of Research, Dead Sea Works, was that the ring might make slight rotatory movements in the cavum uteri and in doing so sweep the ovum out of the uterus. Whether the ring effects a change in the hormonal production is a further question. The work done by Pincus and co-workers[29] could point in this direction. Examinations are still going on in different directions.

Summary

1. For the prevention of pregnancy I use a variant of the Graefenberg ring, viz., a silkworm gut ring consisting of 3 or 4 threads to which a short piece of silver thread is fastened in order to ascertain at any time by x-ray whether or not the ring is still in place.

2. I have inserted a total of 866 rings in 329 patients, and a further 150 since the beginning of the writing of this paper. Some women have worn rings for more than 20 years—one patient for more than 27 years—the rings being changed every 9 to 12 months.

3. The method is absolutely harmless. In the course of 28 years of experience I have not observed a single inflammation of any kind whatever, even in the presulfa and prepenicillin era. Histological examinations of the uterine mucosa immediately upon removal of the ring have never shown any inflammatory or other pathological changes; the examination of the tissue formed on the ring merely showed signs of foreign body reaction such as are formed after operation and which result from silk threads which have been sewn in.

4. I have in no case used sulfa preparations or antibiotics.

5. The ring method proved to be 25 times as safe as the diaphragm method.

6. The insertion of the ring is practically painless and requires no anesthesia. After insertion the patient can immediately resume her usual occupation.

7. The silver ring with its 1.3 per cent failures proved safer than the silk-worm gut ring in its original form (2.4 per cent failures). In spite of that I have given up the silver ring for reasons mentioned in this paper. In recent years since I have formed the ring of 4 instead of 3 silkworm gut threads, and intertwined them thrice instead of twice, there have been no failures at all. In view of the fact that before that change, in about 5 per cent of the cases, the ring slipped out of place, I would recommend regular examinations in order to discover this in time for the ring to be removed and a new one inserted before conception occurs.

8. No miscarriage occurred in those cases where pregnancy took place while the ring was in situ. No malformation of the fetus or placenta was seen in these cases. No cases of sterility have occurred after removal of the ring. All women who wished to become pregnant became so spontaneously without any treatment, generally within one to 4 months and in 2 cases within 6 months.

9. In 28 years of experience I have not seen a single case of carcinoma of the cervix or the corpus in ring-wearers.

10. Ovarian tumors and fibroids among ring-wearers were not more frequent than in other healthy women; I observed, among 329 women, 2 benign ovarian tumors and 6 fibroids, some of which appeared only several years after removal of the ring.

11. No endometriosis occurred.

12. No extrauterine gravidity occurred as a consequence of the ring.

13. Increased and prolonged bleedings occur sometimes in the early stages of wearing the ring, but usually disappear within 2 to 3 months. There is usually a slight brownish secretion one or 2 days before and after menstruation. In some cases, on the other hand, I have observed a shortening of prolonged menstrual bleedings, probably for psychological reasons.

14. In some women menstruation which previously had occurred only every 2½ to 3 months became perfectly normal while they wore the ring.

15. In hypoplasia of the uterus the ring may stimulate growth. In one severe case I have seen gravidity after years of sterility. Further experience in this field is necessary.

16. I had to remove the ring in only 2 of my cases; in one of them because of heavy menstrual bleeding and in the other because of recurrent slight inter-menstrual bleedings. In both cases, the ring had been introduced about 8 weeks post partum. Although cases of this kind account for less than 0.25 per cent of the total, I recommend that the ring should not be inserted until 3 months post partum. For the majority of cases 2 months post partum is sufficient.

17. The cause of the effectiveness is not known. Different possibilities are discussed in this paper; investigations are still being pursued in various directions.

I would like to thank Professor Unger for the pathological examination of the curettage material and the tissue adhering to the ring.

References

1. Mensinga, W. P. J.: Ueber facultative Sterilität, Leipzig, 1882, L. Heuser.
2. Leunbach, J. H.: International Congress for Birth Control, Zurich, 1930.
3. Murphy, M. C.: Lancet 2: 1369, 1933.
4. Stefko, W. H., and Lourié, A.: Deutsche Ztschr. ges. gerichtl. Med. 8: 536, 1926.
5. Mall, F.: Handb. Entwickl. ges. 1: 208, 1900.
6. Mall, F.: J. Morphol. 19: 3, 1908.
7. Mall, F., and Meyer, A. W.: Contrib. Embryol. No. 56, Vol. 12; Carnegie Inst. Washington Pub. No. 275, 1921.
8. Keibel, F., and Mall, F. P.: Man. Human Embryol. 1: 202, 1910.
9. Hertig, A. T.: Ann. Surg. 117: 596, 1943.
10. Rock, J.: New England J. Med. 223: 1020, 1940.
11. Hertig, A. T., and Livingstone, R. G.: New England J. Med. 230: 797, 1944.
12. Hertig, A. T., and Rock, J.: AM. J. OBST. & GYNEC. 47: 149, 1944.
13. Hertig, A. T., and Rock, J.: AM. J. OBST. & GYNEC. 58: 968, 1949.
14. Corner, G. W.: Am. J. Anat. 31: 523, 1923.
15. Loeb, L.: Proc. Soc. Exper. Biol. & Med. 4: 93, 1907.
16. Loeb, L.: J. A. M. A. 53: 1471, 1909.
17. Corner, G. W., and Warren, S. L.: Anat. Rec. 16: 168, 1919.
18. Weichert, C. K.: Proc. Soc. Exper. Biol. & Med. 24: 490, 1928.
19. Goldstein, L. A., and Tatelbaum, A. J.: Am. J. Physiol. 91: 14, 1929.
20. Shelesnyak, M. C.: Anat. Rec. 56: 211, 1933.
21. Long, I. A., and Evans, H. M.: Mem. Univ. California 6: 1, 1922. Cited in Am. J. Physiol. 179: 304, 1954.
22. Blandau, R. J.: Anat. Rec. 97: 322, 1947.
23. Shelesnyak, M. C.: Am. J. Physiol. 170: 522, 1952.
24. Loeb, L., and Kountz, W. B.: Am. J. Physiol. 84: 283, 1928.
25. Shelesnyak, M. C.: Endocrinology 54: 396, 1954.
26. Eichner, E., Goler, G. G., Reed, J., and Gordon, M. B.: AM. J. OBST. & GYNEC. 61: 253, 1951.
27. Carleton, H. M., and Phelps, H. J.: J. Obst. & Gynaec. Brit. Emp. 40: 81, 1933.
28. Bloch, R, M.: Personal discussion, 1957.
29. Pincus, G., Rock, J., Garcia, C., Rice-Wray, E., Paniagua, M., Rodriguez, I., and Pedras, R.: AM. J. OBST. & GYNEC. 75: 1333, 1958.
30. Haire, N.: Lecture 22nd Cong. Deutsche ges. Gynäk., Frankfurt am Main, 1931.

Reprinted from *Yokohama Med. Bull.*, **10**, 89–105 (1959)

34

CLINICAL STUDIES ON INTRAUTERINE RINGS ,

ESPECIALLY THE PRESENT STATE OF CONTRACEPTION IN JAPAN AND THE EXPERIENCES IN THE USE OF INTRAUTERINE RINGS

By Atsumi ISHIHAMA

Department of Obstetrics and Gynecology, Iwate Medical College, Morioka, Japan
(Director: Prof. YOSHIMARO HATA)

INTRODUCTION

Contraception has been encouraged in Japan by every means since the World War II, as she has had a serious problem of the natural increase of her population. On the other hand, indication of induced abortion has greatly spread after the war to the extent of social and economical indications besides medical. For this reason, contraception is not much popularized, however it is encouraged. The present state of contra-

Table 1. The present state of contraception in Japan.

No.	Author	Year	Total number	Practiced number	%
1	Tanaka	1950	900	102	11.4
2	Kimi	'950	6,747	1,754	26.0
3	Tahata	1951	4,054	1,267	31.8
4	Kojima	1951	1,760	517	29.4
5	Kojima	1951	412	41	10.0
6	Sakai	1952	1,060	307	29.0
7	Hori	1952	530	147	27.7
8	Hika	1952	3,760	1,224	32.6
9	Fukita	1952	1,384	509	36.9
10	Takeda	1952	2,115	680	32.0
11	Terauchi	1952	4,539	2,225	49.0
12	Moriyama	1952	1,902	454	23.9
13	Komiyama	1952	351	48	13.7
14	Yasui	1953	9,980	6,410	64.2
15	Ishihama	1953	623	194	31.2
16	Nagao	1953	1,558	805	51.7
17	Sugimoto	1953	700	242	38.4
18	Furuya	1953	418	78	18.7
19	Ogino	1953	716	106	14.8
20	Ishihama	1955	2,527	574	22.7

89

ception reported is summarised in Table 1.　Only 30% (average) are practising it.

The main reasons for the difficulty of popularizing contraception seem to be the followings:

1.　As it has been stated above, many people think that contraception is an artificial interruption of pregnancy and induced abortion can be made so easily.

2.　There is no reliable, harmless and cheap method of contraception.

3.　Every method hitherto used disturbs sexual intercourse to some extent.

4.　The structure of Japanese houses is not befitting for the use of contraceptives.

Table 2 shows five methods of contraception used in this country in the order of

Table 2.　Contraceptive method used in Japan.

No.	Author	Order				
		I	II	III	IV	V
1	Kubo	Condom 21.0 (%)	Ogino's method 12.3 (%)	Ogino+contracept. 8.7 (%)	Contraceptive 5.3 (%)	Coitus interrupt. 5.3 (%)
2	Komiyama	Ogino 41.7	Condom 39.6	Pessary 10.4		
3	Kimi	Ogino 42.6	Condom 17.0	Contraceptive 16.1	Another method 12.0	
4	Fukida	Condom 41.0	Ogino's M 30.8	Contraceptive 16.4	Ring 11.2	
5	Terauchi	Ogino 19.5	Condom 17.5	Condom+Ogino 13.9	Contraceptive 8.6	Pessary 4.4
6	Sugimoto	Condom 23.7	Ogino 22.7	Condom+Ogino 21.0	Pessary+contrac. 8.6	Condom+contrac. 4.1
7	Shinozaki	Condom 63.7	Ogino 41.0	Contraceptive 25.3	Coitus interrupt. 13.4	Pessary 11.5
8	Moriyama	Contracept. 34.4	Condom 20.8	Ogino 12.5	Condom+Ogino 7.9	Contraceptive 6.1
9	Hika	Ogino 31.4	Condom 31.5	Pessary 8.7	Contraceptive 20.3	Coitus interrupt. 8.1
10	Tabata	Condom 32.4	Ogino 14.1	Contraceptive 28.6	Pessary 10.0	Coitus interrupt. 4.1
11	Nagao	Condom 46.2	Ogino 29.8	Ogino+condom 23.5	Contraceptive 7.1	Condom+contrac. 5.7

Table 3.　Effect of contraceptive methods (Result from Japanese Institute of Population Problems).

Method	Number	Success (%)
Condom	115	58.3
Ogino's method	70	55.7
Coitus interruptus	37	6.2
Ogino's method+condom	27	66.7
Another method	79	57.9
Average	286	48.6

their popularization: they are used in the order of condom, periodic continence (OGINO method), and contraceptive medicine. Diaphragm pessary is not much used in Japan.

Varying effects have been reported. However, this appears to be rather due to the insufficient knowledges, incorrect use of contraceptives delinquency in use, or to the use of the various kinds of materials. The results which have been reported from the Japanese Institute of Population Problems are as shown in Table 3.

I have chosen so-called "intrauterine rings" as a method of contraception. These are inserted by doctors of the field; therefore the way of their use is always the same, and the effects can be judged easily and accurately. So, I have done this study in the hope that if intrauterine rings are effective at all, those who have difficulty in the practice of contraception can use them and get some effects from them.

A woman who has some foreign body in the uterus does not readily conceive. We can see it in the fact that myoma uteri makes a cause for sterility. UCHIGAKI (1928) succeeded in the experimental sterility implanting a piece of cartilage on the uterine wall of a rabbit. GRAEFENBERG (1928) succeeded in the experimental sterility inserting a foreign body in the uterus. Later, this experiment was repeated by LEHLFELD, HAIRE, RETSMERSKY, LEUNBACH, CARLETON and PHELPS. In our country, OTA (1932) repeated it around the same time. It was PUST who experimented it on the human uterus for first time. He inserted a ring of silk thread in the uterus and applied its glass board to the portio vaginalis. GRAEFENBERG thought that the parts of the instrument which were to be applied to the cervical canal and the portio vaginalis were not only unnecessary but also would increase infection. Therefore, he advocated a ring of silk thread or silver line was to be placed only in the uterus. This was called GRAEFENBERG's ring. Many experiments were made on GRAEFENBERG's ring by KLEIN, LEUNBACH and ANDREW, and they opposed to it as it caused endometritis. In our country, too, some scholars still oppose to the contraception by means of rings. This method seems pretty popularized in actuality, however, as it is best adapted to the Japanese way of life and also it does not harm so much as it is supposed. The effects of intrauterine rings which I have examined recently will be reported as follows:

RESULTS OF EXPERIMENTS

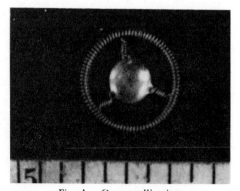 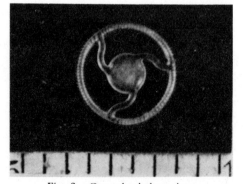

Fig. 1. Ota metallic ring.   Fig. 2. Ota polyethylene ring.

623 cases of OTA metallic rings (data A, Fig. 1) and 350 cases of OTA polyethylene rings (data B, Fig. 2) which I inserted by myself, and 18,594 cases reported from 149

Table 4. Evaluation of result.

A) The course after insertion of 623 cases of metallic rings.

Course after insertion	Cases	%
Non-disturbance	440	70.6
Slight disturbance	155	24.2
Removed ring due to serious disturbance	33	5.2
Total	623	100.0

B) 350 cases of polyethylene rings.

Course after insertion	Cases	%
Non-disturbance	280	80.0
Slight disturbance	58	16.5
Removed ring due to serious disturbance	12	3.5
Total	350	100.0

C) 18,594 cases reported from different hospitals.

Course after insertion	Cases	%
Non-disturbance	14,570	78.4
Slight disturbance	4,024	21.6
Removed ring due to serious disturbance	Unknown	
Total	18,594	100.0

hospitals in Japan (data C) were used in this study. The courses after the insertion in data A, B, C are shown in Table 4. The relation between the time of insertion and the courses was also studied as the rate of disturbances seemed to be varied depending on the time of insertion (Table 5).

Using data A, B, C, I have made some investigations on intrauterine rings, dividing into following items:

Table 5. Relations between side-effects and inserting time.

A) 623 cases of metallic rings.

Course \ Insertion time	Post-menstruation	Interval	Before menstruation	Directly after induced abortion	Few days after induced abortion	During puerperium	Total
Non side-effect	271	58	15	3	54	39	435
Slight disturbance	30	4	2	46	43	25	150
Removed ring due to serious disturbance	6	0	2	13	6	6	33
Total	307	62	19	62	103	70	623

B) 350 cases of polyethylene ring.

Course \ Insertion time	Post-menstruation	Interval	Before menstruation	Directly after induced abortion	Few days after induced abortion	During puerperium	Total
Non side-effect	56	35	14	157	7	11	280
Slight disturbance	10	0	2	31	12	3	58
Removed ring due to serious disturbance	0	0	1	6	3	2	12
Total	66	35	17	194	22	16	350

1. Relations between conception and rings

a. Frequency of conception

The frequency of conception in two years after the insertion of rings is shown in Table 6: 8 of 623 cases (1.2%) in data A, and 6 of 350 cases (1.7%) in data B. In data C 425 of 18,594 cases (2.2%) conceived, but the period of observation in these data was longer than two years. However, these results alone, which were obtained by observations for only two years, may not be sufficient to indicate all about the effect of intrauterine rings. Therefore, I have calculated the rate of conception in 350 cases of data B by STIX-NOTESTEIN's method.

Table 6. Frequency of conception during insertion of ring.

Material	Total	Conception	%
A	623	8	1.1
B	350	6	1.7
C	18,594	425	2.2

Rate of conception before contraception is practiced:

$$E = \frac{a}{b} \times 1,200$$

a: Total conceptions before contraception is practiced.

b: Total months available for conception before contraception is practiced
  =(married period)−(months during fetuses are in the uterus).

Rate of conception after contraception is practiced:

$$H = \frac{c}{d} \times 1,200$$

c: Unexpected conceptions after contraception is practiced (failure).

d: Total months available for conception after contraception is practiced.

The results obtained by the above formulas is as follows:

a: Total conceptions before the insertion of rings=1,400.

b: Total months available for conception before the insertion of rings=(married months) − (months during fetuses are in the uterus)=33,142−(8,300 + 1,700)=23,132 (months).
  deliveries abortions

c: Total conceptions after the insertion of rings (failure)=6.

d: Total months available for conception after the insertion of rings=2,867 (months).

$$E = \frac{1,400}{23,132} \times 1,200 = 72.6$$

$$H = \frac{6}{2,867} \times 1,200 = 2.5$$

The rate of conception before the insertion of rings is 72.6 and the one after the insertion is 2.5.

The effect of contraceptives is generally figured in the following way:

$$\frac{E-H}{H} \times 100 = \text{effectiveness}$$

Therefore the effect of rings is:

$$\frac{E-H}{H} \times 100 = \frac{72.6-2.5}{72.6} \times 100 = 96.5 \ (\%)$$

That is 96.5%.

b. How intrauterine rings act contraceptively

It is still unknown why a ring prevents contraception. OTA explained that a spermatovum was disturbed by the ring from being buried when it was to be implanted on the endometrium. GRAEFENBERG said that the existence of a foreign body caused non-inflammatory hypertrophy of the endometrium and that disturbed the implantation of a spermatovum. CARLETON and PHELPS explained that the oppression by a foreign body caused necrosis of the endometrium. However, histological figures like inflammation, necrosis, hypertrophy and atrophy are not always seen on the endometrium. Besides, polyethylene and nylon rings which do not cause so much oppression and necrosis as metallic rings are even more effective than metallic ones. SUZUKI, RETSCHMERSKY and others stated that the chemical activities of metal and the change of pH were the cause of sterility. Again it is hard to agree with this opinion as the effectiveness of rings do not differ by the materials: metal, nylon and polyethylene. Therefore it is probably most appropriate to think that intrauterine rings act contraceptively simply by the mechanical activities of their own.

c. Investigations on the cases of conception

As already stated there are some cases of conception even after the insertion of

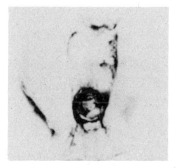

Fig. 3–a. Ring which is inserted in a enlarged uterus.

Fig. 3–b. X-ray picture of the same uterus.

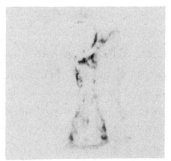

Fig. 3–c. Correct insertion.

Fig. 3–d. X-ray picture of the same uterus.

rings. It is impossible to find the exact reason for such conception, because we do not know how the rings act contraceptively. Investigating the cases of conception, however, I have found that conception occurs often in the following instances: 1) when a ring is inserted after induced abortion (Fig. 3, a, b, c, d), 2) when prolapses of ring is unnoticed and 3) when a ring is not inserted in the uterus properly as it does not fit the size of the uterus (Fig. 4). In data A, 8 of 623 cases conceived. In 4 cases of

Fig. 4. Ring which is inserted in the cervical canal.

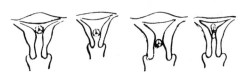

Fig. 5. Supposed figures when rings are inserted in the various shaped uterus.

these the rings were inserted after induced abortion. In data B, 6 of 350 cases conceived. Rings were inserted after induced abortion in all cases. It is considered that when a ring is inserted into the enlarged uterus by pregnancy, it will go down and a space is made between the ring and the uterus. A spermatovum can be implanted there. Figs. 5 are supposed figures when rings are inserted in the various shaped uteri.

d. Time of conception

As is shown in Table 7, conception occurs mostly in one or two years after the insertion of rings. Therefore it will be rash premature to critisize the effect of the contraception by rings within two years.

e. Conception after removal of rings

A ring is used for the purpose of temporary

Table 7. Time of conception.

Time of conception	Material		
	A	B	C
One month	0	0	0
2~6 ″	1	1	36
7~12 ″	2	2	170
1~2 year	5	3	201
2~3 ″	0	0	16
3~5 ″	0	0	0
5~7 ″	0	0	0
Total	8	6	425

contraception; therefore it must be the one which enables conception after its removal. Table 8 shows the cases in which conception occurred immediately after rings were taken out. It might be rash to conclude the effect of rings, with these few cases alone. However, all the women conceived several times before, but not 1 to 4 years after ring-insertion, and all conceived within 2~3 months after removal of the rings. Therefore we may attribute it to the effect of rings. Especially three of these five cases conceived the next months after the rings were taken out. Case 3 was removed of

Table 8. Conception after removed rings.

Cases No.	Name	Profession	Frequency of conception	Date of insertion	Time of insertion	How long inserted	Date of removed ring	Remove why	Conceive within
1	T. Z.	Mine-worker	4	Dec. 1948	After mens.	4 years	May 1952	Except conception	3 months
2	T. F.	Government official	3	Dec. 1952		1 year	Dec. 1953		2 months
3	N. K.	//	1	Nov. 1952	Directly after abortion	8 months	July 1953	Slightly bleeding	3 months
4	T. K.	Farmer's wife	5	Nov. 1953	Interval	1 year	Jan. 1955	Exchange ring	1 month
5	K. M.	//	4	July 1949	//	3 year	Sept. 1952	Hope for baby	2 months

the ring owing to continous bleeding since the insertion, and then conceived. From this fact we may think that even when there was some disturbance during the use of a ring, no after-effect is left after the ring is taken out and she can conceive again. The cases which I have experienced by myself are very few, but similar observations have been reported by many workers. For instance, TORII reported that 94.7% of 151 cases conceived within 6 months after rings were taken out. MURAKAMI also reported that a woman who had a ring for seven years conceived right after the ring was removed. Many others have reported similar experiences.

2. On side-effects of rings

a. Frequency and details of side-effects

The frequency of side-effects in data A, B and C is shown in Table 4. In data A, 183 of 623 cases (29.4%) had some disturbances and rings were removed in 33 cases (5.2%) for that reason. In data B, 58 of 350 cases (16.5%) had some disturbances and rings were taken out in 12 cases (3.5%). In data C, 4,024 of 18,594 cases (21.6%) complained of disturbances, but the number of cases in which rings were removed was unknown. Thus 16.5~29.2% (average 23.4%) had some disturbances, but some of these were very light, and it was only 3~5% that had to have rings taken out because of the serious disturbances. The details and kinds of disturbances are shown in Table 9. Main disturbances were menstrual disorders, hemorrhagic discharge, atypical vaginal bleeding, hypogastric pain, lumbago, and a few nervous symptoms. Let us investigate on each of them.

b. Menstrual disorders

After the insertion of rings, the increase of menstrual discharges and the extension of menstrual periods were often seen. These were seen in 19.2% in my experiments. The actual percentage must be higher as the patients with light symptoms did not come for examination. The cause is unknown, but it is considered that the regenera-

Table 9. Details of side-effects after insertion.

A) 623 cases of metallic rings.

Symptoms / Degree	Hyper-menorrhoe	Atypical bleeding	Pain	Discharge	Examina-tion	Concep-tion	Another symptoms	Total
Slight	112	14	9	3	9	0	3	150
Serious	6	10	4	3	0	8	2	33
Total	118	24	13	6	9	8	5	183

B) 350 cases of polyethylene rings.

Symptoms / Number	Hyper-menorrhoe	Atypical bleeding	Pain	Discharge	Wish to examina-tion only	Conception	Another symptoms	Total
Slight	36	10	9	1	2		0	58
Serious	0	4	1	1	0	6	0	12
Total	36	14	10	2	2	6	0	70

C) 18,594 cases from different hospitals.

Symptoms / Number	Hyper-menorrhoe	Atypical bleeding	Pain	Discharge	Fever	Concep-tion	Another symptoms	Uncer-tainty	Total
Cases	1,318	942	456	387	7	425	16	173	4,024

tion of the ablated endometrium is disturbed by rings. These disturbances, however, are often seen only in the first two or three menstruations, and then become normal after that. Disturbances are seen less when polyethylene rings are used.

c. Atypical vaginal bleeding

Atypical vaginal bleeding is the most unpleasant side-effect which can be called the weak point of rings. The frequency was 3.5% in data A, 2.8% in data B, and 4.3% in data C. HASHIMOTO reported that 28 of 868 cases (3.2%) had metallic rings. Therefore, it seems impossible to avoid 3~5% of hemorrhagic discharge or atypical vaginal bleeding. The frequency varies depending on the kinds of rings, ways of insertion and time of insertion. It is seen especially often when rings are inserted after induced abortion. The three cases in Table 10 had heavy bleeding by the insertion

Table 10. Heavy bleeding cases during insertion.

Case No.	Name	Age	Profession	Conception	Date of insertion	Time of insertion	Notice
1	K. U.	25	Worker	3	Feb. 2, 1953	Directly after abortion	
2	S. S.	39	Teacher	3	April 2, 1953	Before mens.	Abortion ?
3	S. H.	26	Worker	4	May 9, 1953	After mens.	

of rings after induced abortion. If the bleeding is caused merely by a ring, it will stop immediately when the ring is taken out and no disturbance will be left after that. Therefore, a ring should be taken out immediately when atypical vaginal bleeding is seen. In light cases, it sometimes stops naturally by rest and styptics. Also reinsertion of rings after a while causes no more bleeding in some cases. The causes are entirely unknown.

d. Pain

The main pain after the insertion of rings is hypogastric pain and lumbago. The frequency is 13 of 623 cases (2.5%) in data A, 10 of 350 cases (2.8%) in data B, and 456 of 18,594 cases (2.2%) in data C. It is doubtful that hypogastric pain and lumbago are caused essentially by rings because these symptoms are most common in the gynecological field. It is also considered that a nervous woman feels uncomfortable to the insertion of ring, which can cause unpleasantness and abdominal pain psychologically. Pain is often caused when a ring is let down to the internal os or in the cervical canal. However, the symptoms are light in most cases and there are hardly any cases in which rings have to be taken out because of the pain.

e. Inflammation

Chronic endometritis by the stimulation of a foreign body and ascending inflammation by infection have been most feared by the insertion of a foreign body in the uterus. The clinical symptoms are fever, discharge, and pain. In my experiments, only three cases (0.4%) had to have the rings removed because of the increase in discharge. Fever was seen only in one case in which adnexitis sinistra was caused by the insertion of a ring after induced abortion. These three cases had endometritis and it proved that rings were inserted carelessly. It can be said that there is no need of worry about the inflammation by rings, because their materials and disinfection have been improved and antibiotics have been discovered.

f. Period of time to occurrence of disturbances

The interval between the insertion of the rings and the occurrence of disturbances is shown in Table 11. Most disturbances occur within 1~3 months. Therefore, if no abnormality is seen in 1~3 months after the insertion, it is fairly safe to think that no disturbance will occur in 1~2 years.

Table 11. Time when disturbance occur after insertion.

	1 month after	2~6 m. after	7~12 m. after	1~2 year after	2~3 y. after	3~5 y. after	Total
A	134 40.9%	26 31.3	16 19.2	4 4.8	3 3.8	0 0	183 100.0
B	39 48.3	18 30.0	11 18.3	2 3.4	0 0	0 0	70 100.0

g. Serious disturbances

There was no serious side-effect in my experiments. MURAKAMI et al. reported on a case in which a ring was taken out surgically from the abdominal cavity. The ring had entered there perforating the uterus. Recently DÖRFFLER (1957) also found a ring in the abdominal cavity (Fig. 6). In these cases, probably the uteri were perforated by the insertion of rings and rings were introduced to the abdominal cavities through the holes. Especially, DÖRFFLER's case passed twenty years without any abnormality and conception was experienced twice during that period. The ring was found by chance on a X-ray picture. Therefore, such perforation is perhaps

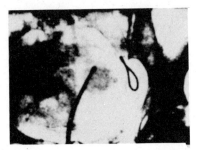

Fig. 6. Ring in the abdominal cavity (DÖRFFLER).

a disturbance provoked by induced abortion or an accident in the inserting operation rather than a disturbance of a ring itself. It is imprudent to attribute all of these to the side-effect of rings.

3. Endometrium after the insertion of rings

The endometrium of all the patients was examined histologically after the insertion of rings, as it was feared that the stimulation by rings might cause chronic inflammation on the endometrium. Some preparations are shown in Fig. 7, a, b. No particular

Fig. 7-a. T. S. 28 age. Endometrium in which ring was inserted for 12 months and removed it for exchange of ring (25 days after menstruation).

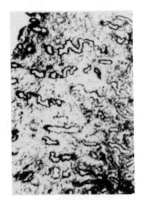

Fig. 7-b. S. M. 27 age. Endometrium in which ring was inserted for 6 months and take out it following hypermenorrhoe (20 days after menstruation).

change was seen on the tissue in either cases in which disturbance was seen or no disturbhnce was seen. A little bleeding was observed in the stroma, but no such findings of inflammation as enlargement of the glands, hyperplasy of gland cells, hypertrophy of stroma, edema and infiltration with round cells were seen. No serious necrosis was observed either in the parts where rings were placed. HASHIMOTO also reported that no particular pathologic change was observed on the endometrium in his investigation on 50 cases. Thus, I oppose to the opinion that the insertion of a ring always causes some inflammatory change on the endometrium.

4. Relations between rings and malignant neoplasms

It has been a matter of prime concern that the insertion of a foreign body in the uterus might cause a cancer. LOURE, BOWLESS and CARLETON stated that there was such danger if a ring was inserted for a long period. However, there has been no reported case which verifies this opinion. SHIMOMURA (1950) had a chance to operate carcinoma of the cervix of a patient, aged 46, who had a metallic ring for nine years. On his histological examination of the endometrium, he reported that only light hypertrophy and infiltration with round cells were observed on the part where the ring was placed and no direct relation between the ring and the squamous cell carcinoma on the cervix was certified.

Fig. 8. Carcinoma of the uterus with ring.

Recently, I also experienced a case of carcinoma of the uterus which had a ring inserted. The patient was a 37 year-old woman who had eight deliveries and had a ring inserted in October, 1956. She had no abnormality until September, 1957 (one year since the insertion), when she came to the hospital complaining of the atypical vaginal bleeding. Carcinoma colli, II stage was diagnosed. Panhysterectomy was done on Oct. 7, 1957 (operator Prof. HATA) (Fig. 8).

Fig. 9-a. Squamous cell carcinoma on portio vaginalis of the same uterus.

Fig. 9-b. The tissue on the cervical canal of the same uterus.

Serial sections from the portio vaginalis to the uterine cavity where the ring had been inserted were made. On the histological examination of the sections, the squamous cell carcinoma of the cervix disappeared about 1.3 cm from the external os, and did not pass over the internal os (Fig. 9a, b). Therefore, there was no relation between the ring inserted in the uterine cavity and the squamous cell carcinoma of the cervix. MIYAHARA also experienced a case of KURKENBERG's tumor which had a ring inserted (Fig. 10). In his case, too, no abnormality was found on the endometrium histologically, and this tumor was found after the operation of gastric cancer. As far as we have experienced and investigated, no malignant change of the uterus by the insertion of a ring was observed.

Fig. 10. KURKENBERG's tumor with a ring.

5. Shapes and materials of rings

More studies are needed on the shapes and materials of rings. Various rings, as shown in Fig. 11, have been made in Japan. Metallic rings are convenient for disinfection and X-ray examination, but cause more side-effects and have a possibility of intruding into the basal layer. Nylon and polyethylene rings which have been made recently seem to cause less side-effects.

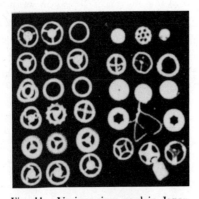

Fig. 11. Various rings used in Japan.

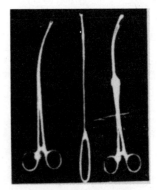

Fig. 12. Special forceps.

6. Insertion and removal of rings

Metallic rings should be sterilized by boiling. Nonmetallic rings should be left in mercurochrome, iodine-tincture and hyamine solution for 5~10 minutes. Such disinfection was enough bactericidal typhoid-, coli-, dysentery bacilli and staphylococci in our experiments. The cervical canal should be enlarged by HEGAR's dilatator 9~12 to insert a ring. Special forceps shown in Fig. 12 should be used in insertion. In the removal, the cervical canal should be enlarged again, and the ring should be removed by the forceps for removal or KOCHER's forceps.

SUMMARY

Investigations have been made on so-called "intrauterine rings" using my own experiences and data from the hospitals all over Japan. The effect is high and the serious disturbances are very few. Of course, as in any other method, it is impossible to expect 100% effect from it. Conception occurs even after tubal ligation which is supposed to be the most reliable way of contraception, and so it is only natural that the contraception by any other instrument or drug is more unreliable. A ring is, of course, a foreign body; therefore the living body naturally shows the disposing reaction against a foreign body. However, it is a matter of degrees. If the reaction is light, the living body will be adapted to it and shows no serious symptoms. If rings are opposed only because of their foreign bodies, opposition should also be made to the various foreign bodies used in the recent surgery and orthopedics. Even diaphragm pessary and tampon which are supposed to be entirely harmless can cause vaginitis when they are put for a long time. A serious case of diaphragm pessary is shown in Fig. 13.

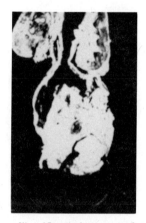

Fig. 13.   Serious case of diaphragm pessary.

Rings are still opposed by some scholars. The first reason of their opposition is that they are not contraceptives but to cause abortion. If it is true, decidual changes should always be seen and menstruation should always be delayed clinically. However, as stated above, no such changes are seen on the endometrium. Therefore, no spermatovum is implanted when the ring is showing its effect. Of course, conception can occur during the insertion of a ring. The ring seems to be inserted not in the right position in such case. The second reason of their opposition is that the insertion of rings cause carcinoma. The third reason is that they cause endometritis. My studies have clarified that there is no need of such worries.

Of course rings have various side-effects. They are varied depending on the time and technic of insertion and the kinds of rings. It is perhaps a problem left for the further study how to remove these side-effects.

Conclusion

1. Investigations have been made on the effect of intrauterine ring, using 623 cases of metallic rings, 350 cases of polyethylene rings and 18,594 cases reported from the various hospitals in Japan.

2. Although there are still many problems left for the future studies, the contraceptive effect, calculated by Stix-Notestein's method, is 96.5%.

3. For the application of the ring, there should be no abnormality in the sex organs.

4. Post-menstruation period is recommended for the time of insertion. The periods before menstruation, after induced abortion and during puerperium should be avoided.

5. Labor and sexual intercouse should be prohibited for 5~10 days after the insertion. Examination should be done every half a year. It is recommended to exchange a ring with new one after a year.

The author is greatly indebted to Prof. HATA for his instructions and revision, and grateful to those who have shown cooperation.

References

1. ANDREW, C.: Migrating Graefenberg contraceptive ring. J. Am. Med. Assoc., **7**: 271~274, 1936.

2. DOI, J.: Intrauterine ring. Japan. J. Fertility & Sterility, **1**: 6~11, 1956.

3. DAIDO, J.: A case of intrauterine ring which had been inserted for 18 years. Sanfujinka no Shinpo, **6**: 5~6, 1954.

4. FUKIDA, S.: Clinical experience of intrauterine ring. J. Japan. Obst. & Gynec. Soc. (Chugoku Shikoku Bukai), **3**: 25~25, 1953.

5. FUJITA, T.: Conception during insertion of ring. J. Japan. Obst. & Gynec. Soc., **7**: 1216~1216, 1955.

6. GRAEFENBERG, E.: Die intrauterine Methode der Kontrazeptionsverhütung. Kegan Paul, London, 1930.

7. GRAEFENBERG, E.: Einfluss der intrauterinen Konzeptionsverhütung und die Uterusschleimhaut. Arch. Gynäk., **144**: 345~345, 1931.

8. HAIRE, N.: A preliminary note on the intrauterine silver ring. International contraception symposium, 5~6, 1931.

9. HOSAKA, T.: Effect and side-effects of intrauterine ring. Japan. Med. J., 1245: 141~144, 1948.

10. HASHIMOTO, K.: Intrauterine contraceptive method. Clin. Gynec. & Obst., **6**: 664~667, 1952.

11. HASHIMOTO, K.: Clinical experience of Ota intrauterine ring. Sanfujinka no Jissai, **1**: 395~398, 1951.

12. HIROKAWA, I.: Clinical experience of intrauterine ring. J. Japan. Obst. & Gynec. Soc., **7**: 1955.

[13] ISHIHARA, T.: Effects of intrauterine ring and histological changes after its insertion. Sanfujinka no Shinpo, **4**: 20~21, 1952.

[14] ISHIHAMA, A.: Clinical experiences of 600 cases of intrauterine ring. Sanfujinka no Jissai, **3**: 616~619, 1954.

[15] ISHIHAMA, A.: Disturbances of intrauterine ring. Obst. & Gynec., **21**: 714~717, 1954.

[16] ISHIHAMA, A.: Clinical experiences of temporary contraception by inserting ring. Iwate Med. J., **6**: 47~49, 1954.

[17] ISHIHAMA, A.: The present state of contraception in Japan. Japan. Med. J., 1664: 34~36, 1956.

[18] ISHIHAMA, A.: Disturbances of intrauterine ring due to insertion in cervical canal. J. Japan Med. Assoc., **37**: 364~366, 1957.

[19] ISHIHAMA, A.: Studies on intrauterine ring. J. Japan. Obst. & Gynec. Soc. (Tohoku Chihobu-kai), **1**: 17~24, 1956.

[20] ISHIGURO, E.: Attention for insertion of ring. J. Japan. Obst. & Gynec. Soc., **7**: 1666~1667, 1955.

[21] KLEIN, H.: Zur Frage der intrauterine Konzeptionsverhütung. Arch. Gynäk., **144** B: 345~345, 1931.

[22] KAWADA, S.: Contraceptive method for intrauterine cavity. Obst. & Gynec., **3**: 1036~1038, 1935.

[23] KURIHARA, J.: Serious disturbance due to insertion of ring. Nichidai Igaku Zasshi, **7**: 50~53, 1943.

[24] KIDO, Y.: Conception during insertion of ring. Obst. & Gynec., **16**: 352~353, 1949.

[25] KONDO, K.: Experience of Ota rings. Sanfujinka no Shinpo, **4**: 20~21, 1952.

[26] KAMIYAMA, M.: Case report of intrauterine ring. World Obst. & Gynec., **5**: 470~471, 1953.

[27] KASEKI, T.: Clinical experience of intrauterine ring. J. Japan. Obst. & Gynec. Soc., **7**: 1216~1216, 1955.

[28] KANASUGI, T.: 700 cases of intrauterine ring and histological examination of its endometrium. J. Japan. Obst. & Gynec. Soc., **8**: 1058~1058, 1955.

[29] LEUNBACH, H.: The Graefenberg ring. The Practice of Contraception. 1931.

[30] LEUNBACH, H.: A new abortus provocatus method. The Practice of Contraception. 1931.

[31] LEUNBACH, H.: Erfahrungen mit Graefenbergschem intrauterinem Silberring. Arch. Gynäk., **144** B: 354~354, 1931.

[32] MURAKAMI, K.: On the contraception. Sanfujinka no Jissai, **2**: 1133~1137, 1951.

[33] NAKASHIMA, K.: Conception during insertion of ring. J. Kyoto Pref. Med. Univ., **14**: 153~155, 1943.

[34] MATSUMOTO, K.: On the case of myoma uteri which had a ring inserted. Obst. & Gynec., **16**: 548~549, 1949.

[35] MATSUOKA, K.: Experience of ring which was inserted for long time. Hakuai, **5**: 71~73, 1952.

[36] NOGI, A.: Effect of intrauterine ring. Sanfujinka no Shinpo, **3**: 5~7, 1951.

[37] OTA, T.: A new method of temporary contraception. Kinki Fujinka Gakkai Zasshi, **18**: 147~149, 1933.

[38] OTA, T.: Result of intrauterine ring. Sanfujinka no Shinpo, **3**: 5~7, 1951.

[39] OTA, T.: Intrauterine ring. J. Japan. Obst. & Gynec. Soc. (Tokyo Chihobu Kaiho), **1**: 5~6, 1952.

[40] OTA, T.: Prevention of ascending ring. J. Japan. Obst. & Gynec. Soc. (Tokyo Chihobu Kaiho), 2: 7~7, 1953.

[41] OKUDAIRA, T.: One case of intrauterine ring which was inserted for 3 years. J. Japan. Obst. & Gynec. Soc. (Kumamoto Chihobu Kaiho), 4: 53~54, 1952.

[42] PUST, D.: Ein brauchbarer Frauenschütz. Dtsch. med. Wschr, 29: 952~956, 1923.

[43] OMORI, K.: Clinical experience of Ota nylon ring. Sanfujinka no Jissai, 4: 590~591, 1955.

[44] STÖCKEL, W.: Die Konzeptionsverhütung als Gegenstand der klinischen Unterrichts. Zbl. Gynäk., 5: 1450~1453, 1931.

[45] SAWASAKI, S.: On the contraceptive implement which is inserted intrauterine cavity. J. Japan. Obst. & Gynec. Soc., 32: 1576~1578, 1937.

[46] SAWASAKI, S.: Prescaring. Tokyo Med. J., 3033: 1144~1144, 1937.

[47] SHIMOMURA, T.: One case of carcinoma colli which had a ring inserted for 9 years. Sanfujinka no Shinpo, 2: 12~15, 1949.

[48] SEKIGUCHI, K.: Disturbance about intrauterine ring. Nichidai Igaku Zasshi, 7: 670~673, 1953.

[49] SANO, K.: Endometritis which was occurred by insertion of ring. Osaka Daigaku Igaku Zasshi, 15: 152~156, 1956.

[50] TAGAMI, M.: Disturbance which was occurred by stimulation of intrauterine contraceptive implement. Sanfujinka no Shinpo, 2: 184~184, 1949.

[51] TORII, S.: Application of metallic ring. Med. J. Kagoshima Univ., 2: 228~231, 1956.

[52] TAKAHASHI, T.: One case of disturbance by intrauterine ring. Obst. & Gynec., 21: 210~213, 1955.

[53] UCHIGAKI, S.: Biological study on the sterility. Kinki Fujinka Gakkaishi, 1: 150~153, 1928.

[54] YOSHIDA, T.: 700 cases report of intrauterine ring. Obst. & Gynec., 24: 525~528, 1957.

[55] YASAKI, K.: One case of intrauterine ring which was inserted for 20 years. Hokkaido Fujinka Zasshi, 1: 100~104, 1950.

[56] YASUDA, Y.: Caesarean section due to intrauterine ring. Obst. & Gynec., 24: 76~79, 1957.

[57] SUZUMURA, M.: A case of placenta praevia totalis with a contraceptive ring penetrated into its parenchym. World Obst. & Gynec., 9: 1038~1040, 1957.

[58] FUJIMORI, H.: On the histological changes of uterus in which contraceptive ring remains inserted. World Obst. & Gynec., 9: 629~631, 1957.

[59] NAWA, S.: Clinical observation upon contraceptive ring. World Obst. & Gynec., 9: 1008~1011. 1957.

[60] GREEN, B.: Intrauterine foreign body and pregnancy. Am. J. Obst. & Gynec., 66: 678~680, 1953.

[61] DÖRFFLER, P.: Über ein im Parametrium gelegenes Intrauterin-Pessar. Geburtsh. u. Frauenh., 17: 743~747, 1957.

35

INTRA-UTERINE CONTRACEPTIVE DEVICES

PROCEEDINGS OF THE CONFERENCE
APRIL 30 - MAY 1, 1962, NEW YORK CITY

edited by

CHRISTOPHER TIETZE and SARAH LEWIT

INTERNATIONAL CONGRESS SERIES NO. 54

EXCERPTA MEDICA FOUNDATION

AMSTERDAM · LONDON · TOKYO · MILAN · NEW YORK

383

A STUDY OF INTRA-UTERINE CONTRACEPTION:
DEVELOPMENT OF A PLASTIC LOOP

by

JACK LIPPES, M.D.*

It is unfortunate that Gräfenberg never lived to see the acknowledgement of the value of his great idea. There is a saying in medicine that an idea is never accepted because it is good or logical but because the opposition dies off. This was certainly true of Gräfenberg. A study of the history of the ring reveals more than academic excellence, more than medical knowledge. It reveals another example of man's eternal struggle to enlighten himself.

Materials and Methods

My first work merely repeated that of Gräfenberg and Oppenheimer.[1] I made silk rings by hand and inserted them. When I learned of the availability of the Japanese Ota ring,[3] I tried inserting these. The disc of solid polyethylene in the center of the Ota ring made it necessary to dilate the cervix to Hegar size 12. This was difficult for both the doctor and the patient. My first modification was to cut out the disc. Although insertions were easier, I soon learned that removing rings was far more difficult than inserting them. With Gräfenberg's instrument, which resembles a crochet hook, one is guided entirely by a sense of touch in removing these devices. I have acquired this skill with time, patience, and practice. My nurses at the Planned Parenthood Center in Buffalo named me the 'Jimmy Valentine of the contraceptive world.'

If these devices are to become universal, inserted by general practitioners, perhaps by nurses and/or midwives, an easier means of removal and insertion is necessary. To accomplish this, I tied to the Ota ring a suture, which dangled through the cervix. This was, of course, contrary to the principles that Gräfenberg taught.[2] Friends and colleagues warned me not to do this—not to bridge the gap between the sterile uterine cavity and the infected vagina. However, I have now done so 271 times (171 rings and 100 loops, all

* Department of Obstetrics and Gynecology, University of Buffalo School of Medicine, Buffalo, New York.

I want to take this opportunity to express my gratitude to Dr. Clyde Randall, Chairman of the Medical Advisory Committee of the Planned Parenthood Center of Buffalo. Were it not for his courage in allowing me to carry on this project at our Planned Parenthood Center, my work on intra-uterine contraception would never have come to fruition.

I must acknowledge the help of the social workers, nurses, and volunteers of the Planned Parenthood Center of Buffalo. Their aid went above and beyond the call.

Acknowledgment with gratitude is made to Dr. Herbert Lansky, Director of Laboratories at the E. J. Meyer Memorial Hospital in Buffalo, for interpreting the endometrial biopsies and to Dr. Ernest Witebsky, Professor of Bacteriology and Immunology at the University of Buffalo, School of Medicine, for assistance in the bacteriological portion of this study.

69

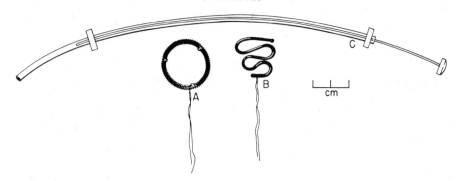

Fig. 1. Intra-uterine devices and instrument for insertion. *A:* plastic Ota ring with center removed; *B:* polyethylene loop, both with suture attached; *C:* flexible plastic inserter with plastic plunger.

with cervical appendages). All of these patients are clinically well. They are all multi-parous, of proven fertility, and were between 18 and 38 years old. Of the total of 271 insertions, 160 were in clinic patients and 111 in private patients.

Bacteriological Study

Intra-uterine cultures from 20 clinic patients (10 from controls and 10 from patients wearing rings) were taken with an Ayre curette in order to avoid vaginal and cervical contamination of the cultures. The results of the culture examination were negative for five patients in each of the two groups. For the remaining five patients in each group, the results were quite similar.

Number of patients	*Cultures*
Ring-wearing:	
1	Streptococcus (nonhemolytic)
1	B. coli, B. aerogenes, and Streptococcus (nonhemolytic)
1	B. coli
1	B. coli and Streptococcus (nonhemolytic)
1	Bacteroides
Control:	
1	Streptococcus (nonhemolytic) and Diphtheroids
1	Staphylococcus albus (nonhemolytic) and Enterococci
1	Enterococci
1	Streptococcus viridans
1	Bacteroides

I have convinced myself that a suture dangling through the cervix provides an easy and harmless way to remove the ring or loop and to detect its presence. My belief that a cervical suture is harmless was confirmed by Zipper.[5] However, in 18 patients among the 171 in whom rings had been inserted, the suture was not visible at the cervix. These rings had to be removed by the original Gräfenberg technique. I believe that these 18 rings rotated when the uterine musculature contracted and, like the roller on the window shade, wound up the cervical suture.

I began thinking about a new design for an intra-uterine contraceptive device. I wanted a device that would fill the uterine cavity in a stable manner and that would not rotate.

70

At this time, Margulies demonstrated his spiral to me. He had originated a new and revolutionary principle, which I believe is a most important advance, by inserting the device through a narrow tube introduced into the cervix. I might have asked to use Margulies' device, but I wanted to get away from the circular shape because I believe it rotates.

As you know, the uterine cavity is triangular or trapezoid in shape. The uterine musculature runs in diagonal and transverse diameters[1] but not vertically. I wanted a device such that the muscular contractions of the uterus would not press on the entire piece of plastic but on one section at a time only. Since uterine contractions are rhythmic, this design and the nature of the plastic used would allow the device to assume its original shape. With this in mind, I designed a device which I call a 'loop.' The device corresponds to the shape of the uterine cavity. I insert the loop through a plastic tube, which is oval in cross section, so that I might know and control the plane in which my loop exits from the tube and enters the uterine cavity. The suture I am now using is a very fine monofilament of linear polyethylene, size 0000. My patients have been successful in learning to identify the presence of the loop by feeling the suture at the external os of the cervix.

Months of Exposure and Pregnancy Rate

A total of 171 modified plastic rings made of nylon and 100 polyethylene loops have been inserted, with a total observation of 1,660 months of exposure for the combined group. The following is a breakdown of months of exposure by type of patient and type of device:

Type of patient	Months of exposure		
	Ring	Loop	Total
Private	699	105	804
Clinic	697	159	856
Totals	1,396	264	1,660

Four failures or pregnancies have occurred, or 2.9 per 100 woman-years. Three pregnancies, or a pregnancy rate of 2.6 per 100 woman-years, have occurred during 1,396 months of exposure for the ring and 1 pregnancy, or a rate of 4.5 during 264 months, for the loop. Since we first began working with the loop in November, 1961, the number of months accumulated is necessarily small.

With regard to the one pregnancy among patients wearing the loop, it is possible that I inserted this loop into a uterus which was already pregnant. This woman had such irregular periods, I cannot be certain. I usually try to insert my loop at the end of a menstrual period because I believe it is easier at that time. The cervix is partially dilated and I am more certain of not interrupting a pregnancy. More patients and more months of exposure will be needed before I can speak with any authority on the loop's effectiveness.

Discontinuation

A total of 34 patients, or 12.5 per cent, discontinued the use of the intra-uterine device. Of these, 31 were ring patients and 3 were loop patients (see Table 1).

Expulsion has been a major problem. Since we began in October, 1959, 13 out of 171 ring wearers discontinued use because of spontaneous expulsion. The loop project is young but, as you can see, 2 loop wearers discontinued because of spontaneous expulsion. Four 'ring expellers' have been re-inserted with a loop and have been successful in using this second device over the past 6 months. Three of these 15 expulsions were responsible for 3 pregnancies because the device had been expelled without the patient's knowledge.

71

TABLE 1

Reason for Discontinuation of Intra-Uterine Device, by Type of Device

Reason	Total		Ring		Loop	
	Number	Per cent[1]	Number	Per cent[2]	Number	Per cent[3]
Expulsion	15	5.5	13	7.6	2	2.0
Bleeding	12	4.4	11	6.4	1	1.0
Pain	5	1.9	5	2.9	—	—
Leukorrhea	2	0.7	2	1.2	—	—
Total	34	12.5	31	18.1	3	3.0

[1] Refers to 271 insertions.
[2] Refers to 171 ring insertions.
[3] Refers to 100 loop insertions.

Most expulsions seem to occur within the first 4 months of use. Eleven of the 15 expulsion occurred during the first 4 months after insertion, and 4 occurred later (see Table 2).

The second major problem is bleeding. Eleven of 171 ring wearers insisted on having their devices removed because of persistent and annoying bleeding. This bleeding is usually not enough to alarm the physician. However, it does create fear and anxiety in the

TABLE 2

Duration of Use prior to Discontinuation of Intra-Uterine Device:
by Reason and Type of Device

Type of device and duration of use (months)	Expulsion	Bleeding	Pain
Ring			
1	3	3	2
2	3	1	1
3	1	1	—
4	2[1]	1	1
5–8	1	5	1
9–12	3[2]	—	—
Total	13	11	5
Loop			
1	2	—	—
2	—	—	—
3	—	—	—
4	—	1	—
5–8	—	—	—
9–12	—	—	—
Total	2	1	—

[1] One pregnancy.   [2] Two pregnancies.

72

387

patient. The bleeding usually stops after the second menstrual period after insertion. In the meantime, I have used Vitamin K, flavonoids, and mostly reassurance, to tide the patient over the first two months of use. Where the bleeding has persisted beyond the second month, I have been compelled to remove the ring or the loop. Only one loop has been removed for bleeding, perhaps because of the small number of loop insertions. However, I have the impression that the loop causes less bleeding than the ring. This may be due to the fact that the ring has a coil of nylon around it, while the loop is made entirely of polyethylene.

About one-half of the 12 removals for bleeding were done during the first 4 weeks and the rest later.

The third problem of ring wearers is pain. Five ring wearers have had their rings removed because of pain. This pain is described as backache or vague lower abdominal cramps. Usually, I attempt to treat pain with reassurance, aspirin, codeine, bed rest, and a hot water bottle. In the five patients who had their devices removed, the pain was persistent enough to necessitate removal. No loops have yet been removed because of pain. Again I have the impression that the loop gives less pain than the ring.

There were two ring patients who developed leukorrhea and insisted that their rings be removed. One of these had a monilia infection and the other, trichomonas. These two patients could not be convinced that the devices had nothing to do with their discharge. I was again compelled, at the patients' requests, to remove two more rings.

I believe the number of patients who have discontinued the loop, is low even for this early six-months period over which I have been working with the loop. I hope, of course, it continues to be low. However, time and further observation will be needed.

Nine patients have had their loops or rings removed because they were desirous of becoming pregnant. All are currently pregnant and none had more than 3 menstrual periods after removal. In fact, 2 patients missed the very next period. Both of these patients had their devices removed on day 17 of their cycle, 2 to 3 days after expected ovulation. Bleeding after removal prevented intercourse until day 22 of the cycle. This would suggest that intra-uterine contraception does prevent nidation, as Gräfenberg originally thought.

Among my patients, I have thus far taken 225 endometrial biopsies. A total of 146 biopsies were taken prior to insertion and used as controls and 79, during the use of intra-uterine contraception, 3 months to 1 year after insertion. As the following figures show, decidual reactions thus far have been the same in the control group as in the patients wearing rings or loops.

Type of reaction	Before insertion	After insertion
Decidual	2	2
Endometritis	2	7
Normal	142	70
Total	146	79

The one big difference that is readily noted is that 7 biopsies among ring wearers have shown endometritis, compared with 2 in the control group. I must point out, however, that all of these patients are clinically well. I believe that the inflammatory reaction in the endometrium, associated with intra-uterine contraception, is due to a foreign-body reaction and not infection. I will call it a 'sterile endometritis.' After all, these patients are well. Their bacterial flora has not changed.

73

No loop-wearing patients have shown endometritis. There has been no cancer, no hyperplasia, and no polyps found in any of my biopsies. This portion of my study is not yet complete. I shall continue to take endometrial biopsies on ring and loop wearers until their number reaches 146 also.

Engineering Principles

Recently, I have been taking readings to determine the amount of force which is needed to remove one of my loops. Thus far, the normal range runs from 70 to 80 grams. These readings have been taken with a spring scale which is attached by a thread to the loop's cervical appendage. I have taken one reading on a patient who has consistently expelled all loops. In this case, only 50 grams of pull was required to remove the loop. If this study continues to show that patients who expel loops and rings need less force to remove their devices, it may be possible in the future to predetermine the patients who are most likely to expel them. The physician in such a case could change the patient to another contraceptive technique. At the very least, the patient would be forewarned that she is liable to expel the device. Here, too, more work is needed. After all, these measurements must be an expression of the diameter of the cervical canal, or at least of the distensibility of the cervical canal, since the loop needs a constant amount of force to be deflected or straightened.

This technique opens up new avenues of research into uterine physiology, and perhaps the study of cervical incompetence.

Summary

A review of intra-uterine contraception through use of either the nylon ring or the polyethylene loop, both with cervical appendages, has been presented. With the evidence at hand, neither the ring nor the loop can be considered harmful. Furthermore, the presence of a cervical appendage, which bridges the uterine cavity and the vagina, is perfectly safe and without serious side effects. Both the ring and the loop provide an effective means of contraception for both private-type patients and clinic-type patients.

Inserting the contraceptive device through a tube has many advantages among which are:
(1) Elimination of the use of a tenaculum except for the occasional case.
(2) Elimination of cervical dilation except for the occasional case.
(3) The carrying of bacteria from the lower cervix into the uterine cavity must reasonably be reduced by the protective action of the tube through which the device is inserted.

About one patient out of eight discontinued intra-uterine contraception because of expulsion, bleeding, pain, and leukorrhea. All of these side effects were annoying enough to force discontinuation of this method. However, none of the side effects could be classified as a serious threat to health or life.

Conclusion

It would not be right to draw conclusions from a study that is as yet incomplete. Further work is obviously needed. Already mentioned are the additional biopsies that will be taken. The engineering principles are just beginning to be evaluated.

However, it is safe to say in this conclusion that intra-uterine contraception does provide a safe, effective, and acceptable means of birth control for both private and clinic patients.

74

BIBLIOGRAPHY

1. DICKINSON, R. L.: *Atlas of Human Sex Anatomy*. Baltimore: Williams and Wilkins, 1949.
2. GRÄFENBERG, E.: 'An intrauterine contraceptive method,' *Seventh International Birth Control Conference*, 33-47, 1930.
3. ISHIHAMA, A.: 'Clinical studies on intrauterine rings, especially the present state of contraception in Japan and the experiences in the use of intrauterine rings,' *Yokohama Medical Journal*, 10: 89-105, Apr. 1959.
4. OPPENHEIMER, W.: 'Prevention of pregnancy by the Graefenberg ring method,' *American Journal of Obstetrics and Gynecology*, 78: 446-454, Aug. 1959.
5. ZIPPER, J.: Personal communication.

Addendum (November 20, 1962)

In an effort to improve results with the loop technic of intrauterine contraception, loop #2 has been designed and produced.

Loop #2 overall measurements:
The top bar measures 30 mm and the trapezoidal outline then narrows to 16.7 mm. The cross sectional diameter of loop #2 is 2 × 2.8 mm. The overall height is 27.5 mm.
Loop #2 was designed in an effort to reduce the number of expulsions and also to improve the effectiveness of this device.

At the present time all multiparous patients at the Planned Parenthood Center at Buffalo are having the #2 loop inserted exclusively. Only nulliparous patients are having loop #1 inserted.
Not enough months have lapsed to publish any of the results with loop #2.

J. L.

75

Reprinted from *Obstet. Gynecol.*, **24**, 515–520 (1964)

Intrauterine Contraception:
A New Approach

36

LAZAR C. MARGULIES, M.D.

G RAFENBERG devised rings for intrauterine contraception in the mid-1920's; the method has been highly controversial in some countries ever since. Use has been sporadic in England, former British dominions, and other areas. On the other hand, modified devices—both metal and plastic—have been used in tens of thousands of women in the Far East, especially Japan.

In the United States, there was general condemnation of intrauterine contraceptive devices (IUCD), mainly because complications such as inflammation, perforation, and cervical tears were observed, because it was assumed that an IUCD induced early abortion, and because it was feared that cancer might ensue. Only one favorable paper on intrauterine contraception, that by Halton et al., was published here from 1934 to 1958.

Halton's method was to load a compressed silkworm gut ring into a gelatine capsule for insertion into the uterus and subsequent expansion. A similar approach, using thin polyethylene tubing instead of gut, was initiated by the author in 1959. However, this method required cervical dilatation to Hegar

size 6—painful for many patients and thus unsuitable for mass application.

The following year was spent searching for a suitable IUCD material and, even more important, for a painless method of insertion. The latter problem was solved by means of a Teflon tube, 3.75 mm. outside diameter, introduced cervically without need for dilatation and only rarely with need for a tenaculum. An IUCD loaded into this tube can be slipped into the cavity by using a pusher.

For the device itself, the material selected was polyethylene. This is inert and also has a good "memory"—that is, ability to revert resiliently to its original molded shape after intrauterine insertion. The form finally chosen for the IUCD was a spiral; its inner end curls in immediately after leaving the tube, thus obviating uterine perforation. Barium sulfate (22%) was mixed with the plastic to permit X-ray visualization.

During that year (1959), the field of IUCD investigation was encouragingly enlightened by the publications of Oppenheimer and Ishihama, reporting the complete absence of observed carcinoma even in women equipped with IUCD for 20 years or more.

In the author's initial work, performed from August 1960 to the end of 1961, spirals of increasing diameter (20–30 mm.) were inserted into some 400 patients. During that period there were 13 pregnancies—9 after unnoticed expulsions and 4 with IUCD in situ. There are 137 patients who still wear these devices, but the number of pregnancies

From the Department of Obstetrics and Gynecology, The Mount Sinai Hospital, New York, N. Y.

The work reported here was aided by grants of the Population Council of New York in the years 1961–1964.

Presented at the Twelfth Annual Clinical Meeting of The American College of Obstetricians and Gynecologists at Bal Harbour, Fla., May 20, 1964.

Submitted for publication May 12, 1964.

has increased to 24–15 after unnoticed ejections, 8 with a device in situ, and 1 ectopic.

Since the beginning of 1962 and to date, the IUCD has been altered by the addition to the spiral of a long tail terminating in 7 spherical beads set 6 mm. apart (Fig. 1). After insertion, any beads in excess of 3 protruding from the cervix are clipped off close, to avoid irritation or trauma. The tailed spiral has turned out to be more effective than the initial plain device; it has also answered the problem that a means be found whereby the location of the IUCD can be checked more simply and more readily than by x-ray visualization: In 2100 cases, over a period of 2200 woman-years of use only 4 patients became pregnant after unnoticed ejections.

The basic advance, however, is the painless method[6] of inserting an IUCD via small diameter tube.[6] This was one of the points discussed at the fact-finding conference held by the Population Council of New York in 1962.[1] Since that meeting, active work has been conducted in many research centers all over the world, to compare and evaluate the present-day intrauterine devices—spiral, loop, modified Grafenberg ring,[2] and bow.

CLINICAL RESULTS

The present report deals with results in 2100 cases—both private and clinic patients —fitted with tailed spiral IUCD between Jan. 1, 1962, and Mar. 15, 1964 and compiled May 1, 1964.

Table 1 presents data on the contraceptive effectiveness of the tailed spiral device. It may be seen that the larger the IUCD, the better the protection apparently provided.

As for the relative efficiency of the device, the data cited in Table 1 may be compared with those for other methods,[1] expressed in pregnancies per 100 woman-years of use: condom, 13.8; diaphragm, 14.4; withdrawal, 16.8; rhythm, 38.5; no method, 80.

Table 2 lists the lengths of time between insertion of the spiral device and conception in the 13 patients who became pregnant.

Table 3 lists the reasons given by patients for discontinuing use of the spiral device. These figures are self-explanatory, except for the 137 listed under "lost contact." Only 4 of these are private patients (4 of 300); the others are clinic patients fitted with devices before Nov. 1, 1963, who have not returned for check-up 3 months after their appointments. The clinic population consists very largely of Puerto Rican women; they travel to the island and often appear after a year or two of absence with a comment about "feeling so well that I didn't think I needed to have a check-up."

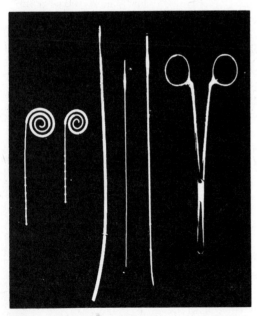

Fig. 1. From left to right: regular and small spiral; inserter tube with oval marker; plunger for pushing device into uterus; probe with a circular mark at 6 cm. from tip; clipping forceps with square jaws for smooth detachment of stem close to bead.

SIDE EFFECTS AND COMPLICATIONS

EMBEDDING. In 7 cases, retraction of the tail of the spiral ended with an embedding of the terminal bead into cervical tissue. If the patients returned soon after the embedding had occurred, it was easy to extract the bead; but if they came later, the procedure

TABLE 1. CONTRACEPTIVE EFFECTIVENESS OF TAILED SPIRALS

	No. of patients		
	Total	Using regular-size spiral	Using small-size spiral
Number of patients	2100	1700	400
Woman-years of use	2200*	1900	300
Total pregnancies	13	7	6
Rate per 100 woman-years of use	0.6	0.32	2.0
Pregnancies after unnoticed ejection (checked after first missed menstruation)	4	3	1
Pregnancy rate per 100 woman-years of use	0.18	0.15	0.33
Pregnancies with device in situ	7	3	4
Pregnancy rate per 100 woman-years of use	0.32	0.15	1.3
Ectopic pregnancies	2	1	1
Rate per 100 woman-years of use	0.09	0.05	0.33

* The 2200 woman-years of use include 160 women in whom tail-less spirals were exchanged for tailed ones. The reason for the inclusion was that one of these patients became pregnant after unnoticed ejection of a tailed spiral and that both ectopics occurred in patients who originally had had tail-less devices inserted. All 3 are included in the data of the table.

TABLE 2. NUMBER OF MONTHS ELAPSED AFTER INSERTION BEFORE PREGNANCIES OCCURRED

Regular-size device	Small-size device
WITH SPIRALS IN SITU	
7, 14, and 18	1, 7, 10, and 10
AFTER UNNOTICED DISPLACEMENT	
4, 4, and 6	15
ECTOPICS	
22	36*

* This patient used a No. 3 tailless spiral device.

was difficult. In 2 cases I cut the stem off and left the bead in the cervix.

In 5 cases there was a complete or partial disappearance of the IUCD into the uterus, confirmed by x-rays. Our practice is not to try and retrieve the spiral but rather to insert another one for increased protection. We also saw three spirals high in the uteri of patients who became pregnant with the device in situ or were pregnant at insertion. Pregnancies continued undisturbed.

BLEEDING. Occasional heavy bleeding at the first menses after IUCD insertion has been a difficulty from the beginning. It made 6 patients so panicky that they preferred to have the devices removed. In 15% this first period was extremely heavy. The problem has been alleviated very considerably by our current routine of dispensing 20 Methergine* or Ergotrate† tablets, 0.2 mg. The patient is instructed to take one tablet every 2-3 hours for moderately heavy bleeding, and 2 tablets twice every 30 minutes for really heavy bleeding. A few patients who could not tolerate oral medication did tolerate

* Sandoz Pharmaceuticals, Hanover, N. J.
† Eli Lilly and Company, Indianapolis, Ind.

TABLE 3. REASONS FOR DISCONTINUING USE OF TAILED SPIRAL DEVICES

Reason	No.	%	No. of patients resuming use of device
RELATED TO METHOD			
Bleeding	35	1.6	
Expulsion	43	2	
Infection	10	0.5	
Pain, cramps, discharge	17	0.8	
Pregnancy with device in situ	6	0.3	1
Pregnancy after unnoticed ejection	2	0.1	2
Insertion into a pregnant uterus	11	0.5	2
Ectopic pregnancy	1	0.05	1
Disturbance to husband	6	0.3	
SUBTOTAL	131	6.15	
UNRELATED TO METHOD			
Pregnancy desired*	29	1.4	1
Poor motivation, patient or husband	19	0.9	
Religious reasons	4	0.2	
Lack of confidence	0	0	
Leaving country, separation from husband, or death	9	0.43	
Ca. work-up	2	0.1	1
Returned to hospital for planned tubal ligation or hysterectomy	10	0.5	
Lost contact with patient	137	6.5	
SUBTOTAL	210	10.03	
TOTAL	341	16.18	

* Eleven of these patients are known to be pregnant.

intramuscular injections of the same drugs.

A second type of bleeding or spotting occurs as a premenstrual, postmenstrual, or intermenstrual symptom. In our experience, it can be completely eliminated by high doses of ascorbic acid (2 gm. daily) for 3 months.

INFECTIONS. There were 16 known infections during the entire 3½-year period. Only 4 of these occurred within a week after insertion; the others started 2 weeks to 8 months after insertion. In 3 cases, gonorrhea was proved either in the patient or the husband.

In 6 cases, the spirals were removed after hospital admission. The remaining 10, treated as ambulatory cases with oral antibiotics, were found a few weeks later to be in good condition, with devices in situ. The 6 hospitalized patients had pelvic inflammation with fever and pain; they were hospitalized for various periods. Five were treated conservatively; in the other patient, one-sided salpingo-oophorectomy was performed because of a tubo-ovarian abscess.

EXPULSIONS. The major unresolved problem, IUCD expulsion, has occurred at a constant rate over the past 2 years: about 12% with regular spirals and almost 25% with small spirals. Most expulsions occur during the first month (5%) the next greatest number are expelled during the second

518

month (2%); in following months percentages are smaller, but expulsions do occur even after 18 months. One encouraging feature is that 60% of the patients who return for reinsertion retain the second spiral, and of those who again eject, between 40% and 50% may retain the next one.

The reasons for IUCD expulsion are probably twofold: (a) the increased irritability of the uterine musculature in the presence of a foreign body, and (b) the interplay between isthmus and fundus, which has been observed in cineradiographic studies.[5] In our experience, almost all expulsions occur during the menses. It can be assumed that in some women the isthmus becomes so hypotonic, or the corpus so hypertonic, or both, that an IUCD can slip down during the premenstruum and be ejected by contractions of the hypertonic corpus. This idea is supported by the fact that expulsions in patients wearing the regular spiral occur at a rate 50% lower than that in those using the small spiral.

PAPANICOLAOU SMEARS. There were three Class IV or Class V Papanicolaou reports among the 2400 smears taken on admission. In 2, there were abnormal cervical cells; biopsies and hysterectomies confirmed carcinomas in situ. The third patient had abnormal endometrial cells on repeated smears and endometrial aspiration. Curettage did not confirm this finding; after frequent check-ups with negative results during the past year, this patient returned for insertion of a new spiral. Three additional patients with Class III findings were studied. Punch biopsies and curettings were normal.

ECTOPIC PREGNANCY. We encountered 3 ectopic pregnancies over a period of 3½ years. The first was in a nulliparous patient who had a spiral inserted on day 23 of her cycle and came to operation on day 35. The ovum must have been implanted in the tube at the time of IUCD insertion. This leaves only 2 patients with tubal pregnancies, instead of the statistically predicted[1] 33, in 2750 woman-years of exposure of all our patients.

NULLIPAROUS PATIENTS. In our experience with 190 nulliparous patients, the insertion of IUCD was frequently troublesome. In contrast to parous patients, who rarely feel slight cramps for a short time during and after insertion, about 80% of nulliparous patients suffer from severe cramps, sometimes vomiting and even syncope. The severe cramps may last for an hour and may recur in short spells for 2–3 weeks. The best and longest-lasting medication is codeine orally or, better yet, parenterally. It is also advisable to keep the patient recumbent for 20–30 minutes after insertion with application of heat to the abdomen; a prescription for codeine may help her over the following nights. In 5 patients we observed tetany-like reactions after insertion, controlled by intravenous calcium injections.

COMMENT

The author's theory of the mode of action of the spiral IUCD is based on various clinical observations, including the rarity of ectopic pregnancies and the frequent occurrence of Mittelblutung and Mittelschmerz in patients with spirals in utero. I assume that the presence of a foreign body of a proper size in the uterine cavity stimulates peristalsis of the tubes at the time of ovulation to such an extent that the ovum, even if fertilized, reaches the unprepared uterus prematurely and does not implant for lack of trophoblast cells.

One closely observed clinical case will illustrate this assumption. A 20-year-old para 2-0-0-2 ejected, for the second time, a regular spiral on day 7 and returned for reinsertion on day 15. Under questioning she conceded unprotected relations on day 11. The spiral was ejected again on day 21. Two weeks later an AZ test was positive.

If this experience is applicable to all patients, it would narrow down the action of

IUCDs to events in the tube between day 11 and day 15. If an ovum can mature and divide during this time as it is slowly propelled through the tube, it will not be prevented from implanting even if a device is inserted as early as the fifteenth day of the cycle.

There is an obvious need for a simple method of permanent contraception on a mass basis. With the technic mentioned, the insertion of an IUCD becomes a 1-minute office procedure. It should, however, be done by specialists or under strict supervision of specialists: The pelvic organs are too easily susceptible to inflammation after even the smallest errors in asepsis. Also, strict rules must be adhered to for the avoidance of IUCD insertion into a pregnant uterus. We now turn away any patient whose uterus measures more than 7 cm.

SUMMARY

A highly reliable technic of contraception has been evolved, using a simplified method to insert plastic contraceptives into the patient's uterus. Over a 2-year period, only 13 pregnancies were recorded among 2100 consecutive patients. Disturbances are mostly minor, and the contraception is quickly and painlessly reversible.

1000 Park Avenue
New York, N. Y., 10028

REFERENCES

1. *Excerpta Medica, International Congress Series,* #54, edited by C. Tietze and S. Lewit, 1962.
2. HALL, H. H., and STONE, M. L. Observations on the use of the intra-uterine pessary, with special reference to the Gräfenberg ring. *Am. J. Obst. & Gynec. 83*:683, 1962.
3. HALTON, M., DICKINSON, R. L., and TIETZE, C. Contraception with an intra-uterine silk coil. *Human Fertil. 13*:10, 1948.
4. ISHIHAMA, A. Clinical studies on intra-uterine rings, especially the present state of contraception in Japan and the experiences in use of intra-uterine rings. *Yokohama Med. J. 10*:89, 1959.
5. MANN, E. C., McLARN, W. D., and HAYT, D. S. The physiology and clinical significance of the uterine isthmus. *Am. J. Obst. & Gynec. 81*: 209, 1961.
6. MARGULIES, L. C. Permanent reversible contraception with an intra-uterine plastic spiral (perma-spiral). *Excerpta Medica, International Congress Series* #54, p. 61, 1962.
7. OPPENHEIMER, W. Prevention of pregnancy by the Gräfenberg ring method. *Am. J. Obst. & Gynec. 78*:446, 1959.

The Pill

XI

Editor's Comments on Papers 37, 38, and 39

37   **Pincus, Chang, Zarrow, Hafez, and Merrill:** *Studies of the Biological Activity of Certain 19-nor Steroids in Female Animals*

38   **Pincus, Rock, Garcia, Rice-Wray, Paniagua, Rodriguez, and Pedras:** *Fertility Control with Oral Medication*

39   **Lipsett et al.:** *Problems in Contraception*

A truly giant step forward was made by what is now generally referred to as "the pill." Writers and dreamers have long imagined that there must be something that could be taken orally to prevent conception. However, the basic knowledge to make this a reality was not available until mid-20th century. Then Gregory Pincus, Sc.D., and his colleagues, principally John Rock, M.D., working at the Worcester Foundation for Experimental Biology in Massachusetts, within a remarkably short period of time, carried out the basic research and conducted a definitive clinical trial. To be sure, there are bits and pieces of evidence that could be cited as contributory to the development of the pill, but the major work is that of the Worcester group. Accordingly, only the two key publications of these scientists are reproduced here.

The first was published in 1956 and is entitled "Studies of the Biological Activity of Certain 19-nor Steroids in Female Animals." It is basic research at its best, and it stands in fascinating contrast to many of the articles published in this collection. There is to be found no philosophy, no theology, nothing but pure experimental physiology. Pincus and his co-workers knew from previous work that progesterone and other related compounds inhibit ovulation in a variety of mammals. Four compounds, in addition to progesterone were selected for detailed study. There were: 17-alpha-ethinyl-19-nortestosterone, 17-alpha-ethinyl-5(10)-estraen-17-beta-ol-3-one, 17-alpha-19-nortestosterone, and 17-alpha-methyl-19-nortestosterone. They were all found to be potent ovulation inhibitors in the rabbit. During administration the animals did not become pregnant although they copulated. And, of particular significance, after discontinuation of medication, they did become pregnant. This showed that no damage had been done to the reproductive system. The authors concluded that the compounds act by inhibition of fertilization and of ovulation. Of the four compounds, the second was found to be the most promising.

The stage was thus set for a clinical trial which is reported in the second paper. The second compound, when combined with small amounts of estrogen, had been found to regulate the menstrual cycle in women. Accordingly, this was the mixture, or "pill," tested in a large group of women. These were Puerto Rican wives living in a low-income housing development project who, prior to medication, had an incidence of pregnancy of 63 per 100 years of marriage in spite of the fact that some had used various contraceptive measures. They were each given the pills and told to take one per day starting on the 5th day of the menstrual cycle and continuing until the 24th. The results were astonishing. In 1,279 cycles in which the pill was taken without fail there was not a single pregnancy! This, of course, was sufficient to establish the effectiveness of the substance as a contraceptive agent. However, some women in the study did report troublesome side-effects such as breast tenderness, nausea, dizziness, vomiting, and pelvic pain. Adjustment of the content of the pill decreased these side-effects, but apparently certain women cannot tolerate it. In the first 18 months of the study, 27 per cent of the subjects discontinued taking the pill because of side-effects. Another drawback is the necessity for daily administration. Some forget to take it, or run out, or are simply too lazy to bother. But, beyond question, the pill is a powerful agent for fertility control, if the woman can tolerate it and if she scrupulously takes it every day. Further, it does not, in any way, interfere with subsequent fertility and reproduction.

In the 15 years since the Pincus study the pill has gained remarkable popularity, especially in the more affluent and educated countries. It requires a prescription, it costs about $2 per cycle (cheaper in some countries), and it requires adequate motivation to take it regularly. Unfortunately, some of the hope for this method faded when reports multiplied of cases of thrombophlebitis. Drug manufacturers, because of the potential profits involved, have frantically sought for compounds that would be free of these disturbing side-effects. The search goes on for a once-a-year pill, a substance that could be injected only infrequently, or a compound that could be implanted under the skin and that would last for many months. In addition, compounds that would render the male temporarily sterile are being examined. These and other possibilities and problems are examined in an interesting conference held at the National Institutes of Health in 1970. The report of this conference was published in 1971 and is included here.

Reprinted from *Endocrinology*, **59**, 695–707 (1956)

STUDIES OF THE BIOLOGICAL ACTIVITY OF CERTAIN 19-NOR STEROIDS IN FEMALE ANIMALS[1]

37

GREGORY PINCUS, M. C. CHANG, M. X. ZARROW[2]
E. S. E. HAFEZ[3] AND ANNE MERRILL

*From the Laboratories of The Worcester Foundation for Experimental Biology,
Shrewsbury, Massachusetts*

INTRODUCTION

IN PREVIOUS publications a number of compounds have been demonstrated as inhibitors of ovulation in rabbits and rats (1, 2, 3). As our standard of reference we have used progesterone, which appears to be effective also in women (4,5). Of especial interest are four compounds: 17α-ethinyl-19-nortestosterone (I), 17α-ethinyl-5(10)estraen-17β-ol-3-one (II), 17α-ethyl-19-nortestosterone (III), and 17α-methyl-19-nortestosterone (IV).

These compounds have been suudied for: (a) progestational activity in rabbits, (b) deciduomagenic capacity in rats, (c) estrogenic activity, (d) ovulation-inhibiting activity in rabbits and rats, and (e) effects on development of the ovulated ovum.

Progestational activity in rabbits

The progestational activity of the various compounds was tested by the Clauberg (6) method. Immature, grey Chinchilla, female rabbits weighing approximately 1 kg. were used in this study. The rabbits were injected daily with 5 μg. of estradiol for 6 days. Following the estrogen priming, the rabbits were injected with the various progesterone-like compounds for 5 days along with 0.5 μg. of estradiol daily for 5 days. The rabbits were killed 24 hours after the last injection and the uteri removed and sectioned

---

Received August 20, 1956.

[1] Investigations described in this paper were aided by grants from the Planned Parenthood Federation of America and G. D. Searle & Company.

[2] Present address: Department of Zoology, Purdue University, Purdue, Illinois.

[3] Present address: Faculty of Agriculture, Cairo University, Cairo, Egypt.

for histological examination. The progestational state of the uterus was then evaluated according to the McPhail (7) technique. All hormones were dissolved in oil or suspended in tween 80 and the injections were given intramuscularly in a volume of 0.1 ml.

In Table 1 we present the comparative assays of these compounds. The table demonstrates that full effectiveness of progesterone is attained at a total dosage of 2.0 mg. in either vehicle. Considering order of magnitude

TABLE 1. THE EFFECTIVENESS OF CERTAIN 19-NOR STEROIDS IN THE CLAUBERG TEST COMPARED WITH PROGESTERONE

Compound	Vehicle	Total dose, mg.	Response
—	Oil	0.5 ml.	—
—	Suspension	1.0 ml.	—
Estradiol	Oil	0.5 μg.	—
Progesterone	Oil	0.2	±
Progesterone	Oil	0.5	1 +, 1 +
Progesgerone	Oil	1.0	3 +
Progesterone	Oil	2.0	4 +
Progesterone	Suspension	0.2	1 +
Progesterone	Suspension	1.0	2 +
Progesterone	Suspension	2.0	4 +
I	Suspension	0.02	—
I	Suspension	0.05	±
I	Suspension	0.1	3 +
I	Suspension	0.2	4 +
I	Suspension	0.5	4 +
I	Suspension	1.0	4 +
I	Suspension	5.0	4 +
II	Suspension	0.5	±
II	Suspension	1.0	2 +
II	Suspension	2.0	3 +, 4 +, 4 +, 1 +
II	Suspension	4.0	4 +
II	Tablet (oral)	50.0	1 +
II	Tablet (oral)	100.0	2 +
III	Oil	0.01	±
III	Oil	0.02	±, ±
III	Oil	0.1	3 +
III	Oil	0.2	4 +
III	Oil	0.5	4 +
III	Oil	1.0	4 +
IV	Suspension	0.02	1 +
IV	Suspension	0.1	3 +, 2 +

I, III and IV are approximately ten times as active as progesterone and II, albeit with some irregularity, is approximately as active as progesterone the activity of II by mouth is considerably reduced, by a factor of 50 to 100 times.

In view of the foregoing, it was our expectation that these compounds would be efficient in maintaining implantation in ovariectomized rabbits carrying fertilized eggs. The demonstration by Allen (8) and Pincus and Werthessen (9) that progesterone in dosages from 1.0 to 1.5 mg. per day is sufficient to establish implantation in the rabbit ovariectomized one day post coitum led us to repeat their experiments using post-partum females mated twice to bucks of known fertility. To ensure ovulation 12 r.u. of a sheep pituitary extract was injected intravenously into the does at the time of mating. Twenty-four hours later the females, in groups of four, were ovariectomized and the number of corpora lutea were counted. Daily injections of the steroids in oil were made, and at ten days post coitum the animals were sacrificed and the uteri were examined to determine the number of implantation sites and the condition of the fetuses.

The frequency and number of implantations obtained with two of the three 19-nor steroids was surprisingly low. In Table 2 we present the data of the series exhibiting successful implantation. The progesterone was

TABLE 2. IMPLANTATION IN OVARIECTOMIZED RABBITS RECEIVING PROGESTINS

Compound	Dosage, mg./day	No. of animals	Av. No. of ova ovulated	Av. No. of implantations	% implanted	% degenerating
Progesterone	from 0.5 to 1.5	4	13.0	5.5	42	23
Progesterone	from 0.3 to 5.0	4	11.3	4.0	36	14
Progesterone	from 0.2 to 10.0	3	9.3	3.3	36	11
Progesterone + estradiol (E)	from 0.5 to 1.5 + 1/1000 E	4	12.0	4.0	33	13
Progesterone + estradiol (E)	from 0.3 to 5.0 + 1/1000 E	4	12.5	3.5	28	8
Progesterone + II	5.0+0.04	4	12.0	3.7	31	0
III	2.0	4	10.3	5.2	53	10
III	10.0	4	10.3	5.5	51	0
III + estradiol	2.0+0.002	3	10.0	2.0	20	10

TABLE 2A

I #2	0.25	2	13.0	11.0	85	55
I #2	2.0	4	7.0	0.5	8	0
I #2	10.0	4	9.8	1.5	15	0

injected in increasing dosage from day to day since we had previously demonstrated (10) that a constant daily dosage of 2 mg. per day regularly induced implantation of approximately 20% of the ova ovulated. In this same test I was administered in daily dosages of 0.2 and 1.0 mg. per day, and in the following combinations 0.2 mg. +0.2 and 0.4 µg. of estradiol, 1.0 mg.+1 and 2 µg. of estradiol, 0.2 mg.+0.25, 1.0 mg. and 4.0 mg. allopregnanedione and 1.0 mg.+0.25, 1.0 mg. and 4.0 mg. allopregnanedione; in no instance was implantation observed. Similarly II in daily dosages of 0.2 and 1.0 mg., of 2.0 mg.+4 µg. estradiol, of 0.2 mg.+5 mg. of progesterone and 2.0+1 mg. of progesterone was ineffective. IV has not been studied in this test. It would appear from the data of Table 2 that III is potent as a maintainer of implantation, and that its efficiency in this respect may be reduced by estrogen. The efficiency of I and II is not established by our data, but it appears certain that it does not parallel their efficiency in the Clauberg test; in fact the data suggest that II may act as an antagonist of progesterone in the implantation process. We have previously shown that progesterone given in single daily doses of 2 or 25 mg. does not succeed in effecting implantation of more than 23% of the ova on the average. Some increase in this percentage (up to 42%) appears to be achieved by staggering the daily dose, and III in constant daily dose (2 or 10 mg.) seems to be more successful in maintaining a high implantation rate than progesterone. Nonetheless the implantation rate of 93% observed in normal pregnancy which we have previously observed (10) is not attained by any replacement regime thus far attempted.

As is demonstrated below, certain preparations of I seemed to have a certain amount of estrogen as a contaminant. Accordingly we obtained a preparation especially prepared to be estrogen-free (I #2 of Table 4). This preparation was injected in the dosages indicated in Table 2A. These data suggest implantation-stimulating activity at low dose but relative ineffectiveness at high dose. Among the ova implanted at the low dose, however, there was a significant (55%) degree of degeneration suggesting marginal ability of I to sustain implantation.

Deciduoma in the rat

Decidual activity was tested in the rat using the classical techniques except that two types of injection schedules were employed. Pseudo-pregnancy was induced by electrical stimulation of the uterine cervix of the rat in estrus. Each animal was castrated 5 days later and the right uterine horn traumatized. The animals were then given a single injection and killed 3 days after the trauma or given 3 daily injections and similarly killed 3 days after the trauma. Ten animals were used for each dosage of each compound tested. The various steroids were dissolved in oil or suspended in Tween 80 and a 0.1 ml. volume used at each injection. Both uterine horns were removed and weighed separately. The degree of stimulation was expressed as the per cent increase in the weight of the traumatized horn over the control horn.

The data presented in Table 3 demonstrate (a) the ineffectiveness of I and II, at least in dosages comparable to those found effective with progesterone, (b) the effectiveness of III and IV at least of the same order of magnitude as progesterone. The results of this test seem to parallel to some extent those obtained in the study of implantation efficiency (Table 2).

Estrogenic activity

Thus far we have studied the estrogenic activity of three of these compounds: I, II and IV have been tested in the Rubin assay (11) using the

TABLE 3. THE EFFECTIVENESS OF CERTAIN 19-NOR STEROIDS IN THE RAT DECIDUAL TEST

Compound	Vehicle	Type of dose	Total dosage, mg.	% increase in weight of traumatized horn
Progesterone	Oil	Single	5	150 ± 15
Progesterone	Oil	Single	10	276 ± 25
Progesterone	Suspension	Single	10	193 ± 33
Progesterone	Oil	Multiple	2	261 ± 38
Progesterone	Oil	Multiple	3	344 ± 21
Progesterone	Oil	Multiple	5	148 ± 35
Progesterone	Suspension	Multiple	0.5	44 ± 13
Progesterone	Suspension	Multiple	2	111 ± 42
I	Suspension	Single	10	30 ± 12
I	Suspension	Multiple	0.3	28 ± 2
II	Suspension	Single	10	8 ± 2
II	Suspension	Single	10	7 ± 6
II	Suspension	Multiple	15	7 ± 2
III	Oil	Single	10	272 ± 44
III	Oil	Multiple	0.05	8 ± 3
III	Oil	Multiple	0.3	43 ± 12
III	Oil	Multiple	0.5	64 ± 12
IV	Suspension	Multiple	0.5	18 ± 1.3
IV	Suspension	Multiple	3.0	190 ± 31

uterine weight of the immature (21 to 22 days old) mouse. In Table 4 we present the data obtained on two samples of I, or which #2 is designated as "highly purified," and on similarly "highly purified" sample of II and IV. It is clear that the two samples of I differ in estrogen activity, #1 being approximately 8 to 10 times as active as #2. Both are, however, considerably less active than the estrone standard. Quantitative comparison with the standard is not possible, however, since I has, in each experiment, a slope constant in the dosage response curve significantly different from that of estrone (Fig. 1). A rough estimate leads to an activity 1/800th to 1/1000th of estrone for #1 and 1/6400th to 1/10,000th for #2. These data suggest an estrogen contaminant in each sample which has been markedly reduced in #2; alternatively, #1 has such a contaminant whereas #2 exhibits an intrinsic uterus-stimulating activity of I with no contaminant.

In Figure 1 we plot the dosage; response data for the various assays of Table 4, along with assay values for progesterone. The most purified sample of I and IV have very similar dosage: response curves whereas II has a higher slope and a lower threshold. II, therefore, appears to have a different order of estrogenic activity; this may be conferred by the shift of the double bond to the 5:10 position. Again the slope of its curve differs from that of the standard but a rough estimate of 1/40th to 1/80th of estrone's activity may be made.

In the vaginal cornification test 120 to 200 gm. female rats were castrated and one week later half of them were injected with estradiol-17β and the other half with II; one week later the two groups were interchanged. Vaginal smears taken morning and night for $2\frac{1}{2}$ days beginning forty-one hours after the first of three injections of sesame oil were stained with Giemsa, and marked positive if only nucleated and epithelial cells

TABLE 4. THE UTERINE RESPONSE (UTERINE WEIGHT IN MG.)/(BODY WEIGHT IN GM.)
OF IMMATURE FEMALE MICE TO CERTAIN 19-NOR STEROIDS

Expt.	Compound	Total dose, μg.	No. of mice	Mean uterine ratio ± S.E.*
A	Control	—	11	0.88 ± 0.065
	Estrone	0.025	14	1.22 ± 0.050
	Estrone	0.05	14	1.80 ± 0.071
	Estrone	0.1	14	3.37 ± 0.231
	Estrone	0.2	13	4.92 ± 0.344
	I #1	20	13	2.26 ± 0.065
	I #1	40	13	2.50 ± 0.079
	I #1	80	13	2.89 ± 0.111
	I #1	160	13	3.43 ± 0.115
B	Control	—	12	1.24 ± 0.006
	Estrone	0.025	12	1.77 ± 0.125
	Estrone	0.05	12	2.39 ± 0.125
	Estrone	0.1	12	2.94 ± 0.276
	Estrone	0.2	11	4.83 ± 0.276
	I #2	15	10	1.61 ± 0.054
	I #2	45	11	1.74 ± 0.071
	I #2	90	12	1.86 ± 0.075
	I #2	270	9	2.17 ± 0.111
C	Control	—	11	1.05 ± 0.089
	Estrone	0.025	11	1.15 ± 0.051
	Estrone	0.05	11	1.73 ± 0.083
	Estrone	0.1	9	3.20 ± 0.380
	Estrone	0.2	11	4.87 ± 0.255
	II	2	11	2.90 ± 1.71
		20	10	4.57 ± 0.234
D	Control	—	15	1.07 ± 0.064
	Estrone	0.025	10	1.38 ± 0.085
	Estrone	0.05	9	1.68 ± 0.105
	Estrone	0.1	10	2.67 ± 0.162
	Estrone	0.2	10	4.20 ± 0.349
	IV	2	10	1.31 ± 0.081
	IV	20	8	1.51 ± 0.067
	IV	100	10	2.05 ± 0.092
	IV	1000	10	2.61 ± 0.104
	Progesterone	100	10	1.75 ± 0.079
	Progesterone	500	10	1.47 ± 0.104
	Progesterone	1000	10	1.87 ± 0.075

* S.E. = standard error.

were present. Scanty smears or smears with 5% or more leucocytes were considered negative. The data of Table V demonstrate some estrogenic activity of II. On the basis of the dose-response curve the 50% response is at 0.065 μg. for estradiol and at 13.5 μg. for II, indicating 1,200th of the activity of estradiol for II, but it should be noted that II has a curve which is less steep than that of estradiol. Since estrone in this assay is approximately 1/5th as active as estradiol, the order of magnitude of activity is that observed in the Rubin test.

Drill and Saunders (12) report no detectable estrogenic activity of III at the 10 μg. level in the Rubin test, but have since found it to have less than 1/200th the activity of estrone. They find it inactive in the vaginal cornification test (13).

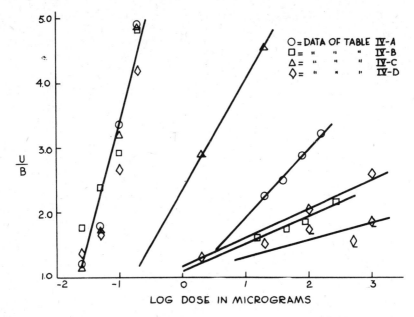

Fig. 1. Relationship between the logarithm of the dose and the uterine weight; body weight ratio in immature female mice receiving estrogens, progesterone and various 19-nor steroids.

Ovulation inhibition in rabbits

Ovulation inhibition in rabbits has been studied using post-partum females which are injected with the test substance twenty-four hours before mating to a fertile male (1). Laparotomy is performed twenty-four hours after mating to determine the presence or absence of ovulation points on the ovary. In Table 6 we present the data on frequency of ovulation in a control series of 62 post-partum females and in females receiving various dosages of the 19-nor steroids. It is clear that they are all potent ovulation inhibitors, and they all have roughly the same order of magnitude of activity. Thus one to two mg. of each compound is practically 100% effective as an ovulation inhibitor, but compound I and II appear to be active at a somewhat lower level. We have previously reported that 1–2 mg. is

TABLE 5. THE ESTROGENIC ACTIVITY OF 17-ETHINYL-ESTRAENEOLONE (II)
IN THE VAGINAL CORNIFICATION TEST

Substance	Total dose, μgs.	No. of rats used	Vaginal cornification	
			No. positive	% positive
Estradiol	0.1	10	10	100
Estradiol	0.075	20	19	90
Estradiol	0.05	10	1	10
II	20.0	10	8	80
II	15.0	20	7	65
II	10.0	10	2	20

the lowest level at which progesterone is active (3, 4). Oral administration of these compounds also leads to effective ovulation-inhibition.

Ovulation inhibition in rats

The methods which we have used for the study of the inhibition of ovulation and early development in rats have been previously described (2, 4). Thus far I, II and III have been administered to mature breeding female rats which are placed with fertile males at the time of initial (or only) administration. We have found that the significant indicator of anti-

TABLE 6. THE EFFECTS OF CERTAIN 19-NOR STEROIDS ON OVULATION IN THE POST-PARTUM RABBIT. (ALL BY SUBCUTANEOUS INJECTION UNLESS OTHERWISE NOTED)

Compound	Dosage	No. of animals	% ovulating
Vehicle	—	62	82 ± 4.88
I	0.1	4	50
	0.25	4	0
	0.5	8	0
	2.0	4	0
	10.0	4	0
	5 (oral)	4	0
II	0.1	5	40
	0.2	5	40
	1.0	5	0
	5.0 (oral)	5	20
	10.0 (oral)	5	40
III	0.2	4	25
	1.0	5	20
	5.0	5	0
	10.0 (oral)	5	40
IV	0.1	4	50
	0.5	4	25
	2.0	4	0
	5.0 (oral)	3	33

fertility effect is the latent period between cohabitation with the male and the successful mating that culminates in pregnancy. This is evident in the data of Table 7 which demonstrate significant effects of I, II and III upon this measurement. I and II are clearly active both by injection and by oral administration and II appears to be somewhat more active than I, particularly by the oral route. III is active by the oral route at the 5 mg. per day dose, but appears to be somewhat less effective than I or II. A significant increase in number of corpora lutea followed the subcutaneous injection of 1 mg. of II, but this failed to occur at higher doses or under any other regime. Similarly, a significant increase in the number of normal embryos occurred following two weeks of feeding of I, but whether this signifies some action to conserve fetuses is difficult to deduce, particularly since this does not occur under other regimes of administration. What the data do suggest generally is that the pregnancy following on the period

TABLE 7. THE EFFECTS OF 19-NOR STEROIDS ON MATING AND PREGNANCY IN THE RAT

Compound	Dosage regime	Dose, mg.	No. of rats	Days between cohabitation and successful mating	Average No. of corpora lutea	Average No. of normal embryos	% of ova failing to implant	Fetal degeneration (as % of total embryos)
Control	—	—	59	4.7±0.57	12.2±0.41	9.4±0.37	9.0	6.9
I	S.I.*	10	11	*38.3±3.12*	13.6±1.19	8.6±0.94	10.0	29.7
	S.F.†	10	12	*9.3±1.48*	13.4±0.87	11.6±1.22	11.7	2.8
	S.F.	25	11	*16.3±1.96*	12.7±0.73	11.1±0.96	10.1	2.4
	F2×2‡	5	11	*17.5±1.50*	14.4±1.11	12.1[1]±0.68	13.9	2.2
II	S.I.	1	12	*13.7±1.43*	15.6[1]±1.21	11.8±0.97	15.5	10.8
	S.I.	2	12	*21.8±2.04*	14.0±0.78	11.3±0.51	8.3	12.3
	S.I.	5	12	*17.8±1.67*	11.7±0.66	10.3±0.65	3.6	8.9
	S.F.	2	10	10.4±3.39	14.7[1]±0.80	12.2±1.30	15.6	1.6
	S.F.	5	12	*16.5±2.66*	13.1±0.77	9.6±0.95	12.1	16.7
	F2×2	2	12	*16.3±1.16*	12.7±0.54	10.3±1.17	8.6	11.5
III	F2×2	1	10	9.2±2.61	12.8±0.49	11.6±0.65	6.5	3.5
	F2×2	5	10	*9.5±1.96*	11.6±1.09	10.3±1.09	11.0	2.6

[1] Significantly higher than control value.
* S.I. = single subcutaneous injection.
† S.F. = single feeding.
‡ F2×2 = feeding twice a week for two weeks.
Italicized values differ significantly from the control.

of delay proceeds normally; a single possible exception is the high percentage (29.7) of fetal degeneration following the 10 mgm. injection of I, but this may be adventitious since it is not observed under the other regimes.

To test the effects of prolonged administration II was given in 2 mg. dose by stomach tube every other day over a period of 70 days to mature adult nonpregnant female rats. These animals were divided into two groups, one of which was caged with fertile males at 18 days, and the other at 39 days following the initiation of medication. Control females were similarly caged with males at these two intervals following the initiation of administration of the oil vehicle. Fertility records were kept and the data of these records are presented in Table 8. In the first control group the mean latent period to conception was 28 days. This is quite unusual (*cf.* Table 7 controls) and immaturity of the male is suspected since vaginal sperm was not observed in these animals until $3\frac{1}{2}$ to $4\frac{1}{2}$ weeks after caging with the male. Nonetheless, on comparison with the experimental animals which exhibited an average delay of 78 days to conception a

TABLE 8. THE EFFECTS OF THE ORAL ADMINISTRATION OF 17-ETHINYLESTRAENEOLONE UPON THE REPRODUCTIVE BEHAVIOR OF ADULT FEMALE RATS. EACH EXPERIMENTAL ANIMAL RECEIVED 2 MG.-IN-OIL BY STOMACH TUBE EVERY OTHER DAY, EACH CONTROL ANIMAL RECEIVED AN EQUAL AMOUNT OF THE OIL SOLVENT EVERY OTHER DAY

Type of animal	No.	Total dosage, mg.	Caged with males after	Latent period to conception, days	Sterile period following medication, days
Control	4	—	18 days	28±1.63	—
Experimental	4	70	18 days	78±0.91	26
Control	5	—	39 days	7.4±0.71	—
Experimental	4	70	39 days	59.5±4.85	28.5

clearly significant difference is observed. In the second group the prompt conception of the control contrasts clearly with the 59.5 day delay to conception in the medicated animals. In Table 8 we have calculated the mean period of sterility ensuing following discontinuance of medication in the two experimental groups, 26 and 28.5 days respectively. This is calculated as follows: in the first group the animals were with males for 52 days during medication; they conceived after 78 days of cohabitation with the male—therefore $78-52=26$ days of sterility followed discontinuation of regular medication. The remarkable similarity in length of the post-medication sterile period with the two groups suggests an inhibitory effect from which recovery is had regardless of the length of exposure to males, i.e. it is intrinsic to the rate of readjustment of the reproductive process of the medicated animals. It should be noted that mating took place from time to time with the medicated animals as judged by the presence of sperm in the vaginal smears which were taken daily. In spite of such matings sterility supervened.

Effects on ovum development

We had assumed that the mechanism of this effect in the rat is due to inhibition of ovulation. It may, however, be ascribable to failure of fertilization or of implantation of the fertilized ovum. To examine this point six female rats were given a single injection of 10 mg. of II and caged with fertile males 24 hours later. One of them mated within 24 hours (as judged by the presence of sperm in the vagina) and four days later she was sacrificed. Fifteen corpora lutea were found in the ovaries and 15 eggs in the oviducts, none of them fertilized. A second female mated twice, once within 24 hours and again within 72 hours of caging; four days after the second mating we found 20 corpora lutea and 20 unfertilized eggs in the oviducts. A third female mated on three successive occasions, at 3, 6 and 9 days following caging; four days after the third mating we found 14 corpora lutea and 14 unfertilized ova. A fourth female mated fifteen days after caging, and five days later we found 18 corpora lutea and 18 unfertilized ova. The remaining two females failed to mate over a 30-day period and on sacrifice gave no evidence of recent ovulations. These data suggest, therefore, a dual effect, at least of II: (a) an inhibition of fertilization in animals mating shortly after its administration and (b) an inhibition of ovulation for a greater or lesser period of time; where the period of time is lesser, e.g., 15 days, the fertilization-inhibiting effect may still persist.

In the case of the rabbit the ovulation-inhibiting effect is plain. Nonetheless, a possibility that effects on the ovum may obtain still exists. Accordingly, we undertook the following experiment. Ten post-partum rabbits were injected with 5 mg. of II per day for three successive days, and on the fourth day they were mated to proven fertile males. Immediately after mating they received an intravenous injection of 12 rat units of a sheep pituitary gonadotrophin to ensure ovulation. All ten did in fact ovulate as determined by laparotomy 24 hours later. One fallopian tube was removed from each of three females at this laparotomy, the ova were flushed from the tubes and examined for evidence of fertilization. All of the ova from two females were clearly fertilized, and some of the ova from the third were fertilized. It would therefore appear that in the rabbit II does not inhibit fertilization as it does in the rat. The uterus on the remaining side of two of the rabbits was examined for blastocysts 5 days later,

TABLE 9. A COMPARISON OF ESTIMATED MINIMAL ACTIVE DOSES OF PROGESTERONE AND THE 19-NOR STEROIDS IN SIX TESTS OF ACTIVITY

	M.E.D. in Clanberg assays, mg.	Minimum uterotrophic dose in mice, μg.	Minimum deciduomagenic dose in rats mg.	Minimum oral antifertility dose in fertile rats, mg.	Minimum ovulation-inhibiting dose, mg.	Minimum implantation sustaining dose in rabbits, mg./day
Progesterone	1–2	87	2	5–10+	1–2	0.5–1.5
I	0.1–0.2	29	>10	5	0.25	0.25*
II	2–4	0.24	>15	2	>0.2<1.0	>2.0
III	0.1–0.2	±100†	0.5	5	>1.0<5.0	2.0
IV	0.1+	19	2	not studied	0.5–2.0	not studied

* Less active at higher dose.
† Data of Drill, Saunders and Edgren (11).

but none were found. Furthermore, the remaining rabbits were allowed to go to term, but no young were born, and palpitation of the uteri at intervals gave no evidence of living embryos. In the rabbit, then, this compound may act to inhibit normal development of the fertilized egg. We are examining this point in further studies.

DISCUSSION

One of these 19-nor steroids, I, has previously been reported as an active progestin by conventional assay in rabbits (14) and in women (15, 16). On closer scrutiny of the array of tests which we have employed complete characterization of these compounds as progestins becomes rather difficult. This is illustrated in Table 9, which compares the calculated minimum effective doses of the various 19-nor steroids with those of progesterone in six tests of activity. The data on the mimimum uterotrophic dose for I, II and IV are derived from the extrapolation of the curves of figure 1 to a uterine weight:body weight ratio of 1.30. The remaining values are calculated from the data of this and previous publications. On a quantitative basis there is no complete parallelism. Thus, compound I which is approximately 10 times as active as progesterone in the Clauberg assay is clearly much less active as a deciduomagenic agent. Compound II which is somewhat less active than progesterone in the Clauberg assay is many times more potent as a uterotrophic agent in the mouse, and is not detectably deciduomagenic. Compounds III and IV are the only ones which exhibit a rough parallelism to progesterone, but both are more active in the Clauberg and uterotrophic assays and approximately as active as progesterone in the other tests.

Compound II would appear to be uniquely distinguishable from the others on the basis of its high uterotrophic activity and also the fact that it is active in the rat vaginal smear assay. This gives to it a clear estrogenic activity in the conventional sense. It is a not very potent progestin compared to the other compounds, is either not at all or only feebly deciduomagenic and appears to be unable to sustain implantation in the dosages thus far employed. If we add to these findings the evidence for its inhibitory effects on the development of early ova, i.e., inhibition of fertilization in the the rat and of blastocyst implantation in the rabbit it might almost be denominated an estrogen. In the human female it does act upon the endomentrium as a progestin (5); it and II and III also appear to act as ovulation inhibitors (4, 5). Compound III, on the basis of our tests, would appear to be the most effective as a progesterone substitute. It has all of the qualitative activities of progesterone and especially in its dosage: response relationship in the uterotrophic assay it resembles progesterone quite markedly. Nonetheless in the human female it appears to be unable alone to sustain normal endometrial development (5).

Each of these compounds would appear to offer the possibility of acting as anti-fertility agents. Of them, Compound II would appear to be most promising for this purpose since it not only is an effective ovulation inhibitor but also may act to prevent development of the free ovum. The ratio of ovulation-inhibiting to ovum-inhibiting dosages has, however, not been established. Furthermore, the etiology of the period of sterility which we have observed following prolonged administration to the female rat requires elucidation.

SUMMARY

Four 19-nor steroids—17α-ethinyl-19-nortestosterone (I), 17α-ethinyl-5(10)estraen-17β-ol-3-one (II), 17α-ethyl-19-nortestosterone (III), and 17α-methyl-19-nortestosterone (IV) have been assayed in a series of tests designed to demonstrate progestational and/or estrogenic activity. All of them are active in the Clauberg test with I, III and IV having approximately ten times the activity of progesterone and II having about $\frac{1}{2}$ the activity of progesterone. All of them are active as ovulation inhibitors in the rabbit, I and II appearing to be somewhat more active than progesterone, III and IV of the same order of magnitude as progesterone. In the uterotrophic assay in the mouse I, III and IV have a dosage:response curve resembling that of progesterone whereas II has one more nearly resembling that of estrone; II also has a much higher order of activity than the other compounds. The deciduomagenic activity of III and IV resembles that of progesterone, but neither I nor II has proven active in doses 5 to 7 times that of progesterone. Compounds I, II and III are effective anti-fertility agents in the female rat; I and especially II appear to be more active than progesterone when administered by injection; III has been tested only orally and appears to be about as active as I and somewhat less active than II. Compounds I, II and III have also been studied as maintainers of implantation in the rabbit; III has the order of magnitude of activity of progesterone, II has been inactive at a dosage at which progesterone is regularly active and I appears to be relatively ineffective over a wide dosage range although at low dosage (0.25 mg. per day) implantation of a larger percentage of ova occurs but with much accompanying fetal degeneration. No compound tested, including progesterone itself, regularly effects a normal percentage of implantation of fertilized eggs. Special studies with II indicate that (a) it acts as an inhibitor of fertilization in the rat, but not in the rabbit, (b) it prevents implantation or the maintenance of implants in the normally pregnant rabbit, (c) during a 70-day regime of injection of 2 mg. every other day in female rats conception does not occur although copulation may occur, and that the period of administration is followed by a 26 to 28-day period of sterility regardless of when the male is caged with the females.

Acknowledgments

We gratefully acknowledge the technical assistance of Mrs. A. Dorfman, Miss P. Longo, and Mr. P. Bodurtha.

REFERENCES

1. PINCUS, G. AND M. C. CHANG: *Acta Physiol. Latino-Americana* **3**: 177. 1953.
2. SLECHTA, R. I., M. C. CHANG AND G. PINCUS: *Fertility and Sterility* **5**: 282. 1954.
3. PINCUS, G.: Aspects du Métabolisme des Steroides Hormonaux, Mason et Cie, Paris, 1955.
4. PINCUS, G.: Proc. Vth International Planned Parenthood Conf. (in press).
5. ROCK, J., G. PINCUS AND C. R. GARCIA: Recent Progress in Hormone Research 13 (in press).
6. CLAUBERG, C.: *Zentr. Gynäkol.* **54**: 2757. 1930.
7. McPHAIL, M. K.: *J. Physiol.* **83**: 145. 1934.
8. ALLEN, W. M.: *Cold Spring Harbor Symposium on Quan. Biol.* **5**: 66. 1937.
9. PINCUS, G. AND N. T. WERTHESSEN: *Am. J. Physiol.* **124**: 484. 1938.
10. HAFEZ, E. S. E. AND G. PINCUS: *Proc. Soc. Exp. Biol. Med.* **91**: 531. 1956.
11. RUBIN, B. L., A. S. DORFMAN, L. BLACK AND R. I. DORFMAN: *Endocrinology* **49**: 429. 1951.
12. DRILL, V. A. AND F. J. SAUNDERS: In ENGLE and PINCUS: Hormones and the Aging Process. Academic Press, New York. 1956.
13. DRILL, V. A., J. F. SAUNDERS AND R. A. EDGREN: Personal communication, 1956.
14. HERTZ, R., W. TULLNER AND E. RAFFELT: *Endocrinology* **54**: 228. 1954.
15. TYLER, E.: *J. Clin. Endocrinol. and Metab.* **15**: 881. 1955.
16. GREENBLATT, R. B.: *J. Clin. Endocrinol. and Metab.* **16**: 869. 1956.

Reprinted from *Amer. J. Obstet. Gynecol.*, **75**, 1333–1346 (1958)

FERTILITY CONTROL WITH ORAL MEDICATION*

GREGORY PINCUS, Sc.D., SHREWSBURY, MASS., JOHN ROCK, M.D.,
AND CELSO-RAMON GARCIA, M.D., BROOKLINE, MASS., AND
EDRIS RICE-WRAY, M.D., MANUEL PANIAGUA, M.D., AND
IRIS RODRIGUEZ, B.S., RIO PEDRAS, P. R.

(From the Worcester Foundation for Experimental Biology, Shrewsbury, Massachusetts; the Reproductive Study Center, Free Hospital for Women, Brookline, Massachusetts; and the Family Planning Association of Puerto Rico, Rio Piedras, P. R.)

FOLLOWING the demonstration of the ovulation-inhibiting effectiveness of several oral progestational 19-nor steroids in animals,[1-3] and in a group of selected patients,[1, 4-7] a field trial in Puerto Rico was undertaken, with the use of one of these compounds. Norethynodrel [Compound II—17α-ethinyl-5(10)-estraeneolone—of our previous studies] was chosen since in animal experiments it appeared to be somewhat more potent than the others in suppressing ovulation. It also gave some indication of preventing fertilization in rats.[3] Moreover, in low dosages, combined with a subeffective estrogen, it regulated menstrual cycles when given cyclically.[7-9]

The most effective estrogen supplement appeared to be the 3-methyl ether of ethinyl estradiol. In 1,467 of the cycles studied in this investigation, the subjects received tablets each containing 10 mg. of norethynodrel and 0.22 mg. of the ethinyl estradiol 3-methyl ether, or, in a very few instances, 0.23 mg. In the remaining 390 cycles reported, the estrogen supplement was somewhat lower, i.e., 0.08 mg. in 157 cycles, 0.15 mg. in 61 cycles, and 0.18 mg. in 172 cycles.†

The procedures employed in assembling subjects, the instructions given, the regime of medication, the problems encountered, and some of the results of the first 8 months of the Puerto Rican study have been described previously by Rice-Wray[10] and by Pincus and his associates.[7, 9] This paper extends the data to Aug. 31, 1957, i.e., to include a total of 16 months of investigation.

Subjects and Methods

Since the details of the procedures used with the married Puerto Rican subjects have been published,[10] it suffices here to state them briefly.

Considered in this report are 1,857‡ cycles of 265 Puerto Rican wives "from the low income population living in a housing development project in a

*The investigation described in this paper has been aided by a research grant from G. D. Searle & Company which, with the medication used, was obtained through the kindness of Dr. A. L. Raymond and Dr. I. C. Winter.

†Tablets containing 10 mg. of norethynodrel and 0.15 mg. of 3-methyl ether of ethinyl estradiol constitute the trademarked product Enovid, G. D. Searle & Company.

‡A total of 1,857 cycles was studied in this investigation. These comprised 1,712 cycles for which we have data on lengths (Table I), plus 118 for which such data were not available, plus an additional 27 in the 19 women who became pregnant.

1333

Am. J. Obst. & Gynec.
June, 1958

TABLE I. DISTRIBUTION OF LENGTHS OF MENSTRUAL CYCLES AS INFLUENCED BY DISCONTINUITY OF MEDICATION
(265 Women: 1,712 Cycles)

TOTAL NO. OF CYCLES	NO. OF TABLETS MISSED		LENGTH OF CYCLE												
			7-12	13-18	19-23	24-25	26	27	28	29	30	31	32	33-36	37-48
1,279	(A) 0	No.	6	13	26	90	163	322	276	130	67	67	65	33	21
		%	0.5	1.0	2.0	7.0	12.7	25.2	21.6	10.2	5.2	5.2	5.1	2.6	1.6
282	(B) 1-5	No.	19	45	55	7	4	7	8	16	19	32	32	29	9
		%	6.7	16.0	19.5	2.5	1.4	2.5	2.8	5.7	6.7	11.3	11.3	10.3	3.2
151	(C) 6-19	No.	1	4	10	2	1	10	3	3	11	9	20	53	24
		%	0.7	2.6	6.6	1.3	0.7	6.6	2.0	2.0	7.3	6.0	13.2	35.1	15.9

slum clearance area.''[10] The ages of 262 were known. They extended from 16 to 44 years with a median of 27.4* Prior to the beginning of medication, the incidence of pregnancy in these women had been 63 per 100 years of marriage (i.e., 0.625 ± 0.0135 per year) in spite of some use of contraceptive measures.

Every woman was given one or two vials, each containing twenty 10 mg. tablets of the drug, with instructions to take one tablet a day, beginning on day 5 of the menstrual cycle, until one vial of 20 tablets was consumed, i.e., through day 24 of the cycle. If a tablet was not taken on any given day, the subject was instructed to proceed with the one-a-day regime nonetheless until all 20 tablets were used.

A schedule of visits by a trained social worker was arranged so that in every medication cycle each subject was seen shortly after she should have taken the last tablet. Initially only one vial was distributed to each woman. This was replaced on the social worker's visit. Since, in a number of instances, the housewives were not at home when she called, it was decided, after a few months, to leave two vials with each subject so that the continuity of the regime of medication (day 5 through day 24) might not be broken. Visits on the same schedule were nonetheless made, and missed interviews were followed by another visit within one to two weeks.

At each consultation, information was elicited concerning the length of the menstrual cycle, the occurrence of side effects, the frequency of coitus, and the number of missed tablets. A rough check, in some instances, on the number of tablets omitted was made by counting those remaining in the vial. As subjects discontinued the study, replacements were sought, so that an average monthly load of approximately 130 women was maintained.

In the course of the investigation, many of the participants came to the office of the Family Planning Association, or of an affiliated physician, for pelvic examination. At this time, an endometrial biopsy was taken and blood drawn for hemoglobin determinations, bleeding time, and clotting time. A limited number of individuals also furnished urine for assays of certain steroids.

Results

Lengths of Menstrual Cycles.—Adequate information for analytical purposes was obtained from 1,712 cycles of 265 women. In Table I are presented the data on lengths of menstrual cycles, arranged according to the number of days that tablets were omitted.

It is shown that out of a total of 1,712 medication cycles, 1,279 (A) were reported with no omissions of medication, 282 (B), with one to five tablets missed, and 151 (C), with six to nineteen tablets unused. The mean lengths of cycles in the three groups are: (A) 27.86 ± 0.515; (B) 25.34 ± 1.529; and (C) 32.01 ± 0.923 days, respectively. Statistically significant are differences between the means for A and C, as well as between those for B and C, but not between A and B, because of the large variability in the data for B.

Table I presents the frequency distribution of the different cycle lengths. It is apparent that in the patients who missed no tablets, this is monomodal, with a peak at 27 days. In contrast, where one to five tablets were omitted, a clear

---

*The age distribution was as follows:

AGE IN YEARS	NO. OF WOMEN
16 to 19	20
20 to 24	77
25 to 29	72
30 to 34	50
35 to 39	40
40 to 44	3
	262

bimodal distribution is seen, with peaks at 19 to 23 days and at 31 to 32 days. When more than five tablets were unused, we observe a minor mode at 19 to 23 days, with a major peak at 33 to 36 days. The degree of variability is expressed by the standard deviation (S) of the distribution, which is highest in B (25.67 ± 1.08), lowest in C (11.37 ± 0.65), and intermediate in A (18.44 ± 0.36). Each of the S's differs significantly from the two others.

In seeking explanations for the nature of the distributions of cycle lengths in each case, it should be recalled that cessation of medication with this compound was found in previous studies[5, 7] to be followed in most cases by withdrawal bleeding within 4 days.

It can be seen from Table I, however, that among 1,279 cycles of the Puerto Rican housewives who took medication from day 5 through day 24, there were 981 cycles in which the flow began at intervals from 3 to 24 days after the last pill was taken. There were, among these, 8 cycles which were of 41 to 48 days' duration.* Postmedication flow in these 8 did not occur until 17 to 24 days after the consumption of the last tablet. There was no constancy in position of the long cycles among the others. Each of these women had but one such lengthened cycle, none having exhibited this phenomenon in any other cycle in which no pills were missed.

The ages of the 8 women ranged from 21 to 38 years (mean, 29.4 ± 5.4; median, 29.5 ± 8.5). Thus age was not a factor. Unfortunately, we have no accurate knowledge of pretreatment cycles. Nor in any of the 8 cycles was a biopsy obtained after medication was completed. We do have one endometrial specimen, however, taken after medication in a 38 day cycle of one of these women. This was obtained on the ninth day after 20 daily increments of 10 mg. of the medication, i.e., on the thirty-third day of the cycle. Flow began on the thirty-ninth day.

Microscopic examination of this tissue showed the stroma to be made up of widely separated cells the nuclei of which were not dissimilar to, unless slightly smaller than, predecidual nuclei. In one small area, there was the ordinary stainless edema commonly seen in early progestational endometrium. Elsewhere, with their attenuated fibrinous cytoplasm, the stromal cells formed a reticulum of strands and vacuoles.

The glands were sparse, small, straight, and lined by pseudocuboidal epithelium in which there was no mitotic activity. The venules were not remarkable in number, although all but two larger ones were filled with blood. No characteristic spiral arterioles could be identified in the biopsy fragments.

We are not prepared to explain the peculiarly long latency preceding withdrawal flow in these women. In the single biopsy available, there was no suggestion of involution to a pretreatment condition; but also there was neither evidence of persistent progestational action, nor of proliferation. Except for the reticulation of the formerly contiguous pseudodecidual stroma cells, the endometrium seemed to be in a suspended state and gave us no indication of what transpired in the ovary or hypophysis to account for the delay in catamenia.

The integrity of the endometrium was not always maintained by the compound. In a previous communication,[7] it was reported that in about 8 per cent of women who received estrogen-supplemented norethynodrel, a breakthrough bleeding occurred before the nineteenth day of medication. In group A of the present series (where no pills were omitted), the distribution of cycle lengths simulates that seen in normally menstruating women as closely as would appear possible by artificial control. To illustrate this, we present in Fig. 1 our data and, for comparison, those of Haman[11] on 2,410 menstrual cycles of 150 normal

*Two recently disclosed cycles, not among the 1,279 under discussion, were even 57 and 58 days long, although no pills were missed.

American married women, along with the statistical constants for each set of observations. It may be seen that in the two tabulations there is no significant difference in the mean length of cycles. Haman's curve on the normal American housewife shows a broader, flatter distribution, however. This implies that medication with norethynodrel tends to narrow the range of cycle lengths.

The 19 to 23 day mode (19.5 per cent) for group B in which one to five tablets were omitted suggests the frequent occurrence of either withdrawal or breakthrough bleeding. Since in Haman's group of normal women the frequency of cycles of 23 days or less was 5.2 per cent, and in group A of our series it was even lower (only 3.5 per cent), it appears that the higher incidence (42.2 per cent) of such short cycles in B was due chiefly to withdrawal bleeding; i.e., the omission of medication occurred sufficiently early in the cycle to precipitate flow.

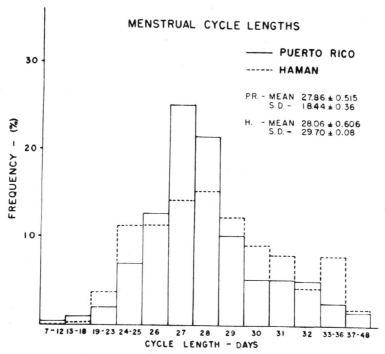

Fig. 1.—Comparison of lengths of menstrual cycles of Puerto Rican women during medication versus those of untreated American women (Haman[11]).

The second mode of B at 31 to 32 days represents approximately 40 per cent of the medication cycles in which, despite an occasional missed tablet, withdrawal bleeding did not occur. These were presumably cases in which the sustenance of the endometrium from the medication was adequate to compensate for the temporary omission of one to five pills. The length of the cycle was therefore increased until the ingestion of the last tablet was followed by the usual withdrawal flow.

In group C, where 6 to 19 tablets were omitted, the minor mode at days 19 to 23 presumably represents the few women with withdrawal bleeding caused by skipping tablets early in the cycle, whereas the 33 to 36 day mode again reflects the delay due to the longer time necessary for the consumption of all 20 tablets. In this connection, it is also possible that women with longer cycles typify those whose endometrial response thresholds to the drug are so low that sustainment might be expected to occur despite missed pills. Lacking data as to the exact days when tablets were unused, we cannot be more specific in regard to this possibility.

The foregoing observations indicate: (a) that, if the regime of day 5 through day 24 is followed strictly, a normal frequency of menstrual cycle lengths may be expected; (b) that the skipping of days may result in either a shortened cycle due to withdrawal bleeding, or in a lengthened cycle, owing to the extension of medication. Actually, in view of the ability of this compound to prevent menstrual bleeding as long as it is taken,[12] a cycle of any desired length could presumably be produced. We had chosen our standard day 5 through day 24 regime in the expectation that "normal" cycle lengths would occur.

Inhibition of Ovulation.—Our belief, on the basis of previous studies, that this compound is ovulation inhibiting was strengthened in these subjects, who continued their usual coital habits, by the inverse correlation between the incidence of pregnancy and the constancy of medication.

In the 1,279 cycles during which the regime of treatment was meticulously followed, there was not a single pregnancy. On the other hand, in the 282 cycles wherein one to five tablets were omitted, conception occurred in 2 instances; while in those cycles (151) where six or more tablets were unused, there were 3 pregnancies.

As has already been noted previously, the premedication pregnancy rate in these women was 0.625 ± 0.0135 pregnancies per year of marriage. In those who faithfully followed the schedule of medication with no omissions, this rate was 0, a reduction of 100 per cent; among individuals who missed one to five tablets the rate was 0.092, while among those who omitted six or more tablets it was 0.259. The rate for the entire group of medicated subjects was 0.038, representing a reduction of 93.9 per cent from the mean premedication pregnancy value.

In spite of what is, in all probability, an inhibition of ovulation during the cycles in which the regime of medication was meticulously followed, the fact that 2 women conceived during cycles in which not more than five tablets were missed suggests no deleterious effect on the ovary from this drug. Further evidence that it does the ovary no permanent harm is given by the occurrence of pregnancies in 14 women after cessation of medication which had been taken from one cycle to as many as 17 cycles (in one case).

Endometrial Biopsies.—In the course of the medication cycles, intermittent endometrial biopsies were obtained from some of these subjects. Such fragments, if taken from high on the anterior or posterior wall, ordinarily give a true picture of the over-all condition of the responsive portions of the endometrium; but, it must be noted, they may show only an isolated, atypical condition. Thus, when we use endometrial biopsies to detect the estrogenic or progestational potency of an experimental hormone, we must realize the limitations of the method, hence the possible inexactness of the conclusions.

Preliminary studies of Hitschmann and Adler[13] and of Schröder,[14] extended by O'Leary,[15] Bartelmez,[16] our own group,[17-19] and others, have established general criteria by which we judge the potency of an experimental estrogen or progestin against the respective standard action of a familiar estrogen or progesterone.

As we have noted previously,[5] the endometrium appears to be somewhat thinner than one might expect in women of these ages. The histology of the endometrial specimen varies with the duration of medication.

Norethynodrel is a potent progestin by conventional endometrial standards, and, by virtue of its supplementation with the 3-methyl ether of ethinyl estradiol, the combined product (Enovid) has at least temporarily some of the effects of estrone. When given from days 5 through 24 of a menstrual cycle to women who habitually ovulate, its cytologic effects on the endometrium mimic mucosal changes seen with normal ovulation, but with some significant differences (Fig. 2).

In the first place, with medication as described, at a time when we know that in all probability there is no luteinized ovarian follicle and no gonadotrophic influence which would evolve a corpus luteum from such a follicle (i.e., the ninth day of the cycle for example), we see the normal effect on glands of a 4-day-old corpus luteum (Fig. 2, 18 day normal ovulatory cycle). Since biologists have found no gonadotrophic action, tumultuous or otherwise, in these compounds, we must conclude that the morphologic changes reflect only the *direct* influence of the ingested material on the endometrium, and do not indicate premature ovulation on, or soon after, the day treatment was begun, i.e., day 5 of the cycle.

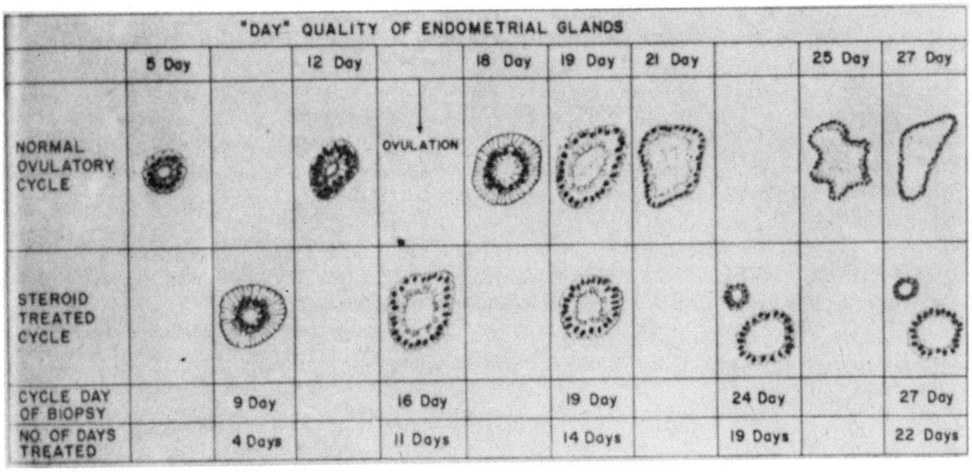

Fig. 2.—Time differential in development of endometrial glandular epithelium in normal and medicated women.

A second aspect of the dissimilarity between endometrium subject to the 19-nor steroids and that of the untreated normal cycle is the short duration of this immediate, so-called secretory response in the glands. With continued medication, it rarely progresses to full, typical secretion by glandular epithelium. Nor, as treatment progresses, do the glands themselves increase in size or change in shape to resemble those subject to a 5, or 6, or 7 day corpus luteum (nineteenth, twentieth, or twenty-first day of the schematic normal cycle).

Instead, in their shapes and in their epithelial structure the glands give the appearance of gradual regression, not to the condition typical of late proliferation but to a condition suggestive of the fifth postovulatory day (nineteenth day of the normal cycle), when actual discharge of vacuole material is beginning. Although the glands themselves remain of proliferative caliber, they are straight or only slightly ribboned. To escape necessity of description, we have called them 19 day glands, because pseudostratification has passed and vacuoles are above the nuclei. After 18 days of treatment, biopsy on the twenty-forth day of the cycle reveals the lumina to be narrower and the epithelium pseudocuboidal, as in the very early proliferative phase. After 3 weeks of medication,

there may be slight variation in caliber of the glands, but most are small and
lined by flat cuboidal cells. They closely resemble glands characteristic of
the fifth day of a normal cycle.

A third difference between treated and nontreated endometria is that the
generalized edema of the functional layer, typical of the week-old corpus luteum
effect, appears in the first few days of treatment and, with continued medication, persists with gradual decline until the twenty-first day; whereas, with
normal ovulation, the edema begins to subside only *after* the twenty-first day.

Fourth, with treatment starting on day 5, the predecidual cytoplasmic enlargement of stromal cells appears 7 days later, on the twelfth day of the
cycle, and progresses rapidly. As early as the twenty-first day of the cycle
the stroma closely resembles that of the untreated cycle day 27 (thirteenth
postovulatory day). By the twenty-second day of treatment, the stroma so
closely simulates that of early pregnancy as to mislead the unwary.

Also significant is the fact that the endometrial diagnosis does not vary
with the number of previous cycles of drug administration. A sample taken
at a given time in an early medication cycle is indistinguishable from one taken
at the same time in a subsequent cycle of treatment. This suggests that the
material imposes a sequence of endometrial change which is repeated cycle
after cycle.

Steroid Excretion.—Twenty-four hour urine samples were obtained from
42 subjects, 10 of whom had withdrawn from the project at least 2 months before the inception of the steroid excretion study. These 10 served as controls
for the 32 on medication when urine was collected.

TABLE II. EFFECTS OF MEDICATION ON THE URINARY EXCRETION OF CREATININE (CR), 17-
KETOSTEROIDS (17 KS), AND 17-HYDROXYCORTICOSTEROIDS (PS) IN 42 PUERTO RICAN WOMEN
(32 During Medication: 10 Controls)

NO. OF CYCLES ON MEDICATION	NO. OF SUBJECTS	MEDIAN AGE (YEARS)	CR (GM. PER 24 HOURS)	17 KS (MG. PER 24 HOURS)	PS* (MG. PER 24 HOURS)
"Withdrawn" (control)	10	28	1.20 ± 0.027	4.24 ± 0.74	3.45 ± 0.41
1-4	17	27	1.22 ± 0.113	2.92 ± 0.40	2.00 ± 0.24
5-10	15	27	1.13 ± 0.113	2.76 ± 0.50	2.29 ± 0.38
1-10	32	27	1.17 ± 0.078	2.85 ± 0.31	2.14 ± 0.22

*Underlined values differ significantly from values of the "withdrawn" group.

In Table II are listed the mean data obtained on urinary output of creatinine,* 17-ketosteroids (determined on an aliquot by the method of Pincus[20]),
and 17-OH-corticosteroids (determined on an aliquot by a modification of the
Porter-Silber[21] method).

Although the mean 17-ketosteroid excretion (KS) of 2.85 mg. per 24
hours in the medicated group (1 to 10 cycles) is 33 per cent less than the
value for the control group, it is not quite significant statistically. On the
other hand, the 38 per cent difference between output values of 17-OH-corti-
costeroids (PS) in control and medicated groups (1 to 10 cycles) is highly
significant statistically ($p < 0.001$). These data suggest an inhibition of excretion of adrenocorticosteroids with the establishment of a constant lowered output level during medication. In this connection, it should be pointed out that
in a study of 7 psychotic women on whom similar determinations were made
during the same regime of medication, each subject having served as her own

*In view of the known constancy of creatinine excretion, determinations were used merely
as a check on the completeness of the 24 hour urine specimens submitted for analysis.

control prior to taking the drug, the decline in mean output of 17-OH-corticosteroids was only 16 per cent, and of 17-ketosteroids only 18 per cent.[9] There is therefore some doubt as to whether the 10 "withdrawn" subjects of the present study serve as adequate controls to the subjects on medication. A small but definite decrease in excretion of 17-ketosteroids has been reported previously in several series of observations.[6, 7] This lowered output was, however, still within the normal range, and no symptomatic evidence of decreased adrenal function was noted.

Blood Studies.—Routine bleeding time, clotting time, and hemoglobin values were determined, at indefinite intervals, on 39 of the subjects of this study during medication, as well as on 10 women after discontinuance of the treatment 3 to 8 months previously. To serve as controls, 26 women were tested who were untreated patients in the Family Planning Association Clinic.

Cases of medication for 1 to 12 cycles are represented in this blood study, but since no difference in values was seen between those on short-term and those on long-term medication, we averaged all the data for patients taking the drug.

TABLE III. THE EFFECT OF MEDICATION ON BLOOD OF PUERTO RICAN WOMEN
(49 Medicated: 26 Controls)

SUBJECTS	NO.	BLEEDING TIME* (SECONDS)	CLOTTING TIME* (SECONDS)	HEMOGLOBIN	
				%	GM.
Control	26	145.9 ± 8.21	278.8 ± 10.7	75.4 ± 1.09	11.77 ± 0.21
Medicated	39	116.8 ± 6.31	261.5 ± 7.02	73.8 ± 1.02	12.04 ± 0.17
After medication	10	103.4 ± 12.4	223.9 ± 15.5	75.2 ± 2.51	12.75 ± 0.4

*Underlined values differ significantly from the control values.

As shown in Table III, the average bleeding time, both during and after medication, is significantly shorter than in the controls. It also appears that the clotting time in the postmedication subjects is significantly less than in either the control or the medicated group. No significant differences in hemoglobin content are seen among the three groups, however. While there is a tendency toward higher hemoglobin in the medicated and postmedicated subjects as compared to the controls, this difference is not significant.

Side Effects.—Some of the women on this medication occasionally exhibited troublesome symptoms which, in a number of instances, led them to discontinue the tablets. Reactions which may be attributable to the compound are breast tenderness, nausea, dizziness, vomiting, and pelvic pain. We have recently analyzed the incidence of such reactions in two groups of patients who received norethynodrel on the day 5 through day 24 regime over periods of a few months.[7] Two findings were outstanding: (a) the incidence of untoward effects was very low with norethynodrel itself, but increased when estrogen was added as a supplement, and (b) the frequency of such reactions was highest during the first cycle of medication and was significantly lower in later cycles. In the Puerto Rican series reported here, we studied the incidence of reactions in 390 cycles of patients receiving norethynodrel with supplements of 0.08 mg. (157 cycles), 0.15 mg. (61 cycles), and 0.18 mg. (172 cycles) of the 3-methyl ether of ethinyl estradiol per 10 mg. of norethynodrel, instead of the usual 0.22 mg. There was no difference in the incidence of reactions in the three groups, although a significant increase of early bleeding occurred at 0.08 mg. of the estrogen supplement. It appears, therefore, that the threshold estrogen dose for these reactions is lower than that for adequate endometrial support.

Since norethynodrel, as administered to these Puerto Rican subjects, has had estrogen supplementation varying from 0.08 mg. to 0.23 mg. per 10 mg. of norethynodrel (in the great majority of cycles, the supplement was 0.22 mg.), we may consider that a suprathreshold level for reaction stimulation has been employed. Let us examine the consequences.

TABLE IV. PERCENTAGE OF PUERTO RICAN WOMEN WHO DISCONTINUED MEDICATION AFTER ONE OR MORE CYCLES BECAUSE OF REACTIONS

| CYCLE NUMBER | NUMBER OF SUBJECTS | LEFT BECAUSE OF REACTIONS | | SURVIVORS PER 1,000 WHO STARTED |
		NO.	%	
1	265	5	1.9	981
2	234	5	2.1	960
3	208	4	1.9	942
4	186	5	2.7	917
5	163	8	4.9	872
6	137	1	0.7	866
7	119	3	2.5	844
8	101	5	4.9	801
9	83	0	0.0	801
10	76	1	1.3	791
11	64	1	1.6	778
12	57	1	1.8	764
13	52	2	3.8	735
14	45	0	0.0	735
15	41	0	0.0	735
16	32	0	0.0	735
17	22	0	0.0	735
18	18	0	0.0	735
19	8	0	0.0	735
20	2	0	0.0	735
21	1	0	0.0	735

In Table IV are presented the data on the number of patients who withdrew from the project because of side effects. From the percentages of women who stopped medication, we have calculated the crude survival rates per 1,000 starting. These survival data are charted in Fig. 3. From the shape of this curve, it is clear that the rate of discontinuance of medication caused by untoward reactions declines with time in such a manner that 13.4 per cent will have left after 6 cycles of medication, 23.6 per cent after 12 cycles, and 26.5 per cent after 18 cycles. The departure rates in these 6 cycle increments are thus 13.4, 10.2, and 2.9 per cent, respectively. In the initial 1½ years, therefore, approximately 27 per cent of the subjects stopped medication because of troublesome symptoms, while thereafter the loss from this cause was negligible. This remainder represents either subjects who have become habituated so that the reactions are not troublesome to them, or women who have high thresholds of reaction stimulation. With the information available, we cannot at present decide just which explanation applies.

Because of these complaints, a special observation period of 3 months was instituted, during which the incidence of reactions was noted, and to a number of the patients tablets of a magnesium aluminum glycinate antacid were dispensed. Fifty-two women in all had reported reactions in 502 medication cycles. Of 39 of these patients, who took from 1 to 10 antacid tablets, 32 reported disappearance of their symptoms: an apparent "cure rate" of 82 per cent. Of the remaining 13 women subject to reactions, who did not take the antacid, however, 6 observed a spontaneous disappearance of symptoms, while 7 did not, suggesting a spontaneous "cure rate" of 46 per cent, or an incidence of 54 per cent of continued reactions. We would therefore expect that 46 per cent of the group of 39 who took the antacid (or 18) would have shown spontaneous remission. This leaves 21 who would be expected to show continued untoward effects, and since only 7 did so, the true "cure rate" by the use of antacid tablets is 67 per cent.

Regardless of these considerations, if our data be taken literally, we would expect, by administering antacid, to inhibit reactions in 82 per cent of the reactors, presumably reducing by this percentage the number of women who discontinue medication. Further tests of the control of untoward effects are in progress.

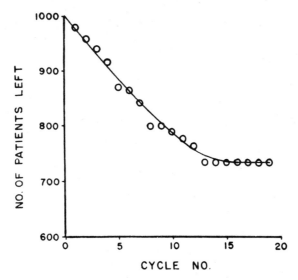

Fig. 3.—Rate of discontinuing medication because of reactions (expressed as per 1,000 women starting medication).

Fertility Control.—As of Aug. 31, 1957, there were 141 patients continuing on medication, while 123 had, for various reasons,* discontinued it. In Table V are listed the reasons for dropping out and the number of women in each of the categories.

From the point of view of contraceptive practice, the subjects in categories a, c, d, i, j, and k, i.e., 64 of the 123,† are susceptible to conception in the test population. Some of these 64 have adopted other means of contraception.

The 14 patients listed as "pregnant with disuse" (c) consist of 10 who failed to take medication through carelessness and 4 who discontinued because of troublesome symptoms. Because the latter 4 are included under "pregnant with disuse," they do not contribute to the 37 listed under "reactions." The 14 in group c are 9 who became pregnant in the first cycle after they stopped medication, and 5 others who, having failed to adopt any other means of contraception, conceived within 2 to 5 months after discontinuation.

Those listed as "pregnant during use" (d) are the 5 already mentioned who missed 3 to 17 tablets.

*It should be noted that 56 other subjects, who volunteered to take part in the project but who did not continue, are not included in this discussion. Twelve of them were pregnant before they began the medication, while, for the remaining 44, adequate information is not available, either because they moved and could not be traced, lived too far away for visits, or apparently failed even to start medication. Some "bootleg" sales of the drug were traced to the latter group.

†The reason why 54 of the remaining women, i.e., groups b, e, f, g, h, discontinued medication are obvious (Table V). The members of group i included 1 menopausal woman, 1 with an "uncooperative attitude," and 3 prostitutes.

Although all of these pregnancies are obviously attributable to failure of the subject, rather than of the method, we have an over-all incidence of 19 pregnancies in 1,857 cycles, or 143 marriage years, an incidence of 13 pregnancies per 100 years. When this figure of 13 is compared with the premedication pregnancy rate of these same women (63 per 100 marriage years), we find a reduction of 80 per cent in the pregnancy rate during the use of this compound. It is of interest, also, to compare our figure of 13 with pregnancy rates reported in a previous study of Puerto Rican women who used other types of contraceptives, i.e., 29 pregnancies per 100 exposure years with diaphragm and jelly, and 33 with foam powder and sponge.[22]

Finally, to enable us to compare our figures with the pregnancy rate when no contraceptive measures were used, Dr. Clarence J. Gamble[23] has furnished us with data on pregnancy rates based on his observations on 1,443 patient years with Puerto Rican couples. For all ages "under 20" to 44, the rate was 76 pregnancies per 100 couples per year. Correcting for the age distribution of our subjects, we would expect 67 pregnancies per 100 years of marriage. Our observed incidence of 13 per 100 years is 19 per cent of this, suggesting an "effective" reduction in the pregnancy rate of 81 per cent.

TABLE V. REASONS FOR DISCONTINUING MEDICATION
(123 Puerto Rican Women)

	NO.	% OF TOTAL DISCONTINUING	% OF TOTAL SUBJECTS
(a) Reactions	37	30.1	14.0
(b) Moved or too distant	19	15.4	7.0
(c) Pregnant with disuse	14*	11.4	5.5
(d) Pregnant during use	5	4.1	2.0
(e) Sterilized	11	8.9	4.0
(f) Separated from husband	10	8.1	4.0
(g) Husband sterilized	7	5.7	2.5
(h) Unrelated illness	7	5.7	2.5
(i) Husband against practice	4	3.3	1.5
(j) No interest	3	2.4	1.0
(k) Religion	1	0.8	0.5
(l) Miscellaneous causes	5	4.1	2.0
Total	123	100.0	46.5

*Four of these stopped medication because of reactions.

Summary

As the outstanding findings resulting from this investigation, we may state the following:

1. Length of the Menstrual Cycle.—

A. The ingestion of 10 mg. of norethynodrel, supplemented by varying amounts of estrogen, on a prescribed day 5 through day 24 regime, resulted in a normal distribution of lengths of menstrual cycles.

B. If this regime is altered by omission of medication, there may ensue either shortened menstrual cycles, caused presumably by withdrawal bleeding, or lengthened menstrual cycles, resulting from adequate maintenance of the endometrium despite intermittent lack of medication or from prolonging of the treatment by use after the twenty-fourth day of the tablets missed earlier.

2. Ovulation.—

A. Presumption of suppression of ovulation is strengthened by the fact that conception did not occur in any instance in which the medication schedule of day 5 through day 24 was followed faithfully.

B. Among those who omitted medication for 3 or more days, the low incidence of pregnancy was roughly proportional to the number of unused tablets.

3. Endometrium.—

A. This compound appeared to exert a prompt progestational effect on the endometrium which, after 5 to 7 days of medication, did not progress in terms of glandular response, but did advance with reference to the stromal reaction.

B. No pathological endometrial changes were observed in specimens taken at different times in the cycle and after varying periods of medication up to 10 months. The sequence of endometrial response to medication, as well as of regression following medication, was generally quite regular, and no distinction could be made between endometrium from short-term and that from long-term treated subjects.

4. Steroid Excretion.—

Studies of urinary excretion of steroids indicated a decrease in 17-hydroxycorticosteroids and, to a questionable extent, of 17-ketosteroids. This decline did not seem to vary with the number of medication cycles, nor did it appear to be accompanied by any discernible signs of adrenocortical hypofunction.

5. Blood Studies.—

No significant differences in hemoglobin level were noted during or after medication as compared with those of untreated women. The average bleeding time, however, both during and after medication, was found to be significantly shorter than in the controls, while the clotting time in the postmedication subjects was significantly less than in either the control or the medicated group.

6. Side Effects.—

A. The treated subjects reported certain untoward reactions, the incidence of which did not vary with 0.8 to 1.8 per cent estrogen supplementation of the 10 mg. dose of norethynodrel.

B. It had been calculated that, over an 18 cycle span of medication, troublesome symptoms would cause approximately 27 per cent of the subjects enrolled in the project to discontinue treatment. Actually, in the course of the study to date, only 18 per cent have ceased medication because of side effects.

C. The administration of a magnesium aluminum glycinate antacid has led to the reported disappearance of untoward reactions in 82 per cent of the subjects who took the antacid.

7. Fertility Control.—

In practice, several difficulties have been encountered in maintaining complete fertility control, so that there have occurred 19 pregnancies, 5 of which were in women who had omitted 3 to 17 tablets from the advised regimen, and 14 in individuals who had stopped medication because of "reactions" or carelessness. These 19 produced a pregnancy rate of 13 per 100 marriage years, which may be compared with an expected incidence of 67 pregnancies per 100 marriage years from Puerto Rican women of this age range not known to be practicing contraception; or an actual incidence of 63 per 100 marriage years among these women (some of whom had been using contraceptives) before entering on the study.

We believe that our data demonstrate the action of a powerful agent for fertility control among the women utilizing it. Thus far, in the subjects of our study, it has clearly lowered the pregnancy rate. The fact that 14 women who had discontinued medication after 1 to 17 cycles became pregnant within 1 to 3 months thereafter suggests that the drug, as thus used, does not interfere with subsequent fertility.

References

1. Pincus, G.: Acta endocrinol., supp. 28, 1956.
2. Pincus, G., Chang, M. C., Hafez, E. S. E., Zarrow, M. X., and Merrill, A.: Science 124: 890, 1956.
3. Pincus, G., Chang, M. C., Zarrow, M. X., Hafez, E. S. E., and Merrill, A.: Endocrinology 59: 695, 1956.
4. Rock, J., Pincus, G., and Garcia, C. R.: Science 124: 891, 1956.
5. Rock, J., Garcia, C. R., and Pincus, G.: In Pincus, G., editor: Recent Progress in Hormone Research, New York, 1957, Academic Press, Inc., vol. 13, p. 323.
6. Garcia, C. R., Pincus, G., and Rock, J.: AM. J. OBST. & GYNEC. 75: 82, 1958.
7. Pincus, G., Rock, J., and Garcia, C. R.: Ann. New York Acad. Sc. (In press.)
8. Rock, J., and Garcia, C. R.: Proceedings of Symposium on 19-Nor Progestational Steroids, G. D. Searle & Company, Chicago, Ill., 1957.
9. Pincus, G.: Proceedings of Symposium on 19-Nor Progestational Steroids, G. D. Searle & Company, Chicago, Ill., 1957.
10. Rice-Wray, E.: Proceedings of Symposium on 19-Nor Progestational Steroids, G. D. Searle & Company, Chicago, Ill., 1957.
11. Haman, J. O.: AM. J. OBST. & GYNEC. 43: 870, 1942.
12. Kistner, R. W.: AM. J. OBST. & GYNEC. 75: 264, 1958.
13. Hitschmann, F., and Adler, L.: Monatschr. Geburtsh. u. Gynäk. 27: 1, 1908.
14. Schröder, R.: Der normale menstruelle Zyklus der Uterusschleimhaut, Berlin, 1913, A. Hirschwald.
15. O'Leary, J. L.: Anat. Rec. 50: 33, 1931.
16. Bartelmez, G. W.: Contrib. Embryol. 24: 141, 1933.
17. Rock, J., and Bartlett, M. K.: J. A. M. A. 108: 2022, 1937.
18. Rock, J.: Am. J. Surg. 48: 228, 1940.
19. Noyes, R. W., Hertig, A. T., and Rock, J.: Fertil. & Steril. 1: 3, 1950.
20. Pincus, G.: J. Clin. Endocrinol. 5: 291, 1945.
21. Romanoff, L. P., Rodriguez, R. M., Seelye, J. M., and Pincus, G.: J. Clin. Endocrinol. 17: 777, 1957.
22. Beebe, G. W., and Belaval, J. S.: Puerto Rico J. Pub. Health & Trop. Med. 18: 3, 1942.
23. Gamble, C. J.: Personal communication.

Reprinted from *Ann. Intern. Med.*, **74**, 251–263 (1971)

Problems in Contraception

Moderator: MORTIMER B. LIPSETT, M.D., F.A.C.P.

Discussants: JERRY W. COMBS, JR., Ph.D., KEVIN CATT, M.D., Ph.D., and

DANIEL G. SEIGEL, S.D., Bethesda, Maryland

39

Earlier projections of birth rate were erroneous because of inadequate appreciation of the many and changing variables: rates of industrialization, educational levels, changes in economic activity, rates of family formation, marriage, timing of births, and so forth. Although a decline in fertility may be projected over the next few years, the rising proportion of women of child-bearing age will result in higher birth rates. Many women still have more children than they say they want, and family planning has been accepted by most American women. Although only a few women receiving oral contraceptives become hypertensive, almost all women show an increase in plasma renin activity, plasma renin substrate, and angiotensin II. Hemodynamic studies show small but consistent increases in cardiac output and mean arterial blood pressure. The oral contraceptives have been associated with an increased risk of thromboembolic disorders and death from pulmonary embolism. The relative risk of venous thromboembolism increases with increasing dose of estrogen, leading to the recommendation that the oral contraceptives contain no more than 50 μg of mestranol or ethinyl estradiol. Survey of the processes in sperm and ovum maturation and fertilization shows many areas where other approaches to contraception may be fruitful. These include several areas of basic scientific interest: the meiotic stage of spermatogenesis, the control of follicle-stimulating hormone secretion, regulation of corpus-luteum life span and steroid synthesis, and the role of progesterone in maintaining a secretory endometrium.

► An edited transcript of a Combined Clinical Staff Conference at the Clinical Center, Bethesda, Md., by the National Institute of Child Health and Human Development, National Institutes of Health, U.S. Department of Health, Education, and Welfare.

DR. MORTIMER B. LIPSETT*: This conference is confined to a single aspect of the science of reproductive biology—contraception. In view of the recent publicity and notoriety surrounding several contraceptive agents and their side effects, it would be wise not to lose sight of many important scientific and practical developments in reproductive biology. Although these may not be of immediate concern to internal medicine, they do indicate the breadth and significance of this area of biology and medicine.

Among the practical consequences of research in reproduction are several important economic measures that have resulted from research in this area. For example, ovulation can be synchronized in pigs, and this permits artificial insemination of large groups of animals in a few days with almost simultaneous farrowing of the animals; superovulation has been induced in sheep, thereby significantly increasing the number of lambs. The identification of the sex attractants, the pheromones, has provided methods of control of insects, and mammalian pheromones may prove equally valuable in other ways.

In the human the obverse of contraception—that is, induction of ovulation with enhanced fertility—is now available. But our future ability to further the development of healthy infants will depend on increasing our knowledge of the phenomena of ovulation, fertilization, sperm maturation, nidation, and fetal nutrition. In all these areas research is accelerating because of the stimulus of the thrust in family planning and research in allied areas.

The internist has become more immediately con-

* Associate Scientific Director (RB), Intramural Research, National Institute of Child Health and Human Development.

cerned with problems of reproductive biology with the simultaneous advent of the so-called population explosion and the "pill." As a citizen and as a physician interested in the individual and his environment, he must be concerned with the consequences of an ever-increasing population. As an internist, he must be aware of the multiple side effects and activities of the oral contraceptive agents. The gamut of side effects, which range from deviations of fat and carbohydrate metabolism and altered liver function to blood clotting and thromboembolic phenomena, to mention only a few, have been discussed recently in many publications. In this conference we consider only several isolated problems concerned with population growth and contraception.

Evaluation of Recent Trends in the Birth Rate

Dr. Jerry W. Combs, Jr.*: The rise and fall of the birth rate in the United States raises a wide range of both interpretive and predictive problems. The birth rate in the United States began to decline in the nineteenth century, possibly near the beginning of it; since then in each census but one the child-woman ratio was lower than in the preceding one. By the time a national registration system was established in 1910, the birth rate, adjusted for underreporting, had dropped to 30.1 births per 1,000 population (Table 1). That decline continued until the birth rate reached a level of 18.4 per 1,000 in 1933. It rose somewhat thereafter in the later 1930's but remained below 20 per 1,000 until 1940.

During the World War II years the birth rate began to rise, reaching a peak in 1947. After 1957, when it was 25.3, it began to decline and reached 17.5 in 1968. In 1967 and 1968 the birth rate was lower than 1933, not because of actual lower fertility per woman but because of the larger proportion of children and, particularly, older persons in the population, which swells the denominator on which the birth rate is based. The fertility rate (the number of births per 1,000 women 15 to 44 years of age) was not as low as in 1933. As a matter of fact, it was about 12% higher, 85.7 in 1968 as compared with 76.3 in 1933.

In 1947 an eminent American demographer, P. K. Whelpton, predicted that the United States faced a declining population before the year 2000 (1). He relied on the established trend of declining fertility which accompanied increased urbanization, industrialization, and education. The very low levels of the birth rate in the 1930's were discounted to some extent as owing to the depression, and the rise thereafter to 1945, taken explicitly into account, was likewise discounted as a making-up of births postponed during the depression and as births from war-stimulated early marriages. The forecast was based on what were considered to be sound observations and sound theory at the time. By the time the report was published, the birth rate had jumped to 26.6. But even when it remained at moderately higher levels for the next several years, the usual explanation was that this was an understandable reaction to the low levels of the 1930's and the increased prosperity after World War II. It was only after higher levels were maintained into the decade of the 1950's that serious and widespread doubts arose as to the soundness of the theories on which the forecast had been based.

A detached appraisal of this erroneous, if not embarrassing, prediction is that the general theory on which it was based was essentially correct—that is, that the kind of industrial, urban society that we have in the West has led and will probably lead to a reduction of fertility. The general theory and the observations on which it was based, however, were inadequate to predict the level to which fertility will decline or the level at which it will remain. For predictive purposes, knowledge of a variety of other developments (for example, the level of economic activity and the ways in which conditions may reflect themselves in the rate of family formation, marriage, the timing of births, and so forth) also requiring predictions are needed. The difference between a birth rate of 18 or 19 and a birth rate of 24 to 25 over a period of years has enormous demographic consequences. Thus it made the difference between a predicted population of about 170,000,000 in 1975 and what will now actually be about 215,000,000 and a predicted population of less than 175,000,000 by the year 2000 and one now estimated by the Bureau of the Census "projections" of between 266,000,000 and 321,000,000.

The upshot of the demographic discomfiture over these forecasts was the pursuit of two lines of inquiry. Demographers began to examine cohort fertility and orders of birth. Analysis of cohort fertility examines the pattern of fertility among cohorts of women (women born in the same calendar year) both with respect to the total number of births and the order of births. Such analysis can show whether changes in marriage patterns over time result from women in two different cohorts bearing children of given orders virtually at the same time, so that the doubling up leads to an abnormally high birth rate without any change in average family size. It can also show whether the pattern of birth orders suggests that fluctuations in the birth rate are caused by ex-

* Chief of Behavioral Sciences Branch, Center of Population Research, National Institute of Child Health and Human Development.

† Births 1909 to 1959 corrected for undernumeration. Births 1959 to 1968 are registered births only.
‡ Births per 1,000 population.
§ Births per 1,000 women 15 to 49 years of age.
‖ Sum of age-specific fertility rates for women 15 to 49 years of age. This measure is equivalent to a measure of completed fertility per 1,000 women, assuming that a cohort of women throughout their childbearing period experience the age-specific fertility observed in that particular year.

Table 1. Live Births, Birth Rates, and Fertility Rates, 1909 to 1968*

Year	Live Births†	Birth Rate‡	Fertility Rate§	Total Fertility Rate‖
1909	2,718,000	30.0	126.8	—
1910	2,777,000	30.1	126.8	—
1911	2,809,000	29.9	126.3	—
1912	2,840,000	29.8	125.8	—
1913	2,869,000	29.5	124.7	—
1914	2,966,000	29.9	126.6	—
1915	2,965,000	29.5	125.0	—
1916	2,964,000	29.1	123.4	—
1917	2,944,000	28.5	121.0	3,332
1918	2,948,000	28.2	119.8	3,313
1919	2,740,000	26.1	111.2	3,078
1920	2,950,000	27.7	117.9	3,273
1921	3,055,000	28.1	119.8	3,349
1922	2,882,000	26.2	111.2	3,125
1923	2,910,000	26.0	110.5	3,116
1924	2,979,000	26.1	110.9	3,144
1925	2,909,000	25.1	106.6	3,027
1926	2,839,000	24.2	102.6	2,910
1927	2,802,000	23.5	99.8	2,826
1928	2,674,000	22.2	93.8	2,656
1929	2,582,000	21.2	89.3	2,524
1930	2,618,000	21.3	89.2	2,509
1931	2,506,000	20.2	84.6	2,376
1932	2,440,000	19.5	81.7	2,288
1933	2,307,000	18.4	76.3	2,149
1934	2,396,000	19.0	78.5	2,205
1935	2,377,000	18.7	77.2	2,163
1936	2,355,000	18.4	75.8	2,119
1937	2,413,000	18.7	77.1	2,147
1938	2,496,000	19.2	79.1	2,200
1939	2,466,000	18.8	77.6	2,154
1940	2,559,000	19.4	79.9	2,214
1941	2,703,000	20.3	83.4	2,314
1942	2,989,000	22.2	91.5	2,532
1943	3,104,000	22.7	94.3	2,616
1944	2,939,000	21.2	88.8	2,466
1945	2,858,000	20.4	85.9	2,392
1946	3,411,000	24.1	101.9	2,829
1947	3,817,000	26.6	113.3	3,158
1948	3,637,000	24.9	107.3	3,013
1949	3,649,000	24.5	107.1	3,030
1950	3,632,000	24.1	106.2	3,030
1951	3,823,000	24.9	111.5	3,209
1952	3,913,000	25.1	113.9	3,307
1953	3,965,000	25.1	115.2	3,378
1954	4,078,000	25.3	118.1	3,501
1955	4,104,000	25.0	118.5	3,521
1956	4,218,000	25.2	121.2	3,634
1957	4,308,000	25.3	122.9	3,724
1958	4,255,000	24.5	120.2	3,654
1959	4,295,000	24.3	120.2	3,669
1959†	4,244,796	24.0	118.8	3,669
1960	4,257,850	23.7	118.0	3,655
1961	4,268,326	23.3	117.2	3,620
1962	4,167,362	22.4	112.2	3,476
1963	4,098,020	21.7	108.5	3,331
1964	4,027,490	21.0	105.0	3,197
1965	3,763,358	19.4	96.6	2,922
1966	3,606,274	18.4	91.3	2,728
1967	3,520,959	17.8	87.6	2,562
1968	3,501,564	17.5	85.7	2,480

* Source: U.S. Department of Health, Education, and Welfare, National Center for Health Statistics, "Natality Statistics Analysis, United States, 1965-1967," Series 21, No. 19, Tables 1 and 2, Washington, U. S. Government Printing Office, 1970.

traordinarily large numbers of first- and second-order births, reflecting an undue concentration of new family formation, or to increases in family size reflected in higher-order births.

Such analysis has shown that high fertility rates in the United States from 1946 to 1963 were caused by a rise in both the size of completed families and a lowering in the age at which women bore their children. Thus, part of the high birth rate was caused by a rise in family size; part was caused by the fact that older cohorts of women, who had relatively low fertility before World War II, had children later in life, and younger cohorts had them earlier in life. Considering the entire period 1920 to 1965, then, changes in the size of family and the timing of births "reinforced each other" to produce a wider variation in the birth rate than would have resulted from changes in completed fertility alone (2).

Completed size of family cannot be known until the end of the childbearing period. Hence, analysis is always delayed. It has been reported, however, that women 35 to 39 years of age in 1969 are known to be the most fertile cohort of women born in the twentieth century (3). They already have 3,205 children per 1,000 women and may add another 100 before they reach age 45. Only 2.13 children per woman are necessary for replacement, and these women exceed this number by 50%. Women 30 to 34 years of age in 1969 had more children by age 25 to 29 than the cohort 5 years older, but by age 30 to 34 they had almost as many as the older group. Women 25 to 29 years old have already had 2,104 children per 1,000 women and will fall below the cohort 10 years older unless they increase their fertility in later years. An implication of these observations is that the current period of low fertility may be caused either by a reduction in family size, a tendency toward later childbearing, or both.

Analysis by marriage cohorts (women married in the same calendar year) has shown that the marriage cohorts of 1930 to 1934, depression years, although marrying at a slightly younger age than later cohorts, had the lowest average number ever of children born; whereas the cohort of 1955 to 1959 had more children in shorter intervals than any prior cohort dating back to 1900. The fertility of the latter, of course, is not completed. Analysis of marriage cohorts has also indicated that half the children in the average marriage are born in the first 5 years and roughly seven tenths by 10 years of marriage. The implication of this for projections is that "within a short time the bulk of the nation's births will come from women who are not now married and who may differ from those now married with respect both to the number of children they want and the timing of the births" (2).

Therefore, developments of the past few years, if extrapolated, may indicate a further decline in fertility. Three qualifications need to be made, however. First, young women reaching the childbearing ages in recent years have been caught in what has been referred to as the "marriage squeeze." This means that the increasing number of females born in 1943 to 1947 considerably outnumber males born a few years earlier, from among whom many select husbands. Second, preliminary figures for births of the period 1943 to 1969 will mean a rising proportion of women in the childbearing years, so that even reduced fertility rates may result in higher birth rates computed on the basis of total population. All these considerations suggest a rise in the birth rate in the next few years.

IDEAL, DESIRED, AND EXPECTED FAMILY SIZE

Another approach to the problem of understanding fertility behavior and improving population projections is the effort to measure fertility intentions of American women. Major studies so far carried out have contributed considerable information about attitudes of women toward contraception and changes that have taken place in various subgroups of the population. In the Growth of American Family (4) studies only married women were interviewed. Thus, women who will marry at later ages and may therefore expect lower fertility are omitted.

Wives interviewed in the three studies show a preference for a completed family size of more than three children. In 1960 ideal family size of all women was 3.4, size wanted at the time of interview was 3.3, and the most likely expected number was 3.1. Comparisons made in 1965 of data from the three studies indicated that wives of the same age at time of interview in 1965 expected to bear more children than those interviewed at that age in 1960 or 1955, but the differences were not large.

So far the studies have allowed reasonably good projections of fertility in the succeeding 5-year period, although Westoff and Ryder (4), the investigators in the 1965 National Fertility Survey, have concluded that they were right for the wrong reasons. They are right primarily in predicting total cohort fertility be-

cause most of the fertility has already occurred. I ut Westoff and Ryder (4) note substantial intracoh -t changes in expectations, which are not always in t e same direction. These changes may become more su - stantial if the socioeconomic situation in the nati n changes radically in one direction or another.

The studies confirm higher fertility of Catholics < s compared with Protestants and show a decline i 1 Protestant fertility, with increasing education, an 1 some slight decrease in fertility expectations as family income rises, whereas Catholic fertility tends to show a U-shaped distribution. Interestingly, Protestant fertility shows little decline as husband's income rises, so apparently it is the lower fertility of working wives that makes the association with family income.

Rural wives expect larger families than urban wives, but the differences are small. The fertility expectations of nonwhites are higher than those of whites, but the number of children nonwhite wives wanted, when compared with matched whites by region of residence, farm and nonfarm residence, and education, was lower than for whites.

As expected, the use of contraceptives is lower among Catholics than among Protestants and lower among nonwhites than among whites. But Westoff and Ryder report an increasing acceptance of contraceptive use among all groups and an increasing approval and use of contraceptive practice among younger women as compared with older women. By 1965, 84% of married white women 18 to 39 years of age reported having used some form of contraception, and, if subfecund women are excluded, 97% either have used or expect to use some form. This figure does, however, include the rhythm method.

Westoff and Ryder (4) summarize:

> The major findings in connection with changes in attitudes since 1960 are: 1) American women have become increasingly favorable toward the principle of fertility control; 2) the greatest change has occurred among Catholic women, many of whom have moved away from exclusive endorsement of the rhythm method; 3) this change in Catholic attitude has been especially marked among the better educated Catholic women; and 4) the gap between white and non-white attitudes has narrowed considerably by 1965 because of the rapid change in non-white attitudes, due in part to increasing education.

With respect to use, which parallels to some extent the change in attitudes, Westoff and Ryder noted especially that "due to a substantial increase in use among non-white women, especially young women in the South, the white-non-white differences in proportions using contraception will probably disappear in the near future."

The studies have also made a signal contribution in showing that, although for all women ideal family size is actually higher than they have or expect to have, there are still many women who have more children than they say they want and who, because of religious and other restraints, practice relatively ineffective methods of contraception. This underlies the Westoff-Ryder claim that if more effective and acceptable contraception were available to eliminate unwanted childbearing, the problem of population growth in the United States would virtually be solved.

These studies were addressed primarily to intermediate variables and left certain relationships unexplored. The basic question of what it is in the social-cultural-economic milieu that actually influences family planning ideals and affects the timing of desired births has not been investigated. And beyond that, how are these conditions likely to change? Until we can answer these questions we will not be able to predict with assurance; but even more important, we will not know how to influence the course of fertility if it ever becomes the national consensus that it is desirable to do so.

In addition, the analyses do not provide us with entirely satisfactory mechanisms for assessing individual factors. Two examples may be cited. First, it has been claimed that introduction of "the pill" in 1960 made some contribution to the decline in fertility after that. Insofar as it is a more effective contraceptive, it has undoubtedly contributed to the control of fertility among those women using it. As long as it can be viewed as a substitute for other methods that could have been used, however, it is extremely difficult to assess just what the fertility would have been had it not been for "the pill" or the intrauterine device (IUD). The ghost of the decline of fertility up to 1933 haunts the picture. A second major problem is in assessing the contribution of family planning programs. The problem is not only to assess the extent to which women will substitute the facilities available to them under a family planning program for other means but also to assess the context in which effective family planning programs operate. Each analysis, therefore, can answer only a limited number of questions that can refine our understanding of processes involved in increases or decreases in the birth rate and illuminate the probable short-run trends in fertility to aid in prediction of what may happen over the next 5 years but that leave quite unanswered the fundamental question of why people have certain family size ideals and whether social factors can be altered to influence levels of fertility.

Effects of Estrogens on Renin Substrate, Angiotensin, and Other Plasma Proteins

Dr. Kevin Catt*: Many of the striking metabolic effects of oral contraceptive preparations are caused by a primary action on the liver, which acts as an extremely sensitive target tissue for sex hormones (5). In addition to alterations of carbohydrate and lipid metabolism, numerous changes in proteins synthesized by the liver have been observed during estrogen treatment and pregnancy (6). Similar changes occur in women taking oral contraceptive preparations that contain estrogen, leading to a characteristic spectrum of changes in plasma proteins (Table 2).

Many of the estrogen-stimulated plasma proteins are transport or binding proteins concerned with the circulation of smaller molecules such as steroids, thyroid hormones, and metals. Corticoid-binding globulin (CBG) and thyroxine-binding globulin (TBG) are markedly increased by estrogen treatment, causing elevation of the total plasma cortisol and protein-bound iodine (PBI) beyond the normal range. The free levels of these hormones in plasma, however, are not increased, the urinary excretion of cortisol metabolites being in fact slightly reduced. In contrast, the excretion of aldosterone is frequently increased by estrogen therapy, reflecting a true rise in aldosterone secretion rate from the adrenal gland. The high level of TBG during estrogen therapy and pregnancy can give a false impression of hyperthyroidism by raising the PBI or of hypothyroidism by reducing the tri-iodothyronine (T_3) resin uptake. The product of these two values, the "free thyroxine index," remains normal during estrogen treatment, in

* Visiting Scientist, Reproduction Research Branch, National Institute of Child Health and Human Development.

Table 2. Effects of Estrogen-Progestagen Oral Contraceptive Therapy on Serum Proteins

Protein	Effect of Oral Contraceptives
Albumin	±
Prealbumin	+
Immunoglobulins	+
Alpha$_2$-macroglobulin	+
Antitrypsin, alpha$_1$	+ +
Orosomucoid	−
Haptoglobin	−
Transferrin	+
Ceruloplasmin	+ + +
Thyroxine-binding globulin	+ +
Cortisol-binding globulin	+ +
Testosterone-estradiol-binding globulin	+ +
Plasminogen	+ +
Fibrinogen	+
Renin substrate	+ + +
Renin	−

keeping with the normal levels of free thyroxine observed in women during oral contraceptive therapy.

There is also a marked rise in the circulating testosterone-estrogen-binding globulin (TeBG) during oral contraceptive therapy and pregnancy, with substantial increases in the plasma binding capacity for both estradiol and testosterone. During pregnancy this protein is appropriately saturated with estrogen arising in the fetoplacental unit, with plasma estradiol levels up to 20 ng/ml, about 500 times normal.

During oral contraceptive therapy there is also a marked increase in the plasma level of TeBG, but in this case the binding protein is not saturated with steroid. The synthetic estrogens used in combined oral contraceptive preparations have low affinity for TeBG, and the endogenous estradiol production is suppressed to extremely low levels because of the inhibition of follicular development by the administered steroids. Other binding proteins such as ceruloplasmin and transferrin are also increased by estrogen and by a group of plasma proteins that act as precursors of more active compounds by behaving as substrates for appropriate enzyme systems. They include plasminogen, fibrinogen, and angiotensinogen, also known as renin substrate. Oral contraceptive therapy has also been found to elevate plasma levels of IgG, alpha$_2$-macroglobulin, and alpha$_1$-trypsin inhibitor and to decrease haptoglobin and orosomucoid (7).

RENIN-ANGIOTENSIN SYSTEM

The change in renin substrate during estrogen treatment is of particular interest because it leads to activation of the renin-angiotensin system and in rare cases is accompanied by severe hypertension. The physiological functions of the renin-angiotensin system are still unclear despite intensive study of its relationship to the regulation of blood pressure and sodium metabolism. There is good evidence that renin secretion is responsive to changes in sodium balance and intravascular volume and that aldosterone secretion is influenced by angiotensin, although to various degrees in different species. The classical view of the renin-angiotensin system is summarized in Figure 1. Renin secreted by the juxtaglomerular cells acts on circulating renin substrate to form the decapeptide angiotensin I, which is rapidly cleaved into a C-terminal dipeptide (histidyl-leucine) and the octapeptide angiotensin II, which is a highly active pressor substance. This conversion of angiotensin I to angiotensin II occurs predominantly in the lung, which, in effect, secretes angiotensin II into the arterial circulation. The octapeptide has the capacity to contract smooth muscle and to stimulate aldosterone secretion by the glomerulosa layer of the adrenal cortex; it also directly suppresses the release of renin by the kidney. Metabolism of angiotensin II occurs rapidly in the tissue vascular bed, which inactivates 80 to 90% of the plasma angiotensin in a single circulation. The half-life of angiotensin II in arterial blood is about 1 min, and the metabolic clearance rate approximates the cardiac output.

It was formerly believed that renin secretion was the major factor determining blood angiotensin levels and that renin substrate was always present in excess. If this were so, the elevation of renin substrate during oral contraceptive therapy would be of little biological significance. The importance of renin substrate, however, in determining the overall activity of the system has been clearly demonstrated, and there is no doubt that elevations of renin substrate can lead to increased activity of the renin-angiotensin system (8).

Until recently the methods used to study the renin-angiotensin system have relied on the bioassay of angiotensin generated during incubation of plasma

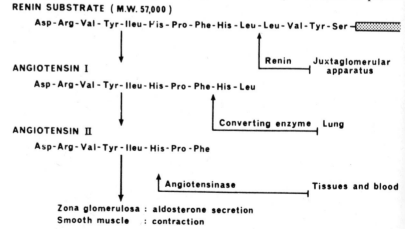

Figure 1. The renin-angiotensin system.

432

s, mples in vitro under various conditions that reflect the activity of the entire system or the individual activities of the components (9). The standard technique has employed the pressor response of the ganglion-blocked rat to infused angiotensin. The commonly measured variables are as follows:

1. Plasma renin activity (PRA): angiotensin generated during incubation of a plasma sample, which represents the result of the interaction between endogenous renin and endogenous substrate.

2. Plasma renin concentration (PRC): angiotensin generated during incubation of a plasma sample with added excess renin substrate (commonly, renin-free plasma). The PRC reflects the rate of renin secretion from the kidney and affects angiotensin formation in vivo to an extent determined by the prevailing level of renin substrate.

3. Plasma renin substrate: angiotensin generated by incubation of a plasma sample with added excess renin, as a semipurified renal extract from the same species. It is now known that variations in renin substrate can cause changes in PRA, blood angiotensin, and PRC.

4. More recently, measurement of blood angiotensin II levels has been achieved by the use of sensitive and specific radioimmunoassays that use antibodies to angiotensin II (10-13).

Previously, measurement of the extremely low circulating levels of angiotensin II in blood had been extremely difficult to perform because the sensitivity and specificity of the rat pressor assay were barely adequate for the purpose. Radioimmunoassays for blood angiotensin II are of adequate sensitivity to measure angiotensin blood levels under normal and abnormal conditions (Table 3). Similar radioimmunoassays have also been developed for angiotensin I and are replacing the rat bioassay for measurement of angiotensin I generated during assays for renin activity, concentration, and substrate (14, 15).

The first indication that oral contraception could activate the renin-angiotensin system was provided in 1966 by Crane and co-workers (16), who observed that PRA was elevated, both under basal conditions and in response to sodium restriction and upright posture, in a patient taking oral contraceptive therapy. Since that time further studies have shown that elevation of plasma renin activity and aldosterone excretion can result from oral contraceptive therapy, analogous to the changes that occur during pregnancy (17). A detailed study by Skinner, Lumbers, and Symonds (9) confirmed that renin substrate was more important than PRC as a determinant of PRA during oral contraceptive therapy because PRC is suppressed during such treatment, whereas PRA and renin substrate are elevated about twofold. Similar studies in both rats (18) and humans have confirmed these findings, showing elevation of renin substrate and activity after estrogen treatment and decrease of plasma renin concentration.

HYPERTENSION

Since 1967 several reports of severe reversible hypertension in women taking oral contraceptives have appeared (17, 19-21), and the aggravation of existing hypertension has become recognized as a possible side effect of estrogen-containing contraceptive preparations. In such patients the values for PRA, renin substrate, and aldosterone excretion are usually not more elevated than those of normotensive women on oral contraceptive therapy, so that excessive renin substrate formation is not responsible for the hypertension of susceptible individuals. Our recent observation that blood angiotensin II levels are markedly elevated during oral contraceptive therapy provides an apparent paradox in that most estrogen-treated women do not develop hypertension despite blood angiotensin II levels that are equivalent to those present in severe essential and renal hypertension and in excess of those known to elevate the blood pressure during infusion of angiotensin II.

When blood angiotensin II levels were measured before and during a single cycle of contraceptive therapy (Ovulen®, 1 mg), a marked rise in blood angiotensin II occurred within 5 days of the commencement of treatment and persisted during therapy, even for up to 3 months, and then returned to normal after cessation of treatment. Equally rapid elevations of PRA have been shown to occur during estrogen treatment in the human (17) and in the rat (18). In a study with Drs. M. D. Cain and W. A. W. Walters, measurements of renin substrate, PRA, PRC, and blood angiotensin II during oral contraceptive therapy showed marked activation of the renin angiotensin system, with simultaneous suppression of renin secretion and elevation of plasma renin substrate, renin activity, and angiotensin II (Table 4). It has been suggested that susceptible women fail to sup-

Table 3. Blood Angiotensin II Levels in Human Beings (Mean ± SD)

Individuals (Number)	Blood Angiotensin II
	ng/100 ml
Normal males and females (124)	1.9 ± 1.2
Females on oral contraceptive therapy (44)	8.6 ± 2.8
Renal hypertension (12)	15.4 ± 9.3
Malignant hypertension (7)	13.9 ± 7.4

Table 4. Effect of Single Cycle of Oral Contraceptive Therapy on the Renin-Angiotensin System in 17 Recumbent Normal Women (Mean ± SD)*

Measurement	Control	Oral Contraceptive
Angiotensin II, *ng/100 ml*	2.7 ± 0.9	8.2 ± 2.2
Renin activity, *ng/ml per hr*	1.6 ± 0.3	5.9 ± 1.6
Renin substrate, *μg/ml*	2.0 ± 0.5	5.7 ± 2.4
Renin concentration, *ng/ml per hr*	8.8 ± 1.9	4.7 ± 1.5

* From Cain, Catt, and Walters, unpublished data.

press their renin secretion during oral contraceptive therapy, leading to uncontrolled rise of PRA and blood angiotensin II (9). Women who develop hypertension during oral contraceptive therapy, however, do not show excessive rises of PRA (21), and an alternative explanation for their hypertension must be sought.

Careful hemodynamic studies (22) have shown that combined oral contraceptive therapy increases cardiac output and stroke volume, with a small but significant increase in mean arterial pressure. The reason for the occasional development of hypertension during oral contraceptive therapy may lie in abnormal metabolism of angiotensin II or in altered sensitivity to the pressor effects of the peptide, in combination with the effect on cardiac output. Estradiol and progesterone do not affect the pressor action of angiotensin and are therefore unlikely to cause diminished responsiveness during oral contraceptive therapy.

The possibility of altered metabolism should be seriously considered because recent studies have shown the presence of immunoreactive angiotensin metabolites in venous blood of normal individuals, reflecting the metabolism of angiotensin II by peripheral tissues. The high levels of angiotensin II in venous blood of patients taking oral contraceptives have not yet been evaluated by bioassay but can be assumed to reflect high arterial angiotensin concentrations because arterial and venous levels of the peptide correlate well over a wide range in normal and hypertensive individuals (23).

Therefore, the production rate of angiotensin II is probably abnormally high in women taking oral contraceptive preparations, yet the circulating peptide seems to be unable to exert more than a minimal pressor effect.

The small mean rise of arterial blood pressure which occurs in women during oral contraceptive therapy may be a highly significant indication of a compensated pressor effect of angiotensin II. Such a compensation could occur by at least two mechanisms, either of which could be defective in the wo-

men who develop hypertension as a result of estrogen therapy.

First, the peripheral metabolism of inactivation of angiotensin II may increase to prevent a substantial constrictive effect on vascular smooth muscle. Women with impaired peripheral inactivation of angiotensin II could therefore show an inappropriate pressor response caused by the unhindered action of the peptide on vascular smooth muscle. Interestingly, the heptapeptide fragment of angiotensin II retains the ability to stimulate aldosterone secretion by the adrenals (24), even though it has greatly reduced pressor activity. The formation of such fragments in vivo would provide a mechanism for expressing the sodium-retaining activity of the renin-angiotensin system while minimizing its pressor effects and could contribute to the minor elevation of aldosterone secretion which occurs during estrogen therapy.

Second, the vasoconstrictive effect of increased angiotensin II secretion may be rapidly and largely compensated by renal adjustment of fluid output as described by Guyton and colleagues (25), and persistent hypertension may occur only in those women with an underlying renal lesion that impairs the normal pressure-induced diuresis and compensation to vasoconstrictive agents. This could explain the differential effects of high blood angiotensin II levels in women taking oral contraceptives and in patients with renal disease. The presence of renal disease could itself be a major factor in determining the sustained pressor response to a prevailing high level of angiotensin II because renal adjustment to the initial pressor effects of the peptide cannot take place, whereas normal women show renal compensation that almost completely nullifies the pressor effect of angiotensin II.

The demonstration that oral contraceptive therapy increases cardiac output is an additional important factor that favors the development of hypertension. The occurrence of increased cardiac output together with increased blood angiotensin II levels provides a potential pressor situation that could readily be expressed as hypertension in the presence of subtle abnormalities of renal compensation or angiotensin II metabolism.

Oral Contraceptives and Thromboembolic Disorders: Epidemiologic Studies

Dr. Daniel G. Seigel*: Three types of studies are represented in the data that I shall present: a case-control study in which most of the more definitive epidemiologic research has been conducted; an analy-

* Acting Chief, Biostatistics Section, Epidemiology and Biometry Branch, National Institute of Child Health and Human Development.

of trends in mortality, a useful supplementary source of information; and an analysis of adverse reactions, such as the analysis reported to the Committee on Safety of Drugs in England, which was important for the impact that it has had on medical care both in England and in this country (26).

CASE-CONTROL STUDIES

This method consists of obtaining samples from women who have experienced thromboembolic disorders; these are called the cases. Comparable samples are also obtained of controls, women who are similar to those in the cases but who have not experienced thromboembolic disorders. Information is then obtained from both groups about the use of oral contraceptives. The proportion of case women who have used oral contraceptives is then compared with the proportion of control women who have used oral contraceptives. The reasoning is that if the former proportion is greater, there is an increased risk of thromboembolic disorders for women using the oral contraceptive. This technique does not permit estimation of the probability that a women who uses the oral contraceptive develops thromboembolism. It does permit estimation of the ratio of risks of such disorders in women who use this drug as compared with women who do not. This ratio is referred to as the relative risk.

Inman and Vessey (27) reported in 1968 on 120 deaths caused by thromboembolic disorders in Great Britain (Table 5). The first line of this table presents the results for deaths from pulmonary embolism. There were 26 such women; 16 were oral contraceptive users, 10 were not. The numbers in brackets, [4.2] and [21.8], are the expected numbers in these two categories if their relative risk was one. The number of women using oral contraceptives who died was greater than what was expected. Excesses occurred for coronary thrombosis and cerebral thrombosis as well, and for the total sample the number of user deaths observed (39) was more than twice than expected [17.1]. Vessey and Doll (28) presented similar data for hospital admission patients with thromboembolic disorders (Table 5). There were 120 such cases, most with venous thromboembolism. Both for the total group and for venous thromboembolism there is a considerable discrepancy between the observed and the expected number for oral contraceptive users. Sartwell and associates (29) presented the first American study of this type on 175 cases of thromboembolic disorder patients admitted to hospital; 67 of these women had been oral contraceptive users. Most recently Vessey and co-workers (30) reported the results of a study of thromboembolism after surgery. In 30 such cases 12 women had been oral contraceptive users as compared with an expected number of 4.5. These studies may be summarized as follows: Women taking oral contraceptives have a fourfold to eightfold greater risk of dying from a thromboembolic disorder than women not receiving these agents.

TRENDS IN MORTALITY

Table 6 presents the observed numbers of deaths in the United States for the years 1962 to 1966 from causes in categories 460 to 468 of the International Classification of Diseases (ICD), which includes thrombophlebitis, pulmonary embolism, and in-

Table 5. Summary of Data Obtained in Case-Control Studies*

Source	Pathology	Total Users	Nonusers	Total
Inman and Vessey, 1968 (27)	Pulmonary embolism	16 [4.2]	10 [21.8]	26
(deaths)	Coronary thrombosis	18 [11.4]	66 [72.6]	84
	Cerebral thrombosis	5 [1.5]	5 [8.5]	10
	Total	39 [17.1]	81 [102.9]	120
Vessey and Doll, 1969 (28)	Venous thromboembolism	42 [11.5]	42 [72.5]	84
(hospital admissions)	Coronary thrombosis	2 [2.1]	15 [14.9]	17
	Cerebral thrombosis	11 [3.5]	8 [15.5]	19
	Total	55 [17.1]	95 [102.9]	120
Sartwell et al, 1969 (29)	Thrombophlebitis, lower extremity, superficial	6 [2]	21 [25]	27
	Thrombophlebitis, lower extremity, deep	26 [9]	55 [72]	81
	Thrombophlebitis, other	6 [1]	5 [10]	11
	Thrombophlebitis and pulmonary embolism	7 [6]	12 [13]	19
	Pulmonary embolism alone	14 [3]	4 [15]	18
	Retinal vascular or intracranial lesion	8 [2]	11 [17]	19
	Total	67 [23]	108 [152]	175
Vessey et al, 1970 (30) (postoperative patients)	Deep vein thrombosis or pulmonary embolism	12 [4.5]	18 [25.5]	30

* Numbers in brackets are expected numbers.

Table 6. Expected and Observed Deaths, by Year, for Combined Ages 20 to 44 from Diseases of Veins, Including Thrombophlebitis, Pulmonary Embolism, and Infarction

	1962	1963	1964	1965	1966
Observed deaths	389	422	492	565	669
"Expected" deaths*	323	342	371	385	401
"Excess" deaths	66	80	121	180	268

* "Expected" deaths estimated in Seigel (31).

farction. The expected number of deaths computed on the basis of experience with women in the years before 1962 and from the experience with men in the years 1962 to 1966 is shown (31). There is a sizeable discrepancy in the expected and the observed number of deaths, the excess deaths in 1966 amounting to about 40% of those observed. Vessey and Weatherall (32), in an analysis of British mortality experience, found a similar unexpected rise in the thromboembolic deaths during the years that the oral contraceptive came into use. From these data we estimate a ninefold relative risk of death for women during the years of oral contraceptive use. This is the same order of magnitude as that yielded by the case-control studies. About half of the deaths in the ICD 460 to 468 categories were from pulmonary embolism and infarction, the rest from phlebitis, thrombophlebitis, and other venous embolism and thrombosis. Although the analysis of such mortality trends is heir to all the problems resulting from the questionable validity of death certificate data, such analyses play a useful and supportive role and are clearly justified in light of the large number of users and the very large relative risks reported by the case-control studies.

ADVERSE REACTION REPORTS

Inman and associates (33) correlated adverse reactions after use of oral contraceptives in England with type and dose of estrogen. Their data are summarized in Table 7. Seven hundred and eighty such reports were submitted for venous thromboembolism; 58 of these reactions were with the use of mestranol at 150 µg, 333 with mestranol at 100 µg, and so forth. From knowledge of sales the expected distribution of the 780 reactions was determined; 31.1 would have been expected to occur with the mestranol at 150, for example. The mestranol 150-µg dose then occurs in excess of that expected, the ratio of observed to expected being 1.83. For all venous thromboembolism there is a trend in the ratio of observed to expected, the lowest ratio noted with the lowest levels of estrogen. This is true for mestranol and for ethinyl estradiol. This trend can be found throughout the table, with the exception of other venous thrombosis of the lower limb. For the very serious category, fatal pulmonary embolism, it is especially striking, although the numbers are rather small in several categories. It should be emphasized that ratios of observed to expected less than one do not imply a protective effect for that regimen, only that toxicity is lower than that at other levels. Indeed, using the data from this table alone, no comparisons are possible with risks in the absence of oral contraceptive usage. The results of Table 7 should not be too surprising. It would be remarkable if the effects demonstrated in the case-control studies were not dose dependent.

The relative risk of contraceptives with high amounts of estrogens versus those with lower estrogen content can be computed from Table 7. For fatal pulmonary embolism the relative risk is approximately three (combining mestranol and ethinyl estradiol and defining "high dose" either as 100 or greater or 75 or greater). The relative risk for all

Table 7. Observed and Expected Reactions in Relation to Type and Dose of Estrogen in Combined Oral Contraceptives*

	Estrogen						Total
	Mestranol				Ethinyl Estradiol		
	150 µg	100 µg	75-80 µg	50 µg	100 µg	50 µg	
All venous thromboembolism†							
Observed (O)	58	333	80	22	21	266	780
Expected (E)	31-71	281-90	85-76	19-42	11-1	350-20	780-00
Ratio (O/E)	1-83	1-18	0-93	1-13	1-91	0-76	
Cerebral thrombosis							
Observed (O)	10	33	6	1	0	29	79
Expected (E)	3-12	28-32	9-10	1-98	1-9	35-39	79-00
Ratio (O/E)	3-21	1-17	0-66	0-51	—	0-82	
Coronary thrombosis							
Observed (O)	6	26	2	2	2	23	61
Expected (E)	2-32	21-62	7-12	1-78	1-11	27-5	61-0
Ratio (O/E)	2-59	1-20	0-28	1-12	1-80	0-85	

* From Inman et al, (33).
† O = observed; E = expected.

v nous thromboembolism is approximately one and a half, comparing high- and low-dose estrogens.

Remember that these data moved the British authorities (26) and subsequently the American authorities to recommend use of steroid contraceptives at low levels of estrogen where possible. Given the data in this table and the previous results from the case-control studies, we can estimate the level of relative risk for the low-dose estrogens alone as compared with use of alternate forms of contraception. For all venous thromboembolism the relative risk would be approximately five; for fatal pulmonary embolism the relative risk would be approximately four. That is to say, if the British were to repeat their studies today, they would probably see these new levels of relative risk rather than that seen in their original studies (six for all venous thromboembolism and eight for fatal pulmonary embolism). It is difficult to make similar estimates for the United States because the relative risk in the study by Sartwell (29) was somewhat lower, and no data such as that presented in Table 3 have been published.

DISCUSSION

There is no doubt but that serious questions can be raised about the merits of each study. Indeed, such questions have been raised. The most serious and the most persistent has been the question of whether women using oral contraceptives are having their morbidity diagnosed more frequently than women who do not use oral contraceptives. This could arise for a variety of reasons: the patient's awareness of the potential hazards of oral contraceptives, which have been so widely discussed in the lay literature; the greater surveillance that they may receive from their physicians, and the higher level of suspicion in their physicians, who may be more inclined to hospitalize and to look for thromboembolic events as an explanation for symptoms. There is certainly very little information available on this area of medical care and the extent to which it affects the epidemiologic studies. The consensus at this time, however, is that a considerably increased risk has been demonstrated and that biases of the type described are not likely to be sufficient to entirely explain the array of data presented here. Further, it should be remembered that these epidemiologic findings do not require bizarre hypotheses from a biomedical point of view. Alterations in physiologic mechanisms that are related to clotting have been extensively studied. A recent review by Dugdale and Masi (34) concluded that the literature indicated that platelet numbers increased, coagulation accelerated, level of activity of coagulation factors increased, and fibri-

nolysis increased. They were unable, though, to provide a theory to explain easily the clinical and epidemiologic observations. They suggest that "the answer may well be elsewhere, for example, in changes in the endothelium and vessel wall and in slowing of blood flow." Clearly, there is more work to be done that would help us to understand the mechanism of these changes and to further define the characteristics of women who experience these adverse reactions.

A review of this type would be incomplete without some discussion of the way in which these risks compare with those to which women who do not use the oral contraceptives are exposed. Tietze (35) has provided an analysis of the risk of death for women who use oral contraceptives that helps to provide perspective to the findings of these studies. He points out that use of oral contraception leads to very few births and a rate of excess deaths associated with contraception of approximately 3 per 100,000 women. Under a regimen of moderately effective contraception, such as the diaphragm, there would be a risk of maternal mortality introduced as the result of unplanned births amounting to 2.5 per 100,000. The added risk associated with oral contraceptive use for this disease entity, 0.5 per 100,000, is really rather small. It presumably has been decreased, moreover, with the trend toward use of low estrogen formulations.

It must be remembered, however, that the risks we are discussing are those from thromboembolism. The real concern at present is directed toward the implications of the alterations that have been seen for carbohydrate and lipid metabolism and the hypothetical hazards of carcinoma, and we must look to extension of these kinds of studies into new diagnostic areas.

Other Approaches to Contraception

Dr. Mortimer B. Lipsett: The complexity of the processes of maturation of sperm and ovum, gamete transport, fertilization, and nidation implies the existence of many critical junctions at which appropriate interference would prevent completion of the process. Some of these are of interest to endocrinology and internal medicine and seem to have more immediate promise than others.

The process of spermatogenesis in man is a complex process taking about 74 days for the progression from primary spermatogonium to mature sperm (36). A striking feature of this process is the 30 days required for the meiotic prophase and meiosis. Since meiosis occurs only in the germ cell, here is a unique series of events shared by none of the somatic cells. This distinguishing characteristic of the germ cell must constitute a vulnerable site for interference. Unfortunately, the events of meiosis are understood at a descriptive level only, and the basic biologic phenomenon has escaped intensive effort.

Many cancer chemotherapeutic agents have been noted to depress spermatogenesis (37). This is not surprising since the germ cells are radiation-sensitive. It is just these characteristics that have been exploited in the design of agents for cancer chemotherapy. The alkylating agents arrest spermatogonial division so that sterility ensues several weeks later after completion of the subsequent stages of spermatogenesis (37). Other toxic chemicals have been described that affect meiosis, but none of these exclusively stop meiosis and are without systemic effect. The development of agents with selective toxicity lies ahead, but one may view this with at least as much optimism as the hope of designing selective chemotherapy for cancer.

The separate control mechanisms for spermatogenesis and testosterone synthesis offer possibilities for the suppression of spermatogenesis without affecting androgen synthesis. There are several data suggesting that follicle-stimulating hormone (FSH) and luteinizing hormone (LH) may be, at least in part, under different regulatory influences. Castration of the male rat differentially affects pituitary FSH and LH content (38). Testosterone will consistently lower plasma LH levels in man but has much less effect on plasma FSH (39). If FSH secretion is regulated by a substance other than androgen, its nature and source remain unknown. This important topic in endocrinology gains increased significance when considered as a potential area for male contraception. It is, of course, true that *large* doses of exogenous androgens can suppress spermatogenesis by depressing FSH secretion. Those agents, however, alter hepatic function tests, and the depression of spermatogenesis is not complete.

The corpus luteum and progesterone remain the focus of many investigations in reproductive biology. Control of corpus luteum life-span in man is in the process of definition, but continued low secretion of LH is probably necessary for a full 14 days of luteal function (40). The secretion of progesterone during this time prepares the endometrium for implantation and maintains the endometrium throughout pregnancy. If it were possible to interrupt progesterone secretion for periods of a few days, endometrial shedding would occur.

The search for a luteolytic factor received its impetus from the finding that hysterectomy in certain animals prolonged the life-span of the corpus luteum (41). The uterus, however, apparently does not have a regulatory function for corpus luteum life-span in man (42). Whether the constant low level of LH secretion is dependent on hypothalamic releasing factors is not certain. When the LH-releasing factor is identified, there is a real possibility that antagonists can be synthesized that will interrupt LH secretion and thereby interrupt corpus luteum function.

If fertilization occurs, however, the zygote implants 9 to 10 days later, and trophoblastic cells secrete human chorionic gonadotrophin, which maintains luteal progesterone secretion at a high level for 6 to 8 weeks (43). At this point the control of progesterone secretion has passed to the fetus, and the maternal pituitary secretions are no longer significant.

A variety of chemical agents have been found that interrupt steroid synthesis in the adrenal cortex (44). Systematic attempts to prevent progesterone synthesis in the corpus luteum have not been published. Our attempts to use aminoglutethimide, an inhibitor of adrenal steroid synthesis, have not been successful in humans or in the monkey. An alternative to the inhibition of progesterone synthesis is the development of antagonists to progesterone at the effector site. Pincus (45) tested almost 200 steroids for their capacity to inhibit progesterone effect in one standard bioassay, and results favorable for antiprogestational activity were obtained. These studies should be pursued because the availability of such compounds would offer a relatively simple way of inducing menstruation in the woman with a secretory endometrium.

These areas of research represent but a small sample of those frontiers of reproductive biology that should be examined intensively because of their intrinsic scientific interest as well as their potential importance in family planning. Thus, understanding the process of maturation of the sperm in the male genital ducts, the influence of cervical secretions on sperm mobility and fertilizing capacity, and the control of Fallopian tube mobility are critical for human biology. The impetus provided by public awareness of population problems and family planning has spurred research in these segments of reproductive biology.

ACKNOWLEDGMENTS: Received 23 November 1970; accepted 24 November 1970.

► Requests for reprints should be addressed to Mortimer B. Lipsett, M.D., F.A.C.P., Associate Scientific Director (RB), Intramural Research, National Institute of Child Health and Human Development, Bldg. 10, Room 12-N-204, National Institutes of Health, Bethesda, Md. 20014

438

Ref rences

1. WHELPTON PK: *Forecasts of the Population of the United tates, 1945-1975*, U.S. Bureau of the Census. Washington, D.C. Government Printing Office, 1947
2. KISER CV, GRABILL WH, CAMPBELL AA: *Trends and Variaions in Fertility in the United States.* Cambridge, Harvard University Press, 1968, p. 283
3. U.S. DEPARTMENT OF COMMERCE, BUREAU OF THE CENSUS: *Changes in the Average Number of Children Ever Born to Women: 1960 to November 1969*, Current Population Reports, Series P-20, No. 203. Washington D.C., Government Printing Office, 6 July 1970
4. WESTOFF CF, RYDER WB: Recent trends in attitudes toward fertility control and in the practice of contraception in the United States, in *Fertility and Family Planning*, edited by BEHRMAN SJ, CORSA L JR, FREEDMAN R. Ann Arbor, University of Michigan Press, 1967, pp. 388-412
5. SONG CS, KAPPAS A: The influence of estrogens, progestins and pregnancy on the liver. *Vitamins Hormones (NY)* 26: 147-195, 1968
6. SEAL US, DOE RP: Effects of gonadal and contraceptive hormones on protein and amino acid metabolism, in *Metabolic Effects of Gonadal Hormones and Oral Contraceptives*, edited by SALHANICK HA, KIPNIS DM, VANDE WIELE RL. New York, Plenum Press, 1968, pp. 277-318
7. LAURELL CB, KULLANDER S, THORELL J: Effect of administration of a combined estrogen-progestin contraceptive on the level of individual plasma proteins. *Scand J Clin Lab Invest* 21:337-343, 1968
8. HELMER OM, JUDSON WE: Influence of high renin substrate levels on renin-angiotensin system in pregnancy. *Amer J Obstet Gynec* 99:9-17, 1967
9. SKINNER SL, LUMBERS ER, SYMONDS EM: Alteration by oral contraceptives of normal menstrual changes in plasma renin activity, concentration and substrate. *Clin Sci* 36:67-76, 1969
10. CATT KJ, CAIN MD, COGHLAN JP: Measurement of angiotensin II in blood. *Lancet* 2:1005-1007, 1967
11. BOYD GW, LANDON J, PEART WS: Radioimmunoassay for determining plasma levels of angiotensin II in man. *Lancet* 2:1002-1005, 1967
12. VALLOTTON MB, PAGE LG, HABER E: Radioimmunoassay of angiotensin in human plasma. *Nature (London)* 215:714-715, 1967
13. GOODFRIEND TL, BALL DL, FARLEY DB: Radioimmunoassay of angiotensin. *J Lab Clin Med* 72:648-661, 1968
14. BOYD GW, FITZ AE, ADAMSON AR, et al: Radioimmunoassay determination of plasma-renin activity. *Lancet* 1:213-218, 1969
15. HABER E, KOERNER T, PAGE LB, et al: Application of a radioimmunoassay for angiotensin I to the physiologic measurement of plasma renin activity in normal human subjects. *J Clin Endocr* 29:1349-1355, 1969
16. CRANE MG, HEITSH J, HARRIS JJ, et al: Effect of ethinyl estradiol (Estinyl) on plasma renin activity. *J Clin Endocr* 26: 1403-1406, 1966
17. CRANE MG, HARRIS JJ: Effects of gonadal steroids on plasma renin activity and aldosterone secretion rate, in *Metabolic Effects of Gonadal Hormones and Contraceptive Steroids*. New York, Plenum Press, 1968, pp. 446-463
18. MENARD J, MALMEJAC A, MILLIEZ P: Influence of diethylstilboestrol on the renin-angiotensin system in male rats. *Endocrinology* 84:774-780, 1970
19. WOODS JW: Oral contraceptives and hypertension. *Lancet* 2:653-654, 1967
20. NEWTON MA, SEALEY JE, LEDINGHAM JGG, et al: High blood pressure and oral contraceptives. *Amer J Obstet Gynec* 101:1037-1045, 1968
21. WEINBERGER MH, COLLINS RD, DOWDY AJ, et al: Hypertension induced by oral contraceptives containing estrogen and gestagen. Effects on plasma renin activity and aldosterone excretion. *Ann Intern Med* 71:891-902, 1969
22. WALTERS WAW, LIM YL: Cardiovascular dynamics in women receiving oral contraceptives. *Lancet* 2:879-881, 1969
23. CAIN MD, CATT KJ, COGHLAN JP: Effect of circulating fragments of angiotensin II on radioimmunoassay in arterial and venous blood. *J Clin Endocr* 29:1639-1643, 1969
24. COGHLAN JP: Personal communication
25. GUYTON AC, COLEMAN TG, BOWER JD, et al: Circulatory control in hypertension. *Circ Res* 27 (suppl 2):135-147, 1970
26. Combined oral contraceptives. A Statement by the Committee on Safety of Drugs. *Brit Med J* 2:231-232, 1970
27. INMAN WHW, VESSEY MP: Investigation of deaths from pulmonary, coronary, and cerebral thrombosis and embolism in women of childbearing age. *Brit Med J* 2:193-199, 1968
28. VESSEY MP, DOLL R: Investigation of relation between use of oral contraceptives and thromboembolic disease. A further report. *Brit Med J* 2:651-657, 1969
29. SARTWELL PE, MASI AT, ARTHES SG, et al: Thromboembolism and oral contraceptives: an epidemiologic case-control study. *Amer J Epidem* 90:365-380, 1969
30. VESSEY MP, DOLL R, FAIRBAIRN AS, et al: Postoperative thromboembolism and the use of oral contraceptives. *Brit Med J* 3:123-126, 1970
31. SEIGEL DG: The association of mortality from thromboembolic disorders and oral contraceptive use. *J Reprod Med* 3:44-49, 1969
32. VESSEY MP, WEATHERALL JAC: Venous thromboembolic disease and the use of oral contraceptives. A review of mortality statistics in England and Wales. *Lancet* 2:94-95, 1968
33. INMAN WHW, VESSEY MP, WESTERHOLM B, et al: Thromboembolic disease and the steroidal content of oral contraceptives. A report to the Committee on Safety of Drugs. *Brit Med J* 2:203-209, 1970
34. DUGDALE M, MASI AT: Effects of the oral contraceptive on blood clotting, in *Second Annual Report on the Oral Contraceptives*, Advisory Committee on Obstetrics and Gynecology, Food & Drug Administration. Washington D.C., Government Printing Office, 1 August 1969
35. TIETZE C: Mortality with contraception and induced abortion. *Studies Fam Planning*, No. 45, Sept. 1969
36. HELLER GC, CLERMONT Y: Kinetics of the germinal epithelium in man. *Recent Progr Hormone Res* 20:545-571, 1964
37. JACKSON H: Antispermatogenic agents. *Brit Med Bull* 26:79-86, 1970
38. STEINBERGER E, DUCKETT GE: Pituitary "total" gonadotropins, FSH and LH in orchiectomized or cryptorchial rats. *Endocrinology* 79:912-920, 1966
39. PETERSON NT JR, MIDGLEY AR, JAFFE NB: Regulation of human gonadotropins. III. Luteinizing hormone and follicle stimulating hormone in sera from adult males. *J Clin Endocr* 28:1473-1478, 1968
40. VANDE WIELE RL, BOGUMIL J, DYRENFORTH I, et al: Mechanisms regulating the menstrual cycle in women. *Recent Progr Hormone Res* 26:63-95, 1970
41. ROWSON L: The evidence for luteolysin. *Brit Med Bull* 26: 14-16, 1970
42. BELING CG, MARCUS SL, MARKHAM SM: Functional activity of the corpus luteum following hysterectomy. *J Clin Endocr* 30:30-39, 1970
43. YOSHIMI T, STROTT CA, MARSHALL JR, et al: Corpus luteum function in early pregnancy. *J Clin Endocr* 29:225-230, 1969
44. GAUNT R, CHART JJ, RENZI AA: Inhibitors of adrenal cortical function. *Ergebn Physiol* 56:114-172, 1965
45. PINCUS G: Experimental studies of fertility control by hormonal steroids in mammals, in *Proceedings of the Second International Congress Hormonal Steroids, Milan*, Excerpta Medica Congress Series 111:100-110, 1966

Prostaglandins

XII

Editor's Comments on Paper 40

40 **Karim:** *Action of Prostaglandin in the Pregnant Woman*

Prostaglandins constitute a series of closely related fatty acids which are found in many different tissues of the body. They are present in interestingly high concentration in semen. Since they appear so ubiquitously throughout the body, considerable research is being carried out to ascertain their physiological role or roles. Of interest in connection with contraception is the remarkably prolific work of S. Karim of the Makerere University Medical School in Kampala, Uganda. Between 1966 and 1971, he published over 20 articles on the action of prostaglandins on the induction of labor, abortion, and the onset of menstruation. In 1970, he participated in a conference on prostaglandins held at the New York Academy of Sciences. The papers were published in 1971. The presentation of Dr. Karim is reproduced here.

Karim's work began with a detailed study of uterine contractions. These contractions can bring about menstruation, abortion, or live children. The reader will recall that about 100 years ago a leading physiologist of the day suggested that violent coughing could do the same!

Prostaglandins are normally present in high concentration in the maternal circulation; thus their role in spontaneous abortion or induction of labor was investigated and evidence obtained which strongly suggests that these substances do indeed play a physiological role in these activities. Of significance to contraception are the findings that prostaglandins are present in the menstrual fluid and in the circulation at the time of menstruation. Further, the administration of these substances induces menstruation.

Once these facts were established the use of prostaglandins for fertility control became obvious. Karim then carried out experiments to determine the best route of administration. The substances proved effective whether given orally, intravenously, subcutaneously, or intramuscularly. For contraception, injection is undesirable and the oral route proved to have unpleasant side-effects, such as diarrhea and vomiting. However, prostaglandins in appropriate form can be placed in the vagina, from where they are quickly and effectively absorbed into the circulation with no apparent side-effects. In this way they can be used to induce labor, to bring about abortion, or to cause menstruation. Karim administered prostaglandins intravaginally to a group of women who had passed their expected dates of menstruation by two to seven days. Intense uterine activity resulted and menstruation quickly followed. Uterine contractions may not be the only reason for inducing menses or bringing about abortion. There is some evidence that prostaglandins cause regression of the corpus lutum—thus the secretion of progesterone would decrease, and this alone could cause menstruation and abortion.

Whatever their action, the possiblities are exciting because the compounds have to be used but once a month, and only when pregnancy is a possibility. A large scale clinical test is clearly indicated, to be followed by the long wait for side-effects. At this writing, though, if prostaglandins live up to their promise they should supplant "the pill" and become widely used.

443

Reprinted from *Ann. N.Y. Acad. Sci.*, **180**, 483–498 (1971)

ACTION OF PROSTAGLANDIN IN THE PREGNANT WOMAN

S. Karim

Department of Pharmacology and Therapeutics
Medical School
Makerere University
Kampala, Uganda

40

The human uterus serves many important functions. These include: i) participation in the process of menstruation, ii) delivery of the live fetus after maintaining pregnancy for nine months, iii) rejection of pregnancy - spontaneous abortion or expulsion of the fetus before it becomes viable. In order to serve these functions, the uterus has to produce regular and rhythmic contractions.

Uterine contractions recorded from three different subjects during menstruation, spontaneous abortion and labour at term, are shown in Fig.1. Qualitatively, the contractions produced by the uterus in the three situations are similar. They are regular and rhythmic. There are, however, quantitative differences, and the amplitude, frequency and tone vary. The main function of these contractions is to expel the contents of the uterus and, depending upon the particular situation, they bring about menstruation, abortion or live childbirth. In recent years, evidence for the physiological roles of some prostaglandins in the three processes described above has been accumulating.

Evidence for the role of prostaglandins in spontaneous labour and abortion

PGE_2 and $PGF_{2\alpha}$ are present in human amniotic fluid samples obtained during labour or spontaneous abortion only (Karim, 1966; Karim & Devlin, 1967; Karim & Hillier, 1970).

In addition, the same prostaglandins are present in the maternal circulation, in high concentrations, during labour and spontaneous abortion (Karim & Hillier, 1970; Karim, 1968 a,b; 1970a).

The presence of a biologically active substance at the site of action is considered indicative of a physiological role. However, the evidence for a role of endogenous prostaglandin in spontaneous abortion or induction of labour would be more convincing if it could be shown firstly that administration of prostaglandins can induce abortion or labour, depending upon when it is given, and secondly, that a prostaglandin antagonist would prevent spontaneous labour or abortion.

Such evidence is forthcoming from studies carried out in Uganda. From these studies, the use of PGE_2 and

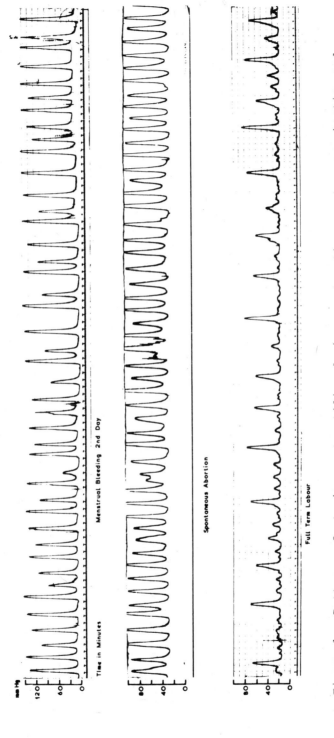

Figure 1. Patterns of uterine contractility during menstruation, spontaneous abortion and spontaneous labour at term.

$PGF_{2\alpha}$ for the induction of labour and for therapeutic abortion has developed.

With i.v. infusion of PGE_2 and $PGF_{2\alpha}$ it is possible to produce uterine contractions similar to those seen in normal physiological labour and to effect delivery of a live fetus or produce abortion. Prostaglandin induced uterine activity is shown in Fig.2,3.

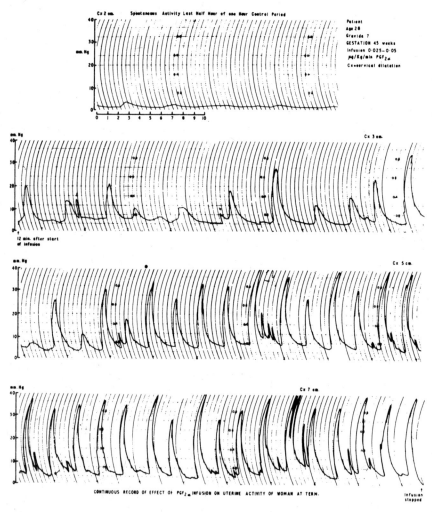

Figure 2.   Labour induced with i.v. infusion of prosta-
            glandin.

In Mulago Hospital Makerere Medical School,Kampala, Uganda,we used PGE_2 and $PGF_{2\alpha}$ in approximately 1000 women to bring about live childbirth or to induce

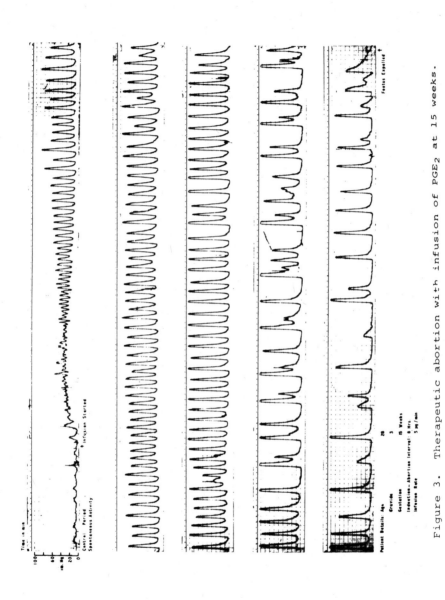

Figure 3.   Therapeutic abortion with infusion of PGE₂ at 15 weeks.

abortion when this is indicated on medical grounds. The
results of some of these studies are summarized in Tables
1,2.

Table 1. Summary of induction of labour with prostaglandins
in 500 women at term.

Gravida	Prostaglandin	No.of Cases	Average Induction Delivery Interval. Hours	Successful Inductions
1	PGE_2	56	12	55
2 - 13	PGE_2	344	7	342
1	$PGF_{2\alpha}$	14	17	9
2 - 12	$PGF_{2\alpha}$	86	10.5	84

PGE_2: 17 Caesarean Section: 2 for failed induction;13 for
cephalopelvic disproportion;2 fetal distress.
$PGF_{2\alpha}$: 2 Caesarean Section: 7 failed inductions(induced
successfully with PGE_2).
Infusion Rate: PGE_2 0.5-2.0 µg/min. $PGF_{2\alpha}$ 5.0-10.0 µg/min.

.More recently other investigators have reported the use
of prostaglandins for the induction of labour and for abortion and in most cases our findings have been confirmed
(Embrey 1970a,b;Beazley et al.,1970;Roth-Brandel et al.,
1970;Roth-Brandel & Adams 1970).
The very high success rate with PGE_2 in our series was
confirmed by us recently in a double blind clinical trial
using PGE_2,$PGF_{2\alpha}$ and oxytocin. A total of 300 patients in
three well matched groups of 100 were involved. The dose
schedule and the results are summarized in Table 3.

Table 2. Summary of therapeutic abortion with prostaglandins in 200 women.

Gravida	Prostaglandins	No.of Cases	Average Abortion Interval
0 - 10	PGE_2	150 (5 failures)	14.5 hr
0 - 7	$PGF_{2\alpha}$	50 (6 failures)	19 hr

Infusion Rate: PGE_2 5.0 µg/min. $PGF_{2\alpha}$ 50 µg/min.

Selective antagonists of prostaglandins for use in
humans are as yet not available. However,it is known that
i.v. infusion of ethanol will inhibit spontaneous uterine
contractions at all stages of gestation(Fuchs et al.,1967).
In a recent study we have shown that ethanol will antagonize
PGE_2 and $PGF_{2\alpha}$ induced uterine activity in pregnant women,
but not that induced by infusion of oxytocin(Karim & Sharma
1970a). (Fig.4.)

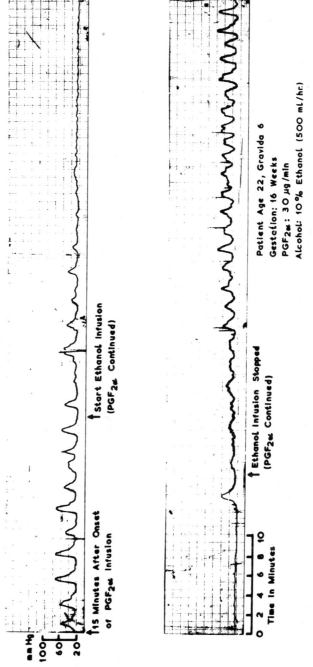

Figure 4. Inhibition of prostaglandin $F_{2\alpha}$ induced uterine activity by infusion of ethyl alcohol.

Table 3.   Results of a double blind clinical trial with
PGE_2, $PGF_{2\alpha}$ and oxytocin for induction of labour.

Drug Used	Dose Range	No.of Cases	Successful Inductions	Failed Inductions
PGE_2	0.3 - 1.2 µg/min	100	96	4
$PGF_{2\alpha}$	2.5 - 10 µg/min	100	67	33
Oxytocin	2 - 8 mU/min	100	56	44

Additional evidence implicating prostaglandins in
physiological labour and spontaneous abortion in the human,
stems from the findings that administration of PGE_2 and
$PGF_{2\alpha}$ stimulates the pregnant uterus to contract and can be
used to induce labour at term and for termination of pregnancy throughout gestation(Karim 1969,1970b;Karim & Filshie
1970a,b;Karim et al.,1968,1969,1970a,b). Furthermore,the
pattern of prostaglandin induced uterine activity is similar
to that of spontaneous labour. In addition,intravenous infusion of ethanol inhibits uterine contractions of spontaneous and prostaglandin induced labour. Oxytocin induced
contractions are not affected. PGE_2 is also effective for
the treatment of missed abortion,missed labour and hydatidiform mole(Karim & Filshie,1970a).

Implication of prostaglandins in process of menstruation
     The evidence implicating prostaglandins in the process
of menstruation has developed from the initial findings that
PGE_2 and $PGF_{2\alpha}$ are present in menstrual fluid,uterine endometrium,and also in the maternal circulation at the time of
menstruation(Pickles et al.,1965;Hall 1966).
     Intravenous infusion of PGE_2 or $PGF_{2\alpha}$ 2-3 days before
the expected date of menstruation will induce uterine
bleeding(Karim et al.,1970c). We have also used infusion of
these prostaglandins to induce menstruation in six women on
two days before,and up to six days after the due menstruation date.

Different routes of prostaglandin administration
     Recently we have been exploring the administration of
prostaglandins by other than the continuous intravenous
infusion route.

Single intravenous injection: With a single injection of
prostaglandin it is possible to stimulate the uterus
throughout gestation. However,the onset of action by this
method is too rapid and the effect is not prolonged(Karim
et al.,1970c).

By intramuscular and subcutaneous injection: PGE_2 and $PGF_{2\alpha}$
administered intramuscularly or subcutaneously have been
used by us and by others to successfully induce abortion
(Roth-Brandel et al.,1970;Karim et al.,1970c). However,the

injections are extremely painful and have to be repeated every 2 hr(for 12-24 hr)for successful abortion.

Oral: PGE$_2$ and PGF$_{2\alpha}$ administered by mouth are absorbed in concentration sufficient to stimulate the pregnant human uterus at term(Karim 1970c). Orally administered prostaglandins produce contractions of the term uterus similar to that produced by intravenous infusion of PGE$_2$ and PGF$_{2\alpha}$ (Fig.5).

In a recent study,PGE$_2$ and PGF$_{2\alpha}$ administered orally were used successfully to induce labour in 100 women at or near term(Karim & Sharma 1970b). The results are summarized in Table 4. Ten times higher concentrations of these prostaglandins have to be given by mouth to stimulate the uterus during early pregnancy,and at these dose levels they produce severe diarrhea and vomiting. For this reason PGE$_2$ and PGF$_{2\alpha}$ cannot be used as oral abortifacients(Karim & Sharma 1970b).

Table 4. Results of induction of labour with oral administration of prostaglandins.

Gravida	Prostaglandin	No.of Cases	Avg. Induction Delivery Interval	No.of Doses Average
1	E$_2$	30	15 hr	5
2 - 9	E$_2$	50 (1 failure)	7.5 hr	3
1 - 8	F$_{2\alpha}$	20	23.5 hr (4 failures)	10

Dose: PGE$_2$ 0.5-1.0 mg; PGF$_{2\alpha}$ 5.0-10 mg; every 2 hr until labour established.

Vaginal administration: Both PGE$_2$ and PGF$_{2\alpha}$ administered intravaginally are absorbed into the circulation and with appropriate doses can be used to stimulate the human uterus (Karim 1970d). Intravaginally administered prostaglandins have been successfully used by us for induction of: (i) labour,(ii) abortion,and for(iii) menstruation.
(i) Induction of labour: PGE$_2$ and PGF$_{2\alpha}$(2 mg or 5 mg respectively)administered intravaginally every 2 hr have been used successfully for the induction of labour at term. Since PGE$_2$ and PGF$_{2\alpha}$ can be given by mouth for the induction of labour,the vaginal route does not appear to offer any advantages over the oral route.
(ii) Induction of abortion: Intravaginal administration of PGE$_2$ and PGF$_{2\alpha}$(20 mgm or 50 mgm respectively)every 2.5 hr is effective for producing abortion(Fig.6). In one recent series involving 45 patients in the first and second trimesters,abortion was successfully induced in all subjects (Karim & Sharma 1970c). The results are summarized in Table V. The vaginal route of administering prostaglandins for

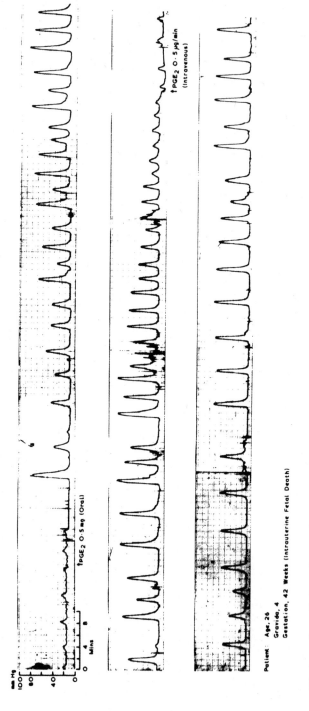

Figure 5. Induction of labour at term with oral and intravenous administration of PGE_2 on pregnant human uterus at 42 weeks.

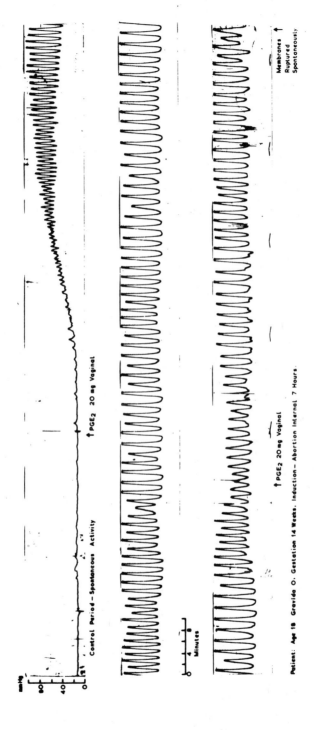

Figure 6. Therapeutic abortion with intravaginal administration of PGE2 on the pregnant human uterus at 14 weeks.

Table 5. Results of induction of abortion with vaginal administration of prostaglandins E$_2$ and F$_{2\alpha}$ in 45 women.

Gravida	Prostaglandin	Gestation Weeks	No.of Women	Average Abortion Interval Hr
1 - 9	PGE$_2$	6 - 23	30	12.5
1 - 8	PGF$_{2\alpha}$	7 - 22	15	14.5

PGE$_2$ 20 mg or PGF$_{2\alpha}$ 50 mg; administered every 2.5 hr until abortion took place.

termination of pregnancy is more acceptable and practical than continuous i.v. infusion.

(iii) Induction of menstruation;once-a-month antifertility agent: An exciting prospect for the future in the fertility control area is a drug which could be taken once-a-month at the time of expected menstruation in a cycle during which the woman had been exposed to the possibility of an unwanted pregnancy. If the preparation need be taken only when pregnancy was likely,as evidenced by delayed onset of menstruation and further if it could be self-administered,such a drug would be even more acceptable. Evidence from many quarters suggest that prostaglandin might fulfill these requirements. The possible role of the endogenous prostaglandins in menstruation is forthcoming from the work of Pickles and his collaborators,and intravenous or intravaginal administration of prostaglandins during the advanced secretory phase of the cycle will induce uterine bleeding.

In a recent study,intravaginal administration of PGE$_2$ or PGF$_{2\alpha}$ was carried out in twelve women who had passed their expected dates of menstruation by 2-7 days;this procedure resulted in menstruation in 11 women(Karim 1970e). The menstrual bleeding was always preceeded by an increase in uterine activity(Fig.7),which was similar to that recorded during spontaneous menstruation(Fig.8).

The mechanism by which PGE$_2$ and PGF$_{2\alpha}$ induce menses in the human is not clear. From studies in animals it is known that PGF$_{2\alpha}$ causes regression of the corpus luteum. Such a luteolytic effect has been detected in the rat,rabbit and rhesus monkey,but it does not seem likely that the corpus luteum is the primary target organ for prostaglandin action in the human,since no decrease in serum progesterone level following prostaglandin treatment were shown by Bygdeman and Wiqvist in early pregnant women. The strong and frequent uterine contractions which precede the onset of menstruation could dislodge the fertilized ovum and initiate uterine bleeding. It is,of course,possible that impairment of corpus luteum function is an additional factor for the induction of menses.

The potential for the use of prostaglandins in the control of fertility is obvious. The advantages of once-a-month contraceptive with abortifacient,luteolytic and menses inducing properties are many. They include convenience of

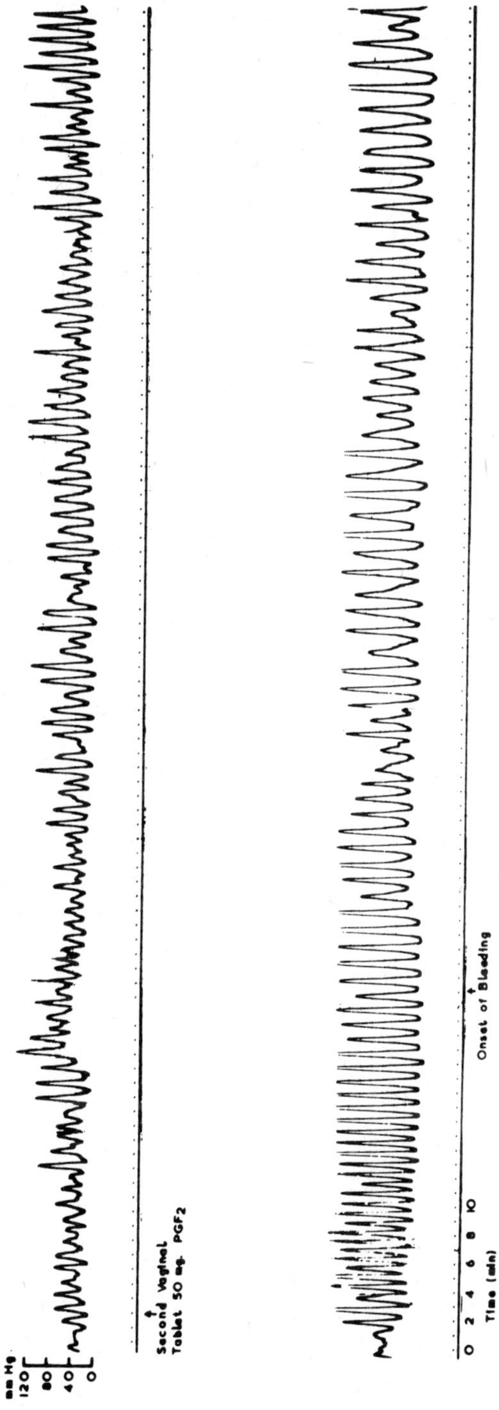

Figure 7. Uterine activity in a 30-year-old subject on the 6th day after first missed period. Record started 4 hr after intravaginal administration of 50 mg $PGF_{2\alpha}$ to induce menstruation.

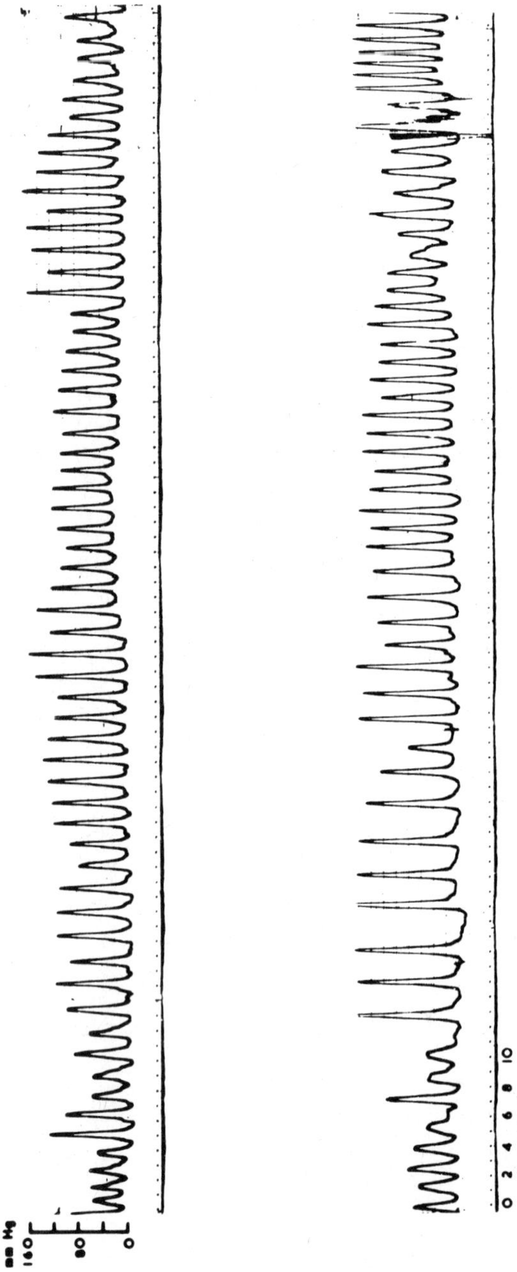

Figure 8. Uterine activity in a 24-year-old subject from 3-6 hr during spontaneous menstruation.

administration and fewer side effects because of the need for periodic short-term administration.

ACKNOWLEDGEMENTS

Part of the work presented in this paper was carried out in collaboration with Professor R.R. Trussell,Professor K. Somers, Dr. S.D. Sharma,Dr. K. Hillier,Dr. G.M. Filshie, Dr. R.C. Patel,Dr. S. Tamusange,Dr. J.R. Patel and Dr. J. Alluwalia. The excellent technical assistance of Mr. R. Raja,Mr. Ogoye,Mr. Sunderjee,Mr. J. Phadke,Mr. Jaffer and Mrs. N. Mulimezi is gratefully acknowledged.
The work was supported in part by the Wellcome Trust, U.K.;Makerere University Research Grants Committee;the Upjohn Company,Michigan,Kalamazoo,U.S.A.;and Muljibhai Madhvani and Co. Ltd.,Uganda.
Prostaglandins were generously supplied by Professors Bergstrøm and Samuelsson(Sweden);and the Upjohn·Company, Kalamazoo,Michigan,U.S.A.

REFERENCES

Beazley,J.M.,C.J. Dewhurst and A. Gillespie 1970. The induction of labour with prostaglandin E_2. J.Obstet.Gynaec. Brit.Comm. 77:193.

Embrey,M.P. 1970a. Induction of labour with prostaglandins E_1 and E_2. Brit.Med.J. 2:256.

Embrey,M.P. 1970b. Induction of abortion by prostaglandin E_1 and E_2. Brit.Med.J. 2:258.

Fuchs,F.,A.R. Fuchs,V.F. Poblete and A. Risk 1967. Effect of alcohol on threatened premature labour. Amer.J.Obstet. Gynec. 99:627.

Hall,W.J. 1966. Prostaglandins in human menstrual fluid and endometrial curettings. Mem.Soc.Endocr. 14:65.

Karim,S.M.M. 1966. Identification of prostaglandins in human amniotic fluid. J.Obstet.Gynaec.Brit.Comm. 73:903.

Karim,S.M.M. 1968a. Appearance of prostaglandin $F_{2\alpha}$ in maternal blood during labour. Brit.Med.J. 4:618.

Karim,S.M.M. 1968b. The role of prostaglandin $F_{2\alpha}$ in human parturition. In: Prostaglandins,Peptides and Amines. p.65. Academic Press(Lond.).

Karim,S.M.M. 1969. The role of prostaglandins in human par-trurition. In: Proc. Royal Soc.Med.Symp.Kinins and Prostaglandins. Nov. 1969.

Karim,S.M.M. 1970a. Prostaglandin E_2 in maternal circulation during spontaneous labour and abortion(in preparation).

Karim,S.M.M. 1970b. Use of prostaglandin E_2 in the management of missed abortion,missed labour and hydatidiform mole. Brit.Med.J. $\underline{3}$:196.

Karim,S.M.M. 1970c. Effect of oral administration of prostaglandins E_2 and $F_{2\alpha}$ on the pregnant human uterus and the motility of the gastrointestinal tract. Brit.J.Pharmacol.(in press).

Karim,S.M.M. 1970d. Absorption of prostaglandins after intravaginal administration in pregnant women(in press).

Karim,S.M.M. 1970e. Once-a-month vaginal administration of prostaglandins E_2 and $F_{2\alpha}$ for fertility control. J.A.M.A.(in press).

Karim,S.M.M. and J. Devlin 1967. Prostaglandin content of human amniotic fluid during pregnancy and labour. J.Obstet. Gynaec.Brit.Comm. $\underline{74}$:230.

Karim,S.M.M. and G.M. Filshie 1970a. Therapeutic abortion using prostaglandin $F_{2\alpha}$. Lancet,$\underline{i}$:157.

Karim,S.M.M. and G.M. Filshie 1970b. Use of prostaglandin E_2 for therapeutic abortion. Brit.Med.J. $\underline{3}$:198.

Karim,S.M.M. and K. Hillier 1970. Prostaglandins and spontaneous abortion. J.Obstet.Gynaec.Brit.Comm.(in press).

Karim,S.M.M. and S.D. Sharma 1970a. The effect of ethyl alcohol on prostaglandins E_2 and $F_{2\alpha}$ induced uterine activity in pregnant women. J.Obstet.Gynaec.Brit.Comm.(accepted for publication).

Karim,S.M.M. and S.D. Sharma 1970b. Oral administration of prostaglandins E_2 and $F_{2\alpha}$ for the induction of labour. Brit. Med.J.(in press).

Karim,S.M.M. and S.D. Sharma 1970c. Therapeutic abortion and induction of labour with intravaginal administration of prostaglandins E_2 and $F_{2\alpha}$. Brit.Med.J.(in press).

Karim,S.M.M.,R.R. Trussell,R.C. Patel and K. Hillier 1968. Response of pregnant human uterus to prostaglandin $F_{2\alpha}$-Induction of labour. Brit.Med.J. $\underline{4}$:621.

Karim,S.M.M.,R.R. Trussell,K. Hillier and R.C. Patel 1969. Induction of labour with prostaglandin $F_{2\alpha}$. J.Obstet.Gynaec. Brit.Comm. $\underline{76}$:769.

Karim,S.M.M.,K. Hillier,R.R. Trussell,R.C. Patel and S. Tamusange 1970a. Induction of labour with prostaglandin E_2. J.Obstet.Gynaec.Brit.Comm. $\underline{77}$:200.

Karim,S.M.M.,R.C. Patel,S.D. Sharma and R.R. Trussell 1970b. Two years experience with prostaglandin E_2 for the induction of labour. J.A.M.A.(in press).

Karim,S.M.M.,K. Hillier,K. Somers and R.R. Trussell 1970c. The effects of prostaglandins E_2 and $F_{2\alpha}$ administered by different routes on uterine activity and the cardiovascular system in pregnant and nonpregnant women. J.Obstet.Gynaec. Brit.Comm.(in press).

Pickles,V.R.,W.J. Hall,F.A. Best and G.N. Smith 1965. Prostaglandins in endometrium and menstrual fluid from normal dysmenorrhoeic subjects. J.Obstet.Gynaec.Brit.Comm. 72:185.

Roth-Brandel,U. and M. Adams 1970. An evaluation of the possible use of prostaglandin E_1,E_2 and $F_{2\alpha}$ for induction of labour. Acta.Obstet.Gynec.Scand. Suppl.5,49:9.

Roth-Brandel,U.,M. Bygdeman,N. Wiqvist and S. Bergström 1970. Prostaglandins for induction of therapeutic abortion. Lancet,1:190.

Rejection, Chauvinism, Trends

XIII

Editor's Comments on Papers 41, 42, and 43

In the United States alone there are at least one or two million undesired pregnancies per year. And yet, in the United States there are excellent means of communication, sophistication, affluence, and a choice of methods to suit most everyone. Still women become pregnant. Why? In a superb article, Drs. Sandberg and Jacobs discuss this problem. They conclude by stating: "More and better contraception is not the answer to the population crisis, nor is it likely that even free and available abortions or abortifacients are the answer, although each and all of these items would be of general aid. The elimination of population growth is not principally a medical or a scientific problem. It is a social, psychological, political, and attitudinal problem. . . ."

Coitus interruptus can be easily used in an emergency, condoms are ubiquitously available and cheap, a prompt douche effective, the diaphragm highly successful, "the pill" practically foolproof, and the intrauterine device can be inserted and forgotten. Yet women become pregnant without wanting to and either bear the child or seek an abortion. Sandberg and Jacobs present many reasons for this. They point out that women are ambivalent about pregnancy throughout most of their reproductive lives. This causes them to vacillate, to reject contraception. And there are other reasons, such as denial that coitus is even occurring, or denial that contraceptives work, or denial of any personal responsibility for contraception. The latter is particularly true of many men.

And there is love, that marvelously irrational state that is so often equated with self-sacrifice and the willingness to take risks, perhaps to prove one's love or to shut out anything that might impinge upon the "deep and beautiful relationship."

On and on flow the reasons discussed in this paper; guilt, shame, coital gamesmanship, sexual identity conflicts, hostility, masochism, eroticism, nihilism, fear and anxiety, availability of abortion, opportunism, and iatrogenesis.

Despite the fact that since earliest times the man has prevented conception first by the use of coitus interruptus and then by using the condom and now through vasectomy, the very blatant women's lib screams discrimination while insisting that ". . . women have always had to bear most of the risks associated with sex and reproduction." They insist that little or no effort is being made to develop male contraceptives comparable to "the pill" and the IUD. This is simply not true and in a superb, informative, and entertaining article, Dr. Sheldon Segal sets the record straight. He discusses the possibilities for male procedures, outlines the research underway, and explains the problems. Amusingly, he includes the possibility of using heat to destroy sperm, in situ so to speak, but concludes, as has already been concluded earlier in these comments, that the ineffectiveness of the method combined with the danger of genetically abnormal sperm preclude serious consideration of the method. He also takes note of our Aboriginal Australians and goes on to observe: "Through the years sperm have been confronted with various forms of vulcanized road blocks and, more recently, plunged into lethal pools of jellies, creams or effervescent foams."

Finally, the concluding article is an excellent statistical survey of the use of contraception in the United States as of 1970. This analysis by Dr. Charles Westoff reveals many fascinating trends. Although between 1965 and 1970 there was only a small increase in the percentage of married couples using any type of contraception, there were significant changes in the methods used. Perhaps the most surprising finding is that by 1970, voluntary sterilization had become widespread. In couples aged 30–44 it is the most popular method, with 25.2 per cent selecting this procedure; greater than any other. Equally startling is the growth of acceptance of "the pill." These contraceptives have been on the market only since 1960, yet for all couples, over 34 per cent rely on them. For black women they are the overwhelming method of choice.

Looking at trends we see that coitus interruptus is losing favor, as is the diaphragm, the condom, and the rhythm method. The biggest gainer is the IUD. In 1965, only 1.2 per cent of couples used the device; in 1970, it was up to 7.4 per cent.

Dr. Westoff concludes that there is now available high protection against pregnancy and, most significantly, low-income couples have almost caught up to the level of contraceptive protection experienced by higher-income couples.

In summary, the happy prediction by Francis Place that if suitable "checks" were available, population would be controlled, marriage would be ideal, even idyllic, has hardly resulted from an array of suitable "checks." Still, the conditions that ensued from a series of unwanted pregnancies have been ameliorated, at least in the more advanced societies. The last chapter in this saga cannot yet be written.

463

Reprinted from *Amer. J. Obstet. Gynecol.*, **110**, 227–242 (1971)

Psychology of the misuse and rejection of contraception

EUGENE C. SANDBERG, M.D.

RALPH I. JACOBS, M.D.

Stanford, California

It is obvious from the large number of illegitimate births, legally and illegally induced abortions, and legitimate but undesired pregnancies in this country and abroad that contraceptive measures are commonly ignored or actively rejected by a substantial proportion of coitally active human beings who consciously deny procreative intent. While many of the reasons for misuse or rejection of contraception are included within the commonly discussed areas of contraceptive knowledgeability, acceptability, availability, cost, religious proscription, etc., innumerable other reasons, principally in the psychological and interpersonal relationship realms, are also operative, consciously and unconsciously, in both partners. Many of these other reasons have been examined, and their ultimate influence on the concept of control of population growth by contraceptive means is discussed. Even with the future availability of an "ideal" contraceptive, it is probable for reasons of psychology rather than technology that social systems which require or allow volitional and individually initiated contraceptive use as the sole method for population control will fail to accomplish that goal.

HALF OF THE PEOPLE who ever lived are living today. The world population will increase by 73 million this year, more than the combined current population of the 15 largest cities in the world. Statistics such as these are being used by demographers, social scientists, biologists, and innumerable others to drive home the message that a population-induced catastrophe is in the making. Others have pointed out that the first symptoms of this overpopulation disease are already at hand (acute accentuations of man's old problems of poverty, crime, hunger, violence, war, pollution, social alienations, drug abuse, racial antipathies, etc.). Social and ecologic disaster seems imminent.

Although induced abortion and steriliza-

From the Department of Gynecology and Obstetrics, Stanford University School of Medicine.

Presented at the Thirty-seventh Annual Meeting of the Pacific Coast Obstetrical and Gynecological Society, Kauai, Hawaii, November 9-14, 1970.

tion operations have been allowed, and in a few areas even encouraged, the political and economic support given world population–control efforts thus far have been almost solely in the area of contraception. It is noteworthy also that this has been invariably predicated on the "right" of personal volition as is practiced in essentially all of the world.

It is apparent that the efforts to date have failed. Declines in birth rate have occurred in some areas of concentrated contraceptive distribution, but these have occurred only in areas or countries with emerging industrialization and urbanization in which a decline in population growth rate had already begun. In not a single country has population growth been prevented by contraception.

In as contraceptively sophisticated a country as the United States, neither population stabilization nor even the prevention of presumably unwanted pregnancies has been accomplished. Three hundred thousand illegitimate births are predicted for 1970. Two hundred thousand to one million two hundred thousand induced abortions are estimated to occur annually. One third of the national total of "first births" is conceived out of wedlock.[8]

Conservatively, one or two million pregnancies that are presumed to be undesired occur in the United States yearly. The mass of copulative humanity involved in these pregnancies can hardly be considered to be without contraceptive information. While some specific segments of our society are underprivileged and underschooled in this regard, it is apparent, if the 4,000 patients receiving legal abortions at our hospital within the past three years are any indication, that the majority are not. Why such a sizable portion of our population fails to exploit fully the apparent advantages to themselves of current contraceptive science is a question of fundamental social concern. Undoubtedly, as has been repeatedly pointed out, social, religious, scientific, cultural, economic, and political forces influence patients' contraceptive use both consciously and unconsciously. More specific and precise influences such as contraceptive knowledgeability, physical acceptance of the method, apparent safety, availability, cost, etc., have also been cited. But a major influence which has been intuitively accepted as operative but never fully probed (although it is, in truth, the working level) is the personal and interpersonal psychological makeup of the coupling individuals.

Women are ambivalent about pregnancy throughout most of their reproductive lives. Psychic conflict regarding contraception is to be anticipated, as conscious and unconscious reasons for and against its use commonly exist simultaneously. This will include the conflict between wanting evidence of fertility but not wanting to have a child, a conflict which often results in pregnancy and the acquisition of a legal or illegal abortion.

A physician who accepts proffered statements for the whole truth is soon confounded by the apparent irrational action of some patients in their misuse or rejection of the prescribed contraceptives and by the unreasonable and inconsistent explanations as to why none of the various methods are utilizable. It is obvious that behavior in contraceptive use does not always conform to apparently rational, externally voiced attitudes and that conflicted psychological forces, conscious and unconscious, are extremely influential. A great many of these forces appear to be changeable in type and strength and vary with time, age, situation, partner, etc. This leads to the necessity for repeated decision-making which may be part of the reason for the two-year dropout rate of approximately 50 per cent for essentially each of the contraceptive methods.[4, 13, 15]

From information acquired from the literature, from gynecologic and psychiatric practitioners, and from a large number of patients, the majority of whom were in the process of acquiring a legal abortion, we have attempted to discern the major psychological reasons why presumably undesired pregnancies have been allowed to occur through the misuse and/or rejection of contraception. These have been arbitrarily divided into 14 general categories which will be listed and discussed. There has been no attempt, and no claim, to be all inclusive. In some, the psychological forces result in the nonuse of contraception with pregnancy being an incidental aftermath. In others, quite plainly, pregnancy is the goal, with contraceptive nonuse being a required but incidental factor.

We have deliberately eliminated from this consideration contraceptive nonuse due to mental derangement, contraceptive unavailability, forced intercourse, and any other specific causes or instances precluding volitional contraceptive use. We have also eliminated that due to ignorance even though it is clear that some ignorance is of a determined nature and is psychologically based.

None of the following should be confused with reasons why people have intercourse, licitly or illicitly, even though the psychodynamic categorization would undoubtedly be very similar. This compilation concerns only the psychological reasons why people who profess not to desire pregnancy fail to use methods to prevent it (i.e., willful exposure to "unwanted" pregnancy).

A brief description of the features of each category will be presented along with an occasional illustrative quotation or anecdote. We hope by this means to adequately illustrate the degree and the diversity of the personal and interpersonal psychological relationships that can lead to rejection of contraception or can provoke sufficient conflict or ambivalence to lead to misuse or the intermittent disuse of these measures.

The superficial aspects of the examples cited in several categories are similar, and, indeed, a significant overlap of certain of the categories will seem obvious and possibly predictable. The differentiating qualities are to be found in the psychodynamic forces at work and the motivation of the individual(s) being considered, features which are operating at both conscious and subconscious levels.

1. *Denial*. Denial may be seen in at least three principal forms: (1) denial of the possibility of pregnancy (and, in the rare instance, denial that coitus is even occurring), (2) denial that contraceptive measures work, and (3) denial of any personal responsibility for contraception.

We have seen denial of the possibility of pregnancy (or coitus) most frequently in high school and college students whose common attitude is expressed in statements such as, "I can't understand how it happened," or, "I just put the possibility of pregnancy out of my mind," or, "God loved me so much he wouldn't make me pregnant."

Denial of the effectiveness of contraceptives or their safety is most often a rationalization which hides features of a different category of psychological conflict regarding contraceptive use. Rarely is the lack of faith voiced in regard to many or all methods, the elimination of one being irrationally adequate to dismiss all. Condoms may be dismissed with, "Anything so cheap can't be much good." The IUD is dismissed with, "It doesn't really prevent pregnancy and it may cause cancer." The oral contraceptives are dismissed with, "They're not thoroughly proved safe," or, "The only foolproof method is the pill and I'm afraid to use it because of clots." As a result, no contraceptive is used.

Denial of any personal responsibility for contraception is seen very frequently in men, and also in hysterical women who quite typically shift contraceptive responsibility to the man. This form of denial, in the true psychiatric sense of the word, may represent an unwillingness to acknowledge the reality of a personal requirement for responsibility. Or it may represent simply an intentional renunciation of responsibility, often unspoken. In general, any individual who is reluctant to accept responsibility in other spheres of life will tend to avoid it in sexual and contraceptive matters as well. It is tacitly understood that the contraceptive user will be blamed, should pregnancy occur. The possibility of being blamed is eliminated if responsibility is shifted or if one can rationalize to the point of believing that the coital partner does not want contraception to be used. "I was counting on him to pull out and he didn't," and, "He should use protection. Sex is for him. He's the only one who enjoys it," are fairly typical comments.

2. *Love*. Love is commonly equated with self-sacrifice and the willingness to take risks. The demonstration of love by risk-taking is romantically accepted and occasionally even encouraged. This may be through risking physical injury in "showing off" or fighting to prove one's love, or through the risk of social injury when the courtship is illicit or in other circumstances in which the couple risks social penalty in the event of exposure. A simple extension of this principle is frequently seen in the nonuse of contraception.

In some instances the concept of love may become so ethereal that the realities of biology are, at least superficially, ignored. This is illustrated in statements such as, "I wanted to totally surrender to demonstrate fully my love," and, "I didn't use contraception because sex was a totally unimportant part of our deep and beautiful relationship."

An even fuller sacrifice in the name of love may be seen in the situation in which the woman offers a demonstration of her love by the gift of pregnancy, a frequent and highly acceptable aspect of married love but a complicating element in unmarried love. This gift may or may not have been solicited or known to be intended and may or may not be accepted with equanimity. Even more directly, whether motivated by love or by other considerations, an occasional girl has explained that her pregnancy has resulted from acceding to her lover's request that she permit him to demonstrate his virility.

3. *Guilt.* One might anticipate that the specter of pregnancy arising from contraceptive nonuse in individuals not desiring pregnancy would provoke more worry or guilt than would be provoked by contraceptive use, almost regardless of the situation. While this is true for a substantial number of individuals, there are innumerable others who feel greater guilt with contraceptive use than from its nonuse.

Pregnancy, to some, is a "normal" aftermath of coitus. The lack of pregnancy following coitus suggests that something is abnormal. The use of an agent to provoke such an abnormality may initiate considerable conflict and remorse. The guilt may also emanate from a denial of God and nature and from a frustration with having coitus for "no purpose." Intrinsically mixed with this in the minds of some individuals is the betrayal of conscience arising from their socioreligious teachings that sexual activity is permissible for procreative purposes but is highly immoral and sinful if used for pure sensuality. Or guilt arising from participation in any coitus may be the "normal" state for a given individual, but the action may be adequately rationalized as necessary for procreation and/or as a marriage duty. Contraceptive use may eventuate in an increased desire or demand for coitus by the spouse. In such circumstances, the sensual aspects of coitus may be accentuated and may balloon guilt to a degree beyond the other's compensatory capacities. Each individual's tolerance for guilt will probably be the deciding factor in the use or nonuse of contraception.

Additionally, contraceptive use must be considered to be synonymous with coital preparedness. This realization may arouse considerable guilt in some through its implication of promiscuous behavior or through its implied consent and commitment to a continuation of conflictual coitus. In other words, rationalization of coital readiness may require more time and energy than is required for rationalizing the coital activity itself. The intermittent and impulsive use of coitally related methods or total nonuse of contraception would be expected in this group.

Guilt adequate to eliminate consideration of contraception may also arise from a belief that the nonmechanical means are really abortive, in which event menstrual clots may be viewed as adequate evidence. This may be stated as a socioreligious feeling against abortion or simply as a rationalization to avoid contraception for some other reason.

In many, simply the guilt arising from their involvement in coital activity may require that they forsake contraception and assume at least a risk of punishment through possible pregnancy if coital activity is to continue. The associated penalties of anxiety and trepidation may also help to assuage the guilt. Even beyond this, many individuals actually feel a need for punishment for having sinned, punishment being considered to be almost a requirement for redemption by members of certain religious faiths.

4. *Shame (embarrassment).* Closely allied to the etiologic aspects of guilt, but sufficiently distinctive to warrant separate categorization, are those of shame and, its lesser dimension, embarrassment. Some individuals who would prefer to use contraception reject it on the basis of the shame or embarrassment that would be engendered if others (e.g., their children, parents, relatives, friends, neighbors, etc.) were to discover that they were using it, in other words, having intercourse. This applies to a large number of unmarried individuals, especially women whether living at home or elsewhere, and to a number of married persons as well. This also applies to many of the intended recipients of the services of poorly planned and hastily established storefront contraceptive

clinics, especially in ghetto areas. It is glaringly obvious that these clinics dispense only a single commodity, and the private activities of any individual seen entering, leaving, or seated within the frequently visible waiting areas are not simply suspect, they are known. Many potential patients would prefer that they not be seen and for this reason avoid the clinics and never obtain contraception. Nonuse because of religious or cultist proscription will also often fit in this general category.

Embarrassment that is equally counter productive to contraceptive use may develop in others simply from an apparent necessity for admission of ignorance. This is seen in individuals who will not seek contraceptive advice for fear of exposing their ignorance in this and possibly other sexual areas to either a physician or to clinic personnel. It is operative in many other circumstances as well. For example, some girls will indulge in coitus without contraception purely because of their potential embarrassment over exposing their ignorance if they broach the subject to their partners.

5. *Coital gamesmanship.* Sexual intercourse is not always undertaken for the purpose of procreation or for obtaining pure sensual delight but may be used for a seemingly vast array of other purposes. Many of these are directed toward the achievement of dominance or control of the relationship. The choice of a contraceptive or the decision not to use contraception may be a reflection of the power struggle or the power balance between the pair. Either one pushed to assume the responsibility for conception control may resent this as being servitude and may respond in any of a number of ways including mutiny against contraceptive use. Contraception may also be rejected in these circumstances because its use would diminish the possibility of using sexuality to manipulate the relationship. A contraceptively protected woman, for instance, may no longer be able to control the frequency of sexual activity through statements regarding a reasonable fear of pregnancy. The same is true for an individual of either sex in whom fear of pregnancy is the rationalization for sexual inhibition or distaste for coitus, regardless of whether the latter is due to pain, maltreatment, boredom, fatigue, hate, etc. The encouragement of contraception would be so anxiety-provoking in these individuals that one could almost anticipate its rejection. Discordance between coital partners on reproductive and contraceptive matters and a lack of communication requiring rationalizations in these areas are symptomatic of poor sexual adjustment within the coital unit.

A situation which has recently come to our attention demonstrates well the variety of psychodynamic construct possible in this sphere of contraceptive nonuse. An unmarried man refused to use, and refused to allow his unmarried partner to use, contraception in their coital relationship. His obvious motivation was to control their sexual activity and, consequently, their emotional investment. By not releasing her from the continuing and repressive fear of pregnancy, he could manipulate and hold down her expressiveness and keep himself from being forced into a deeper, and possibly marital, commitment. Also, he never "let himself go" in any other area of his extremely well-ordered life and, by this personal repression, he avoided a threat to the controllability of his own sexual behavior.

Possibly also falling into the area of poor sexual adjustment, so common in coital gamesmanship, are the instances in which the man insists on the nonuse of contraception. He may fear that his partner's release from the anxiety of pregnancy will lead to an accentuation of her sexual drive which he will be unable to accommodate, or possibly even to her infidelity. In other instances, the man may develop anxiety simply over the concern that contraceptive use will lead to a reduction in his partner's sexual desire. Indeed, contraceptive practice may be so anxiety-related as to be itself directly productive of sexual dysfunction. Masters and Johnson have noted occasional instances in which sexual inadequacy or dysfunction was relieved simply by discontinuation of the contraceptive.[7]

May 15, 1971
Amer. J. Obstet. Gynec.

6. *Sexual identity conflicts.* In the majority of the world's cultures, a woman who senses herself to be fertile feels more feminine, more attractive, more desirable. The man also finds her to be more attractive, consciously or unconsciously, as a prospect for the demonstration of his virility via impregnation. For both men and women, sexual identity and sexual adequacy are very closely allied with self-esteem and feelings of self-worth. The establishment and demonstration of virility by impregnation of the woman is well understood and inherently accepted in essentially all cultures, and almost deified in some. A significant number of men will feel a strong need to repeatedly impregnate as proof, to themselves and to society, of their strength and thus their worthfulness, and additionally of their mastery over the woman. This variety of ego-building or ego-reinforcement was noted by Rainwater and Weinstein[11] to be especially prevalent in unskilled or jobless men who are "unable to express themselves socially." Men having low self-esteem and sexual identity conflicts will feel thwarted by the lack of fertility engendered by their partner's use of contraception. In some men, contraceptive use may even precipitate panic through the initiation of a severe castration anxiety. Impotence may develop simply through a partner's use of contraception. Or the inadequacy of a male's ability or potency, disguised and nonjeopardized by the woman's reluctance to indulge in intercourse with frequency for fear of pregnancy, may be exposed by her release from such fear and her increase in demand for sexuality following initiation of contraception. Needless to say, contraceptive disuse will be encouraged or possibly even demanded under these circumstances.

These conflicts over sexual identity are seen just as commonly in the woman in whom development or preservation of self-esteem is accomplished through a demonstration of fertility. Fertility is the epitome of femininity and for some the sine qua non. Pregnancy is a release from the fear of not being a woman; it is fulfillment of self-image. It is a means of being creative, of producing something, of being worthwhile, and is of special compensatory importance for those who are or consider themselves to be uncreative, unproductive, and unfulfilled in other areas of life. It is also a means of achieving respect, deference, and attention customarily accorded motherhood in our society as well as most others.

Fertile feministy is equated with youthfulness, and this is highly valued. The elements of vanity and narcissism in this equation are seen in the common desire to sustain fertility and may be especially noted in the fantasy of rejuvenation through pregnancy and childbirth in older women.

Some women measure their feminity (show their potency) by the number of children they produce. Many compete with their mothers, sisters, friends, or even men by becoming pregnant. This may evolve through a conflict over their sexual identity as it may suffer in comparison to their evaluation of femininity in others, through hostility toward these individuals, or through a host of other psychological dynamics. This measurement of femininity by number of children produced has also been emphasized by Clarkson[2] who found that women with stereotypically feminine concepts have significantly larger families than those women with relatively masculine self-concepts.

Contraception may be regarded as being tantamount to sterility and viewed as producing a degrading lack of femininity. Women with low self-esteem are not likely to do well with any of the contraceptive methods as the prevention of fertility is too threatening to their femininity. Depression, impotency, and innumerable other symptoms or dysfunctions may result or may be simply prevented by ignoring contraception.

While outlets for the procreative instincts of women will become increasingly available, none are likely to be so specific, so obvious, so certain, so reassuring, so demonstrative to self and others, as pregnancy. It is unlikely that even the availability of the most ideal contraceptive will retard or prevent the seeking of pregnancy, consciously or unconsciously, by men and women who are in doubt or in conflict regarding their sexual identity.

7. *Hostility.* The acting-out of hostile impulses arising from conflicts in the areas of sexual and social adjustment may also lead to the misuse or nonuse of contraception. It is usually an immature, revengeful act in which pregnancy is sought in an attempt "to get even." Occasionally this may be self-directed as a continued protest and anger against men (her husband, father, brother, lovers, those of the Church, or others), an irrational, self-punishing, martyristic revenge. When projected, the hostility may be directed toward the current partner, toward an old partner or peer, toward parents or parent surrogates, or toward society or a specific segment thereof.

A husband may demonstrate hostility toward a wife by seeing that she is in a fairly constant gravid state, or he may intentionally impregnate her to force her into a specific desired action (to prevent her from taking a job, going elsewhere, etc.).

As discussed in the section on coital gamesmanship, a woman may employ the nonuse of contraception as a method to manipulate the interpersonal relationship and to "control" the man by preventing coitus in some situations. She thereby demonstrates her superiority and power through her ability to deny his desire. When this is ineffective, however, and "control" is lost, whether in the sexual or other spheres of the relationship, hostility and a regaining of "control" may be initiated by the acquisition of pregnancy and the opportunity to force the partner into bad conscience with cries of "I told you so," or, "All you think of is yourself."

The deliberate misuse or disuse of contraception may be used by either of the partners to produce pregnancy and hopefully thus to capture or recapture the other person, to initiate marriage or other constancy, or to prevent divorce or separation. In the latter circumstances, this is not infrequently employed by the reluctant one of the pair during the last few "for old times' sake" sexual unions, as has been described by a substantial

number of our abortion applicants. Pregnancy can also be used in a hostile fashion by attempting to force the partner into increased stability and responsibility on the basis of another child to mother or another mouth to feed.

If one partner requests the other to assume contraceptive responsibility, hostility may cause refusal because of resentment from this shift in responsibility, resentment from having to be the user (the responsible person), or resentment from this intrusion into his or her basic right to trust nature. Or refusal may simply be to deny the partner any control of the person's actions, to straightforwardly injure, displease, or provoke the partner, or to develop guilt in the partner for this projection of responsibility. Imposition of contraceptive responsibility will not infrequently be met with the prophecy, "I'm sure it won't work," which may well become self-fulfilling.

Hostility toward a coital partner or other emotionally involved individual may be demonstrated by initiation of coital activity with another with pregnancy being sought, or at least not prevented, in the anticipation of even more deeply injuring the subject of the hostility. This subject could be a boyfriend, husband, girlfriend, wife, homosexual paramour, etc. More than a few of our patients have calmly admitted that they became pregnant "on purpose" by another in retaliation for rejection or emotional injury by their principal partner. A sulking and hostile woman drinking in a bar following an argument with her husband, adulterously bedded without contraceptive concern, and occasionally impregnated before the end of the evening, is a picture not infrequently seen. Nor is the jilted, depressed, unmarried woman in a similar setting.

The attempt to injure the parents or parent surrogates through the hostile action of coitus and contraceptive abandonment is also a common event. The young are taught in most homes that nonmarital sex is sinful and reprehensible and that illegitimate pregnancy is a stigma on the entire family. A rebellious attitude and a desire to injure may lead an individual to active behavior in an area in which the parents are most anxious, most repressed, and most sensitive. Impulsive, open sexual activity with intentional courting of pregnancy through contraceptive nonuse may thus be a hostile reprisal against parental authority, rejection or maltreatment. As one of our patients who had begun promiscuous coitus at the age of fourteen said, "It was exciting because my parents were so much against it." The instigation of pregnancy, consciously or unconsciously, may also be simply a means by which to escape the home or current undesirable environment, but even here an element of hostility is usually apparent.

Hostility can also be directed against society or toward social groups outside the home by the nonuse or rejection of contraception. Persons or groups believing that others who are encouraging their contraceptive use are trying to eliminate, diminish, or weaken their numbers for personal gain or prejudice may, ███ spite alone, not use proffered and available contraception even when logic would dictate its use. This applies equally to racial groups, ethnic groups, religious sects, poverty groups, and others.

Also a desire for revenge emanating from a projection of a feeling of self-degradation and humiliation may be sufficiently operative in some that pregnancy may be actually sought in order to obtain all available payments or benefits from a despised source ("I'll make them pay"). A direct attempt is made to hurt the feeding hand as its very presence implies a childlike dependency and inferiority of the recipient. A retaliatory and rebellious attempt to assert independence and to demonstrate self-worth is often made through reproduction. Many perenially reproducing welfare recipients fall within this group. Frequently, too little attention is paid to these psychodynamics by individuals operating birth control programs in poverty ghettos.

8. *Masochism.* The dynamics operative in the hostility category are not far removed psychologically from those operative in another category, that of masochism. The punishment resulting from the hostility motive is usually directed externally. When contraceptive nonuse is chosen as the weapon by the woman, however, the wielder often "cuts off her nose to spite her face." This masochistic infliction of self-punishment is at least accepted by such individuals, even though possibly not directly pursued.

In others, however, a more clear-cut, self-directed punishment is sought. Gestures of proof of worthlessness and gestures of self-destruction, with contraceptive nonuse and pregnancy as the vehicle, may be seen with any of a host of nonpregnancy-associated psychopathological states, especially those having depressive aspects. A sense of worthlessness may be verified by allowing oneself to be used sexually by another (and usually discarded thereafter). The vilification can be accentuated by contraceptive nonuse and the infliction of the additional punishment of pregnancy. Thus, degrading behavior, irresponsibility, and emotional and physical punishment are all brought together to prove that one is reprehensible and socially and morally wretched. It is interesting to note that, in the dynamics of sexual identity conflict, pregnancy may be used to enhance self-worth while in depressed, masochistic patients it may be used to further degrade the ego.

A masochistic type of suicide gesture may also be made by this means. Vandervoort[12] has described a patient who deliberately became pregnant 5 times, had 5 illegal abortions, all self-induced, all infected, and all life-threatening, in order "to test the gods to see whether she could still live."

9. *Eroticism.* A wholly different and totally unrelated stimulus to contraceptive nonuse or misuse is eroticism. In some individuals, sexual pleasure is accentuated by or principally derived from the thrill in risk-taking. Either or both may seek this with the acquiescence of the other or one may never be told.

Contraception may also be abandoned during the risk-taking associated with boastfulness and coercion, a game of coital "chicken." This action is more a product of immaturity than a quest for sensuality as noted for the group above, and, depending on the innate motivation, might more appropriately be included under a different category.

The nonuse of contraception may also be associated with a special variety or philosophy of eroticism sought by a youth subculture in the separation of mind from body and the use of the body as an emotion-divorced recipient of sensual stimulation. Expression of libido is a requirement of the group but so is the dissociation of deep intimacy and love from the coital experience. Johnson[6] speaks of sophisticated college coeds in this subculture who, in the process of separating their rational mentality from pure body sensuality, felt it necessary "to feign spontaneity by not taking adequate contraceptive precautions." He assumes that the same eroseparatist philosophy and contraceptive irrationality exists in certain adulterous liaisons as well.

10. *Nihilism.* The abject apathy so frequently associated with financial poverty influences all of an individual's attitudes and actions, including those relating to sexuality and reproduction. The influence is essentially nihilistic. Individuals in this circumstance are generally too apathetic to make plans and carry them through. Inasmuch as positive, usually recurring, action is required to prevent pregnancy and no action of a foreign nature is required to produce pregnancy, the latter occurs simply because of inertia and ennui. The contraceptive idea is not likely to penetrate soon the "unapproachable fatalism of the hopelessly poor."[4]

The nihilism associated with the helplessness and hopelessness of neurotic and psycotic depressional states (the emotional stupor expressed as, "I just don't care.") is also, of course, conducive to contraceptive nonuse.

A certain variety of nihilism is also seen in instances of affectional poverty. There are a large number of lonely and love-deprived women to whom natural sources of sustained adult emotional gratification are unavailable for any of a host of psychological, physical,

or social reasons. Some of these women depend on babies for emotional gratification, seeking an infant to fill their emotional void and often seeking a new one whenever the preceding one "outgrows maternal closeness." Symptomatic of this affectional poverty is the statement, "Sex is for men; babies are for women."

11. *Fear and anxiety.* Fear and anxiety, initiated or increased by the use or contemplated use of contraception, can evolve from many sources. Zell and Crisp[16] have described these in excellent detail principally as they pertain to the oral contraceptives but with sufficient generality to be pertinent to other contraceptive measures as well. Anxiety may develop over vanity-disturbing side effects or a fear of bodily damage, for example, uterine perforation, cancer, thrombosis, etc. This anxiety may be rationally evolved or may be a superficial manifestation in some women of resentment related to castration fears. Side effects or physical changes, even if not potentially dangerous, may be inte▇▇▇▇ for ▇/ these women as a castration threat, especially if they serve as a forcible and regular reminder of their deprived female status.

Anxiety may also occur from concern regarding the control of sexual impulses. Some women may be fearful that they will become sexually aggressive if the controlling force of the fear of pregnancy is removed. The use of contraception may arouse latent fantasies of prostitution and a woman may fear that she will become promiscuous and irresponsible and be totally unable to control her sexual behavior. The opposite reaction may be seen in others who fear that contraceptive practice will lead to a loss of libido or frigidity. The associated anxieties in the man regarding an accentuation or decline in his partner's sexual urge and fidelity have already been noted.

Anxiety may also develop from concern regarding the influence of contraception on future reproductive possibilities. This may reflect realistic fears regarding the physical situation or may reflect sexual identity conflicts and an anxious desire for preservation of a valuable route to self-esteem.

Anxiety may also be aroused by an individual's recognition of the personal controllability of one's reproductive fate and the manipulability of one's life. The specter of such control and power and the degree of responsibility one inherits with the acceptance of contraception is threatening to dependent and immature individuals with low self-esteem. The more effective and absolute the method, the greater the anxiety. Volitional contraceptive use is a recognition and a declaration of independence. Many women (and men) neither desire nor are psychologically prepared to accept or deal with independence in general or with sexual and reproductive independence in particular.

On the other hand, a modestly immature but contraceptively normally functioning woman may suddenly discontinue contraception in the event of a particularly stressful situation. Consciously or unconsciously, she may seek pregnancy if she can anticipate that others will sympathize, comfort and otherwise support her physically and emotionally. By this method she can shift or eliminate her responsibility by retreating to the dependent state of pregnancy.

12. *Abortion availability.* During the past three years, as legal induction of abortion has become increasingly available, it has become evident that some women are now intentionally using abortion as a substitute for contraception. This alternative to contraception is especially appealing to women who have any one of innumerable reasons for desiring pregnancy but not reproduction. It is also appealing to perceptive women in appropriate circumstances who note that it is cheaper to have a welfare-supported abortion than it is to personally purchase contraception. This substitution is also being embraced by certain women and couples who consider themselves to have a minimal risk of pregnancy because of infrequent or erratic coitus or because of known or suspected low fertility. It has also been used by hostile feminists who harbor the belief that "Abortion is my right. Why should I use contraception if I don't want to?" The availability of abortion is also largely the basis for the pretentious rejection of contraception by an apparently growing body of young nonconforming social dissenters who declare, "Why sweat? So it happens. So we'll take care of it."

It seems certain that for some time to come there will be an increasing number of women who will reject contraception purely on the basis of the availability of legal abortion.

13. *Opportunism (desperation).* While there are no statistics available regarding incidence, the most common reasons for contraceptive nonuse should predictably fall in the category of opportunism or desperation. This should be particularly true for young, unmarried individuals, especially during their early experimentation. Except in instances of force, deceit, misunderstanding, or complete masculine disregard, each of the partners is aware of the lack of contraception and each presumably has the option of declining to indulge on the basis of the risks involved. If coitus occurs, each will have decided, frequently for very different reasons, to willfully accept the possibility of pregnancy for the advantage(s) to be gained from intercourse at that particular time.

For both partners the advantage may be simply lustful pleasure that they are unwilling to deny to themselves and unwilling to delay. This is probably the major psychological basis for male involvement in contraceptively unprotected coitus and may be the basis repeatedly for any given man as men have less to lose from the consequence of pregnancy. However, the more frequently it is invoked by any individual woman, the more likely it is that the true basis for her contraceptive nonuse lies within one or more of the other categories. The advantage, on the other hand, may be the initiation, maintenance, or prolongation of a relationship which the individual considers might not occur unless coitus is undertaken in that immediate situation. All too commonly the advantage is simply the obtaining of some infrequently available and wholly unanticipated acceptance, status, attention, affection, experience, etc.

Seizure of an available coital opportunity

for these or other reasons and the unacceptability of postponement to acquire contraception almost invariably connotes a degree of desperation, hence the inclusion of the two in a single category.

14. *Iatrogenesis*. We must also recognize that there is an iatrogenic basis for contraceptive nonuse. The influence of the physician and his associated personnel is substantial. Negative attitudes or ambivalence, derived from one's own guilt and anxiety concerning contraceptive use, from moralistic judgments regarding the individual patient, from a lack of commitment to contraception and population control, etc., will almost invariably be transferred to patients and in many instances will set the pattern for the patient's contraceptive actions. Even more explicit, though perhaps no more influential, are the instances in which physicians have flatly refused to give contraceptive advice and some other instances in which actual physical sabotage of contraceptive prescriptions by associated personnel has occurred.[14]

Even highly motivated, contraception-selling physicians may work against their own ideals and efforts on occasion. Overenthusiastic authoritarian urging, a demeaning attitude, or many other types of behavior which may be interpreted adversely by the patient can create sufficient suspicion, resentment, or rebellion to cause him or her to reject the advice and thus contraception. Individuals generally desire ego attention and selling contraception to them on the basis of nonpersonal reasons (e.g., social good, population control, etc.) is not likely to be highly successful.

Other iatrogenic reasons for contraceptive nonuse or misuse, possibly but not positively psychologically based, are those associated with apparent physician ignorance, oversight, or unconcern. Incomplete or erroneous instructions regarding use of the contraceptive method are not unusual. Also, the irresponsible and reprehensible practice of advising a patient to temporarily or permanently discontinue a particular form of contraception without simultaneously counseling the individual regarding alternative or interval methods is by no means infrequent.

A physician must also guard against leaving a patient with misconceptions that may lead to contraceptive rejection. A patient may misconstrue a physician's explanation regarding the potentiality of this or that condition diminishing fertility to mean that he or she has no need for contraception. For some patients, such an explanation will lead to a simple, fertile disuse of contraception. In others, however, the explanation may constitute a threat to the patient's sense of femininity or masculinity adequate to cause the patient to reject contraception and to pursue pregnancy to reinforce a depleted feeling of sexual identity. Obviously a total clarification of potentiality and an attempt to understand patients' interpretations and psychological responses to explanations regarding their virility or fertility are absolute requirements for responsible and compassionate patient care.

Characterization of the contraceptive rejector

If it is possible on the basis of the foregoing to characterize the personality that will fail most consistently in contraceptive usage, it is the immature, dependent, self-punishing individual who has a feeling of low self-esteem and self-worth and who has little, if any, desire to control his or her life. Also characteristic of such an individual would be the inability to assume responsibility, to control impulses, to appreciate long-range goals, and to develop good sexual adjustment. These findings, or anticipations, are in keeping with the results of personality assays of contraceptive misusers or disusers reported by others.[1, 9, 15] In general, as Pohlman[10] has shown, success in life, in marriage, in business, etc., correlates well with success in contraceptive usage as does maturity, intelligence, and motivation. The less the general life success and the greater the neurosis or psychosis and the greater the compulsiveness, the more frequent the use of sex for expressions of hostility and acting out of emotional troubles and the greater the frequency of contraceptive failure.

Comment

This has been, at best, an overview of the innumerable and exceptionally prevalent psychological factors that have been operative to some extent and in some combination in essentially all individuals who have engaged in coitus without contraceptive protection. There has been no attempt to be all inclusive. That the list is lengthy despite its incompleteness and that it intentionally and totally disregards other highly influential nonpsychological factors serves to point out the enormity and universality of the forces working against the potentiality of control of population growth by volitional contraceptive means.

It is apparent that contraceptive effectiveness is not simply a matter of technology but is also a matter of the influences of psychological, sociologic, and many other factors. Additionally, while it may appear that increased efficiency in contraception would be highly valued by all users, this is by no means the case. Many individuals are far more comfortable with less than totally efficient methods and some even relish the risks attendant on intermittent use or nonuse. Regardless of the method and regardless of its inherent qualities in terms of simplicity, availability, safety, low cost, efficiency, etc., as long as it is contrary to conception there will always be a large number of people who will not employ it or not use it correctly despite the fact that they will say superficially that they do not desire pregnancy.

The current concentration of attention and money on the development of new contraceptive techniques with the wistful hope of evolving an "ideal" contraceptive, or a bevy of contraceptives to satisfy all faiths, is almost certainly misplaced. Volitional contraception has never been shown to be adequate to the task of gaining control over the birth rate to the point of preventing population increase despite the availability for the past fifty years in industrialized countries of adequate techniques to this end. Davis[3] has pointed out that even in showplace areas of concentrated contraceptive distribution in the past two decades this approach has failed to halt population growth. While the birth rate may have been shown to decline, the total population continues to increase. One of the obvious reasons he cites is that people simply want more children than can be accommodated in the zero population change context. As he has pointed out, it has never been demonstrated that even restricting births to those "wanted" would be adequate to eliminate population growth.

This is a problem that "has no technical solution."[5] More and better contraception is not the answer to the population crisis, nor is it likely that even free and available abortions or abortifacients are the answer, although each and all of these items would be of general aid. The elimination of population growth is not principally a medical or a scientific problem. It is a social, psychological, political, and attitudinal problem, one which will require wholly new approaches for solution. It is well beyond the time that social foundations and governments awoke to this fact and moved a substantial portion of their mental talent and funded efforts to the discovery, development, and distribution of these approaches.

REFERENCES

1. Bakker, C. B., and Dightman, C. R.: Fertil. Steril. 15: 559, 1964.
2. Clarkson, F. E.: Ob. Gyn. News 5: 52, 1970.
3. Davis, K.: Science 158: 730, 1967.
4. Goldzieher, J. W.: J. Reprod. Med. 5: 49, 1970.
5. Hardin, G.: Science 162: 1243, 1968.
6. Johnson, A.: Med. Aspects Hum. Sexual. 3 (No. 10): 33, 1969.
7. Kolodny, R. C.: Med. Aspects Hum. Sexual. 4 (No. 7): 47, 1970.
8. Kovar, M. G.: Report by National Center for Health Statistics, San Francisco Chronicle, April 8, 1970, p. 1.
9. Lidz, R.: Fertil. Steril. 20: 761, 1969.
10. Pohlman, E.: Psychology of Birth Planning, Cambridge, Massachusetts, 1969, Schenkman Publications.

11. Rainwater, L., and Weinstein, K. K.: And the Poor Get Children, Chicago, 1960, Quadrangle Books, Inc.
12. Vandervoort, H. E.: Personal communication.
13. West, J.: Ob/Gyn Digest 11 (No. 1): 46, 1969.
14. Wolf, S. R., and Ferguson, E. L.: AMER. J. OBSTET. GYNEC. 104: 752, 1969.
15. Zeigler, F. J., Rodgers, D. A., Kriegsman, S. A., and Martin, P. L.: J. A. M. A. 204: 849, 1968.
16. Zell, J. R., and Crisp, W. E.: Obstet. Gynec. 23: 657, 1964.

Discussion

DR. LEROY E. SMALE, Bakersfield, California, Drs. Sandberg and Jacobs have explored the "personal and interpersonal psychological make-up" of 4,000 patients seeking abortion at the Stanford University Hospital. They have classified into 14 psychological categories why these 4,000 women did not practice conception control adequately to prevent their then-current pregnancy. These categories range from denial, love, guilt, coital gamesmanship, sexual identity conflicts, etc., to iatrogenesis. In addition, the authors have framed their principal body of material by a relating discussion of contraception as a method of population control, which is "finally a social, psychological, political, and attitudinal problem, which will require wholly new approaches for solution."

If Dr. Sandberg implied that the United States is a contraceptively sophisticated country, I cite a recent study by Bauman[1] on selected aspects of the contraceptive practices of unmarried university students. Sixty per cent of unmarried men and women at the time of first coitus used no "reliable method of conception control," and "about forty per cent usually used nothing or an unreliable technique." Also, "less than three per cent of the men and women were protected by the pill during their first intercourse." Since such a presumably informed group depicted by Bauman's material regularly does not use contraception, it is not surprising that unplanned and unwanted pregnancy is as frequent as it is. College students have had no recent fundamental changes in sexual attitude. Though not confined to college students, coitus among the group frequently is opportunistic in nature, and thus may become an aftermath of a "beer party." I have delivered quite a number of sophisticated women of "unwanted" children who found to their dismay that "candy is dandy, but liquor is quicker," who found that the erotic aspects of their activities while somewhat disabled by alcohol simply made for carelessness. Many of these pregnancies because of the ready availability of abortion now do not terminate in obstetric deliveries. It occurs to me the psychological aspects of these situations are not significant, until the girl or wife has found herself undesirably pregnant.

Bumpass and Westoff[2] in an article dealing with the extent and implications of unwanted fertility in the United States found that unwanted pregnancies increased rapidly by birth order, were inversely related to dollar income, and were also related to the parents' ethnic group. For the same birth order, Negroes desired the pregnancy less often than Caucasians. In addition, Sarell[3] related a study of one hundred and fifty pregnant teen-age girls seventeen years or younger who when exposed to careful social, psychiatric, and obstetric attention were prevented from being "transformed from a young, frightened girl 'caught' by a pregnancy into a depressed, defeated, and dependent unwed mother of 5 or 6 young children." Data such as these demonstrate in a minuscule way that psychologically, socially, and educationally deprived persons are driven to limit reproductivity.

Data of these kinds bring me to take exception with the authors that individual effort will bring about no significant population control. Only within this present generation has contraception been openly and freely discussed. It is only in the last five to six years that one finds still infrequent but frank discussion of birth control within pages of local newspapers. And, it is only within the last two to three years (if that long) that television and radio stations were brave enough to include this subject material in their programming. Even as recently as Eisenhower's administration, government was too much afraid to take any kind of stand on this subject.

Before making the statement that "it is apparent that the efforts to date have failed," the authors ought to look at certain data. A partial failure, yes, but the birth rate in the United States has declined since about 1961 and the enrollment in the elementary grades is down significantly since 1967. In my county, the birth rate has fallen from 28 to

18 per 1,000, and in Taiwan the birth rate of
45 per 1,000 in 1954 dropped to about 28
in 1968; in addition, in the Republic of Korea
the 1968 crude birth rate was about 31 to
33 per 1,000, a drop from the estimated 40
per thousand for 1961.[4, 5] It thus seems to
me that contraceptive information has had an
obvious effect in the last few years. I can't
recall anyone claiming that everyone would
stock up on contraceptives without a mass
educational program. Perhaps we should emu-
late the tobacco companies and advertise in
the Madison Avenue fashion. Very few people
now argue about the desirability of smallpox
vaccination, and fewer people resent flourida-
tion today than five years ago.

For many millions of years, man has been
breeding at an unregulated rate. Prior to
modern health practices, through plague, smallpox, starvation, malaria, cholera, syphilis, measles, and pneumonia were his numbers periodically decimated. Since only in the last generation
have we had effective methods of conception
control, we have not had time to develop
fully the medical, technical, social, emotional,
educational, and political structures and attitudes necessary to cause man to control his
unrestricted breeding, either voluntarily or, if
necessary, by edict. But I agree with the authors,
with Hardin,[6] and with Ehrlich[7] that time
is short and we must move quickly if we are
to frustrate the disasters that are close upon us.

I found the authors' paper informative, interesting, and enjoyable. It is generally anecdotal
and easy to read. Though it is well substantiated,
I would have felt better informed if they had
placed relative importances upon their various
psychological categories and if they had told
us something of the age, education, and social,
mental, professional, and ethnic composition of
their material.

This paper is a good example of how many
scientific papers are the result of change rather
than a cause of/or impetus for change. It is
because of social pressure of overpopulation
man now finds it necessary to talk about this
particular subject. Scientists write erudite papers
giving a hierarchical stamp of approval for
people to go ahead and think the way they
are thinking or are starting to think. It is
quite necessary for the intelligensia and the
power structure to embrace a social concept
for it to get off the ground and to succeed
without revolution. This is the principle value
of papers like that of Drs. Sandberg and Jacobs.

REFERENCES

1. Bauman, K. E.: Amer. J. Obstet. Gynec. 108: 203, 1970.
2. Bumpass, L., and Westoff, C. F.: Science 169: 1177, 1970.
3. Sarell, P. M.: Amer. J. Pub. Health 57: 1308, 1967.
4. Country Profiles: The Republic of Korea, Population Council and The International Institute for the Study of Human Reproduction, New York, April, 1970, Columbia University.
5. Country Profiles: Taiwan: Training for Family Planning, Population Council and The International Institute for the Study of Human Reproduction, New York, December, 1968, Columbia University.
6. Hardin, G.: Population, Evolution, Birth Control, San Francisco, 1964, W. H. Freeman & Company.
7. Ehrlich, P. R.: The Population Bomb, New York, 1968, Ballantine Books.

Dr. Donald M. Minkler, Berkeley, California. We are indebted to Dr. Sandberg for
two things. One is for pointing out what has
been shown by others, namely, that simply
relying on family planning is by no means the
answer to the world's population problem. My
friend Stephen Plank says it better when he
states, "We must not delude ourselves into
thinking we are just going to contracept our
way to the great society." The other debt we
owe to Dr. Sandberg is in emphasizing the
importance of the unconscious in the attitudinal
elements that surround the decisions pertaining
to human fertility. But to go from there to his
conclusion that an attempt to influence population dynamics on the basis of individual
and voluntary conception control is therefore
futile is a big jump with which I find it hard
to agree. It has been said that, "those who
fail to read history are destined to suffer the
repetition of history's mistakes." We have learned
from history, as Dr. Smale has pointed out,
that even the unconscious and the subconscious determinants of decisions regarding human fertility can be influenced by societal goals
and by economic and historical events. The
spectacular changes in fertility rates in human
history have not paralleled significant break-
throughs in contraceptive technology; witness
the dramatic drop in birth rates that accompanied the industrial revolution in northern Europe and England in the latter part of the
last century, the drop in birth rates in the
United States in the 30's during the depression
years, and the progressive decline in the American birth rate continuing at the present time
which began in the late 1950s, at least three

or four years before the widespread dissemination of either "the pill" or the intrauterine device. Thus, the premise that the unconscious or the subconscious determinants of fertility control are somehow beyond influence is the premise that I find hard to accept and I would like to have Eugene Sandberg comment on this. I think our key to this that might be helpful in understanding that even the unconscious is "negotiable," if you please, lies perhaps in the great contributions that have been made to later psychoanalytic theory by the writings of Eric Erickson. From studies of such groups as the American Sioux Indian, the German Jew, and the American Negro, he showed the importance of the society and its history on the unconscious and on the determinants of human behavior which Dr. Sandberg has portrayed on the screen for us.

We have not yet done the experiment in human fertility control which combines the easy availablity of up-to-date and efficient contraception on the one hand, with a motivational framework that includes all the indirect determinants of decisions to control fertility on the other hand, which I think do make it possible to have a significant influence on birth rates based on individual and voluntary contraception.

DR. ROBERT A. SACK, Whittier, California. This is an extremely important and timely paper that focuses our attention on probably the gravest dilemma society has ever faced, and I am not referring here to the problem of overpopulation and its attendant pollution of our environment. Rather, I want to refer to the choice that we are all going to have to make, and this is going to be the choice between individual rights and the rights of society. We are now at a point in time when we can no longer afford the luxury of worrying about the psychological or even the spiritual rights of any individual. If the consequences of an individual's act adversely affects society as a whole, then society will have to control these acts.

A few months ago I promised my wife I would no longer get up before groups and propose that motherhood should be licensed so I will stop short of that today.

DR. RALPH L. HOFFMAN, San Diego, California. At the expense of being somewhat facetious, I would like to state a couple of comments and ask a question.

Along with Dr. Sack, I hope that in some way the world, whether the supposedly sophis-

ticated society of the United States or the uneducated unsophisticated countries that produce nearly 70 million people themselves a year, like China and India, can arrive at a solution before it is determined by government edict that abortion or sterilization must be enforced on the population. I think this will come if the present population growth rate continues.

It is unfortunate that birth control and abortion cannot be retroactive. I think it would be a lovely solution to our problem.

My question is do you think the same psychological and other factors you discussed apply to the uneducated countries—Africa, India, China—as they do in this country?

DR. SANDBERG (Closing). I am sorry if I led Dr. Smale, or anyone, to believe that this material was obtained from a personal study of 4,000 patients having therapeutic abortions. It was not. I mentioned this number of legally induced abortions at Stanford University Hospital during the past three years only to point out that a tremendous number of women who profess not to want pregnancy, nonetheless fail to use methods to prevent it. The material presented is a distillate of information obtained from a number of sources including the medical literature, friends, fellow practitioners, and patients. It does not fully envelop the topic and it is not quantitative. I doubt very much that it would be possible to obtain accurate quantitative information in this area. It would often be difficult for the individual to know or to understand the precise psychological reason for his or her rejection of contraception. Several influences are often operative at the same time and the type, number, and strength of these influences may vary from one day to the next, depending upon location, circumstances, time, partner, etc. Additionally, the patient's conscious mind may propound a reason, but this may only be an unconscious rationalization, a substitute for the real basis which he or she prefers not to recognize.

I did not mean to imply that individual effort will be of no value in reducing population growth, only that to date it has been inadequate. I think it is inappropriate to speak in terms of "significant" or insignificant population control. Either population is controlled or it is not. Today it is not. To cite birth rate declines in the United States, Taiwan, Korea, or Bakersfield as proof of partial success in this area is, in my opinion, wishful and suicidal thinking. Anything less than total success will eventually be total failure. Though the birth *rate* may decline,

May 15, 1971
Amer. J. Obstet. Gynec.

the total *population* continues to increase. According to the Population Reference Bureau in Washington, D. C., there is only one country in the entire world where there has been a decline in population since 1965. That is Malta which has a population of 300,000. While a reduction in birth *rate* may extend man's period of survival, any degree of continual population *growth* must eventually lead to disaster. How many human bodies can the earth support? When and how do we call it quits and put an end to population growth?

In response to Dr. Minkler's kind remarks, I would like to emphasize that I was not attempting to state that it is impossible to negotiate with the unconscious. I think it is possible in some areas and I think that we must try. I did not mean to imply that contraception is bad and that we ought to totally dismiss it. I am saying that absolute reliance on volitional contraception is foolhardy under the present circumstances. We need available abortion, we need contraception, we need education, we need attitudinal changes, we need a host of things, many as yet untried, many as yet unconceived. My major premise is that governments and institutions which fund research, development, and distribution studies in contraception in the anticipation of ultimate population control would do well to expand their mental horizons and to desist placing all their eggs in the contraception basket. I think that for our salvation this is absolutely and ultimately going to be required.

In answer to Dr. Hoffman's question, the psychological factors which I mentioned today relate strictly to Americans. I have no reason to believe that this same group of psychological factors, directly and in totality, would be operative in other countries, other cultures, and other circumstances. But those that would not probably would be replaced by other psychological factors which are prevalent there but not here. A few might be universal.

We all would like to maintain our present freedoms, but I believe wholeheartedly in what Dr. Sack has had to say. Freedom to breed is currently universal, unrestricted, and considered to be an unassailable and basic human right. The United Nations has even issued a formal Declaration which emphasizes that choice and decision regarding family size must irrevocably rest with the family. I fear that such a denial of social good in favor of personal freedom is foolhardy and shortsighted.

Reprinted from *Family Planning Perspectives*, **4**, 21–25 (1972)

Contraceptive Research: A Male Chauvinist Plot?

42

By Sheldon J. Segal

Reproductive and contraceptive research, only just beginning to recover from many decades of less than benign neglect by scientific institutions and virtual financial starvation by government, faces a new problem: charges of discrimination against women. I think that I have not attended a single nonscientific meeting in the last two years at which the progress of contraceptive development was discussed that someone – usually a woman – has not asked "What about the men? Why aren't scientists trying to develop a new *male* contraceptive?" Feminists, switched off from their decades-long battle to take the contraceptive decision away from men (at which they were amazingly successful,° in this country at least, even though armed only with so limited an armamentarium as the diaphragm and jellies), now demand more sharing by males of the responsibility and the risks of contraception. Researchers (male) and doctors (male), many believe, conspire to frustrate this demand. As Barbara Seaman puts it:

If you doubt that there has been sex discrimination in the development of the pill, try to answer this question: Why *isn't* there a pill for men? . . . [It is because] women have always had to bear most of the risks associated with sex and reproduction. Therefore, governments and scientists reasoned, it would be all right to substitute one risk for another. One still hears this argument from certain doctors . . . who like to point out that the risks connected with the pill are less than the risks of pregnancy.[1]

Ironic comment comes from Jennifer Macleod, writing in the *Village Voice*, with "advice" for the young bridegroom:

Most likely, you will choose one of the fine methods available to the modern husband. Consult a qualified urologist. She will explain to you several methods. . . . One widely used method is the insertion of sperm-killing liquid into the urethra before intercourse. She (your doctor) will show you how. . . . The other widely used method is of course the Capsule. . . . There are minor undesirable side-effects in some men: you may gain weight around the abdomen or buttocks, get white pigmentless patches on your face (which you may be able to conceal with beard or face-bronzer), or suffer some morning nausea. But be patient – these effects often decrease or even disappear after a few months. The one serious drawback of the Capsule is that you are several times more likely than otherwise to suffer eventually from prostate cancer or fatal blood clots. But these ailments are relatively uncommon anyway, so that many couples consider it worth the risk, especially since this is the one method that is 100 percent effective.[2]

What are the facts about male contraceptive research? Is the failure thus far to find a new male method comparable to the pill indicative of male disinterest in women's well-being? I don't think so. Certainly the extraordinary increase in vasectomy operations in the last decade† and the increased willingness of doctors to perform such contraceptive sterilizations would indicate an opposite trend. Then why have we not developed a good new male method?

Background

In the evolutionary development of live-bearing mammals the adaptations of both form and function needed to keep the species alive and reproducing have occurred most frequently in the female.

With greater reproductive efficiency, reduction of the reproductive rate has been characteristic of the evolutionary changes leading to the development of placental mammals, and it is rare that these changes have involved the male. Male sperm production and secondary sex system function do not differ greatly among most fish, amphibians, reptiles, birds or mammals. The numbers involved in gamete (sex cell) production is an example. The female primate, typically, discharges only one egg during each ovarian cycle, and may release only 400 eggs in a lifetime, compared to the thousands released in each egg clutch, each season, by the female fish or amphibian. The male primate, however, continues to produce uncounted numbers of sperm, a trait reminiscent of lower vertebrate species that derive tremendous survival value from the copious release of sperm in the general vicinity of unfertilized eggs discharged by the female into sea water or tidal marshes. Key events in reproductive evolution can be identified: restriction of the oogonial (primordial egg cell) multiplication phase to the fetal stage of life; the development of an elaborate follicular apparatus to segregate eggs individually; the process of follicular atresia (degeneration of ovarian follicles) – a mammalian characteristic not seen in lower vertebrates. All of these events have contributed to fertility regulation (birth control for species) of monumental success. One cannot help but wonder why Nature has shunned possibil-

° By 1955, the diaphragm was about even with the condom in methods used most recently by white married couples. (See: N. B. Ryder and C. F. Westoff, *Reproduction in the United States 1965*, Princeton University Press, Princeton, N. J., 1971.)

† [See: C. F. Westoff, "The Modernization of U.S. Contraceptive Practice," p. 9. Ed.]

Dr. Segal is Vice President of The Population Council and Director of its Biomedical Division.

ities in the male in the course of this natural family planning program.

Mankind, on the other hand, has been eminently successful in limiting fertility by concentrating on the role of the male. There can be no doubt that in the segment of the world that has, since the industrial revolution, undergone the demographic transition from high to low fertility rates, the preponderance of this change was effected by the use of methods based on the role of the male — chiefly withdrawal before ejaculating (for which there is a vernacular expression in virtually all languages) and the condom (also richly represented in slang vocabularly).

Why, then, has the modern era of contraceptive research shown so much fascination with events occurring in the female: egg maturation, ovulation, egg pick-up and transport, fertilization, zygote (fertilized egg) transport in the fallopian tube, penetrability of the cervical mucus, preparation of the endometrium to receive the fertilized egg, the process of implantation, corpus luteum function, myometrium (uterine smooth muscle) function? In part, at least, the reason would be the sheer number of potentially vulnerable links in the female chain of reproductive events. Even the forces of women's liberation cannot change the fact that the reproductive analogies between male and female end with sperm transport and egg transport, and that all subsequent events potentially subject to controlled interference occur only in the female.

We are left, then, with four broad areas of attack on the male system: sperm production in the testis, sperm storage and maturation in the epididymis, sperm transport in the vas and, perhaps, the chemical constitution of the seminal fluid.

Suppression of Sperm Production

The testis, like the ovary, depends upon stimulation by pituitary gonadotropic hormones to perform its normal function of producing sex hormones and sperm. Like the ovary, the testis can be suppressed secondarily by a procedure that stops the production of gonadotropins.[3] The oral progestins, for example, could be effective agents for the inhibition of sperm production. The doses required to accomplish this, however, also have the unwelcome effect of inhibiting the secretion of sex hormones by the testis.[4] As a consequence, libido and potency are reduced. There are, however, long-acting androgen esters now available that may provide long-term suppression of sperm production while maintaining libido and general well-being.[5]

Although testosterone and other androgens can suppress sperm production in man, the feasibility of such treatment for contraception depends on establishment of a dosage and mode of administration which would not at the same time have more general adverse metabolic ef-

Figure 1. Vulnerable Steps in the Reproductive Process, Male and Female

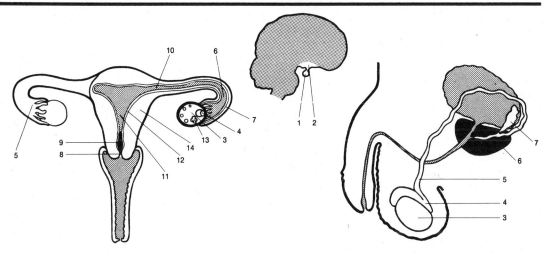

Female

OVULATION

Steroid negative feedback (1 & 2)
Central nervous system drugs (2)
Gonadotropin antagonists (3)
Local action on follicle (4)

OVUM TRANSPORT

Ovum pickup by fimbria (5)
Cilia activity (6)
Tubal fluid secretion (6)
Tubal musculature (7)

SPERM TRANSPORT

External os of cervix (8)
Cervical mucus (9)
Utero-tubal junction (10)

FERTILIZATION

Shedding of zona pellucida of ovum (6)
Sperm capacitation (11)
Sperm penetration of egg membrane (6)
Pronuclei fusion (6)

ZYGOTE TRANSPORT

Tubal fluid secretion (6)
Tubal musculature (7)

PREVENTION OF IMPLANTATION

Estrogen binding (12)
Corpus luteum function (13)
Progesterone binding (12)

PLACENTATION

Trophoblast formation (12)
Chorionic gonadotropin production (12)

MAINTENANCE OF PREGNANCY

Embryogenesis (12)
Placental function (12)
Myometrial activity (14)

Male

Pituitary control (1)
Steroid negative feedback (1 & 2)
Sperm formation in testis (3)
Sperm maturation in epididimis (4)
Sperm transport in vas (5)
Seminal fluid biochemistry (6 & 7)

fects such as stimulation of the prostate and changes in blood chemistry. (Elevated androgen in the blood has been associated with fatal heart attacks, and has been advanced as a possible reason for the shorter life span of men as compared to women.)[6]

An approach that may overcome this problem has been launched by The Population Council's International Committee for Contraceptive Research (ICCR). This team of six specially skilled physician-scientists (all men, from Brazil, Chile, Austria, Sweden, Finland and the United States) has placed the development of 'male' methods high on their list of contraceptive development priorities. The urologist in the group, Dr. Julian Frick—a Tyrolean downhill racer — has been successful in suppressing sperm production in men without loss of libido by using a combination of a progesterone-like compound and an androgen. He is using dosage forms that keep the blood level of androgen within the normal range, thus minimizing the prospect of adverse metabolic effects. Other members of the ICCR are now doing specialized studies on the method and, at the home base in New York, The Population Council's laboratory has started long-term studies on monkeys and rats, all of which would be needed to develop a practicable method as rapidly as possible. Several different methods — oral, injectable, implant — could develop from this work. The 'male combination' method may prove to be the first new method of contraception developed by this all-male group of scientists, who are working also on several potential 'female methods'. (The Council's special ICCR backup staff of five scientists includes one woman.)

Aside from steroid hormones, there are other orally active chemical compounds that stop sperm production without interfering with testicular hormone secretion; but all have accompanying side effects which render them unsatisfactory for contraceptive purposes. One group of such compounds is the nitrofurans, which have had wide use as inhibitors of bacterial growth. They are very effective in stopping sperm production in man, but the doses required are extremely toxic.[7] Compounds that can stop sperm production also have been found among drugs used for treatment of cancer, fungal infections or other types of bacterial or protozoal infections. No single compound, however, has been found to have sperm-inhibiting activity at doses that do not cause serious

toxicity concerns, such as mutation or genetic damage.[8]

In 1960, promise was seen in a group of compounds, the bis-(dichloroacetyl)-diamines, originally of interest for their usefulness in the treatment of intestinal amoebae. When these drugs were tested, using volunteers among penitentiary prisoners, complete suppression of sperm count was demonstrated; when the drug was discontinued, sperm count returned to normal.[9] With high hopes, trials were expanded to include men in more usual social circumstances. The first unexpected observation was that the drug had an antabuse effect enhancing the vascular effects of imbibed alcohol, and causing dizziness, vomiting and loss of equilibrium.[10] More significantly, the studies revealed the presence of abnormal and bizarre forms of spermatozoa[11] which could be associated with genetic damage.[12] Nevertheless, there is current interest in reexamining this series of compounds with a view toward establishing a dose that would have an acceptable activity: toxicity ratio.

Another nonsteroidal compound, a dinitropyrrole, impaired sperm production in rats for as long as four weeks after a single oral dose. An infertile state could be maintained indefinitely by administering single doses at intervals of four weeks. Sperm production recovered fully when treatment was finally stopped.[13] Subsequent toxicologic findings resulted in the withdrawal of the compound from investigation, but a related nontoxic compound may be discovered.

Various physical insults can stop sperm production. Heat and X-ray have been studied, and diathermy, ultrasonic waves and laser beams have been suggested, but none of these has been really tested to any extent. An unusual experiment involving heat effect on the testis was carried out by Dr. John Rock, codeveloper of the pill. He found that sperm production was decreased in volunteer medical students who wore an insulated scrotal supporter continuously. It was inevitable that this would become known as a "Rock strap." The effect was too variable to be an acceptable basis for contraception, but did confirm the earlier work of the late Dr. I. Tokuyama, whose volunteer medical students submerged their scrota in hot water baths for a half-hour per day. An elevation of scrotal temperature each day, of just a few degrees, diminished sperm production, but with considerable variability.

Testicular antigens which can be used for specific immunization to prevent sperm production have been isolated. Indeed, even nonpurified, crude testicular extracts can prevent sperm production in the guinea pig and in the rat.[14] An attempt has been made to immunize human males with testicular extract believed to be purified for this aspermatogenic factor, but the results have not been notable.[15] Immunization with tissue extracts for the purpose of inducing sterility in the male seems distant at this time. Similarly, immunization with protein hormones — particularly those that control testis function — must be considered to be in the early experimental stage.[16] The basic problems of tissue cross-reactions, specificity of antigens, controlled reversibility of the immune response and development of acceptable adjuvants (to enhance the immune reaction) still impede progress in this field.

Whether sperm production is prevented by gonadotropin suppression, direct chemical or physical assault on the testis or by immunological means, a method of fertility control based on this principle must consider a special safety issue: There must be reasonable assurance that during the period of regression of the sperm count, or during recovery, there is not a significant increase in forms that may have fertilizing capacity although they are genetically abnormal. Students of sperm morphology are well aware of the relative increase in abnormal forms as sperm counts decline following x-irradiation, gonadotropin suppression, hypophysectomy (removal of the pituitary) or sperm-antigen immunization. The association of these observed changes in appearance of sperm with significant functional changes has never been sufficiently tested. A complicating problem when using sperm production, with the hundreds of millions of individual cells involved, as the target for contraceptive action, is the requirement for an all-or-none effect, on two levels. First, the effect on the sperm-producing machinery as a whole needs to be complete, for even low-sperm-count ejaculates can be fertile. Second, the effect on individual sperm-producing cells has to be all-or-none, since a partially affected cell could give rise to sperm that are damaged genetically, but could still fertilize, causing an abnormal embryo to develop. In general, one needs to be cautious about all-or-none effects in biological systems.

Maturation and Fertilizing Capacity of Spermatozoa

Mammalian spermatozoa may appear completely normal without possessing the capacity to fertilize ova. The first maturation phase of sperm probably occurs where the sperm first develop, in the 800 or so seminiferous tubules of the testis and in the network of collecting ducts which connect them with the epididymis. Scant attention has been given to this phase of sperm physiology between the time they are released from the nurse-cells that are attached to the tubule walls, and the time that they reach the epididymis. This is technologically difficult because of the inaccessibility of the sperm at that stage. Maturation continues and motility is achieved during the period of epididymal storage. The hormonal environment has a clear influence on this phase of sperm maturation, as suggested by the recent important experiments in rats with cyproterone acetate,[17] imputed to have an antiandrogenic activity leading to the immobilizing of epididymal spermatozoa and subsequent sterility. This interpretation suggests that the epididymis is perhaps the most sensitive of androgen-dependent target organs and can be selectively impaired without interfering with other androgen-dependent systems.

The final maturation stage of sperm has been called "capacitation." Evidence of capacitation has been obtained in a number of mammalian species, including the rabbit, rat, hamster, sheep and ferret.[18] From the viewpoint of fertility control research, the intriguing extension of the capacitation concept is an understanding of the manner in which it can be inhibited. Sperm do not capacitate in the uterus of a rabbit injected with progesterone or in the uterus of a rabbit in the pseudopregnant state (progestational condition). In fact, it has been suggested that fully capacitated sperm can lose their fertilizing capacity by exposure to a female reproductive tract under progestin domination.[19]

The role of progestin in influencing the ability of sperm to capacitate in the female tract raises the question of a possible influence of this class of hormones while sperm still reside in the male storage system. The effect of progestins in the male, at doses below the threshold for inhibition of sperm production, should be examined in laboratory species, as a test of possible use in men.

During the maturation process, sperm develop a complex packaging of enzymes that enable them to penetrate the cell envelope of the egg, the outer zone of the egg and, ultimately, the egg membrane itself. Inhibitors to this enzyme have been found, and are able to block sperm penetration of eggs in vitro.[20] The practical application of these findings (apart from vaginal spermicides) is to find a means to localize these inhibitors in the epididymis or the female reproductive tract. There is no immediate prospect of achieving this goal.

Sperm Transport

Sperm transport has been the element of the system most successfully attacked until now, for methods of contraception used by both men and women. Through the years sperm have been confronted with various forms of vulcanized road blocks and, more recently, plunged into lethal pools of jellies, creams or effervescent foams. Permanent blockage of sperm passage has been achieved by surgical separation of the vas deferens. Even primitive societies have developed ways of preventing sperm transport: Aboriginal Australians, it is reported, create a urethral fistula at the base of the penis with a sharpened twig during puberty rites. The semen flow, mainly, is diverted and lost.[21] (During micturition the hole is covered.)

There is a growing interest in developing new surgical procedures that will be simple and more readily reversible than vasectomy. The basis for this effort, and the priority it should receive, warrant careful evaluation. One frequently hears that vasectomy would be more widely used if there were assurance of reversibility. This reasoning seems to neglect the fact that vasectomy, as a method of fertility control, does not exist in a vacuum. It is one of the few nearly 100 percent effective permanent methods to create planned sterility. There are several, less perfect, reversible methods of conception control. Why would someone be less willing to use one of these, now available, than to use the hypothesized reversible vasectomy?

There is no reason to assume that the high level of effectiveness with the surgical, so-called nonreversible, method would be maintained once reversibility is added. Simplicity of the procedure would almost surely be sacrificed in the

course of seeking reversibility through microvalves,[22] tissue ingrowth-anchored prosthetic devices,[23] intravas rigid plugs carefully placed to prevent pressure necrosis and other means tried and suggested.[24]

An underlying issue that needs investigation is the effect of long-term closing of the vas on sperm production, hormone production and, possibly, autoimmunization. The literature has not been terribly clear on these subjects ever since Dr. Eugen Steinach first claimed that vasectomy leads to hypersexuality.[25] There is no doubt that there are cases of restored fertility after reconnection of the vas deferens, either spontaneously or surgically.[26] The questions are whether the rate of secondary sterility in such cases is abnormally high and, if so, from what cause. Investigators have found an elevated level of sperm agglutinating antibodies in some men following vasectomy.[27] Such reports, however, do not have sufficient numbers or adequate control cases to be conclusive. At the present time there is no evidence that vasectomy has a deleterious effect on health, libido or, in the event that a reanastomosis operation is desired and successfully achieved, subsequent fertility.

Human Seminal Fluid

A primary function of the ejaculate is to carry the sperm from the male to the female reproductive tract. However, the chemical complexity of the seminal plasma suggests other and more subtle relationships to sperm function. The chemical composition of the seminal fluid of man has been analyzed in considerable detail. It is known, for example, that the seminal fluid contains several trace metals, such as iron, copper, zinc and magnesium. Chelating agents (which bind metals, making them unavailable for chemical reaction) at a concentration of a few parts per million can be toxic to ram, bull, rabbit and human spermatozoa, and the addition of copper or zinc enhances the spermatotoxic activity of many chelating agents.[28] Considerable work has been done on seminal carbohydrates, which appear to be an important source of energy for spermatozoa.[29] In human semen, an alcohol (sorbitol) which may be oxidized into a sugar (fructose) by the enzyme sorbitol dehydrogenase, is also present. Fructose is formed in the seminal vesicles and its formation is dependent

24

upon the secretion of testosterone by the testis. It remains to be explored if mild antiandrogenic substances can influence seminal fluid chemistry at doses below the threshold for other undesirable antiandrogenic effects. The influence of such a change on the fertilizing capacity of spermatozoa is at any rate uncertain since the seminal fluid may not be essential to the fertilizing capacity of sperm.

Although such conclusions tend to minimize the significance of the seminal fluids, it remains a distinct possibility that adverse conditions of the fluid medium could influence the spermatozoal surface in a manner that would impair the ability of sperm to reach the fallopian tube or to penetrate an ovum. From experimental data now available, it seems that such an adverse condition is more likely to be caused by the addition of a deleterious constituent to the seminal fluid than the deletion of something normally present. For example, in the rat, zinc, which is believed to be essential for normal sperm metabolism, is contributed chiefly by the dorsolateral prostate; yet removal of this organ does not reduce the fertility of the male rat.[30]

The possibility of exogenous substances finding their way to the seminal fluid is real. Following the administration of estrogen to the male rat or rabbit, for example, estrogen can be found in the ejaculate. Certain medications (sulfonamides, for example) or alcohol, after having been taken orally, have been found in seminal fluid.[31] A pertinent question, therefore, is whether spermicidal substances (or the enzyme inhibitors mentioned earlier) could reach seminal fluid after ingestion or injection, without having general toxicity.

Barbara Seaman may be perfectly correct in her statement that ". . . a man's organs, being handily placed outside the body, are easier to work with than a woman's."[32] But this hardly justifies the truculence with which she and other feminists charge physicians and scientists with proceeding to research and test contraceptives in order to provide more fun for men, while ignoring the health needs of women. The simple fact is that the number of targets — spermatogenesis, sperm maturation, sperm transport and, possibly, the chemical constitution of the seminal fluid — is far more limited in males than females. It is not surprising, then, that the number of approaches under study is fewer for male than for female methods. What is surprising, to this researcher at least, is not that we do not have more male methods, but that we came so far for so long with *only* male methods, and of the most primitive type.

References

1. B. Seaman, *Free and Female*, Coward, McCann & Geoghegan, New York, 1972, pp. 218-219.

2. J. S. Macleod, "How to Hold a Wife: A Bridegroom's Guide," *Village Voice*, Feb. 11, 1971, p. 5.

3. C. G. Heller, M. F. Lalli and M. J. Rowley, "Factors Affecting the Testicular Function in Man," in M. Rocha e Silva, ed., *Pharmacology of Reproduction*, Pergamon Press, Elmsford, N.Y., 1967, pp. 61-73.

4. D. J. Patanelli and W. O. Nelson, "The Effect of Certain 19-Norsteroids and Related Compounds on Spermatogenesis in Male Rats," *Archives d'Anatomie Microscopique et de Morphologie Experimentale*, 48(Supp.):199, 1959.

5. P. R. K. Reddy and J. M. Rao, "Reversible Antifertility Action of Testosterone Proprionate in Human Males," *Contraception*, 5:295, 1972.

6. J. B. Hamilton, L. D. Bunch and A. Hirschman, "Serum Inorganic Phosphorus Levels in Males and Females at Progressive Ages, with Concomitant Measurements of Urinary Ketosteroids and Androgens in Men," *Journal of Clinical Endocrinology and Metabolism*, 16:463, 1956.

7. W. O. Nelson and R. G. Bunge, "The Effect of Therapeutic Doses of Nitrofurantoin (Furadantin) upon Spermatogenesis in Men," *Journal of Urology*, 77:275, 1957.

8. H. Jackson, *Antifertility Compounds in the Male and Female: Development, Actions, and Applications of Chemicals Affecting the Reproductive Processes of Animals, Insects, and Man*, C. C. Thomas, Springfield, Ill., 1966.

9. C. G. Heller, D. J. Moore and C. A. Paulsen, "Suppression of Spermatogenesis and Chronic Toxicity in Men by a New Series of Bis (Dichloroacetyl) Diamines," *Toxicology and Applied Pharmacology*, 3:1, 1961.

10. W. O. Nelson and D. J. Patanelli, "Chemical Control of Spermatogenisis," in C. R. Austin and J. S. Perry, eds., *Agents Affecting Fertility*, Little, Brown, Boston, 1965, p. 78.

11. J. MacLeod, "Human Seminal Cytology following the Administration of Certain Antispermatogenic Compounds," in C. R. Austin and J. S. Perry, eds., *Agents Affecting Fertility*, Little, Brown, Boston, 1965, p. 93.

12. B. W. Fox and M. Fox, "Biochemical Aspects of the Actions of Drugs on Spermatogenesis," *Pharmacological Reviews*, 19:21, 1967.

13. D. J. Patanelli and W. O. Nelson, "A Quantitative Study of Inhibition Recovery of Spermatogenesis," *Recent Progress in Hormone Research*, 20:491, 1964.

14. S. Katsh, "Adjuvants and Aspermatogenesis in Guinea Pig," *International Archives of Allergy*, 24:319, 1964.

15. R. E. Mancini, J. A. Andrada, D. Saraceni, A. E. Bachmann, J. C. Lavieri and M. Nemirovsky, "Immunological and Testicular Response in Man Sensitized with Human Testicular Homogenate," *Journal of Clinical Endocrinology and Metabolism*, 25:859, 1965.

16. A. Cervantes, "FSH as a Reversible Antispermiogenic Agent in Rats," in *Advances in Planned Parenthood*, Vol. 8, Excerpta Medica Foundation, Princeton, N. J. (in press).

17. M. R. N. Prasad, S. P. Singh and M. Rajalakshmi, "Fertility Control in Male Rats by Continuous Release of Microquantities of Cyproterone Acetate from Subcutaneous Silastic Capsules," *Contraception*, 2:165, 1970.

18. M. C. Chang, "Capacitation of Rabbit Spermatozoa in Uterus with Special Reference to Reproductive Phases of Female," *Endocrinology*, 63:619, 1958.

19. C. E. Hamner, J. P. Jones and N. Y. Sojka, "Influence of Hormonal State of Female on Capacitation of Rabbit Spermatozoa," *Fertility and Sterility*, 19:137, 1968.

20. L. J. D. Zaneveld, R. T. Robertson, M. Kessler and M. W. L. Williams, "Inhibition Fertilization in Vivo by Pancreatic and Seminal Plasma Trypsin Inhibitors," *Journal of Reproduction and Fertility*, 25:387, 1971.

21. N. E. Himes, *Medical History of Contraception*, Williams & Wilkins, Baltimore, 1936.

22. J. E. Davis, M. Freund and W. P. Ventura, "A New Reversible Vasectomy Device: A Gold and Stainless Steel Microvalve," paper presented at the twenty-eighth annual meeting of the American Fertility Society, New York, Feb. 28-March 1, 1972.

23. Ibid.

24. H. Y. Lee, "Experimental Studies on Reversible Vas Occlusion by Intravasal Thread," *Fertility and Sterility*, 20:735, 1969.

25. E. Steinach, "Biological Methods against Process of Old Age," *Medical Journal and Record*, 125:77, 1927.

26. R. G. Bunge, "Bilateral Spontaneous Reanastomosis of the Ductus Deferens," *Journal of Urology*, 100:762, 1968.

27. R. Ansbacher, "Sperm-Agglutinating and Sperm-Immobilizing Antibodies in Vasectomized Men," *Fertility and Sterility*, 22:629, 1971.

28. T. Mann, *The Biochemistry of Semen and of the Male Reproductive Tract*, Methuen, London, 1964.

29. Ibid.

30. Ibid.

32. B. Seaman, 1972, op. cit.

Reprints are available at a single copy price of 25 cents. For orders of 50 or more, single copy price is reduced to 20 cents.

Reprinted from *Family Planning Perspectives*, **4**, 9–12 (1972)

The Modernization of U.S. Contraceptive Practice

43

By Charles F. Westoff

Data from the 1970 National Fertility Study (NFS) reveal a dramatic drop in the rate of unwanted fertility between the 1961-1965 period and 1966-1970— a decline of some 36 percent in the number of unwanted births per 1,000 woman-years of exposure to the risk of unwanted childbearing. For whites the decline was 35 percent, for blacks 56 percent.[1] We have estimated that about half of the nationwide fertility decline between the two periods is due to the improvement in the control of unwanted births.[2] Such improvements can result from: earlier or more extensive use of contraception; enlarged or more consistent use of the more effective medical methods; greater motivation to avoid pregnancy, possibly resulting in more regular contraceptive use or recourse to other means of fertility control, or some combination of such changes. This article describes changes in the distribution of types of contraceptive methods currently° used by married couples of reproductive age between 1965 and 1970, based on data drawn from the two National Fertility Studies in those years. These studies were based on extensive interviews conducted with national probability samples of 4,810 and 5,884 married women, respectively, who were younger than 45. The analysis is confined to women currently married and living with their husbands.

Charles F. Westoff is Professor of Sociology at Princeton University. He was Executive Director of the Commission on Population Growth and the American Future, and is Codirector with Norman F. Ryder of the 1970 National Fertility Study. This article is adapted from "Population Growth and Policy in the United States," prepared for a conference sponsored by the Ortho Pharmaceutical Company, Sept. 6-7, 1972 in Buck Hill Falls, Pa. It will be included in a book edited by Dr. Westoff, to be published in 1973 by Prentice-Hall, Englewood Cliffs, N. J.

Contraceptive Use

The proportion of married couples who never used contraception declined slightly between 1965 and 1970 (see Table 1). This was largely due to the decrease in the proportion of "never-users" among younger white couples during this period —from 14.8 to 11.1 percent. The classification "never used contraception" subsumes many diverse categories including younger, recently married couples who have not yet begun practicing contraception, couples with subfecundity problems discovered before they ever used contraception and those who simply have not used any methods for such reasons as ignorance, indifference or slowness in conceiving. This latter group comprises about a quarter of the never-users but only four percent of all married couples at reproductive age —about one million couples. This includes couples for whom conception is possible

Table 1. Percent of Married Couples Who Have Never Used Contraception, by Age and Color: 1965 and 1970

	All Couples (Wife < 45)		Younger Couples (Wife < 30)		Older Couples (Wife 30-44)	
	1965	1970	1965	1970	1965	1970
White	16.0	14.9	14.8	11.1	17.0	18.3
Black	24.3	25.2	15.7	18.4	31.4	30.8
Total	**17.1**	**15.9**	**15.2**	**11.7**	**18.3**	**19.6**

but not easy. In 1970, the fraction who were at risk of unintentional pregnancy but who had never used contraception because of social or motivational reasons is clearly only a very small fraction indeed.

While the proportion who never had used contraception was small, the proportion who were not using contraception

° The word "currently," in this analysis, means at the approximate time of interview.

Table 2. Current Exposure of Married Couples* to the Risk of Conception, Percents, by Age and Color: 1965 and 1970

Type of Exposure	All Couples (Wife < 45)		Younger Couples (Wife < 30)		Older Couples (Wife 30-44)		White Couples		Black Couples	
	1965 (N = 4,810)	1970 (N = 5,884)	1965 (N = 1,918)	1970 (N = 2,743)	1965 (N = 2,892)	1970 (N = 3,141)	1965 (N = 3,771)	1970 (N = 4,972)	1965 (N = 969)	1970 (N = 782)
Pregnant, Postpartum or Trying to Get Pregnant	14.2	14.5	25.4	23.8	7.0	6.4	14.0	14.5	16.1	13.9
Sterile and Subfecund†	14.4	12.9	4.9	4.4	20.5	20.4	14.5	12.6	13.1	16.7
Other Nonusers	7.5	7.5	6.3	6.1	8.2	8.8	6.7	7.2	13.7	10.2
Noncontraceptive Total	**36.1**	**34.9**	**36.6**	**34.3**	**35.7**	**35.6**	**35.2**	**34.3**	**42.9**	**40.8**
Wife Sterilized‡	4.5	5.5	2.0	2.1	6.1	8.5	4.1	4.9	8.3	11.4
Husband Sterilized‡	3.3	5.1	1.9	2.0	4.2	7.8	3.5	5.5	0.3	0.6
Pill§	15.3	22.3	26.2	32.5	8.2	13.3	15.6	22.4	12.4	22.1
IUD**	0.7	4.8	1.1	6.0	0.5	3.8	0.7	4.8	1.7	4.5
Diaphragm††	6.3	3.7	3.9	2.3	7.9	4.9	6.8	3.8	2.9	3.1
Condom‡‡	14.0	9.2	12.2	7.5	15.2	10.7	14.5	9.7	9.7	4.0
Withdrawal	2.6	1.4	1.5	1.1	3.3	1.6	2.7	1.5	1.2	0.4
Foam	2.1	3.9	3.1	5.3	1.5	2.8	2.0	4.0	3.5	3.6
Rhythm	6.9	4.1	4.8	2.7	8.3	5.4	7.5	4.4	1.4	1.0
Douche	3.3	2.1	3.1	1.5	3.5	2.7	2.7	1.9	10.0	4.7
Other§§	4.9	2.9	3.9	2.8	5.4	3.0	4.8	2.8	5.8	3.8
Contraceptive Total	**63.9**	**65.0**	**63.7**	**65.8**	**64.1**	**64.5**	**64.9**	**65.7**	**57.2**	**59.2**
Percent Total	**100**	**100**	**100**	**100**	**100**	**100**	**100**	**100**	**100**	**100**

* Who were living together currently.

† Includes women reporting sterilizing operations (for noncontraceptive reasons) and those who reported that they believed it was not physically possible to have another child.

‡ Surgical procedures undertaken at least partly for contraceptive reasons.

§ Includes combination with any other method.

** Includes combination with any other method except pill.

†† Includes combination with any method except pill or IUD.

‡‡ Includes combination with any method except pill, IUD or diaphragm.

§§ Includes other multiple as well as single methods and a small percentage of unreported methods.

currently in 1970 amounted to more than one-third of married couples of reproductive age—nearly nine million couples (see Table 2). This included wives who were intentionally or accidentally pregnant, in the postpartum or trying to become pregnant (amounting collectively to 14.5 percent in 1970); couples who were sterile or subfecund (12.9 percent); and those who were not using contraception for miscellaneous other reasons (7.5 percent). The proportion not using contraception currently declined very slightly from 36.1 percent in 1965 to 34.9 percent in 1970, a drop concentrated entirely among younger couples and reflecting mainly a decrease in the proportions pregnant, postpartum or trying to become pregnant.

Although there was little change in the overall proportion of couples currently using contraception—63.9 percent in 1965 and 65 percent in 1970,* there were significant changes in the methods used. There was an increase in the proportion of couples sterilized for contraceptive reasons apparent among older couples, an increase in use of the pill and the IUD and a decrease in the use of all other methods except foam. The details of these changes are examined in Table 3, which shows the distribution of methods used by age and color for couples who were currently using any method in 1965 and 1970.† Excluded from this tabulation are many couples who had used or who will use contraception but who were not currently using any contraceptive method.

Contraceptive Sterilization

One of the most dramatic findings in the 1970 NFS is the fact that voluntary sterilization—typically, tubal ligation for women and vasectomy for men—has become the most popular method of contraception currently used by older couples (in which the wife is aged 30-44). One-quarter of all older couples who were currently practicing contraception had been surgically sterilized; the operations were almost equally divided between men and women. The corresponding figure was 16 percent in 1965 (see Table 3). These are all surgical procedures reported by the women to have been elected for contraceptive reasons; they exclude other forms of surgery which produce sterility but which were performed for other reasons. The closest competitor is the pill, used by 20.6 percent of older couples (an increase of eight percentage points over 1965). The jump in reliance on surgical procedures, and the fact that contraceptive sterilization had, by 1970, become the most popular method among older couples, appears to reflect the unsuitability of other methods of contraception for many couples who have already had all the children they want to have. It is estimated that as of 1970 some 2.75 million couples of reproductive age (and, undoubtedly, many more since 1970) had resorted to sterilization, which is usually regarded as an extreme solution to the problem of fertility control.

Reliance on contraceptive sterilization

* This estimate for 1965 and other statistics from the 1965 NFS differ from those published in the main report of that study (N.B. Ryder and C. F. Westoff, *Reproduction in the United States: 1965,* Princeton University Press, Princeton, N.J., 1971) because of changes in classification criteria. The most important changes were to include elective sterilization for contraceptive reasons as a method of contraception rather than as a type of subfecundity and to classify all women currently using contraception *and* subfecund as "current users," and to classify as "other nonusers," rather than as subfecund, women reporting long periods of noncontraceptive exposure without becoming pregnant, and women having two or more fetal deaths (unless they reported that it was impossible for them to become pregnant). The net effect of these redefinitions has been to increase the proportion using contraception, to decrease the proportion sterile or subfecund and to increase the proportion classified as "other nonusers."

† Trends in contraceptive practice by religion, with special attention to Catholics, will be the subject of a subsequent article.

10

is evidently more common among black than among white women, but much less so among black than white men. While almost one-third (32.5 percent) of older black women compared with 11.6 percent of older white women report having been sterilized, only 1.7 percent of older black men compared with 12.9 percent of older white men were reported to have had vasectomies. This difference probably reflects a combination of differences between whites and blacks in the role of the woman in the control of fertility and in the concern for the presumed implications of vasectomies for sexual potency. Thus, the use of the male methods, condom and withdrawal, is much greater among whites than blacks. There is also a considerable difference between black and white women in their belief that a vasectomy will impair male sexual ability: thirty-six percent of black compared with 13 percent of white women held such beliefs in 1970.[3] This appears to be primarily the result of educational differences.

Adding the two types of operations together shows that sterilization is more

common among older black (34.2 percent) than among older white (24.5 percent) couples currently using contraception, a fact that is probably best interpreted to reflect the lesser availability in earlier years to blacks of the more effective medical methods of contraception and the resulting greater desperation by older black women to control fertility. As the dramatic increase in the proportion of younger blacks using the pill and the IUD reveals, this situation is rapidly changing.

Women with less education were more likely than women with more schooling to have experienced a tubal ligation as of 1970 (Table 4, p. 12). Although this was true both of white and black women, contraceptive sterilization was utilized especially by black women with less than a high school education, among whom it was the leading method (31.6 percent) along with the pill (31.1 percent). However, 9.3 percent of white men married to women in the lowest educational group were sterilized, bringing the total to 23.8 percent of low-education white couples, as compared to 32.1 percent of black cou-

ples who have had comparable education.

The Pill

In 1970, nearly six million married women of reproductive age were using the oral contraceptive—more than one out of every five (see Table 2). The pill is by far the most popular method of contraception; it accounted for 34.2 percent of all current contraceptive practice in 1970, taking a commanding lead over all other methods (see Table 3). Its closest competitor was contraceptive sterilization (16.0 percent).

The adoption of the pill by American women has been an amazing phenomenon, considering the various side effects associated with its use, and is an indication of the wide market for effective contraception. It made its first public appearance in 1960. By 1965, 23.9 percent of married women who were currently practicing contraception were using the pill; by 1970 this proportion had grown to 34.2 percent. Most of this increase can be attributed to its widespread acceptance by young

Table 3. Methods of Contraception Used Currently by Married Couples, Percents, by Age and Color:* 1965 and 1970

Current Method	All Couples (Wife < 45)						Younger Couples (Wife < 30)						Older Couples (Wife 30-44)					
	Total†		White		Black		Total†		White		Black		Total†		White		Black	
	1965 (N= 3,032)	1970 (N= 3,810)	1965 (N= 2,441)	1970 (N= 3,273)	1965 (N= 554)	1970 (N= 462)	1965 (N= 1,215)	1970 (N= 1,800)	1965 (N= 922)	1970 (N= 1,540)	1965 (N= 276)	1970 (N= 222)	1965 (N= 1,817)	1970 (N= 2,010)	1965 (N= 1,519)	1970 (N= 1,733)	1965 (N= 278)	1970 (N= 240)
Wife Sterilized‡	7.0	8.5	6.3	7.5	14.4	19.3	3.2	3.2	2.8	2.9	6.9	5.0	9.5	13.1	8.4	11.6	21.9	32.5
Husband Sterilized‡	5.1	7.8	5.4	8.3	0.5	1.1	2.9	3.0	3.1	3.2	0.4	0.5	6.5	12.1	6.8	12.9	0.7	1.7
Pill§	23.9	34.2	24.0	34.0	21.7	37.4	41.4	49.4	42.5	49.4	30.8	54.1	12.8	20.6	12.8	20.4	12.6	22.1
IUD**	1.2	7.4	1.0	7.3	2.9	7.6	1.7	9.2	1.4	8.8	4.7	9.9	0.8	5.9	0.8	5.9	1.1	5.4
Diaphragm††	9.9	5.7	10.4	5.7	5.1	5.2	6.2	3.5	6.5	3.5	3.3	3.6	12.3	7.6	12.8	7.7	6.8	6.7
Condom‡‡	21.9	14.2	22.4	14.8	17.0	6.7	19.2	11.4	19.2	11.9	18.1	6.3	23.7	16.6	24.4	17.3	15.8	7.1
Withdrawal	4.0	2.1	4.1	2.2	2.2	0.6	2.3	1.7	2.3	1.8	1.8	0.5	5.1	2.5	5.3	2.7	2.5	0.8
Foam	3.3	6.1	3.1	6.1	6.1	6.1	4.8	8.0	4.4	8.2	8.0	6.8	2.3	4.3	2.2	4.3	4.3	5.4
Rhythm	10.9	6.4	11.6	6.7	2.5	1.7	7.5	4.2	7.9	4.4	2.9	0.9	13.0	8.3	13.8	8.8	2.2	2.5
Douche	5.2	3.2	4.2	2.9	17.5	8.0	4.8	2.3	3.8	1.9	15.2	5.9	5.5	4.1	4.4	3.7	19.8	10.0
Other§§	7.5	4.6	7.3	4.4	10.2	6.2	6.1	4.0	6.0	4.0	8.0	6.8	8.4	4.8	8.1	4.6	12.2	5.8
Percent Total	100	100	100	100	100	100	100	100	100	100	100	100	100	100	100	100	100	100

* Who were living together currently.

† Includes nonwhites other than blacks.

‡ Surgical procedures undertaken at least partly for contraceptive reasons.

§ Includes combination with any other method.

** Includes combination with any other method except pill.

†† Includes combination with any method except pill or IUD.

‡‡ Includes combination with any method except pill, IUD or diaphragm.

§§ Includes other multiple as well as single methods and a small percentage of unreported methods.

Table 4. Methods of Contraception Used Currently by Married* Couples by Wife's Education and by Color: 1970

Current Method	All Couples								
	Total†			White			Black		
	College (N = 1,066)	HS4 (N = 1,835)	Less (N = 909)	College (N = 948)	HS4 (N = 1,648)	Less (N = 677)	College (N = 103)	HS4 (N = 166)	Less (N = 193)
Wife Sterilized‡	5.7	6.0	17.2	5.6	5.8	14.5	9.7	10.8	31.6
Husband Sterilized‡	7.6	7.8	8.1	7.9	8.2	9.3	1.9	1.2	0.5
Pill§	34.6	36.1	29.7	34.4	35.8	29.1	39.8	43.4	31.1
IUD**	8.2	7.4	6.6	8.4	7.1	6.1	4.9	7.2	9.3
Diaphragm††	9.0	5.5	1.8	8.9	5.5	1.9	10.7	6.0	1.6
Condom‡‡	14.3	15.1	12.1	14.3	15.6	13.3	8.7	7.8	4.7
Withdrawal	1.6	2.0	2.9	1.7	2.0	3.5	0.0	1.8	0.0
Foam	6.3	6.4	5.1	6.1	6.4	5.5	9.7	5.4	4.7
Rhythm	6.8	7.2	3.9	7.0	7.5	4.4	4.9	1.8	0.0
Douche	1.1	2.3	7.8	1.1	1.9	7.8	2.9	9.6	9.3
Other§§	4.7	4.2	5.0	4.6	4.2	4.6	6.8	4.8	7.3
Percent Total	100	100	100	100	100	100	100	100	100

* Who were living together currently.

† Includes women reporting sterilizing operations (for noncontraceptive reasons) and those who reported that they believed it was not physically possible to have another child.

‡ Surgical procedures undertaken at least partly for contraceptive reasons.

§ Includes combination with any other method.

** Includes combination with any other method except pill.

†† Includes combination with any method except pill or IUD.

‡‡ Includes combination with any method except pill, IUD or diaphragm.

§§ Includes other multiple as well as single methods and a small percentage of unreported methods.

women. In 1970 about half of all younger women (49.4 percent) using contraception were relying on the pill, compared with 21 percent of older women.* The growth in popularity of the method has been especially pronounced among young black women among whom its use has increased between 1965 and 1970 from 30.8 to 54.1 percent of all current practice (see Table 3).

In its earlier history, the oral contraceptive was first adopted by more educated women, but by 1970 little of this association remained (see Table 4).

The IUD

About 1.25 million married women in the United States—one out of every 20 couples of reproductive age—now use the highly effective intrauterine device. Although its popularity is still far below that of the pill, its use grew considerably, from 1.2 percent of all wives who were currently

* Another analysis of 1970 NFS data by Norman Ryder will show the month-by-month record of adoption of the pill for the 1960-1970 decade.

practicing contraception in 1965 to 7.4 percent by 1970 (see Table 3). Black and white women in 1970 relied on the method about equally. Although IUD use increased among both younger and older women, it has proven somewhat more popular among wives younger than 30 (9.2 percent) than those 30-44 (5.9 percent).

Opposite patterns of association between education and the use of the IUD prevail for whites and blacks (see Table 4). Whereas the lowest use among whites is by women of the lowest education level, among black women with little education its use is greatest. This probably reflects the greater reliance of black women of lower socioeconomic status on clinics.

Other Methods

Given the sharp increases in reliance on contraceptive sterilization and on the use of the pill and the IUD, the use of the older methods had to decline accordingly. The use of all the older methods declined over the five-year period: the condom de-

clined in use from 21.9 percent of current contraceptors in 1965 to 14.2 percent by 1970, the diaphragm from 9.9 to 5.7 percent, rhythm from 10.9 to 6.4 percent. Other methods, including withdrawal and douche, also declined (see top bank, Table 3). Thus, whereas 59.4 percent of the current contraceptors were using conventional methods (other than foam) in 1965, this had declined by 1970 to 36.2 percent.

Conclusion

The net consequence of all of these changes in methods has been a significant increase in the use of more effective contraception, undoubtedly the main explanation for the decline in the rate of unwanted fertility between 1965 and 1970 and a major factor in the drop in the nation's birthrate. The three most effective methods—sterilization, the pill and the IUD—have increased from 37.2 percent of all contraceptive practice in 1965 to 57.9 percent by 1970. If we add to these three methods the very effective diaphragm, condom and a small fraction of multiple method usage, about four out of five couples using contraception in 1970 were highly protected from the risk of unintentional conception. This high level of protection is being experienced by both blacks and whites and fairly uniformly by couples of widely varying educational levels. Since educational attainment is a measure of socioeconomic status which is closely related to income, the data for 1970 would seem to indicate that low-income couples have almost caught up to the level of contraceptive protection experienced by higher income couples. This is probably in substantial part due to the efforts of public and private family planning programs. A subsequent article will examine the implications of these changes for family planning program needs.

References

1. N. B. Ryder and C. F. Westoff, "Wanted and Unwanted Fertility in the United States: 1965 and 1970," in C. F. Westoff and R. Parke, Jr., eds., *Demographic and Social Aspects of Population Growth*, U.S. Government Printing Office, Washington, D.C., 1972, (in press).

2. Ibid.

3. H. B. Presser and L. L. Bumpass, "Demographic and Social Aspects of Contraceptive Sterilization in the United States: 1965-1970," in C. F. Westoff and R. Parke, Jr., 1972, op. cit.

No. C1297   Distributed by Planned Parenthood-World Population, 810 Seventh Ave., New York, N.Y. 10019   9/72-5 3.61

Author Citation Index

Subject Index